ENGINEERING VALUATION
AND DEPRECIATION

ENGINEERING VALUATION
AND DEPRECIATION

ANSON MARSTON
LATE DEAN EMERITUS OF ENGINEERING
IOWA STATE COLLEGE

ROBLEY WINFREY
FORMERLY PROFESSOR OF CIVIL ENGINEERING
IOWA STATE COLLEGE

JEAN C. HEMPSTEAD
PROFESSOR OF GENERAL ENGINEERING
IOWA STATE COLLEGE

SECOND EDITION

NEW YORK   TORONTO   LONDON

McGRAW-HILL BOOK COMPANY, INC.

1953

ENGINEERING VALUATION AND DEPRECIATION

THE MAPLE PRESS COMPANY, YORK, PA.

PREFACE

"Engineering Valuation and Depreciation" is a discussion of the art of the appraisal of industrial property. The estimation of the monetary measure of the desirability of ownership of commodities and small properties is accomplished daily in the commercial world, often in an informal and intuitive manner. However, the complex society of the present demands systematic and theoretically correct procedures when consideration is given to the appraisal of enterprises and properties not regularly acquired on the market. This book discusses these procedures in detail.

Man has bartered and sold his property throughout history. Today, however, man's industrial and business property is so extensive that its value can be established only by careful study of each factor that gives that property value. Engineering, economics, finance, and business management are each involved in the process of estimating the value of enterprises and industrial properties. The authors realize that the value of property is a highly complicated quality and that, in the end, value is a judgment quantity.

This book, "Engineering Valuation and Depreciation," is written for use as a textbook in the schools of engineering and business wherein a course in valuation of property is offered. However, engineers and others engaged in appraisal practice will find this book a useful reference. Obviously, in a one-volume text, the subject cannot be covered in complete detail; rather, the subjects of valuation and depreciation are covered in sufficient breadth to enable the reader to gain a sound perspective of these two important factors of business and industrial management.

In Chaps. 8, 9, 10, and 11, the authors have endeavored to bring the reader along a new approach to the old and controversial subject of depreciation. Specifically, the *cost, value,* and *accounting concepts* of depreciation are separated and applied within their separate meanings. This discussion of depreciation and its role in valuation forms the core of the book. The experiences of the authors have led them to the conviction that much confusion has been engendered because those who write about depreciation have failed to make clear the distinction between depreciation as an item of cost allocation and depreciation as a measure of the consumed usefulness of property.

Chapters 3 and 7 and Appendix B contain much material of interest to those working in property accounting and those engaged in making

v

analyses of the life experience of property. The authors are convinced that adequate studies of the probable average service lives of groups of property are requisites of an adequate depreciation program for any enterprise.

The sequence of chapters is the order that one might use in the process of making an engineering valuation of an enterprise. Public utility valuation is deemphasized in favor of stress on the valuation of other types of properties and for purposes other than the establishment of rates. As stated in the text, however, the processes and policies evolved largely through public utility rate fixing are the bases used in the establishment of the value of nonregulated enterprise.

The beginning effort on this edition started as a process of bringing "Engineering Valuation" by Marston and Agg (McGraw-Hill Book Company, Inc., 1936) up to date. However, writing had scarcely begun when it was realized that the old edition would have to be largely abandoned in order to produce a text meeting the changed conditions. The revision of "Engineering Valuation" was planned before the death of Anson Marston on October 21, 1949. The writing and organization of this book, however, are entirely that of Robley Winfrey and Jean C. Hempstead. Thomas R. Agg, coauthor with Anson Marston on the first edition, died May 7, 1947.

The two active authors were helped immeasurably by their years of association with Dean Anson Marston, who guided them in their teaching and research up to the time of his death. They also had the privilege of making a material contribution to the first edition, "Engineering Valuation." Although only a small part of "Engineering Valuation" by Marston and Agg is used in this second edition, the authors employed the original edition as a foundation upon which this second edition is built. The present authors gratefully acknowledge their indebtedness to these two noted engineers and educators and honor their memory.

Credit is extended to Dr. William Chester Fitch for his helpful suggestions and critical reading of the manuscript. To our many professional associates, credit is given for the furnishing of illustrative material and consultation. The careful reading of the manuscript by Verne C. Winfrey and Edna W. Hempstead was especially helpful, as was also their sympathetic interest and cooperation throughout the many months required to complete the manuscript.

Robley Winfrey
Jean C. Hempstead

Ames, Iowa
November, 1952

CONTENTS

CHAPTER 1

Valuation and Value

Individuals universally exercise daily the art of valuation without realizing that they do. Each exchange of property, of however trivial a character, involves an appraisal which is at least an elementary valuation. Each exchange of property involves an estimate of the relative worths of the items exchanged. In ordinary trade, value is estimated by the almost instinctive decision that the price quoted is fair or unfair. In all these everyday affairs the exercise of the art of valuation is informal, intuitive, and inexact, as is well recognized; nevertheless, the art of valuation is the basis of the exchange of property comprising the bulk of the world's commerce.

The practices of the industrial world recognize the need for a systematic and theoretically correct procedure in estimating the value of industrial properties, whether in connection with sale, financial management, or the fixing of rates for services. In consequence, there has gradually developed what is recognized as a formal process in the art of valuation.

VALUATION CONCEPTS

Valuation of property is an old art. As applied to industrial properties, however, valuation is a modern art. The following definitions and explanations indicate the concepts of the words *valuation* and *appraisal* as used in this book.

1.1. Valuation. Valuation is defined as the art of estimating the fair monetary measure of the desirability of ownership of specific properties for specific purposes. As used in this book, the terms valuation and appraisal are synonymous.

For each property the value must be expressed in terms of some recognized medium of exchange, usually in the monetary unit of the country in which the property is located. For international exchange purposes, the unit of worth adopted is generally an internationally accepted money unit, such as the United States dollar or the English pound.

1.2. Ordinary Valuation. In ordinary exchanges of property, the value is determined by the judgment of the seller and the buyer, each taking into account his knowledge of the property, the prevailing exchange

1

conditions for such property, and his own exigencies and those of the other party. By a process of barter, the seller and the buyer finally agree upon the sale price. In the majority of cases, only a few simple mathematical computations are needed. Such ordinary valuations are made authoritative and binding only through acceptance of the terms of the exchange by both the seller and the purchaser of the property.

1.3. Formal Valuation. In formal valuations of property, the value is determined by judgment of specially qualified valuators. Such valuations may be for use in property sales or for many other purposes, such as taxing property, securing loans, determining rents, and establishing fair commodity prices. The formal valuation is not computed by mathematical formula but is fixed by expert judgment. However, mathematical computations of varying degrees of complexity often are required; these computations may be technical or nontechnical.

1.4. Engineering Valuation. Engineering valuation is the art of estimating[1] the value of specific properties where professional engineering knowledge and judgment are essential. Examples of such properties are mines, factories, buildings, machinery, industrial plants, engineering constructions of all kinds, and public utilities.

The art of engineering valuation has developed mainly since 1890. Beginning about 1890, engineers, industrialists, economists, and the courts began to be drawn into active participation in formal valuation work. This formal valuation activity shifted from the province of the merchant, the accountant, and the financier to the engineer as extensive industrial expansion took place. The literature of engineering valuation dates almost entirely since 1900.

The art of engineering valuation is continually undergoing improvement. Engineers, accountants, economists, and lawyers are continually studying the various phases of the art. The federal government of the United States and many of the state governments have established commissions to regulate public utilities. These commissions are publishing their opinions and decisions on valuation matters in official reports. The state courts and the federal courts have handed down a long line of decisions which show a gradual evolution toward the development of comprehensive and clearly formulated valuation fundamentals.

Value is the end point of analysis and judgment. The value stated by one person may not agree with that stated by another. Both the methods employed to reach a value and the weights accorded the factors

---

[1] The term *estimate* is used in engineering valuation in the sense in which it is employed in general engineering practice, that is, to indicate a carefully considered computation of some quantity, the exact magnitude of which cannot be determined. The estimate represents the true magnitude as closely as it can be determined by the exercise of sound judgment based on appropriate computations and is not to be confused with offhand approximations that are little better than outright guesses.

which cause value to exist may vary as between appraisers.   Therefore, the student of the art must recognize this situation and maintain an open mind when considering any question relating to valuation of property.

Although the process of appraising industrial properties has been developed largely in connection with the rate-making phase of the regulation of public utilities, more and more these same processes are being applied to properties in connection with settlement of estates, regulation of the issuance of securities, taxation, insurance, and sales.

BASIC CHARACTERISTICS OF VALUE

The word *value* is used in many different well-established meanings. In many of its uses, however, there is reason to doubt that the author himself can make clear to the reader the meaning he wishes the word to convey.   Certainly, many readers fail to interpret the meaning in the sense the author intended.   Uses of the word *value* which apply to other than tangible or intangible property are of no concern in this treatise on valuation; application of the word to property is of primary concern, and an attempt at clarification of the term in the sense that it is usually used in this book is in order.

1.5. Meaning of the Word "Value."   The literature is replete with such terms as appraised value, assessed value, book value, cost value, earning value, exchange value, fair value, forced sale value, imputed value, intrinsic value, investment value, just value, justified market value, market value, normal market value, normal value, nuisance value, objective value, physical value, rate-making value, real value, reasonable value, replacement value, sale value, scrap value, salvage value, sentimental value, sound value, stock and bond value, subjective value, true value, and value in use.

Bonbright discusses many of these terms at length,[1] as do many books on economics.   No attempt is made here to differentiate the various shades of meaning that are implied by these many terms.   In most uses of the word *value* as applied to property there is implied by the author or speaker a sense of worth, a desirability of ownership or possession, or the exchangeability of property as it can be measured in terms of the dollar or other monetary unit.   Usually there is the implication that it is of little consequence whether one possesses at that particular moment the property or the cash dollars stated to be its value.   The terms assessed value, earning value, market value, and replacement value are intended to indicate the basis upon which the value may have been computed, and thus these terms qualify the value as being applied under those conditions.

---

[1] James C. Bonbright, "The Valuation of Property," Vol. 1, pp. 3–109, New York, McGraw-Hill Book Company, Inc., 1937.

Real value, fair value, sound value, and true value are terms that attempt to indicate the justness or reality of the value stated.

1.6. Use of "Value" in This Book.   Throughout this book the value of property will be used in the concept of the desirability of ownership or value to the owner, when *owner* is defined as anyone or everyone who may have or expects to have an interest in the property.   Desirability of ownership of property is measured by the probable returns, benefits, or satisfactions that may accrue in the future to the owner.   Market price, cost of replacing the service rendered by the property, and present value of the future returns from the property are usually relatively good measures of the value of property to the owner.   The basic value of the property to the owner arises from his power to exchange his property for other property in a direct exchange or through the medium of a money exchange.   Sentimental values and values arising from personal pride of ownership are not considered herein.

1.7. Applications of the Word "Value."   The word value in itself is difficult of precise definition and usage.   Value is a relative term by which the desirability of ownership of the property in question is stated in terms of other property or money.   The conditions under which the value is arrived at and the conditions under which the value is applicable must be understood, if the expressed value is to have a real significance. The time, place, purpose, and parties thereto all affect the measure of the value of property.

A development laboratory may value at $12,000 a highly specialized and complicated pressure integrator to be used on a research project for a customer, for whom the integrator was specially designed and constructed.   However, to another person or company this piece of mechanism is worthless, except as scrap metal.   The following month, the customer cancels his contract for the research because results indicate that the original objective cannot be obtained within a profitable cost.   This special pressure integrator, valued at $12,000 the previous month by the owner, thus is now not only useless to him but also valueless, except for salvage, which might amount to $200.

In 1940 many secondhand machine tools were valued by their owners at their worth as scrap metal or as obsolete machines; in 1941 these same machines sold for prices comparable with the prices of new machines because unexpected demand in defense activities for machine tools gave them high values.

A building within an area to be flooded by a reservoir under construction is only of scrap value to anyone so far as its construction materials are concerned.   The owner, however, might place a high value on the building because of the future returns he could earn through its use were it not for the reservoir.   Consequently, the owner is paid an indemnity on the basis that he could continue to operate the property and earn a satisfactory return. Once in the hands of the new owner (the government or other authority constructing the reservoir) the same building ceases to have value, or at least no more than it is worth as scrap material.

Unless the party to whom the property has value is known, any statement of the value of property is usually without significance. Likewise, the time and place are also requirements of a stated value if the value is to have complete significance. Thus, in the process of valuating property, no progress can be made until the purpose of valuation is known and the conditions of valuation established. The assessed value of a property is as much a value of the property as is its market value or replacement value; yet it is safe to state that no two of these three values are ever identical. Money itself has changing value in its purchasing power. The 1939 dollar and the 1952 dollar are widely different in their values. Each year sees some change in monetary values. On the other hand, two men, each under different circumstances, may place different values on the dollar because of their supply of dollars. A man who possesses only a few goods and who has annual earnings of only $1,800 values a dollar much higher than a man whose earnings are $20,000 a year. Their total purchasing powers differ, and thus their personal evaluations of property to be purchased with their dollars also differ.

Reference was made to the fact that periods of time affect values. The changing of value with time comes about not only because of the changing of circumstances which give rise to the value of property in the first instance, but in many cases values of property are not realizable values except as certain future conditions prevail.

1.8. Relation of Time to Value. Values that lie in the future are usually discounted when they are expressed as of the current time or other time short of their expected realization. A given sum of money in hand today is worth more than the same sum to be received at some future date. Figure 1.1 shows the present worth,[1] at different rates of compound interest, of $1 receivable 1 to 100 years in the future. The rate of compound interest used in any calculation of present worth should be that which long-time investments of the particular character being valued must earn to justify the investment risks considered.

1.9. Fundamental Basis of Value. The fundamental basis of the value of any specific property is the present worth, to the present owner and to the would-be purchaser, of the probable future services expected from the property during its probable future productive life in service.

The future service may be of such character as to bring an annual

---

[1] The present worth of a given sum S to be received n years in the future is the sum P which will accumulate to S in n years if kept invested at a given rate of compound interest i.

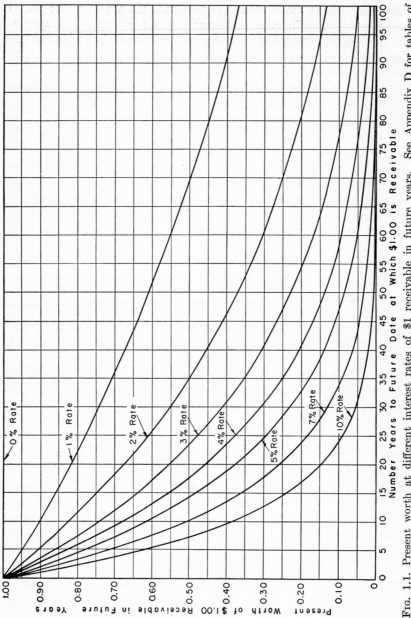

FIG. 1.1. Present worth at different interest rates of $1 receivable in future years. See Appendix D for tables of compound interest factors.

money return to the owner, as in the case of real estate rented; or the future service may be of value to the owner because of his use of the property, as in the case of food consumed or a house occupied; or the service may be of value to the owner mainly because of personal satisfaction in its ownership, as in the case of jewelry or a painting.

Manifestly, the future life in service and a measure of the annual returns during the future service life cannot be determined with exactness and certainty. They are estimated on the basis of judgment. All values are of the nature of forecasts of events and are subject to the uncertainties of all prophecies. Values fluctuate with changes in prevailing opinions of what the future is likely to bring. They can never be determined by formulas or computations alone.

1.10. Relation of Cost to Value. The words *cost* and *value* are to be distinguished from each other. Price is the amount of money paid to the seller by the purchaser of the property. Cost is the price paid plus all other expenses incurred by the purchaser in the acquisition of the property. The terms *actual cost, original cost,* and *historical cost* are used to indicate the outlay which was made by either the present owner or by the owner who first purchased or built the property for use in its normal function. In ordinary bookkeeping, original cost refers to the investment made in the property by the present owner in acquiring possession of the property. However, in valuation work, original cost usually means the investment made in the property by the owner who first used the property when it was new. With land, however, original cost is taken to mean the price paid by the present owner.

The cost of a property is not necessarily equal to its value. On the other hand, cost is considered as an evidence of value, and in establishing value of property it is customary to investigate both original cost and replacement cost. It is usually safe to consider that the value of a property to the owner was at least equal to its cost at the moment he took possession. The cost represents the minimum value to the purchaser, because a shrewd trader pays less than maximum value to him to acquire his property. Certainly, to another person or for another purpose, the original cost bears no positive relationship to the value of the property.

NOMENCLATURE OF VALUATION

The literature of engineering valuation abounds in terms that are used in a special technical sense and as a consequence require a special definition to cover their meaning when used in valuation work. Those terms relating to value are accordingly defined.

1.11. Definitions of Value. As stated in Sec. 1.5, the word *value* has many meanings and many modifiers. The following definitions apply to the meanings of value as ordinarily used in this book.

Value. Value is a measure of the desirability of ownership of property.

Fair Value. Fair value is that estimate of the value of a property which is reasonable and fair to all concerned, every proper consideration having been given due weight.

Market Value. Market value is the value established in a public market by exchanges between willing sellers and willing buyers. The market value fluctuates with the degree of willingness of the buyer and seller and with the conditions of the sale. The use of the term *market* suggests the idea of barter. When numerous sales occur on the market, the result is to establish fairly definite market prices as the basis of exchanges. Such market prices fluctuate to some extent and at any one time may be above or below the level which infallible judgment would adopt when appraising property.

Replacement Value. Replacement value refers to that value of a property determined on the basis of what it would cost (usually at the current price level) to replace the property or its service with at least equally satisfactory and comparable property and service.

Stock and Bond Value. The stock and bond value of an industrial property is the sum of (1) the par values in dollars of the different issues of bonds multiplied by the corresponding ratios of the market price to the par value and (2) the number of shares of each issue of stock multiplied by the corresponding market prices in dollars per share. Stock and bond value is a special form of market value for enterprises which can be owned through possession of their securities.

Earning Value. Earning value of a property is the present worth of its probable future net earnings, as prognosticated on the basis of recent and present expenses and earnings and the business outlook.

Service Worth Value. Service worth value of a property is what its earning value would be if the rates and/or prices charged were just equal to the reasonable worths to customers of the services and/or commodities sold.

Capitalized Value. The capitalized value of a uniform perpetual income is that sum of money whose annual return, at the highest rate which it can certainly earn, is equal to the given perpetual income. Annual incomes to be received at remote future dates do not affect the earning value greatly; if the income in question is reasonably certain to be received for a long period of years, it may often be treated as if it were perpetual. Capitalized value is a special case of earning value.

Taxable Value, or Assessed Value. The assessed value of a property is that value entered on the official assessor's records as the value of the property applicable in determining the amount of taxes to be assessed against that property.

Going Value. Going value is that element of value possessed by an operating enterprise advanced to the state of successful operation as compared with an enterprise not so developed and advanced.

Salvage Value. Salvage value is the net sum (actual or estimated), over and above the cost of removal and sale, realized for a property retired from service. Salvage value and *scrap value* are identical when the property retired from service is scrapped for the value of its materials, in lieu of additional further serviceable use of the property.

Book Value. Book value is the original investment as carried on the company books less any allowance for depreciation entered on the books. In this sense, book value is actually book cost.

1.12. Definitions Related to Value. The definitions of value in the preceding section may be supplemented by other technical terms frequently used in engineering valuations.

Physical Property. The physical property of an enterprise is that part of the property which has a physical existence, so that it can be apprehended by the senses. The physical property of an industrial enterprise consists of many physical units: lands, buildings, machines, poles, wires, ties, rails, roadbeds, culverts, bridges, and dams may be cited as examples.

Intangible Property. Intangible property is that part of the property which does not have a physical existence. Examples are organization, financing, good will, patents, and contracts.

Investment. The investment in an enterprise may be taken to be the sum of the original costs of the several items of existing property that constitute the enterprise.

Present Investment. Present investment in an enterprise is the investment at original cost adjusted for any decreased usefulness of the property brought about by age and prior use of the property.

Prudent Investment. Prudent investment is that amount invested in the acquisition of the property of an enterprise when all expenditures were made in a careful, businesslike, and competent manner.

Reproduction Cost. Reproduction cost of a property is the estimated cost of reproducing substantially the identical property at a price level as of the date specified.

Replacement Cost. Replacement cost of a property is the estimated cost of replacing the service of the existing property by another property, of any type to achieve the most economical and preferred service, but at prices as of the date specified.

Trended Cost. The trended cost of a property is its replacement cost estimated by multiplying the original costs of each item of property by the ratio of the appropriate cost indexes for the two time periods concerned.

Fair Return. The fair return for an enterprise is that amount of annual monetary gain in income above all expenses of operation which represents a fair, reasonable, and appropriate compensation to the owners (1) for their investment in the enterprise, (2) for their assumption of the risks and uncertainties of operation, and (3) for management functions not otherwise rewarded.

Rate Base. Rate base of a public utility is that monetary sum established by the proper regulatory authority as a basis for determining the charges to customers and the "fair return" to the owners of the utility.

FIELD OF ENGINEERING VALUATION

Engineering valuation entails a knowledge of the fundamentals of value and of the cost, service lives, and operating characteristics of the components that comprise modern industrial properties. The field has broadened until valuation has become a part of the accepted responsibility of management in many enterprises aside from those under the regulation of governmental agencies. Consequently, the engineer is likely to encounter valuation assignments in connection with many sorts of employment in which he may engage.

1.13. Fields of Valuation Practice. A few of the many fields where engineering valuation is practiced are next described.

Engineering Executives. Engineers frequently come eventually to fill responsible executive positions in manufacturing and other industrial undertakings; in all such cases a knowledge of the fundamentals of valuation would seem essential.

Consulting Practice. Consulting engineering firms and individuals often find engineering valuation work an important and remunerative part of their practice.

Appraisal Companies. There are a number of firms devoted mainly to valuation work. The need for their services is growing because of the increasing needs of industries for correct valuation and depreciation data without which fair prices cannot be determined, true profits ascertained, or correct financial statements prepared.

Valuation Departments. A large number of public utilities, private industrial enterprises, governmental commissions, and other agencies maintain organized valuation departments.

Salaried Valuation Engineers. Many salaried valuation engineers are employed by consulting firms, appraisal companies, industries, and governmental agencies.

Young Engineers. Judgment and special skill of a character attainable only through experience in positions of responsibility are essential in making the important decisions in engineering valuation work. Nevertheless, much of the extensive detailed work required is particularly well adapted to the service which young engineering graduates, under suitable direction and supervision, are qualified to render. Experience in valuation work gives training extremely valuable to the young engineer, regardless of the branch of the profession he later follows.

1.14. Applications of Engineering Valuation. The purposes of engineering valuation are more often than not related to the legal aspects of the transfer of property, to public utility regulations, and to state and federal laws which concern the value of property. There are transfers of property ownerships and occasions for determining the value of industrial properties in which the government does not have a direct interest, but these cases are few in number in comparison with those in which there is a public interest. As defined in the early part of this chapter, engineering valuation is concerned with the establishment of the value of industrial properties in which the exercise of professional judgment is required and usually with those types of properties not commonly exchanged on the market. Thus, ordinary residential properties, the smaller retail and wholesale business properties, and consumer goods are not considered in this book. Farm valuation is a specialized appraisal field outside the scope of this treatise. The applications of engineering valuation ordinarily encountered are the following:

Utility Rate Making. The process of engineering valuation has received a large part of its development in connection with the regulation of public utilities. Through court cases involving the valuation of utilities, much of the legal background of valuation has been established.

Administration. Valuations of the properties of a corporation afford certain useful information to management. The trends of the replacement cost of the property, investment, and rates of depreciation afford useful information in determining financial policy, competitive position, and selling prices. The basis of certain decisions relating to engineering economy studies may also be found in the reports of valuations.

Taxation. City, county, and state governments are concerned with the value of property which is subject to assessment for ad valorem taxes. Appraisal companies are often hired by governments for the express purpose of establishing the basic information upon which assessed values are determined according to the laws which apply. The federal government is interested in private property in connection with the establishment of proper depreciation rates for income taxation purposes and for excess profits taxes when such laws apply.

Sale or Transfer. When a business is sold or transferred in connection with a consolidation, or when it changes hands because of retirement of personnel, or for other reasons, an appraisal may be made for the purpose of fixing a basis upon which to negotiate the sale or transfer. The value can be found by following the process described in this treatise for all elements of value that are recognized by law.

Condemnations.   The law of eminent domain gives rise to many cases of valuation of property.   As the federal government and the many subdivisions of government expand their activities, many types of properties in private ownership are condemned. Damages and indemnities are paid in accordance with the value of the properties as established through negotiations, condemnation boards, or the courts.

Estates.   The valuation of estates results from a three-cornered interest. The heirs of the property are interested in a valuation of their inheritance as a basis of division of the property; the state government and the federal government may be concerned because of their right to inheritance taxes.

Insurance.   There are two applications of engineering valuations to the field of insurance.   Insurance companies and owners of property alike are interested in knowing the value of insurable property as a basis of determining the amount of insurance to be carried.   When property has been damaged by fire, flood, or other forces, the extent of the damage is ascertained by a process of appraisal.

Security Issues and Financing.   The federal government and the state governments are interested in the value of industrial properties for which funds are raised through sale of securities to the public.   The intent of the laws is to make certain that the prospective purchaser has available the facts relative to the enterprise which affect the value of the securities and to guard against the issuance of securities not backed by property in sufficient value.   A similar interest is held by financial houses which act as trustees or underwriters of security issues.   A third application of engineering valuation in connection with the financing of properties is the determination of the value of the property against which a mortgage loan is desired.   Fourth, in cases of financial reorganization or settlement of enterprises in receivership, a valuation of the property or enterprise may be used as the basis of the reorganization.

PROCESS OF VALUATION

Valuation, in common with other technical activities, adapts itself to an orderly procedure.   This procedure, developed over the past 60 years or so, forms the basis of the chapter sequence of this book.

1.15. General Procedure.   Progress in the engineering valuation of property can be made only after knowing the purpose of the valuation and what property is to be valued.   The basis of valuation is controlled largely by the purpose for which the valuation is being made.   Although the procedures for the valuation of any specific property will follow a plan appropriate for that property, the over-all steps are somewhat common for all industrial properties. Briefly these steps are:

1. Determination of the purpose of the valuation, the parties thereto, the date, and the place of valuation.

2. Determination of the specific property to be appraised, including a study of the geographical and functional classifications.

3. Appraisal of the separate properties, tangible and intangible, by consideration of all the several evidences of value which are applicable.

4. Determination of the value of the whole enterprise or property as an operating entity by consideration of all the several evidences of value which are applicable.

5. By application of judgment to the values arrived at in steps 3 and 4, determine the final over-all value of the enterprise or property, giving each evidence just and right weight.

Following Chap. 2 on the courts, rate base, and process of valuation, the chapters of this book follow in sequence the usual order of conducting a valuation and expand in detail the work incident to the completion of these five steps. The itemization of the property to be valued is covered in the chapters on classification of property and inventories, which are followed by the work of costing the inventory and estimating depreciation. Land, cash resources, and intangible properties are then brought into the valuation. As the final step, the fair value of the property is found by giving just weight to all evidence, including earning value, stock and bond value, and other values not directly based on costs of the property. Mines and other limited life enterprises are discussed separately in Chap. 18.

Eng. Role

CHAPTER 2

The Courts, the Rate Base, and the Process of Valuation

In Chap. 1 the basic concepts of value and the various evidences of value are defined. Certain of these concepts and evidences of value have evolved through a long series of court cases and practices of the art of valuation in connection with the regulation of the rates of public utilities. This chapter is devoted to a discussion of the role of the courts in establishing these concepts and their adaptability to appraisals of properties other than public utilities. A summary of 20 valuation fundamentals and a formal step-by-step process of conducting an appraisal of industrial properties conclude the chapter.

VALUATION AND THE COURTS

The useful service obtainable from a property causes the property to be desired. What one is willing to pay to satisfy this desire is a measure of the value of that property. Thus, the exchange of commodities on the market is a manifestation of this basic principle of valuation. The value of properties not regularly bought and sold on the market is established through a formal process in which the analysis of the several evidences of value is the predominant part of the process. The courts have been an important factor in the establishment of the several fundamentals of valuation set forth in this chapter and on which the process of formal valuation is based.

2.1. Basic Measurement of Value. From the discussion in Chap. 1 it is seen that the value of any property is based fundamentally upon its ability to produce some kind of useful service during its expected future life in service. That service may be of one or more kinds.

The service performed may be measured directly in dollars, as, for example, the income from a parking lot, a water company, or a farm. When an industrial enterprise is considered as an entity, the service which it produces is measured in dollars of net income per year. When it is possible to estimate the magnitude of these incomes year after year, the value of the enterprise is established as the sum of the present worths of these annual amounts for as many years as they are expected to be received.

Although it is generally possible to measure in dollars the value of the service rendered by an entire enterprise, the service rendered by the separate property items comprising the enterprise is frequently difficult or impossible to measure.   For example, the portion of the income earned by the enterprise attributed to a large chimney, a water tower, a transformer, or a meter would be unknown; yet these property items are valuable, as each has the ability to perform a useful service.   It is then necessary that other evidences of the value of property should be considered; perhaps value based on replacement cost, the original cost, or the market value, if it can be established, would be appropriate.

A property may have the ability to perform a service, but yet it in no way contributes toward an annual net income.   Such property has value, because it can command a fair price on a free market.   The demand for the property item may result from sentiment or from some real or imagined utility; but as long as there exists a means whereby a seller can find the highest reasonable price (or the buyer can find the lowest reasonable price), a value of the property can be established.   As long as properties similar to the one in question are being bought and sold, a market price is available, and it is of the utmost importance in establishing value.

It may occur to the reader that the valuation problem is always one of searching until a fair market price of the property in question is obtained. In theory that could be true.   However, there are numerous situations where it is necessary to estimate the value of property when no exchange of the property is contemplated and when no fair free market for such property exists.   For example, think of the property of a railway system or of a manufacturing enterprise.   An authoritative taxing body is going to collect property taxes, based, say, on the value of that property. There is little chance of finding a fair market price for such properties; so the appraiser must resort to other methods to reach his estimate of value.

The value of a property is based fundamentally on its ability to render satisfying services.   The true value then is the present worth of these expected future services, whether they be sentimentalities, pleasures, satisfactions, or monetary returns.

2.2. Role of Courts in Establishing Values.   The fundamentals of valuation, to which the appraiser looks for guidance, have evolved through long years of trial and controversy.   Estimates of value, being judgments, have reflected the interests of those parties concerned about the appraisals.   In tax cases, for example, the property owner is interested primarily in paying as small a tax as possible; the taxing body is interested primarily in having each taxpayer pay his fair share of the total tax to be collected.   These interests can be far apart; they have become bases for controversy.   As a result, the courts of the land have stepped in as arbiters.   Through their decisions there has grown a body of law relating to the value of property.

The basis of the fundamentals of engineering valuation is the law of the land, both common and statute, as interpreted and thereby established by the courts of final resort.

2.3. State and Federal Court Jurisdiction and Procedure.   Valuation questions are sometimes litigated in state and sometimes in federal courts.

State courts deal primarily with intrastate cases, involving questions of the common and statute law of the state.   Appeals may be taken to the state supreme court, but in some states they must go first to an appellate division.   Appeal may be taken to the United States Supreme Court only in those cases in which competent showing is made that some question of federal law or federal constitutional right is at issue.

Federal courts deal primarily with interstate cases and with other cases involving questions of federal common and statute law, including federal constitutional rights.   Most of the cases started in federal courts go first to the United States district courts.   United States circuit courts of appeal are provided to decide most appeals; only certain cases can reach the United States Supreme Court.   The United States Court of Claims and the United States Board of Tax Appeals are examples of special tribunals provided to try, in the first instance, special types of litigations.

The constitutional authority of the federal courts to protect public utility owners against confiscatory rates is conferred by

1. That portion of the Fifth Amendment to the Constitution of the United States which provides that no person shall be "deprived of life, liberty, or property, without due process of law; nor shall private property be taken for public use without just compensation."

2. That part of the Fourteenth Amendment to the Constitution of the United States which provides: "Nor shall any state deprive any person of life, liberty, or property without due process of law, nor deny to any person the equal protection of the laws."

2.4. Classes of Law Cases Involving Valuation.   Law cases involving valuation fundamentals may be roughly classified as follows:

1. Valuation litigations involving individual persons and corporations. The value at issue may be that of either a nonregulated enterprise or a public utility enterprise.   The litigation is initiated by filing a suit in a court of appropriate jurisdiction, either state or federal.   Examples are litigations over: property sales or leases; divisions of estates; divisions of jointly owned properties; issuance of corporation securities.

2. Valuation litigations involving private individuals or corporations and the public or legal representatives of the public.   The value at issue

may be that of either a nonregulated or a regulated enterprise.   In most cases the litigation is started in court only after a public utility or governmental officer, jury, board, commission, or legislative agency has first made an official decision involving the value at issue.   A qualified party at interest may appeal this decision to the appropriate state or federal court.   Examples are litigations over: property tax valuations; income taxes; condemnations of property for public use; public utility rate cases.

Except in interstate cases and in other cases where questions of federal law or federal constitutional rights are at issue, litigations over property rights are most often carried on in state courts.

In public utility litigations, however, the right of appeal to the federal courts exists so often that there is a strong tendency to start such litigations in the federal courts.   The courts decide whether particular rates established by law or by utility commission orders are, or are not, so low as to be confiscatory of property, and therefore in violation of the constitutional rights of the owners.   In practice, the courts give great weight to the authority of legislative bodies and to the decisions and orders of utility commissions.   In general, the rule is that positive and convincing proof of injustice, amounting to the violation of legal rights, is necessary to justify setting aside laws, rates, and commission orders related to public utility regulation.

2.5. Important Court Decisions Affecting Valuation.   Brief, general reviews of 83 important valuation litigation cases are presented in Appendix A, to afford assistance in studying, interpreting, and giving proper weight to court decisions on valuation questions.   The cases briefed are arranged by chronological periods; the progress of the development of valuation fundamentals in each period is stated briefly.   With each decision, one or two of its most important rulings are named.

UTILITY REGULATION AND THE RATE BASE

In the sections which follow there is a discussion of the development of regulation of public utilities and the effect of this regulation on the fundamentals related to the determination of the value of industrial enterprises.   Although these fundamentals in valuation procedures came about through public utility regulation, they form a sound basis of approach to the valuation of all property.

2.6. Historical Development of the Regulation of Public Utilities.   In the literature of jurisprudence, references to businesses endowed with a public interest are to be found in cases arising as early as the year 1400.   One of the earliest of such cases had to do with a common carrier, a stagecoach.

Legal decisions seem to emanate from a treatise by Lord Chief Justice Hale published in 1787,[1] in which he said:

A man for his own private advantage, may, in a port town set up a wharf or crane, and may take what rates he and his customers can agree for cranage, wharfage, housellage, pesage; for he doth no more than is lawful for any man to do, viz., makes the most of his own. . . . If the king or subject have a public wharf, unto which all persons that come to that port must come and unlade or lade their goods as for the purpose, because they are the wharfs only licensed by the queen, . . . or because there is no other wharf in that port, as it may fall out where a port is newly erected; in that case there cannot be taken arbitrary and excessive duties for cranage, wharfage, pesage, &c., neither can they be inhanced to an immoderate rate, but the duties must be reasonable and moderate, though settled by the king's license or charter. For now the wharf and crane and other conveniences are affected with a public interest, and they cease to be *juris privati* only; as if a man set out a street in new building on his own land, it is now no longer bare private interest, but is affected by a public interest.

The above statement of the law by Lord Hale was cited and acted upon by Lord Kenyon in *Bolt v. Stennett.*[2]

Again, in 1810, in *Allnutt v. Inglis,*[3] warehouses used for the storage of wines were held by Lord Ellenborough to be subject to regulation and " . . . obliged to limit themselves to a reasonable compensation for such warehousing. . . . "

One of the first cases in the United States involving the status of businesses affected by a public interest was heard by the Supreme Court of Alabama in 1841. In this case[4] the court was called upon to decide whether the power granted to the city of Mobile to regulate the weight and price of bread was constitutional.

Perhaps the United States Supreme Court decision in the *Munn* case[5] is the landmark in the law relating to businesses endowed with public interest. In the decision, delivered by Mr. Chief Justice Waite, many references were made to earlier decisions leading back to the treatise by Lord Hale. Among other things, the Supreme Court upheld the act of the Illinois legislature to " . . . fix by law the maximum of charges for the storage of grain in warehouses at Chicago and other places in the State. . . . " To quote from Chief Justice Waite's decision:

. . . it is difficult to see why, if the common carrier, or the miller, or the ferryman, or the inn-keeper, or the wharfinger, or the baker, or the cartman, or the hackney-

[1] *De Portibus Maris,* 1 Hargrave, Law Tracts 77–78 (1787).
[2] *Bolt against Stennett,* 8 T.R.606 (June 20, 1800).
[3] *Allnutt and another v. Inglis,* Treasurer of the London Dock Co., 12 East 527 (July 3, 1810).
[4] *The Mayor and Aldermen of Mobile v. Yuille,* 3 Ala. (N.S.) 137 (Ala. Sup. Ct. 1841).
[5] *Munn v. Illinois,* 94 U.S. 113, 132 (U.S. Sup. Ct. Oct. 1876).

coachman, pursues a public employment and exercises "a sort of public office," these plaintiffs in error do not.   They stand, to use again the language of their counsel, in the very "gateway of commerce," and take toll from all who pass. Their business most certainly "tends to a common charge, and is become a thing of public interest and use."   Every bushel of grain for its passage "pays a toll, which is a common charge," and, therefore, according to Lord Hale, every such warehouseman "ought to be under public regulation, viz., that he . . . take but reasonable toll."   Certainly, if any business can be clothed "with a public interest, and cease to be *juris privati* only," this has been.   It may not be made so by the operation of the Constitution of Illinois or this statute, but it is by the facts.

It was largely, however, during the latter part of the nineteenth century that the regulation of businesses endowed with public interest was developed.   This development was accelerated greatly through the establishment and rapid growth of the gas light, railroad, telegraph, telephone, and other service industries which could be developed properly only by restricting the number of operating enterprises within a given area.

The term *public utility* came gradually into use as a general term to apply to certain classes of business that were recognized as being endowed with a public interest.   In the jurisprudence of today any business so endowed is considered to be a public utility.   The layman generally thinks of electric power, water, gas, and railroad properties, streetcar lines, and bus lines as being public utilities without sensing that many other kinds of industrial enterprises are also public utilities.

The regulation of rents has been recognized as constitutional under emergency conditions such as those prevailing during the world wars. Air transportation, the various communication media including television, and, not the least, the utilization of atomic energy have been fields of enterprise vested with great public interest from their earliest beginnings.

2.7. Regulation and Valuation.   As soon as the right of regulation of public utilities by governmental agencies had been established, the question arose of the limits of authority.   For a time, in fact in some cases up to the present, regulation dealt only with operational procedures. For example, in dealing with the radio industry, the Federal Communications Commission concerns itself for the most part with the problems of licensing stations and allocating the available frequencies in the broadcasting bands; thus the interests of individuals, business organizations, and the general public may be accommodated fairly.   But sooner or later, regulation usually involves compensation for services performed.

In the early days of regulation it became clear that if a governmental agency possessed the power to regulate rates charged by a public utility, the agency had in its hands the power to affect the value of the enterprise.

An order to reduce rates can affect the future average return so adversely as to impair the ability of the organization to pay dividends or to obtain new capital. A rate reduction of this character diminishes the value of the property.

In *Smyth v. Ames*,[1] the Supreme Court of the United States set forth the basic tenet of rate regulation. This case arose from a litigation between the state of Nebraska and several railroads serving the state, involving a dispute over proposed intrastate livestock shipping rates. Because of its importance in rate regulation and its contribution to the art of valuation, the following is quoted:

We hold, however, that the basis of all calculations as to the reasonableness of rates to be charged by a corporation maintaining a highway under legislative sanction must be the fair value of the property being used by it for the convenience of the public. And in order to ascertain that value, the original cost of construction, the amount expended in permanent improvements, the amount and market value of its bonds and stock, the present as compared with the original cost of construction, the probable earning capacity of the property under particular rates prescribed by statute, and the sum required to meet operating expenses, are all matters for consideration, and are to be given such weight as may be just and right in each case. We do not say that there may not be other matters to be regarded in estimating the value of the property. What the company is entitled to ask is a fair return upon the value of that which it employs for the public convenience. On the other hand, what the public is entitled to demand is that no more be exacted from it for the use of a public highway than the services rendered by it are reasonably worth.

As a result of this decision, there arose the term *fair value basis of rate regulation* by application of the *Smyth v. Ames* rule. In Secs. 2.10 to 2.15, the controversies which have occurred in the application of the *Smyth v. Ames* rule to rate regulation of public utilities are discussed. But it is to be noted here that this decision had the effect of putting the appraisal engineer into the midst of the rate regulation problem. He has since played an important part in helping to answer the question, "What are just and reasonable rates which a public utility can charge its customers?" even though the final decision of what the rates are to be is not an item of the engineer's responsibility.

2.8. Rule of Smyth v. Ames. In brief, the *Smyth v. Ames* rule states that all factors or evidences of value must be considered and given such weight as may be just and right in each case, as determined by sound judgment.

It is significant that, in enunciating this rule, the United States Supreme Court, in effect, upheld the view that experts and courts should determine the value of property in formal valuations using those same evidences of

[1] *Smyth v. Ames* (No. 49), *Smyth v. Smith* (No. 50), *Smyth v. Higginson* (No. 51), 169 U.S. 466, 546 (U.S. Sup. Ct. Mar. 7, 1898).

value which prevail in ordinary business. These factors are discussed briefly in Chap. 1, but because of their importance a restatement of them is appropriate.

1. *The original cost of the property, adjusted for decreased usefulness and intangible elements.* This factor represents the existing investment in the property. The owner of the property desires to earn at least a fair return on his investment in the business. When the owner is competitively able to earn such a return, the original cost factor may affect the probable future returns of the existing business.

2. *The replacement cost of the property, adjusted for decreased usefulness and intangible elements.* This factor represents the price level at which immediate future replacements of existing properties and immediate future investments in similar competitive properties would be made. Thus, the replacement cost may affect the future returns through the operation of competition in fixing prices when the relative price level of such properties is materially different from the price level at which the existing property was built.

3. *The earning value of the property.* The past record of receipts and expenditures is an indicator of probable future returns upon which the value of the property depends. Because earning value is measured as the present worth of the probable future returns from the property, it is often entitled to great weight in estimating value. For purposes of establishing the rate base of a public utility, earning value may not be given any weight.

4. *The service worth value of the property.* The forecasting of future returns depends upon assumed price levels for commodities or services. Such price levels are determined primarily by the competitive market, which in turn is sensitive to the development of better products or services through changes of production equipment and methods. Customers are prone to measure the worth of commodities or services by the price of comparable alternates. Thus, service worth value is deserving of weight in determining fair value because it affords a check upon both the earning value and the market value of the property.

5. *The market value of the property.* When the stock and bond value can be determined from the prices paid by the investing public in trading the stocks and the bonds of the enterprise, such an estimate is an important factor in finding the fair value. The stock and bond value represents the investors' estimate of what the future returns are likely to be, except when the stock activity results from speculation rather than from a desire to acquire long-term investments.

Some types of properties may themselves be bought on the open market with sufficient frequency to have a market value established. Whether market value is determined by the sales of the stocks and the bonds or by the sales of similar properties, the estimate is evidence of the value of the property, to which the appraiser should give such weight as is just and right.

The market value is not determinable for enterprises whose stocks and bonds are not traded on the open market or for which no recent sales of similar properties are available.

6. *Other pertinent factors affecting value.* The value of a property is affected by such other factors as the purpose of the valuation, community served, type of product or service, materials and labor supply, transportation facilities, governmental supervision, position of enterprise in the industry, general economic conditions and trends, geographical location, and similar items which may affect the future returns of the enterprise. These factors are given weight by the appraiser as may be just in each case.

2.9. Ideal Application of the Smyth v. Ames Rule. The question may well be asked, "How would the *Smyth v. Ames* rule work in the ideal situation?" The following example, greatly simplified, may answer:

Suppose a small telephone utility is at present charging rates for service which produce an annual gross revenue of $500,000. A group of interested parties persuade the regulating agency, the state public service commission, to initiate proceedings to show why the present rate schedule should not be decreased.

Hearings are held, and the following estimates are finally determined by a decision of the commission:

1. The original cost of the fixed capital physical property adjusted for depreciation... $1,008,000
2. The depreciated book cost of the fixed capital physical property (amount paid to predecessor company less balance in the depreciation reserve account).. 1,119,000
3. The estimated reproduction cost of the fixed capital physical property adjusted for depreciation....................................... 1,770,000
4. The estimated present value of intangible properties possessed by the utility... 52,000
5. The estimated average requirement for working capital............. 76,000
6. The fair rate of return, percent....................................... 5½
7. The average annual depreciation charge........................... $ 47,000
8. The average annual operation expense............................. 300,000

By giving an adequate expression of judgment to items 1, 2, 3, 4, and 5, plus any other pertinent factors or evidences of value, the commission decides that the rate base shall be $1,130,000.

The fair annual return which the utility is now allowed to earn is $62,150, found by the multiplication

$$\left. \begin{array}{c} \text{Fair annual} \\ \text{return} \end{array} \right\} = \left(\begin{array}{c} \text{rate} \\ \text{base} \end{array} \right) \left(\begin{array}{c} \text{fair rate of} \\ \text{return} \end{array} \right)$$
$$= (\$1,130,000)(0.055)$$
$$= \$62,150$$

By addition, the maximum allowable gross income is $409,150, found by the sum

Fair annual return...........................	$ 62,150
Fair annual expense for depreciation..........	47,000
Fair annual operation expense................	300,000
	$409,150

Since the existing gross income is $500,000 per year, the commission will undoubtedly order that the rates now in effect be changed in such a way as to produce a decrease in gross income of $91,000 annually.

It should be apparent to the reader that several of the items listed above may be a subject of controversy in a dispute involving the reasonableness of rates charged by the utility.   Those differences of judgments which are of special interest to the appraiser are discussed in Secs. 2.10 to 2.15.

Now a court, if necessary, can test the reasonableness of the rate reduction order by application of the *Smyth v. Ames* rule.   The following questions must be answered: Will the proposed rates

1. Be ample to pay all expenses of operation?
2. Enable the utility to maintain its investment in the property?
3. Provide for payment of interest on its bonded indebtedness?
4. Enable the utility to pay a suitable dividend to its owners?
5. Be so low that, in effect, the value of the property will be significantly impaired?
6. Be unreasonable, exorbitant, or prohibitive?

In the determination of the rate base, has the commission

7. Considered all evidences of value, and has just and right weight been accorded them?

When the answers to questions 1, 2, 3, and 4 appear to be "yes," it should follow that the answer to 5 is "no."   If the answer to 6 is also "no" and if "yes" is the answer to the last question, the rate order has a good chance of being approved by the court.

2.10. Significance of the Fair Value Rate Base.   It seems probable that certain objections to the fair value basis of rate regulation result from a lack of understanding of the real significance of the rate base thus established.   The impression has prevailed that the purpose of a valuation, and the establishment of a rate base as a result thereof, is to fix rates that are as near the confiscation level as is possible without danger of having the courts set aside the rates thus established.   Such is not the goal of fair regulation.

Impartial students of utility regulation recognize the necessity for providing the well-managed utility with an income sufficient to keep its property in good repair and to maintain the credit of the corporation so that it can operate efficiently and render satisfactory service. The rates required to ensure these conditions must be materially above the confiscation level. Just what constitutes a *fair rate of return* has never been defined precisely, but it must be at a level that permits adequate financing.

Judgment must be exercised in fixing the *rate of return*, just as it must be exercised in fixing the *rate base*. It seems perfectly clear that an intelligent and reasonable solution of this admittedly difficult problem is impossible without a knowledge of the value of the property employed in the public service. It is entirely feasible, if all concerned collaborate in the effort, to set up for rate-making purposes a rate base that takes proper account of all factors that should be considered in a given case.

Unfavorable criticism of the fair-value basis for rate regulation has also been attributed in part to the resulting long-drawn-out litigations. While the number of such extended cases has been small in comparison with the total number of rate cases, they have attracted wide attention. Valuation as a means of establishing the rate base, however, has not been responsible for the law's delay, although valuation seems to have borne the onus.

It is not out of place to remark that lack of confidence in fair value as a rate base has resulted from certain indefensible practices that have been all too common in rate cases. It is true that technical experts representing opposing sides in a rate controversy have filed separate valuations differing by large amounts. As a result, it is not surprising that reviewing boards and courts reposed but little confidence in the work of these experts. The testimony of technical experts as to the methods employed in arriving at their amounts has not been convincing because so often one or the other or both of the experts was in error. The valuation of an extensive property is a tedious matter and costs a large sum of money. It often happens that clients are unwilling to finance an adequate formal valuation and consequently make it necessary for their valuation experts to testify on the basis of inadequate data. All these things have contributed to much litigation, confusion, and delay in the field of public utility regulation.

2.11. Minority Court Opinions against the Fair Value Rate Base. In addition to the difficulties mentioned in the previous section, arguments designed to bring out the inherent weaknesses of the *Smyth v. Ames* rule have been presented from time to time. One of the most able of these discussions was that of the minority opinion in the *Southwestern Bell Telephone* case, written by Justice Brandeis and with which Justice Holmes concurred. Justice Brandeis wrote:[1]

---

[1] *State of Missouri ex rel. Southwestern Bell Telephone Co. v. Public Service Commission of Missouri et al.* (No. 158), 262 U.S. 276, 289, 296, 310, P.U.R. 1923C, 193 (U.S. Sup. Ct. May 21, 1923).

I concur in the judgment of reversal.   But I do so on the ground that the order of the state commission prevents the utility from earning a fair return on the amount prudently invested in it. . . . The Court, adhering to the so-called rule of Smyth v. Ames, 169 U.S. 466, and further defining it, declares that what is termed value must be ascertained by giving weight, among other things, to estimates of what it would cost to reproduce the property at the time of the rate hearing.

The so-called rule of Smyth v. Ames is, in my opinion, legally and economically unsound.   The thing devoted by the investor to the public use is not specific property, tangible and intangible, but capital embarked in the enterprise.   Upon the capital so invested the Federal Constitution guarantees to the utility the opportunity to earn a fair return.   (Except that the rates may, in no event, be prohibitive. . . .) The Constitution does not guarantee to the utility the opportunity to earn a return on the value of all items of property used by the utility, or of any of them.   The several items of property constituting the utility, taken singly, and freed from the public use, may conceivably have an aggregate value greater than if the items are used in combination. . . . But so long as the specific items are employed by the utility their exchange value is not of legal significance.
. . .

The efforts of courts to control commissions' findings of value have largely failed.   The reason lies in the character of the rule declared in Smyth v. Ames. The rule there stated was to be applied solely as a means of determining whether rates already prescribed by the legislature were confiscatory.   It was to be applied judicially after the rate had been made; and by a court which had had no part in making the rate.   When applied under such circumstances the rule, although cumbersome, may occasionally be effective in destroying an obstruction to justice. . . . But the commissions undertook to make the rule their standard for constructive action.   They used it as a guide for making, or approving, rates. And the tendency developed to fix as reasonable, the rate which is not so low as to be confiscatory.   Thus the rule . . . has, by the practice of the commissions, eliminated the margin between a reasonable rate and a merely compensatory rate; and, in the process of rate making, effective judicial review is very often rendered impossible.

Value is a word of many meanings.   That with which commissions and courts in these proceedings are concerned, in so-called confiscation cases, is a special value for rate making purposes, not exchange value.

Justice Brandeis felt strongly that fair value could not be a starting point[1] in a rate case and that it was necessary to have a set of rates at hand to test their reasonableness.   He considered the *Smyth v. Ames* rule

[1] Twenty-one years later in the *Federal Power Commission et al. v. Hope Natural Gas Co. Case* (No. 34), 320 U.S. 591, 601, 51 P.U.R. (N.S.) 193 (U.S. Sup. Ct. Jan. 3, 1944) the Court said:
" . . . The fixing of prices, like other applications of the police power, may reduce the value of the property which is being regulated.   But the fact that the value is reduced does not mean that the regulation is invalid.   It does, however, indicate that 'fair value' is the end product of the process of rate-making not the starting point as the Circuit Court of Appeals held."

a "mischievous" one (to quote Justice Black) in that it gave the regulating agencies the wrong guide in setting new rates.

That being the case, the question naturally arises, "What is a proper rate base with which to set up rates if fair value is not appropriate?" The following proposals have been advanced as an answer to this question:

2.12. Reproduction Cost Rate Base Adjusted for Depreciation. *The present as compared with the original cost of construction* was the term used by Justice John M. Harlan in *Smyth v. Ames*, which is comparable with the phrase *reproduction cost*[1] used today. The procedures followed in preparing such an estimate are discussed in Chaps. 5 and 6. However, the impact of its use as the proposed rate base is discussed herein.

The idea of using reproduction cost adjusted for depreciation as the rate base (and, too, as the principal evidence of value) was strongly voiced during the years preceding the First World War and immediately following. Book records of industrial properties were then so incomplete that reliable data for determining original costs could not be obtained.

Starting with 1915 and ending with 1929, the rise in construction cost prices produced situations where the estimate of reproduction cost was 60 to 100 percent higher than the original cost. Those who desired a high rate base naturally supported reproduction cost as the paramount evidence and claimed that the Supreme Court had upheld their contention, citing cases where rate bases had been rejected by the Court in which little or no weight was given to reproduction cost. Some lower courts even adopted the erroneous view that the highest court of the land had held that reproduction cost must be given *dominant weight;* but the United States Supreme Court ruling was merely that reproduction cost shall be given "such weight as is just and right in each case," never that it shall be predominant. In its decision in the famous *O'Fallon Railway* case[2] in 1929, in which the valuations made by the Interstate Commerce Commission were overruled because no weight was given to reproduction costs (except for land), the Court was careful to say:

. . . The weight to be accorded thereto [to reproduction costs] is not the matter before us. No doubt there are some, perhaps many, railroads the ultimate value of which should be placed far below the sum necessary for reproduction.

2.13. Original Cost Rate Base Adjusted for Depreciation. Ordinary, nonspeculative business investments are made for the purpose

---

[1] The term *reproduction cost* as used in the discussion in the following pages is used in the sense found in many utility rate cases. It means the cost literally to duplicate in a new condition the existing property. This term is not to be confused with the more general expression *replacement cost*, which means the replacement of the physical property or service with the most economical substitute without necessarily duplicating the size, weight, style, and character of the existing property.

[2] *St. Louis & O'Fallon Railway Co. et al. v. United States et al.* (No. 131), 279 U.S. 461, 487, P.U.R. 1929C, 161 (U.S. Sup. Ct. May 20, 1929).

of earning profits on the amount invested. Although these investments change in value from time to time, the owners of a business always desire to earn an adequate return on their investment and to be assured that incomes are sufficient to maintain the investment. Hence, it is not surprising that there has been much support from an early date for the contention which would make prudent investment the *dominant factor* in determining the rate base for calculating fair rates or prices. But on the other hand, since business investments change in dollar value, there is justifiable support for the contention that the earnings of a business should be based on value rather than investment.

The Massachusetts rule,[1] that the money honestly and prudently invested and devoted to the service of the public is entitled to a fair return, was established as early as 1914. During the period of high prices following 1915, the public utility commissions of several states favored prudent investment as a rate base, doubtless in order to protect the public from being required to pay returns upon great increases in value gained by utility properties without corresponding increases in investment. A number of engineers and economists supported the idea. Agreement with the idea is also to be found in the minority opinion of Mr. Justice Brandeis in the *Southwestern Bell Telephone* case. His argument in favor of prudent investment as a rate base included the following points:[2]

. . . The adoption of the amount prudently invested as the rate base and the amount of the capital charge as the measure of the rate of return would give definiteness to these two factors involved in rate controversies which are now shifting and treacherous, and which render the proceedings peculiarly burdensome and largely futile. Such measures offer a basis for decision which is certain and stable. The rate base . . . would not fluctuate with the market price of labor, or materials, or money. . . . It would not be distorted by the fickle and varying judgments of appraisers, commissions or courts. It would, when once made in respect to any utility, be fixed, for all time, subject only to increases to represent additions to plant, after allowance for the depreciation included in the annual operating charges.

It may be remarked that the great depression beginning in 1929 demonstrated again that prudent investment and value can bear no positive or preconcluded relationship.

[1] The Massachusetts Department of Public Utilities, *In re New England Telephone and Telegraph Co.* (July 30, 1925). See Robert H. Whitten and Delos F. Wilcox, "Valuation of Public Service Corporations," 2d ed., Vol. 1, p. 318, New York, Banks Publishing Co., 1928.

[2] *State of Missouri ex rel. Southwestern Bell Telephone Co. v. Public Service Commission of Missouri et al.* (No. 158), 262 U.S. 276, 306, P.U.R. 1923C, 193 (U.S. Sup. Ct. May 21, 1923).

There are as many loose ends to be gathered together in setting up the prudent investment as there are in determining fair value. Further, there is a diversity of opinion as to the procedure to be followed. Some of the questions that need to be answered authoritatively before a prudent investment rate base is established are:

1. Who shall determine what expenditures are prudent?

2. By what basis shall expenditures be determined as prudent?

3. Who shall determine and by what basis shall it be decided what property possessed by the enterprise is classified as used and useful and therefore prudent?

4. In determining prudent investment, is the cash money contributed by the owners therein the significant determining factor, or is the original cost of the property used in the business the significant factor to analyze?

5. How shall depreciation be treated in determining the prudent investment? Shall it be ignored? If depreciation is to be brought into the rate base, by what process shall it be determined?

6. What shall be done with property which at the time of installation unquestionably was a prudent investment but now is far from the best and most modern type?

The United States Supreme Court has not directed that prudent investment be the rate base. It is reasonable to assume that prudent investment is a factor to be taken into account, but there is no established dictum for judging the weight to be accorded this factor.

2.14. Federal Legislation and the Fair Value Rate Base. Although the Federal Power Commission was created in 1920, its duties were such that it did not enter significantly into public utility regulation until the passage of the Public Utility Act of 1935 and the Natural Gas Act of 1938. Of interest to the appraiser are the sections relating to the establishment of uniform classifications of accounts and the dictum[1]

The Commission may investigate and ascertain the actual legitimate cost of the property of every public utility, the depreciation therein, and, when found necessary for rate-making purposes, other factors which bear on the determination of such cost or depreciation, and the fair value of such property.

The material just quoted is Sec. 208(a) of the Public Utility Act of 1935; if for the term *public utility* one substitutes *natural gas company* the result is Sec. 6 of the Natural Gas Act of 1938.

It is of further interest to note the content of a section of the proposed public utility act of 1935, which was removed before the act was passed

[1] U.S. Congress, *An Act to Provide for Control and Regulation of Public Utility Holding Companies and for Other Purposes*, 74th Cong., 1st sess., Chap. 687, Sec. 208(a) (Aug. 26, 1935). (Public Laws of the United States, 74th Cong., p. 853.)

because many congressmen considered that such a provision would be unacceptable to the Supreme Court.   This section read:[1]

(c) In determining just and reasonable rates the Commission shall fix such rates as will afford the public utility an opportunity to earn a fair return on a rate base not in excess of the actual legitimate cost of the property used and useful for the service in question less the accrued depreciation therein.

It was not long after passage of these two acts until the Federal Power Commission tried out the provisions of the law.   Companies which neglected to change their accounts over to the new uniform classification found themselves in court.   Two major rate cases[2] were tried, of which the *Hope* case is the more significant.   Here was a utility wholly owned by a large oil company, purchasing gas in large quantities, and wholesaling it to a few customers.   Information brought out by the interested parties included the data given in the accompanying table.

Item	Company estimate, millions	Commission finding, millions
The original cost of the present facilities........	$ 52.7	
The actual legitimate cost of the present facilities	......	$52.0
The trended original cost of the present facilities (original cost converted to current cost by use of indexes)...............................	97.3	
The estimated reproduction cost of the present facilities......................................	105.1	
Development cost of well fields previously charged to operation expense........................	17.0	
The original cost less depreciation..............	......	31.6
Working capital..............................	3.0	2.1
The rate base................................	66.0	33.7

The Circuit Court of Appeals held that the Commission ignored the directions of the Federal Power Act as well as the dictum of *Smyth v. Ames*. However, the Supreme Court in the *Hope* case upheld the rate order of the Federal Power Commission, saying:

We held in *Federal Power Commission v. Natural Gas Pipeline Co.*, supra, that the Commission was not bound to the use of any single formula or combination of formulae in determining rates. . . . Under the statutory standard of "just

[1] U.S. Congress, *A Bill on Control and Elimination of Holding Companies*, 74th Cong., 1st sess., S. 2796, Sec. 208, par. c (May 13, 1935).
[2] *Federal Power Commission et al. v. Natural Gas Pipeline Co. et al.* (No. 265), 315 U.S. 575, 42 P.U.R. (N.S.) 129 (Mar. 16, 1942).
Federal Power Commission et al. v. Hope Natural Gas Co. (No. 34), 320 U.S. 591, 602, 649, 51 P.U.R. (N.S.) 193 (Jan. 3, 1944).

and reasonable" it is the result reached not the method employed, which is controlling. . . . It is not theory but the impact of the rate order which counts. If the total effect of the rate order cannot be said to be unjust and unreasonable, judicial inquiry under the act is at an end. . . . For we are of the view that the end result in this case cannot be condemned under the Act as unjust and unreasonable from the investor or company viewpoint.

Justice Frankfurter and Justice Jackson dissented. Their argument was based on the inadmissibility of a "rate base method" of setting rates in an industry having an irreplaceable asset as its reason for being in business. Justice Jackson said:

The prudent investment theory has relative merits in fixing rates for a utility which creates its services merely by its investment. The amount and quality of service rendered by the usual utility will, at least roughly, be measured by the amount of capital it puts into the enterprise. But it has no rational application where there is no such relationship between investment and capacity to serve. There is no such relationship between investment and amount of gas produced.

. . . As our decisions stand the Commission was justified in believing that it was required to proceed by the rate base method even as to gas in the field. . . . The fact is that this Court, with no discussion of its fitness, simply transferred the rate base method to the natural gas industry. . . . As I see it now I would be prepared to hold that these rules do not apply to a natural gas case arising under the Natural Gas Act.

. . . A price cannot be fixed without considering its effect on the production of gas. Is it an incentive to continue to exploit vast unoperated reserves? . . . The Commission has power to fix a price that will be both maximum and minimum and it has the incidental right, and I think the duty, to choose the economic consequences it will promote or retard in production. . . . In my opinion the "public interest" requires that the great volume of gas now being put to uneconomic industrial use should either be saved for its more important future domestic use or the present domestic user should have the full benefit of its exchange value in reducing his present rates.

. . . This problem presents the Commission an unprecedented opportunity if it will boldly make sound economic considerations, instead of legal and accounting theories, the foundation of federal policy.

Contrary to the opinion of many, there appears to be nothing in the *Hope* case or *Natural Gas Pipeline* case decisions to indicate that the Supreme Court has discarded the *Smyth v. Ames* rule. But by the very wording, the door has been left wide open for a regulatory agency to determine a rate base by any method which can be shown to be reasonable in the light of the results achieved by the rate order.

In the *Hope* case, the Supreme Court found that the test for reasonableness of rates could be made without the need of establishing the fair value of the enterprise, and no attempt was made by the Court to determine a fair value.

Since the passage of the Federal Power and Natural Gas Acts, there have been better records kept by the utilities, improvements in regulation, and better understandings of the objectives of regulation. Such attainments may account for the fact that there have been in recent years but few cases litigated in which it was necessary to show that a proposed set of rates would be so unreasonably low as to indicate actual confiscation of property. In addition, court decisions and the arguments of those coming before the courts, have indicated a tendency to view the regulation of rates of a public utility not as a problem relating to the value of property but as an exercise of the police power of the state, subject to the requirements that the fixing of new rates be reasonable and just and not arbitrary. If such a view were generally taken, only in exceptional situations would it be necessary to resort to the test of the *Smyth v. Ames* rule of fair value and to the protection of the due process clause of the Constitution.

The fixing of rates of a public utility may be more of an economic, social, or moral problem than a legalistic or factual one. A rate which is reasonable in the eyes of the general public could be inadequate to produce a fair return on an acceptable appraisal of the property. Perhaps the general worth of the service produced is as satisfactory a way of setting rates as is the rate base method, whether the base adopted is fair value, reproduction cost adjusted for depreciation, or prudent investment. But the final answer must be left to higher authority and to time.

2.15. Summary of Rate Base Determination. From the evidences of the manner of rate regulation of public utilities gathered during the half century of operation of the *Smyth v. Ames* rule, one sees that a regulating agency may proceed to fix rates along one of these three lines:

1. The commission may find a fair value of the utility and determine a fair rate of return. The rate structure would then be set to produce a fair return on this fair value.

2. The commission may determine the prudent investment and a fair rate of return. The rate structure would then be set to produce a fair return on this prudent investment.

3. The commission may fix a rate structure which will provide in the opinion of the commission a reasonable and adequate income sufficient to keep the utility stable and adequately financed without establishing a rate base or a fair rate of return.

Commissions and utilities have fought many a battle before the courts under the rules of the first procedure. The questions which predominate relate to just and right weights accorded evidences of value. However, under the tendency of price levels to increase, the influence of the Federal Power Commission, and the weight of the *Hope* case decision, many regulating agencies have used the second procedure.   The general results were lower rates to customers than would have prevailed had the first procedure been used.

Eventually it may be that the third operational procedure will be used. The discussion of Justice Jackson in the *Hope* case indicates that possibility.   In fact, the Public Service Commission of Wisconsin attempted to set the rates of a small telephone utility on just such a basis.   However, the Wisconsin Supreme Court set aside the action, saying:[1]

> The principal question raised by this appeal is whether the Commission must file findings of fact which embrace the essentials upon which it bases the reasonableness of its rate order. . . . The Commission's order in this case was appropriately termed by the trial court to be arbitrary and unlawful. . . .
>
> How can the Commission or the reviewing body or the utility or the public determine whether the profit is proper unless the Commission makes specific findings of the "relevant facts and circumstances"?   The Commission must determine what those are and set them forth as required by law.   Those essential facts which control each case will then determine the rate base.

Regardless of the operational procedures followed by the regulating agencies, the valuation engineer will continue to play an important part in helping to establish just and reasonable rates for public utilities.   His services will continue to be required for estimates of:

1. The original cost of construction
2. The proper overhead costs of construction
3. The reproduction or replacement cost of the property
4. The depreciation of the property
5. The average requirement for materials and supplies used in operations
6. The intangible property possessed by the utility
7. The proper annual depreciation charge
8. The average annual expenses of operation

These estimates cannot be obtained in an offhand way; judgment is required.   Although the rate regulation problem may not always be a valuation problem, the appraisal engineer must be on hand with his data and analyses, even though others may make the necessary final decisions setting the rate schedule.

Finally, in the few cases where it would seem that the proposed rate schedules are so unreasonably low as to indicate a drastic reduction in the value of the utility (confiscation), the test of *Smyth v. Ames* will apply. Then the problem is a valuation problem, and again the appraisal engineer has much to contribute.

[1] *Commonwealth Telephone Co., Respondent, v. Public Service Commission, Appellant,* 252 Wis. 481, 482, 73 P.U.R. (N.S.) 97 (Wis. Sup. Ct. May 11, 1948).

VALUATION OF NONREGULATED ENTERPRISES

The process of making a valuation of a public utility gradually evolved as the courts, valuation experts, and regulatory commissions expressed their views on what constituted the law of the land in appraising properties of this character.   It has been pointed out that certain elements of value came to be generally recognized in public utility regulation.   These elements were set forth under the scrutiny of the courts and commissions over a period of the past 50 years and constitute a guide as to the evidences of value.

In the valuation of nonutility properties, there has been no such thorough discussion of the elements of value, nor has the process of valuation been subject to such intense legal scrutiny and expert study.   It is repeatedly stated in this book that, after all, value is a matter of judgment.   The value of any industrial property is correctly arrived at by bringing to bear the judgment of experts who have gathered the various data essential to a correct judgment.   The general process for making an engineering valuation as developed from the experience of those who have been valuing public utilities affords a correct basis for appraisal of other types of industrial properties.

The valuation of nonutility properties may be undertaken for any one of a variety of purposes.   The purpose of the appraisal may determine the degree of detail employed, the items of property included, and the evidences of value considered.   Some of the major purposes of appraisals are discussed briefly to indicate the various phases of the valuation problem.

2.16. Administrative Purposes.   The management of an industrial enterprise ought to know the investment in, the value of, and especially the annual consumption of the useful service of fixed assets employed in the fabrication of its product.   Without this information, it is difficult to fix a selling price that will ensure a real profit.   Without this information, there is the danger that the selling price will be based on assumed costs in which an incorrect allowance for plant depreciation is included.

Management needs to be aware of the long-term rate of return realized by the enterprise on both its present investment and the probable replacement cost adjusted for depreciation.   Making budgets for future construction will require forecasts of the annual retirements of property and the estimated cost of replacements.   The depreciation reserve account balance should be tested frequently in order to ensure that the annual credits to the account are appropriate.   Thus, a valuation made for the purpose of administrative control should show the fair value of the property including both physical and intangible property and a statement of the original and replacement costs.

2.17. Valuation for Taxation. The amount of property tax annually paid by industrial enterprises is significant. However, the laws relating to the manner by which a tax base is determined vary widely. In some areas, the taxable value of industrial property approaches the practical fair market value, or the approximate amount which might be obtained were the property to change hands in a free market. In other areas, the taxable value may be some predetermined fraction of the fair market value or some unscientific minimum designed to make the unadvised taxpayer feel better. But whether the taxing body uses several evidences of value in setting the tax base of property or none at all, it behooves the management to have adequate appraisal data available in order to be able to discuss possible adjustments of tax assessments against the property.

If management maintains an original cost property ledger and if cost indexes and price trends necessary in the process of an engineering appraisal are maintained, the replacement cost of the property could be ascertained with a minimum of effort. When such a replacement cost is adjusted for depreciation, a sound basis is immediately available to management by which to determine whether tax assessments are reasonable.

There exists wide variety in the laws of the several states regarding transfer taxes which will be assessed when a property changes hands. Data which indicate clearly just what property has been sold and at what price are of great aid to management.

The U.S. Bureau of Internal Revenue requires the taxpayer to prove the correctness of his estimates of the annual provision for depreciation of the physical property. The proof includes a record of the original cost of existing property and some indication that the forecasted useful service lives are reasonable. Such data are contained in adequate property ledgers of the enterprise, and management should insist that sufficient effort be made to keep such records adequate. Otherwise it will be necessary to resort to special studies from time to time in order to supply sufficient data for income tax computations.

2.18. Sales, Condemnations, and Estates. When a business is to be sold or transferred, an appraisal may be made for the purpose of fixing a basis upon which to negotiate the sale or transfer. The appraisal that is made for this purpose should take into account every element of value that is recognized in law. As a matter of fact, appraisals of this kind not infrequently find their way into the courts. The fair value of the property can be most reliably established by following the formal process described in this book. In applying the formal valuation process to private industrial properties, it is necessary to take into account each factor affecting the value and to give each element the proper weight in view of the fact that the property under valuation is of a private character and subjected to open competition.

Private property is sometimes taken over for public use through exercise of the right of *eminent domain* and the owner compensated in accordance with the findings of a special jury or board set up in accordance with law.   Except in simple cases it is necessary to present evidence of value to these boards.   Often an appraisal is made for this purpose.   The value sought in such cases is the fair value of the property.   Thus, again, the significant elements of the *Smyth v. Ames* rule, applying to utility property, should be utilized in the appraisal of nonutility property.

For settlement with the heirs and with the governments who claim inheritance taxes, a careful appraisal of the tangible and intangible property of estates must be made.   The appraisal procedure can be determined only after knowing what particular properties are involved.   In general, the answer sought is the value of the property on the basis that it must be disposed of in the settlement of the estate.

If the character of a business is such that its future depends largely on the skill and wisdom of the owner, the value of the business materially decreases at his death.   In the settlement of such an estate, value would be determined more or less on the conditions of a forced sale.

On the other hand, if the property is one whose continuity of operation is not jeopardized at the death of the owner, the value would be determined by the general process outlined in this book.

2.19. Insurance Policies.   In determining the amount of insurance to be carried on a plant and for the appraisal of damages that may have been suffered through fire or other disaster, complete valuation data on the property are needed.   Insurance companies employ short-cut methods for checking the value of a property before they assume a risk thereon, but these methods are not satisfactory for the adjustment of losses.   Here the detailed inventory with the value correctly determined, usually on a replacement basis, affords the most dependable basis for the adjustment.

2.20. Financing.   The necessity frequently arises for additional financing for an industrial enterprise by the issuance of bonds or stock or, to meet temporary stringencies, by borrowing money from banks.   In these instances (except in obtaining limited loans for working capital), it is required that the value of the property be established to the satisfaction of those underwriting the financing.   One of the significant elements of value is the physical property.   Another strong element is the ability of the enterprise to earn returns sufficient to service the loan.   Thus, in the valuation of enterprises for financing purposes, either property value or earning value may be dominant, depending on the character of the financing and its immediate purpose.

Generally, no banking group would ordinarily finance an enterprise wholly on the basis of the established value of the physical property.   Therefore, it is highly desirable that there be available an appraisal which gives the fair value of the enterprise, including intangible elements.   It is also highly desirable to set forth the prospective annual earnings of the enterprise.

The federal government and the several state governments exercise certain controls on the offering for sale to the public of the securities of enterprises, both regulated and nonregulated.   Usually, the investigation which precedes approval of these issues for sale includes some study of the value of the physical properties owned by the enterprise.   The issuance of stocks and bonds is therefore expedited when the corporation can make available the required information on valuation which the government agency requests.

VALUATION FUNDAMENTALS AND THE PROCESS
OF ENGINEERING VALUATION

As previously stated, in ordinary exchanges of property the factors affecting value, enumerated in Sec. 2.8, are usually considered and given proper weight in an informal manner.   In engineering valuation, however, as a result of many years of development of the art, a fairly well recognized formal valuation process has gradually evolved.   Also, certain fundamentals on which the process is founded have become well established.   Chapter 2 is ended with a listing of these fundamental statements and a step-by-step process of conducting an engineering valuation.

2.21. Fundamentals of Valuation.   In summary form are listed in this section 20 fundamental statements pertaining to the basis and process of the art of engineering valuation.   These statements are the interpretations by the authors of the well-established, general economic and legal fundamentals which serve as the groundwork of the process of establishing value of property.   It is not claimed that all authorities on valuation will agree with the authors on each of these 20 statements. These statements, however, do set out the basic tenets which form an excellent guide to the subject of engineering valuation of industrial enterprises.

Fundamental 1.   *Purpose of Establishing Value.*   The value of any property varies with the time, place, conditions, parties thereto, and purpose for which the value is to be established.

Fundamental 2.   *Basis of Value.*   The fundamental basis of the value of any property at any time is the prevailing judgment, at that time, as to the present worth of the *probable future services* to be received from the property.

Fundamental 3.   *Factors Affecting Value.*   *All* factors which affect the value of any particular property must be taken into account in determining the property's fair value, giving each factor just and right weight in each case.

Fundamental 4. *Weights of Factors Affecting Value.* The just and right weights to be given the different factors affecting the values of particular properties may vary widely in different cases, and they must be determined by fair, correct judgment in each case, *not* by any valuation formula.

Fundamental 5. *Property Comprising an Enterprise.* Among other factors, the value of an enterprise as a whole is dependent upon the value of its properties, including (1) the value of its physical property, (2) the value of its intangible property, and (3) the value of its working capital and other liquid assets.

Fundamental 6. *Overhead and Direct Costs.* The original cost and the replacement cost of physical property include (1) the *direct* construction cost (sometimes termed contract cost) and (2) the necessary indirect construction cost, termed *overhead* cost.

Fundamental 7. *Adjustment for Depreciation.* In determining the present value of physical property on the basis of its replacement cost, an adjustment of the replacement cost is necessary in order to measure the reduction of service usefulness (quantitatively and qualitatively) of the present property as compared with the service usefulness of the hypothetical new property.

Fundamental 8. *Annual Depreciation Provision.* The annual operation return of an enterprise is inclusive of the properly allocated depreciation cost.

Fundamental 9. *Past Provisions for Annual Depreciation Costs.* Neither past undercharges nor overcharges of the annual depreciation provision for consumption of the usefulness of the property, as recorded in the financial accounts of the corporation, affect the present fair value of the property but may affect a rate base.

Fundamental 10. *Organization and Financing.* The necessary expense of organizing and financing an industrial enterprise may be capitalized as intangible property.

Fundamental 11. *Going Value.* An industrial property already in successful operation and regularly earning an income has a going value, over and above the sum of the values of the other elements of property.

Fundamental 12. *Good Will Value.* The good will of the customers who habitually patronize a particular enterprise may have a value to the enterprise which should be included as intangible property.

Fundamental 13. *Value of the Other Intangible Properties.* Industrial enterprises may possess intangible properties such as patent rights, water rights, contracts, options, and trade secrets which are valuable.

Fundamental 14. *Interest.* Interest payments on bonds or other securities representing the funded indebtedness of an enterprise should be excluded as an expense and included in the determination of the annual return of the enterprise.

Fundamental 15. *Discounts on Securities.* Discounts and premiums received on the sale of the securities of the enterprise are not valued as property of the enterprise.

Fundamental 16. *Fair Rate of Return.* The fair rate of return of an enterprise is equal to the rate of return generally earned on investments in other enterprises attended by corresponding risks and uncertainties. The return should be such that confidence in the financial soundness of the enterprise and the support of its credit is assured.

Fundamental 17. *Subservience of Public Utilities to Public Regulation.* Public utility rates, operation, and valuation are subservient to just and fair public regulation by (1) legislative bodies, such as Congress and state legislatures, and (2) utility commissions, such as the Interstate Commerce Commission, the railroad and other commissions of the several states, and certain city commissions when duly authorized by constitutional statute laws.

Fundamental 18. *Authority of the Courts in Public Utility Rate Litigation.* The several state and United States courts have jurisdiction and authority to protect both the public and public utility owners against unfair rates or regulation, no matter how imposed.

Fundamental 19. *Function and the Practice of the Courts in Public Utility Rate Cases.* It is the function of the courts to decide whether particular public utility rates, valuation laws, or utility commission decisions and orders are legal; it is not their function to establish utility rates or to make utility valuations on their own initiative.

Fundamental 20. *Legal Principle for Determining Fair Public Utility Rates.* The legal principle which most often applies in determining fair public utility rates is that the utility owners are entitled to a fair return from their property used and useful in rendering the public service. This principle is subservient to the ruling principle that the public is entitled to demand that no more be exacted from it for the services rendered by the public utility than such services are reasonably worth.

2.22. Step-by-step Process of Making an Engineering Valuation. The engineering process of making an engineering valuation of an enterprise is outlined in the following three parts, consisting of 17 distinct steps.

PREPARATORY WORK, INVENTORIES, AND INVENTORY CLASSIFICATIONS

1. Determine the purpose of the valuation, the parties thereto, the time, the place, and special conditions of the valuation.

2. Make a preliminary examination of the enterprise and its property. Study the history and circumstances of the initiation of the organization and its life history. Analyze the periodic financial reports. Plan the valuation; divide the property into appropriate geographical sections.

3. Make a complete detailed inventory of the property.

4. Summarize the inventory by geographical sections.   Classify all similar units by type, size, and age.   Check the property records of the enterprise extensively to verify the count of the units.

DETERMINATION OF THE EVIDENCES OF VALUE

5. Determine the original cost of all fixed capital physical property, excluding land, and adjust this cost for consumed usefulness.

6. Estimate the reproduction or replacement cost of all fixed capital physical property, excluding land, and adjust for consumed usefulness of the existing property.

7. Estimate the fair market value of all land.

8. Estimate the value of the working capital.

9. Estimate the present value of the intangible property possessed by the enterprise.

10. Determine the fair rate of return for the enterprise.

11. Estimate the earning value of the enterprise.

12. Estimate the service worth (fair earning) value of the enterprise.

13. Estimate the market value on the basis of the average market prices of its outstanding securities or on the basis of the market value of similar properties.

ESTIMATION OF THE FAIR VALUE

14. Find an evidence of the total present investment in the enterprise by summing items 5, 7, 8, and 9.

15. Find an evidence of the total value based on the present cost of construction of the enterprise by summing items 6, 7, 8, and 9.

16. Compare or contrast items 11, 12, 13, 14, and 15.   (Some of these evidences of value may not be obtained for particular enterprises.)

17. Find the fair value by giving such weight as may be just and right in each case to each item and to all other factors affecting the value.

2.23. Basic Considerations.   The appraisal process just outlined contemplates that the fair value of an entire enterprise is the goal of the appraiser.   Such an answer suggests a completely disinterested valuation, coming as close to a fair market value as is reasonable.   However, the appraiser may be called upon to make estimates which involve the valuation process but which may not end up as estimates of fair value.

Determination of value for property tax purposes and of the prudent investment in an enterprise employs some of the steps of the valuation process, but these determinations do not include the complete valuation process.   Fundamentally, the valuation process requires an answer to the question, "What appears to be the prospective earnings of the enterprise?"   For example, the determination of loans to businesses, the determination of an appropriate figure representing the purchase price of an operating enterprise, and the amount determined as the condemnation price of a plot of land are valuation problems because such values are dependent upon the future returns.

Whether or not an appraisal is a complete valuation problem need not be of concern to the appraiser.   It is necessary only that he know what he is doing and why and that he recognize a true valuation problem when he encounters it.

CHAPTER 3

Property and Other Accounting Records

The making of a correct engineering valuation of an industrial property requires many data which can be ascertained only from properly kept book accounts of the enterprise. Of foremost importance are the book records of the physical property. No set of information is more useful to the valuation engineer than an accurate, up-to-date property ledger showing description, location, and original cost of every item and group of physical property owned by the company.

In the absence of a satisfactory property ledger, the appraiser is required to conduct extensive field inventories and extensive correspondence and search to establish the original cost of the property (see Chaps. 4, 5, and 6).

Operating statements, balance sheets, and other financial reports are also of importance to the appraiser. From these accounts the appraiser is able to determine the yearly returns, rate of growth of the enterprise, depreciation accounting practices, and other financial information needed in the process of valuation.

3.1. Property Accounts and Property Ledgers. The prime purpose of the accounts of physical property is to afford a means of keeping track of these capital investments in the same manner as other accounts are used to monitor the supplies and raw materials, and as accounts are maintained to keep track of finished goods. Property purchased with cash is no less important in the financial accounting system than is the cash. Balance sheet and operating statements are hardly of value unless they reflect properly the activity in physical assets and depreciation allocations. Property accounts are the basic sources of the entries for property assets and depreciation ledgers.

A system of property accounts consists basically of two sets of records, (1) the property fiscal accounts and (2) the property ledgers. The fiscal accounts are the sources of balance sheet information pertaining to the investment in fixed capital property, both by geographical location and by function. The property ledgers are detailed accounts subsidiary to the property fiscal accounts. Ledgers show the detailed descriptions and costs of the physical properties by many subdivisions and itemizations.

The analysis of work orders, both construction and retirement, is made by use of the property ledgers, and it is from these analyses that much of the fiscal information is furnished for posting to the fiscal accounts.   Especially is this true of retirement work orders.   Though the fiscal property accounts and the property ledgers serve as a check on each other and are always reconciled, the fiscal accounts are considered to be the controlling records.

The operation of property ledgers requires the services of engineers, because of the necessity of making allocations of the cost of the additions and retirements to the many detailed classifications of the items of properties.   Costs must be allocated to the foundation as distinguished from the machine, and to piping, wiring, and other connections as distinguished from apparatus and equipment.   Building costs are allocated to foundations, walls, floors, roofs, wiring, heating, and the like, by types of material as well as by function.   Frequent reference to construction plans and specifications is required in connection with the posting of the property ledger.

The combined system of property fiscal accounts and the property ledger will provide for the following:

1. A detailed description of the property, with itemization of all quantities and their unit costs and identifying technical specifications.

2. A geographical and a functional classification of the property such that all the property in a given location can be identified easily and all the property of a like kind can be grouped.

3. A continuous inventory maintained through a system of prompt work-order analysis by which the property added is brought into the record and the property retired is removed from the accounts, by proper debit and credit entries.

4. Dates of additions and retirements of the property from which satisfactory analyses of retirements can be made to determine survivor curves, average service lives, and age distribution of property in service.

5. Realized salvage values and costs of removal for each class of property.

6. The amounts of overhead costs and the detail of how they were determined and allocated.

7. Itemization of the units of construction and assembly to show both quantities and unit costs, so that cost indexes can be developed.

8. Notation of work-order numbers, construction contracts, and construction plans, as a means of cross reference back to original sources of the supporting information.

Property ledgers are designed to fit the occasion of their use.   In general they provide for three types of properties: (1) structural and com-

TABLE 3.1.   PROPERTY LEDGER FORM 301 FOR UNIT ITEMS

Property Ledger Form 301.   Sac County Electric Company, Sac City, Iowa

Unit: Permutit water softener
Manufacturer: Crane Mfg. Co., Chicago
Supplier: Midwest Supply Co., Des Moines
Mfg's serial no.: 341 289-12
Rating or size: 12,000 gal per day
Type or model: E-4

Date installed: Oct. 5, 1931
Location: Power plant building
Division: Sac City power plant
Account: 316 misc. power plant equipment
Subaccount:
Assigned no.: P-321

Date	Reference and explanations	Quantity and unit	Item and description	Cost f.o.b. or stores	Installation costs	Cost installed / Cost retired	Cost of items remaining in service
(1)	(2)	(3)	(4)	(5)	(6)	(7)	(8)
Oct. 29, 1931	Work order 3064	1	12,000-gal Permutit softener	$4,290.00	$310.00	$4,600.00	$4,600.00
			Piping as follows:				
		10'	6" C.I.B. & S.	9.65			
		1	6" T bell	11.00			
		1	6" gate valve bell	24.00			
		178'	4" C.I.B. & S.	91.60			
		4	4" 90-deg bell	19.70			
		1	4" 45-deg bell	4.80			
		1	4" T bell	7.70			
		2	4" gate valve bell	24.00			
		1	4" float valve bell	60.00			
		1	4" × 4" × 2" Y bell	6.50			
		1	4" × 4" × 2" T bell	7.15			
		20'	2" C.I.B. & S.	3.50			
		1	2" 90-deg bell	4.50			
		1	2" gate valve bell	7.50			
		22'	2½" steel pipe through reservoir	8.10			
		2	2½" 45-deg elbows	1.70			
			Total piping	$ 291.40	104.00	395.40	4,995.40
Dec. 31, 1931	General overheads at 6.1%					304.72	5,300.12
Dec. 1, 1941	Work order 4178	1	6" gate valve bell (broken)	*24.00*	*8.56*	*32.56*	
			Overheads at 6.1%			*1.98*	5,265.58
		1	6" gate valve bell (replacement)	20.90	10.20	31.10	5,296.68
Dec. 31, 1941	General overheads at 8.0%					2.49	5,299.17
Oct. 8, 1951	Retirement work order 5082		Entire softener sold for salvage to J. H. Blank Co., Chicago			*5,299.17*	0.00
			Cost of removal of softener			126.40	126.40
			Sale price for salvage			*175.00*	*48.60*

NOTE: In this table, retirements are indicated by italic figures.

posite properties identifiable largely by location and general description, such as buildings, process machinery and apparatus, and heavy construction; (2) singly identifiable numerous units such as motors, poles, transformers, and meters; (3) numerous small mass units which cannot be economically identified individually, such as insulators, pole hardware, and railroad crossties.

TABLE 3.2. PROPERTY LEDGER FORM 302 FOR VINTAGE GROUPS

Property Ledger Form 302. Sac County Electric Company, Sac City, Iowa

Unit: Distribution poles	Date installed: 1930
Manufacturer: Minnesota & Ontario Paper Co.	Location: Sac City street system
Supplier: Same	Division: Sac City distribution
Mfg's serial no.:	Account: 354 poles, towers, and fixtures
Rating or size: 35 ft, Class 4	Subaccount:
Type or model: Western red cedar, butt-treated	Assigned no.: E-196

Date	Reference and explanations	No. in service	No. installed / No. retired	Unit cost f.o.b. or stores	Unit installation cost	Total unit cost installed	Cost installed / Cost retired	Cost of units remaining in service
(1)	(2)	(3)	(4)	(5)	(6)	(7)	(8)	(9)
Mar. 2, 1930	Work order 2049	50	50	$15.70	$3.24	$18.94	$ 947.00	$ 947.00
June 8, 1930		130	80	15.20	3.24	18.44	1,475.20	2,422.20
July 17, 1930		150	20	15.20	3.24	18.44	368.80	2,791.00
Aug. 20, 1930		179	29	15.20	3.24	18.44	534.76	3,325.76
Dec. 11, 1930		309	130	14.40	3.24	17.64	2,293.20	5,618.96
Dec. 31, 1930	General overheads at 5.263%						295.73	5,914.69
	Average unit cost of 309 poles			14.94	3.24	19.1414		
July 6, 1935	Work order A-635	308	1				19.14	5,895.55
Feb. 6, 1937	Work order A-637	307	1				19.14	5,876.41
Sep. 3, 1940	Work order A-640	304	3				57.42	5,818.99
Apr. 16, 1943	Work order A-643	301	3				57.42	5,761.57
Aug. 18, 1944	Work order A-644	300	1				19.14	5,742.43
May 6, 1946	Work order 6091	290	10				191.41	5,551.02
July 14, 1947	Work order A-647	281	9				172.27	5,378.75
Sep. 30, 1948	W.O. A-648, 6898	266	15				287.12	5,091.63
Oct. 16, 1949	Work order A-649	252	14				267.98	4,823.65
May 19, 1950	Work order A-650	246	6				114.85	4,708.80
Nov. 22, 1951	W.O. A-651, 7282	230	16				306.26	4,402.54

NOTE: In this table, retirements are indicated by italic figures.

The property ledgers in Tables 3.1, 3.2, and 3.3 illustrate satisfactory forms to use for these three general classes of properties.

3.2. Advantages of Property Ledgers to Valuation. A high percentage of the work of making an engineering valuation of an industrial enterprise is directly concerned with the physical properties. An adequate

TABLE 3.3. PROPERTY LEDGER FORM 303 FOR UNIDENTIFIABLE UNITS

Property Ledger Form 303.   Sac County Electric Company, Sac City, Iowa

Unit: Primary line insulators   Date installed: 1938 and later
Manufacturer: Porcelain Insulator Corp.   Location: Sac City distribution system
Supplier: Iowa Electric Supply Co.   Division: Sac City distribution
Mfg's serial no.:   Account: 357 overhead conductors and devices
Rating or size: 6,600-volt   Subaccount:
Type or model: L 62 Pinco   Assigned no.:

Date	Reference and explanations	No. in service	No. installed / No. retired	Unit cost f.o.b. or stores	Unit installation cost	Total unit cost installed	Cost installed / Cost retired*	Cost of units remaining in service
(1)	(2)	(3)	(4)	(5)	(6)	(7)	(8)	(9)
Apr. 15, 1938	Work order 5061	50	50	$0.10	$0.03	$0.13	$ 6.50	$ 6.50
Oct. 21, 1938	Work order 5061	61	11	0.105	0.035	0.14	1.54	8.04
Dec. 31, 1938	General overheads at 5.15%						0.41	8.45
	Average unit cost of 61 insulators					0.1385		
Mar. 26, 1939	Work order 5061	110	49	0.105	0.035	0.14	6.86	15.31
May 13, 1939	Work order 5061	150	40	0.105	0.035	0.14	5.60	20.91
June 22, 1939	Work order 5180	162	12	0.105	0.035	0.14	1.68	22.59
Oct. 6, 1939	Work order 5360	182	20	0.105	0.035	0.14	2.80	25.39
Oct. 13, 1939	Work order 5268	200	18	0.105	0.035	0.14	2.52	27.91
Dec. 31, 1939	General overheads at 5.51%						1.07	28.98
	Average unit cost of 139 insulators					0.1477		
Oct. 20, 1940	Work order 5588	276	76	0.11	0.04	0.15	11.40	40.38
Dec. 31, 1940	General overheads at 4.76%						0.54	40.92
	Average unit cost of 76 insulators					0.1571		
May 18, 1941	Work order A-841	272	*4*			*0.1385*	*0.55*	40.37
Dec. 31, 1941	Work order 5784	322	*50*	0.11	0.04	0.15	7.50	47.87
Dec. 31, 1941	General overheads at 5.16%						0.39	48.26
	Average unit cost of 50 insulators					0.1578		
Aug. 30, 1942	Work order A-842	314	*8*			*0.1385*	*1.11*	47.15
Dec. 31, 1942	Work order A-842	344	*30*	0.115	0.04	0.155	4.65	51.80
Dec. 31, 1942	General overheads at 5.50%						0.26	52.06
	Average unit cost of 30 insulators					0.1637		
Dec. 31, 1945	Work order A-845	334	*10*			*0.1385*	*1.38*	50.68
Dec. 31, 1946	Work order A-845	374	*40*	0.14	0.06	0.20	8.00	58.68
Dec. 31, 1946	General overheads at 6.76%						0.54	59.22
	Average unit cost of 40 insulators					0.2135		
June 30, 1948	Work order 6897	414	40	0.16	0.065	0.225	9.00	68.22
Dec. 31, 1948	Work order 6981	516	102	0.19	0.07	0.26	26.52	94.74
Dec. 31, 1948	General overheads at 7.14%						2.54	97.28
	Average unit cost of 142 insulators					0.2680		
Mar. 28, 1949	Work order 7046		*39*			*0.1385*	*5.40*	91.88
Mar. 28, 1949	Work order 7046	468	*9*			*0.1477*	*1.33*	90.55
Dec. 31, 1949	Work order 6989	556	88	0.205	0.075	0.28	24.64	115.19
Dec. 31, 1949	General overheads at 7.60%						1.87	117.06
	Average unit cost of 88 insulators					0.3013		

NOTE: In this table, retirements are indicated by italic figures.
* Retirements priced on basis of first-in first-out (FIFO).

property ledger system, therefore, has great advantages to the appraiser, among which may be listed the following:

1. A review of the property ledgers affords the appraiser an adequate knowledge of the extent, amount, classification, and location of the property on which to base his preliminary plans for the valuation, including tentative valuation sections, personnel required, cost of the work, and time required.

2. Inventory forms, supplies, procedures, and property classifications can be developed from the property ledger, thus affording many opportunities to shorten the work and to verify results.

3. The complete detailed field inventory may be omitted when, through an adequate system of field spot checking, the physical property ledgers are found to be complete and accurate.

4. Property ledgers furnish unquestionable data on controversial items of overheads, underground work, and similar items difficult to inventory or to estimate.

5. Ages of property, age and amount of property retirements, and original costs are firmly established for use of the appraiser in his study of depreciation allocations.

Thus, when complete and accurate property ledgers are available, the appraiser's work and the cost of the valuation are reduced 50 to 90 percent from what would be required without these ledgers. Moreover, property ledgers supply information which otherwise would be controversial, thus making unnecessary extended conferences on inventory and original costs when the parties to the valuation endeavor to reach an agreement on the value of the property.

It is not easy to keep all the accounts of an enterprise reflecting actual current conditions, and the property accounts by their very nature are those which can become inaccurate most easily. One of the ways, however, to keep accounts currently accurate is to set up uniform accounting classifications and procedures and insist that they be followed.

Comparisons between different property accounts of one enterprise or between similar accounts of different enterprises often prove worth while in providing data for management decisions as well as for solutions to problems encountered by the appraiser. Comparisons to be valid must be based upon similar records. Consequently, much progress has been made in effecting a uniform classification of accounts and the property ledger systems supporting these accounts.

3.3. Uniform Accounting Classification. Regulatory commissions, both federal and state, have been instrumental in getting property accounts and ledger systems established in great detail and in promoting uniform classifications within an industry. However, one of the earliest uniform systems of statistical records and cost accounting was proposed in 1855 by the American Iron and Steel Association.[1] The National Association of Stove Manufacturers began discussion of the cost of manufacturing and adopted a cost formula in 1889. From these early dates uniform accounting spread to many trade associations until in 1931 a study of 500 associations revealed that 131 had developed uniform plans.[2]

Federal agencies prescribing uniform classifications of accounts include the following:

Interstate Commerce Commission—railway, pipe-line, and motor common carriers

Federal Power Commission—natural gas pipe-line, natural gas, and electric power companies

Federal Communications Commission—telephone, radio and television broadcasting, telegraph, and cable companies

Civil Aeronautics Authority—air-line common carriers

Most of the state regulatory commissions have established uniform accounting classifications for water, gas, electric, telephone, and transportation utilities; in most instances the state classification substantially follows the federal system when one applies.

A typical uniform classification of accounts as set forth by federal agencies is shown at the end of this chapter. The accounts shown are those prescribed by the Federal Power Commission for natural gas companies.[3]

3.4. Property Accounting Procedures. Property accounts are maintained to reflect both physical quantities and dollar original costs. Considerable detail is required in the ledgers if the accounting is to continue correctly over a period of years during which many additions and many retirements are made. Success in this respect depends upon close coordination and cooperation among the design, construction, and auditing departments. Construction work, purchase of new equipment, disposal of old property, or alterations to existing property and equipment are undertaken only after detailed work orders are issued by the proper authority. This work order will state in detail the work to be added and the old property to be removed, giving estimated costs for both, and original costs of the property to be removed. Upon completion of the

---

[1] Michael J. Jucius, Historical Development of Uniform Accounting, *Journal of Business of the University of Chicago*, Vol. 16, pp. 219–229, October, 1943.

[2] Metropolitan Life Insurance Company Policy-holders' Service Bureau, "Uniform Cost Activities in Trade and Industry," p. 1 (n.d., probably 1935).

[3] United States Federal Power Commission, "Uniform System of Accounts Prescribed for Natural Gas Companies," Washington, D.C., Government Printing Office, 1940.

work set forth in the work order the construction department prepares a final report describing in detail the work done and itemizing the costs. With this report and complete records of the prior work, the property auditing department analyzes the work order to obtain the debit and credit entries for the several accounts involved.

If a property ledger is to be worth its upkeep, it must be maintained at all times in exact agreement with the fiscal accounts and with the property owned by the company.   For engineering valuation these two requisites are especially important.

Agreement with the fiscal accounts is maintained by fiscal controls through which all expenditures for property reflected in the property accounts are likewise reflected in the property ledgers.   Plant additions which are posted to the property ledger are controlled exactly to the dollars debited to the plant accounts.   In making this set of entries, the fiscal expenditures may be carried in a clearing account until the property auditor has furnished the necessary analysis to indicate what is to be charged to plant additions and what to operation.   Likewise, when plant is retired, the property auditor furnishes to the fiscal auditor the necessary credit entries by accounts.

The property ledger should be proved against the fiscal accounts periodically, at least as often as once each year.   Similarly, the property auditor makes frequent checks in the field to ascertain that the property on his ledgers is in full agreement with that in use.   It is often easy for the operating division to discard property or to build up property through maintenance crews without first getting the proper work order through the property accounting division.

3.5. Maintenance and Additions Compared.   Obviously, property accounting is a procedure which calls for considerable judgment and, to a certain degree, arbitrary decisions.   The distinction between maintenance and repair work (debited directly to production expense), on the one hand, and addition and betterment work (debited to capital investment accounts), on the other hand, involves the borderline area which is not unlike deciding when the color black shades into gray.   Patching an area of a square yard of pavement is certainly a maintenance expense, but when the area grows to cover several hundred square yards, the accounting classification is settled only by predetermined policy.

The accounting classification between maintenance and construction operations is usually based upon the following items:

Size of the physical property involved (quantities of weight, area, volume, or length)
Number of units (itemization)
Cost of the work performed

Frequency of occurrence of the operation

Whether the depreciation rate is based upon retirement of the property
   involved in the operation

In general, operations which leave the property in better condition for
profitable service than when it was new are classed as additions and betterments, a form of construction creating a new investment; operations
which only restore property to a former serviceable state are maintenance operations, unless the property removed falls within the retirement classification. For instance, the replacement of a roof could be
classed either as a maintenance item or as a retirement and addition
operation, in accordance with predetermined accounting policies, which
specify whether the cost of the new roof would be charged to maintenance
or to investment.

To distinguish between expenditures for maintenance and for capital
additions is important.   In the former classification the cost is expensed
immediately and affects the current statement of profit and loss.   When
classed as a capital addition, the cost affects future statements of profit
and loss through the charge for depreciation.   When long-lived property
is added or retired through the maintenance accounts, the stated investment in the property eventually will not agree with the property in
service.   In order to keep the investment accounts in agreement with the
property in service, the necessary debit and credit entries to the property
accounts must be made for all property installed or retired, regardless of
whether the plant work is done by maintenance forces or by contract.

Utility property under regulation is usually closely specified as to
accounting classification, including definitions of retirement units.
Nevertheless, the variations in possible situations are so many and
extreme that considerable judgment must be continually exercised in the
procedures of property accounting.

3.6. Property Ledgers and Depreciation Accounting.   Property
ledger forms should also record the dates from which the age of the
property can be computed, at all times, including property existing in
service as well as that retired.   These ages (both physical units and dollar
units when possible) furnish the basic data from which the average service
lives can be calculated (Chap. 7) and from which a test of the adequacy
of the reserve can be computed.   Subledgers are frequently maintained
by age groups to facilitate making computations involving the age of the
property.   This information is useful currently in determining accounting depreciation rates as well as in valuation studies when average service
lives are wanted.

Should the cost of removal of retired property and the salvage value
received not be recorded in the *depreciation ledger* in a form which identi-

fied these entries with specific property, such data should be recorded in the *property ledger*.

3.7. Costing Property Ledgers.   The costing of the property ledgers should be by original cost with overheads shown separately.   The ledger or subsidiary records need to be complete enough in price data and overhead costs so that any portion of the property when retired can be priced out correctly (see Chaps. 5 and 6 for discussion of pricing and costing procedures).

When unidentifiable items such as those carried on Property Ledger Form 303 (Table 3.3) are retired, there is question of what cost to use. The two methods generally used base the book retirement cost on the cost of the units which were first in and assumed to be first out (FIFO) or last in and assumed to be first out (LIFO).

Under FIFO the book cost of the units remaining in service is that which would prevail should all units remaining in service be younger than the youngest unit actually retired.   The book cost of remaining units under the FIFO system approaches replacement cost based upon prices over a period equal to the average life of the property in the account.

Under LIFO the book cost of the units remaining in service is that which would prevail should all units in service be older than the oldest unit actually retired.   The book cost of remaining units under the LIFO system approaches the original cost of the units from the beginning of the account to an age equal to the average life of the property in the account.

FIFO states the cost balance in terms of the price trend from the latest purchase backward, but never including the units first purchased unless none is retired.   LIFO, on the other hand, states the cost balance in terms of the price trend from the earliest purchase forward, but never including the units last purchased unless no units have been retired.

3.8. Property Ledgers and Valuation Procedure.   The particular forms used in property ledgers vary from enterprise to enterprise, although all exhibit the information discussed in this chapter.   In regulated utilities, original cost property ledgers have virtually made it unnecessary to conduct complete field inventories to establish valuations. For any industry, complete property ledgers are most helpful in all valuation procedures as well as for the establishment of average lives on which to base depreciation rates.

When the appraiser finds that the enterprise under valuation has complete and accurate property ledgers which agree with the property in use and with the fiscal accounts, he is able to establish with only minor effort the following for all fixed capital physical property:

1. Complete original cost
2. Trended original cost (original cost converted to current cost by use of cost indexes)
3. Reproduction or replacement cost

Upon making a field inspection of the property and an analysis of the retirement experience from the property ledgers, the appraiser is then in a position to estimate his allowances for depreciation.

Today's trend in utility rate cases is to settle them by conference rather than by court proceedings, because with the original cost property ledgers and full uniform accounting procedures and classifications there is but little left in the controversial area which cannot be settled over the conference table.

FEDERAL POWER COMMISSION UNIFORM SYSTEM OF ACCOUNTS PRESCRIBED FOR NATURAL GAS COMPANIES

Effective Jan. 1, 1940

Balance Sheet Accounts

ASSETS AND OTHER DEBITS

I. UTILITY PLANT

100.	Gas plant
100.1.	Gas plant in service
100.2.	Gas plant leased to others
100.3.	Construction work in progress
100.4.	Gas plant held for future use
100.5.	Gas plant acquisition adjustments
100.6.	Gas plant in process of reclassification
107.	Gas plant adjustments
108.	Other utility plant

II. INVESTMENT AND FUND ACCOUNTS

110.	Other physical property
111.	Investments in associated companies
111.1.	Investments in securities of associated companies
111.2.	Advances to associated companies
112.	Other investments
113.	Sinking funds
114.	Miscellaneous special funds
114.1.	Depreciation fund
114.2.	Other special funds

III. CURRENT AND ACCRUED ASSETS

120.	Cash
121.	Special deposits
121.1.	Interest special deposits
121.2.	Dividend special deposits
121.3.	Miscellaneous special deposits
122.	Working funds
123.	Temporary cash investments
124.	Notes receivable
125.	Accounts receivable
125.1.	Accounts receivable—customers
125.2.	Other accounts receivable
126.	Receivables from associated companies
126.1.	Notes receivable from associated companies
126.2.	Accounts receivable from associated companies
127.	Subscriptions to capital stock
128.	Interest and dividends receivable
129.	Rents receivable
130.	Accrued utility revenues
131.	Materials and supplies
131.1.	Materials and supplies—gas
131.2.	Materials and supplies—other
132.	Prepayments
133.	Other current and accrued assets

IV. DEFERRED DEBITS

140. Unamortized debt discount and expense
141. Extraordinary property losses
142.1. Preliminary natural gas survey and investigation charges
142.2. Other preliminary survey and investigation charges
143. Clearing accounts
144. Retirement work in progress
145. Other work in progress
146. Other deferred debits

V. CAPITAL STOCK DISCOUNT AND EXPENSE

150. Discount on capital stock
151. Capital stock expense

VI. REACQUIRED SECURITIES

152. Reacquired capital stock
153. Reacquired long-term debt

LIABILITIES AND OTHER CREDITS

VII. CAPITAL STOCK

200. Common capital stock
201. Preferred capital stock
202. Stock liability for conversion
203. Premiums and assessments on capital stock
204. Capital stock subscribed
205. Installments received on capital stock

VIII. LONG-TERM DEBT

210. Bonds
211. Receivers' certificates
212. Advances from associated companies
212.1. Advances on notes
212.2. Advances on open accounts
213. Miscellaneous long-term debt

IX. CURRENT AND ACCRUED LIABILITIES

220. Notes payable
221. Notes receivable discounted
222. Accounts payable
223. Payables to associated companies
223.1. Notes payable to associated companies
223.2. Accounts payable to associated companies
224. Dividends declared
225. Matured long-term debt
226. Matured interest
227. Customers' deposits
228. Taxes accrued
229. Interest accrued
229.1. Interest accrued on long-term debt
229.2. Interest accrued on other liabilities
230. Other current and accrued liabilities

X. DEFERRED CREDITS

240. Unamortized premium on debt
241. Customers' advances for construction
242. Other deferred credits

XI. RESERVES

250.1. Reserve for depreciation of gas plant
  250.11. Reserve for depreciation of gas plant in service
  250.12. Reserve for depreciation of gas plant leased to others
  250.13. Reserve for depreciation of gas plant held for future use
250.2. Reserve for amortization and depletion of producing natural gas land and land rights
  250.21. Reserve for amortization and depletion of producing natural gas land and land rights —gas plant in service
  250.22. Reserve for amortization and depletion of producing natural gas land and land rights —gas plant leased to others
250.3. Reserve for abandoned leases
251. Reserve for amortization of other limited-term gas investments
251.1. Reserve for amortization of other limited-term gas investments— gas plant in service

XII. CONTRIBUTIONS IN AID OF CONSTRUCTION

XIII. SURPLUS

Gas Plant Accounts

I. INTANGIBLE PLANT

II. PRODUCTION PLANT

A. Manufactured Gas Production Plant

B. Natural Gas Production Plant

III. STORAGE PLANT

341. Land and land rights
342. Structures and improvements

IV. TRANSMISSION PLANT

351. Land and land rights
    351.1. Land
    351.2. Land rights
352. Structures and improvements
    352.1. Pumping station structures
    352.2. Measuring and regulating station structures
353. Mains
354. Pumping and regulating equipment
    354.1. Pumping station equipment
    354.2. Measuring and regulating station equipment

V. DISTRIBUTION PLANT

357. Land and land rights
    357.1. Land
    357.2. Land rights
358. Structures and improvements
359. Mains
360. Pumping and regulating equipment

361. Services
362. Meters
363. Meter installations
364. House regulators
365. House regulator installations
366. Other property on customers' premises
367. Street lighting equipment
368. Other distribution system equipment

VI. GENERAL PLANT

370. Land and land rights
371. Structures and improvements
372. Office furniture and equipment
373. Transportation equipment
374. Stores equipment
375. Shop equipment
376. Laboratory equipment
377. Tools and work equipment
378. Communication equipment
379. Miscellaneous equipment
390. Other tangible property
391. Gas plant purchased
392. Gas plant sold

Earned Surplus Account

CREDITS

271. Earned surplus (at beginning of period)
400. Credit balance transferred from income account
401. Miscellaneous credits to surplus
    Total credits

DEBITS

410. Debit balance transferred from income account
411. Dividend appropriations—preferred stock
412. Dividend appropriations—common stock
413. Miscellaneous reservations of surplus
414. Miscellaneous debits to surplus
    Total debits
271. Earned surplus (at end of period)

Income Accounts

I. UTILITY INCOME

Gas operating income:
501.   Operating revenues
Operating revenue deductions:
502.   Operating expenses

503.1. Depreciation
503.2. Amortization and depletion of producing natural gas land and land rights
504. Amortization of other limited-term gas investments

505. Amortization of gas plant acquisition adjustments
506. Property losses chargeable to operations
507. Taxes
    Total operating revenue deductions
    Net operating revenues
508. Income from gas plant leased to others
    Gas operating income
509. Other utility operating income
    Utility income

II. EXPLORATION AND DEVELOPMENT COSTS

510. Delay rentals
511. Nonproductive well drilling
512. Abandoned leases
513. Other exploration costs
    Net utility income

III. OTHER INCOME

520. Income from merchandising, jobbing, and contract work
521. Income from nonutility operations
522. Revenues from lease of other physical property
523. Dividend revenues
524. Interest revenues

525. Revenues from sinking and other funds
526. Miscellaneous nonoperating revenues
527. Nonoperating revenue deductions
    Total other income
    Gross income

IV. INCOME DEDUCTIONS

530. Interest on long-term debt
531. Amortization of debt discount and expense
532. Amortization of premium on debt— Cr.
533. Taxes assumed on interest
534. Interest on debt to associated companies
535. Other interest charges
536. Interest charged to construction— Cr.
537. Miscellaneous amortization
538. Miscellaneous income deductions
    Total income deductions
    Net income

V. DISPOSITION OF NET INCOME

540. Miscellaneous reservations of net income
    Balance transferred to earned surplus

Operating Revenue Accounts

I. GAS SERVICE REVENUES

600. Residential sales
602. Commercial and industrial sales
    602.1. Commercial sales
    602.2. Industrial sales
603. Public street and highway lighting
604. Other sales to public authorities
605. Sales to other gas utilities
607. Interdepartmental sales
608. Other sales

II. OTHER GAS REVENUES

610. Rent from gas property
611. Interdepartmental rents
612. Customers' forfeited discounts and penalties
614. Servicing of customers' installations
615. Revenue from transportation of gas of others
616. Revenue from incidental gasoline sales
617. Revenue from processing natural gas
618. Revenue from incidental oil sales
619. Miscellaneous gas revenues

Operating Expense Accounts

I. PRODUCTION EXPENSES

A. Manufactured Gas Production

OPERATION

B A 701. Operation supervision and engineering

B A 702. Boiler and other power labor

B   703. Coal gas and producer gas labor

A 703.1. Retort labor

A 703.2. Coke oven labor

A 703.3. Producer gas labor

B   704. Gas generating labor

A 704.1. Water gas generating labor

A 704.2. Petroleum gas generating labor

A 704.3. Other gas generating labor

A 704.4. Gas reforming labor

B A 705. Purification labor

B A 707. Miscellaneous production labor

B A 708. Boiler fuel

B A 709. Water

B A 710. Fuel under retorts

B A 711. Fuel under coke ovens

B A 712. Producer gas fuel

B A 713. Coal carbonized in retorts

B A 714. Coal carbonized in coke ovens

B A 715. Water gas generator fuel

B A 716. Oil for water gas

B A 717. Gas enricher

B A 718. Liquefied petroleum gas

B A 719. Oil for oil gas

B A 720. Raw materials for other gas processes

B A 721. Purification supplies

B A 722. Miscellaneous works expenses

MAINTENANCE

B A 723. Maintenance supervision and engineering

B A 724. Maintenance of structures and improvements

B   725. Maintenance of power equipment

A 725.1. Maintenance of boiler plant equipment

A 725.2. Maintenance of other power equipment

B   726. Maintenance of producing and generating equipment

A 726.1. Maintenance of benches and retorts

A 726.2. Maintenance of coke ovens

A 726.3. Maintenance of producer gas equipment

A 726.4. Maintenance of water gas generating equipment

A 726.5. Maintenance of petroleum gas equipment

A 726.6. Maintenance of other gas generating equipment

A 726.7. Maintenance of coal, coke, and ash handling equipment

B   727. Maintenance of other manufactured gas property

A 727.1. Maintenance of gas reforming equipment

A 727.2. Maintenance of purification equipment

A 727.3. Maintenance of other production equipment

MISCELLANEOUS

B A 728. Power from other sources

B A 729. Rents

B A 730.1. Residuals produced—Cr.

B A 730.2. Residuals operation expenses

B A 730.3. Residuals maintenance expenses

B A 731.1. Joint expenses—Dr.

B A 731.2. Joint expenses—Cr.

B A 732. Duplicate charges—Cr.

B. Natural Gas Production

OPERATION

B A 733. Operation supervision and engineering

B   734. Operation labor

A 734.1. Gas well labor

A 734.2. Field line labor

A 734.3. Field measuring and regulating station labor

734.31. Field compressor station labor

734.32. Field measuring and regulating station labor

A 734.4. Other production labor

B   735. Operating supplies and expenses

A 735.1. Gas well supplies and expenses

A 735.2. Field line supplies and expenses

A 735.3. Field measuring and regulating station supplies and expenses

735.31. Field compressor station supplies and expenses

735.32. Field measuring and regulating station supplies and expenses

A 735.4. Other supplies and expenses

B A 736. Purification supplies and expenses

B A 737. Production maps and records

B A 738. Miscellaneous production expenses

MAINTENANCE

B A 739. Maintenance supervision and engineering

B   740. Maintenance of structures and improvements

A 740.1. Maintenance of gas well structures

A 740.2. Maintenance of field measuring and regulating station structures

740.21. Maintenance of compressor station structures

740.22. Maintenance of field measuring and regulating station structures

A 740.3. Maintenance of other production system structures

B A 741. Maintenance of producing gas well equipment

B   742. Maintenance of field lines and equipment

A 742.1. Maintenance of field lines

A 742.2. Maintenance of field measuring and regulating station equipment

742.21. Maintenance of compressor station equipment

742.22. Maintenance of measuring and regulating station equipment

B A 743. Maintenance of drilling and cleaning equipment

B A 744. Maintenance of other natural gas property

MISCELLANEOUS

B A 745. Gas well royalties

B A 746. Natural gas rents

B A 747.1. Residuals produced—Cr.

B A 747.2. Residuals operation expenses

B A 747.3. Residuals maintenance expenses

B A 748.1. Joint expenses—Dr.

B A 748.2. Joint expenses—Cr.

B A 749. Duplicate charges—Cr.

C. Other Production Expenses

OPERATION

B A 750. Operating of storage facilities

B A 751. Gas mixing expenses

MAINTENANCE

B A 752. Maintenance of storage facilities

B   753. Maintenance of other production property

A 753.1. Maintenance of gas mixing equipment

A 753.2. Maintenance of production laboratory equipment

MISCELLANEOUS

B A 754. Gas purchased

754.1. Gas purchased—natural gas

754.2. Gas purchased—other gas

B A 755. Purchased gas expenses

B A 756. Other expenses

B A 757.1. Joint expenses—Dr.

B A 757.2. Joint expenses—Cr.

II. TRANSMISSION EXPENSES

OPERATION

B A 758. Operation supervision and engineering

B   759. Transmission operations

A 759.1. Pumping and regulating expenses

759.11. Pumping and regulating expenses—labor

759.111. Pumping station—labor

759.112. Measuring and regulating station—labor

759.12. Measuring and regulating expenses—supplies and expenses

759.121. Pumping station—
supplies and expenses
759.122. Measuring and regulating station—sup-
plies and expenses
A 759.2. Operation of transmission
mains
759.21. Operation of transmission
mains—labor
759.22. Operation of transmission
mains—supplies and
expenses
A 759.3. Transmission maps and
records

MAINTENANCE

B A 760. Maintenance supervision and
engineering
B A 761. Maintenance of structures and
improvements
761.1. Maintenance of pumping
station structures
761.2. Maintenance of measuring
and regulating station
structures
761.3. Maintenance of other
transmission system structures
B   762. Maintenance of transmission
lines
A 762.1. Maintenance of mains
A 762.2. Maintenance of pumping,
regulating, and miscellaneous
equipment
762.21. Maintenance of pumping
station equipment
762.22. Maintenance of measuring and regulating station
equipment
762.23. Maintenance of other
transmission system
equipment .

MISCELLANEOUS

B A 763. Rents
763.1. Transmission and compres-
sion of gas by others
763.2. Rents
B A 764.1. Joint expenses—Dr.
B A 764.2. Joint expenses—Cr.

III. DISTRIBUTION EXPENSES

OPERATION

B A 765. Operation supervision and
engineering
B   766. Distribution office expenses
A 766.1. Distribution maps and
records
A 766.2. Other distribution office
expenses
B A 767. Operation of distribution lines
A 767.1. Operation of distribution
lines—labor
A 767.2. Operation of distribution
lines—supplies and expenses
B   768. Operation of meters
A 768.1. Removing and resetting
meters
A 768.2. Miscellaneous meter
expenses
B A 769. Services on customers' premises
B A 770. Operation of street lighting
equipment

MAINTENANCE

B A 771. Maintenance supervision and
engineering
B A 772. Maintenance of structures and
improvements
B   773. Maintenance of distribution
lines
A 773.1. Maintenance of mains
A 773.2. Maintenance of pumping and
regulating equipment
A 773.3. Maintenance of services
A 773.4. Maintenance of meters
A 773.5. Maintenance of house regu-
lators
A 773.6. Maintenance of other prop-
erty on customers' premises
B A 774. Maintenance of street lighting
equipment
B A 775. Maintenance of other distri-
bution equipment

MISCELLANEOUS

B A 776. Rents
B A 777.1. Joint expenses—Dr.
B A 777.2. Joint expenses—Cr.

IV. CUSTOMERS' ACCOUNTING AND COLLECTING EXPENSES

B A 779. Supervision
B   780. Customers' contracts, orders, meter reading, and collecting
A 780.1. Customers' contracts and orders
A 780.2. Credit investigations and records
A 780.3. Meter reading
A 780.4. Collecting
B A 781. Customers' billing and accounting
B A 782. Miscellaneous expenses
B A 783. Uncollectible accounts
B A 784. Rents

V. SALES PROMOTION EXPENSES

B A 785. Supervision
B A 786. Salaries and commissions
B   787. Demonstration, advertising, and other sales expenses
A 787.1. Demonstration
A 787.2. Advertising
A 787.3. Miscellaneous sales expenses
B A 788. Rents
B A 789. Merchandising, jobbing, and contract work
789.1. Revenues from merchandising, jobbing, and contract work
789.2. Costs and expenses of merchandising, jobbing, and contract work

VI. ADMINISTRATIVE AND GENERAL EXPENSES

B A 790. Salaries of general officers and executives
B A 791. Other general office salaries
B   792. Expenses of general officers and general office employees

A 792.1. Expenses of general officers
A 792.2. Expenses of general office employees
B A 793. General office supplies and expenses
B A 794. Management and supervision fees and expenses
B A 795. Special services
B A 796. Special legal services
B A 797. Regulatory commission expenses
B A 798. Insurance
B A 799. Injuries and damages
B   800. Employees' welfare expenses and pensions
A 800.1. Employees' welfare expenses
A 800.2. Pensions
B A 801. Miscellaneous general expenses
B   802. Maintenance of general property
A 802.1. Maintenance of structures and improvements
A 802.2. Maintenance of office furniture and equipment
A 802.3. Maintenance of communication equipment
A 802.4. Maintenance of miscellaneous property
B A 803. Rents
B A 804. Commissions paid under agency sales contracts
B A 805. Franchise requirements
805.1. Cash outlays
805.2. Gas supplied without charge—Dr.
805.3. Other items furnished without charge—Dr.
B A 806. Duplicate miscellaneous charges—Cr.
B A 807. Administrative and general expenses transferred—Cr.
B A 808. Joint expenses—Dr.
B A 809. Joint expenses—Cr.

Clearing Accounts

901. Charges by associated companies—clearing
902. Stores expenses—clearing
903. Transportation expenses—clearing

904. Laboratory expenses—clearing
905. Shop expenses—clearing
906. Tools and work equipment expenses—clearing

CHAPTER 4

Preparatory Work, Inventories, and Inventory Classification

The methods used in making engineering valuations vary in their details to suit the characteristics of different properties and the ideas of different practitioners; but a general process has been gradually evolved to which most engineering valuations conform, in a general way, as outlined in Sec. 2.22. The preliminary and preparatory valuation work stated in that outline and the inventory procedures are discussed in this chapter. Pricing and costing of the inventory are given in Chaps. 5 and 6.

PRELIMINARY EXAMINATION OF THE ENTERPRISE AND ITS PROPERTY

The first step toward making an engineering valuation of a particular property is to visit and study it, in order to plan its systematic valuation.

4.1. General Examinations of Properties Preliminary to Valuation. Before the detailed work of the valuation is undertaken, the engineer responsible for the valuation should make a preliminary general examination and study of the whole property; this examination is to gain a correct idea of the general character and sufficient familiarity with the features of the property to enable him to plan his work and organize his staff properly. Clients should be consulted; the owners and managers of the property and others concerned should be interviewed. Appraisal boards often hold public hearings, at which all interested parties may appear and express their views. The general history of the inception, the financing, the construction, and the operation of the property should be studied.

4.2. Studies of the History and Circumstances of the Enterprise. The history and the circumstances of each particular property should be ascertained and given due consideration in its valuation. The book records and annual reports of the enterprise should supply most of the data required.

The inception, organization, promotion, and any reorganizations of the enterprise should be studied. The financial history includes all sales of stocks and bonds, the annual incomes, the operating expenses, annual returns, and the disposition of returns.

Frequently, the appraiser can find a condensed history of the enterprise in standard financial reports such as Moody's "Reports" (Industrials, Railroads, Utilities, Municipals) or Poor's "Index of Manufacturers." Other sources of information are often found in current periodicals. Generally, the appraiser will find that the life history of the enterprise falls into a typical pattern. The several stages of development through which an enterprise must pass before it reaches the status of an established and profitable business may be described as follows:

1. *Preconstruction period*, during which the idea of establishing the enterprise is conceived and its promotion undertaken by one or more persons. Engineers, lawyers, and financiers may be called upon to report on the feasibility of the project, its probable cost, and the estimated returns. A company, corporation, or partnership is formed; capital is secured; water, mineral, land, or other necessary rights are optioned or bought; and, if required, a franchise is secured.

2. *Construction period*, during which the plant is designed and constructed and all facilities provided so that the plant is ready to begin operation.

3. *Development of business period*, which follows immediately after the completion of construction or which takes place during the latter stages of construction. In this period the enterprise frequently operates at a loss or at a low rate of return while a satisfactory volume of business is being developed.

4. *Operation period*, during which the enterprise enjoys a fair return and growth. There may be some overlapping of the development and operation periods because there is not a distinct marking of the transition from a developing to an established business.

The various relationships during the life history of an industrial enterprise are outlined in Fig. 4.1.

The property of the typical successful industrial enterprise will undergo almost constant alteration and improvement throughout the entire operation period, owing to the growth of the business and the progress of invention. Many enterprises in their latter stages may undergo a gradual decline in activity and ultimately may be dissolved.

Once the valuation engineer has obtained and studied the life history of the enterprise, he should have gained a perspective of the problem before him. He should appreciate how large his problem is, how to divide the property into the major geographical and functional divisions, and, most important, the general character of the enterprise. It is necessary that the appraiser have these impressions, for he may make major errors in the planning of the valuation if he does not possess an adequate background.

4.3. Studies of the Periodic Financial Reports. The information contained in the standard primary accounts and financial reports is so extensive and changes so continuously that only by studying several of the periodic statements can a comprehensive understanding be had of the condition of the enterprise at definite dates and of its operations during definite periods. Those periodic statements of special interest to the appraiser are (1) the balance sheet and (2) the statement of operations. These two statements may be supplemented by other reports, such as analyses of the working capital and of the earned surplus account.

	Period of Initial Construction		Period of Operation of Enterprise		
Preconstruction Period; Conception of Idea and its Development	Preoperation Construction	Concurrent Construction and Operation	Period During Which an Engineering Valuation May be Required		
			Development of Business to a Level of Fair Return	Growth and Expansion During Periods of Prosperity and Depression	Decline to Period of Rehabilitation or Abandonment
Some capital received from sale of securities	Additional capital received from sale of securities Limited sales and operating revenues		Additional capital received from sale of additional securities Capital obtained by retention of annual returns in the business Increasing and declining sales and operating revenues Temporary cash needs met by short term borrowings		Declining sales and operating revenues
Expenditures for: Organization Financing Franchise or other business permits	Expenditure for: Plant and equipment (direct costs and overheads) Additional financing Limited operations		Continued expenditures for expansion and replacement of plant and equipment Expenditures incident to the development of sales and revenues to profitable level Expenditures for operation and maintenance Payment of dividends Retirement of funded debt		Declining operating and maintenance expenditures

FIG. 4.1. Diagram of the life history of an industrial plant or of a small enterprise.

The balance sheet shows five important items in summary form which should receive the attention of the appraiser:

1. *Total net investment* in the fixed capital physical property, which is the original cost of the property less the book balance in the account, reserve for depreciation.

2. The investment in *intangible property* (see Chap. 14).

3. The investment in *working capital* (see Chap. 13).

4. The *sources of the funds* used to acquire the property. Although the sources are obvious, there may be need to search for such accounts as Premiums on Sale of Bonds. The balances in the accounts, Notes Payable, Accounts Payable, and Bonds indicate the portion of the total investment procured from creditors. The Stock accounts indicate amounts subscribed by the owners. The Earned Surplus account shows

the amounts now invested somewhere in the business, which were retained by management from the profits of past years.

5. *Debt and equity capital*—information helpful to the appraiser in determining the stock and bond value of the enterprise (see Chap. 16).

A study of a series of yearly balance sheets will give the appraiser an insight into the general character of the enterprise. Time series charts showing the growth of the fixed capital will indicate the kind of expansion. A chart showing the ratio of the current assets to the current liabilities year by year can indicate something about the credit policies of the enterprise. A graph showing the ratio of bonds plus notes to stock and various surplus accounts may indicate the kind of financial policy which guides the management of the enterprise. Tables 4.1 and 4.2 are balance sheets typical of those issued by industrial enterprises.

Careful study of the statement of operations (Table 4.3) of the enterprise will likewise prove fruitful. In summary form this statement shows six important items:

1. *Total income* (not necessarily cash) received by the enterprise from all sources during the accounting period. In addition to sales income there will be some income from miscellaneous sources, such as dividends on those securities owned by the enterprise, but issued by other businesses, and income from subsidiary organizations.

2. *Expenses of operation of the enterprise.* These expenses are numerous and include such items as labor and materials used in operation, taxes, maintenance of the property, overhead costs of production and management (excluding the depreciation expense on the physical property for reasons given in the next paragraph), and selling and distributing expenses.

3. *Depreciation expense* on the physical property. Depreciation cost, although a part of the overhead cost of production, is of especial interest to the appraiser. Frequently it will be second in amount to the cost of labor and materials. In addition, depreciation is so often the subject of intense scrutiny by those who read the completed valuation report that the appraiser will save time by making the depreciation a separate item of study from the very beginning.

4. *Annual return* of the enterprise for the accounting period. As used herein the term annual return is the difference between total income and operating expenses, including depreciation but excluding interest paid on long-term notes and on bonds.

5. *Disposition of the annual return.* The appraiser will ascertain what portion of the total annual return is paid for interest on the debts of the enterprise, the amount paid as dividends to the owners, the miscellaneous

TABLE 4.1. CONSOLIDATED BALANCE SHEET OF THE GENERAL ELECTRIC COMPANY

ASSETS

	Dec. 31, 1951	Dec. 31, 1950
Current Assets:		
Cash..............................	$ 71,927,452	$ 63,038,689
Marketable securities.............	142,730,267	253,864,140
Receivables—after reserves:		
Customers.................	259,453,749	164,220,675
Nonconsolidated affiliates.	65,724,465	60,837,660
Others....................	27,548,026	20,064,390
Inventories—after reserves.......	571,355,191	338,773,773
	$1,138,739,150	$900,799,327
Deduct:		
Progress collections on contracts..	*199,839,577*	*94,740,813*
Price adjustments accrued.........	*42,019,954*	*37,363,752*
TOTAL CURRENT ASSETS......	$ 896,879,619	$ 768,694,762
Investments:		
Nonconsolidated affiliates........	$172,328,497	$167,307,701
General Electric common stock.....	3,717,273	5,958,356
Miscellaneous securities—after reserve.....	14,637,404	7,622,748
TOTAL INVESTMENTS.........	190,683,174	180,888,805
Plant and Equipment:		
Cost.............................	$ 751,783,862	$679,960,085
Deduct:		
Accumulated depreciation..........	*433,062,041*	*403,456,596*
PLANT AND EQUIPMENT—NET....	318,721,821	276,503,489
Assets of Special Funds:		
Fund for payments under U.S. government contracts..	$ 13,094,227	$ 15,096,374
Employee benefit plans and taxes withheld......	22,156,416	18,388,377
TOTAL ASSETS OF SPECIAL FUNDS—PER CONTRA....	35,250,643	33,484,751
Other Assets:		
Receivables not current—after reserves..........	$ 12,297,022	$ 12,604,741
Marketable securities deposited as guarantees.....	3,534,330	3,589,224
Miscellaneous assets—after reserves.............	2,435,920	1,660,035
Patents and other intangible assets..........	1	1
TOTAL OTHER ASSETS........	18,267,273	17,854,001
TOTAL ASSETS..............	$1,459,802,530	$1,277,425,808

LIABILITIES AND SHARE OWNERS' INVESTMENT

Current Liabilities:			
Accounts payable	$ 76,342,149		$ 79,968,280
Due to nonconsolidated affiliates	3,437,421		3,083,471
Dividends payable	21,469,562		17,134,444
Accrued liabilities:			
Federal, state, and local taxes	336,634,532		260,590,548
Other costs and expenses	106,506,090		86,343,733
TOTAL CURRENT LIABILITIES		$ 544,389,754	$ 447,120,476
Accounts Payable and Accruals—Not Current		24,096,737	22,913,086
Liabilities for Special Funds:			
Fund for payments under U.S. government contracts	$ 13,094,227		$ 15,096,374
Employee benefit plans and taxes withheld	22,156,416		18,388,377
TOTAL LIABILITIES FOR SPECIAL FUNDS—PER CONTRA		35,250,643	33,484,751
Deferred Income		2,198,201	1,901,215
Miscellaneous Reserves		65,507,165	69,152,844
Share Owners' Investment:			
Common stock—stated value of no par value shares (authorized 35,000,000 shares; issued 28,845,927 shares)	$ 180,287,046		$180,287,046
Investment in excess of stated value of common stock	18,247,439		16,858,598
Reinvested earnings	589,825,545		505,707,792
TOTAL SHARE OWNERS' INVESTMENT		788,360,030	702,853,436
TOTAL LIABILITIES AND SHARE OWNERS' INVESTMENT		$1,459,802,530	$1,277,425,808

TABLE 4.2. BALANCE SHEET OF THE DETROIT EDISON COMPANY AND SUBSIDIARY COMPANIES

Consolidated Statement of Financial Condition

ASSETS

	Dec. 31, 1951	Dec. 31, 1950
Utility Properties:		
Tangible (at original cost when first devoted to utility service)..	$556,115,052	$504,373,695
Excess over original cost		
Plant acquisition adjustments...................	2,985,618	3,412,136
Plant adjustments.............................	942,726	1,077,401
Organization expense and franchises..............	213,579	263,960
TOTAL UTILITY PROPERTIES..................	$560,256,975	$509,127,192
Other Property, Investments, and Miscellaneous Assets:		
Nonutility property............................	624,138	717,771
Temporary investments in U.S. government securities (at cost, which is approximate market value) to be used for construction purposes.................	40,300,000	————
Casualty and contingency investment fund........	————	3,258,236
Claims for refund of prior years' federal income and excess profits taxes...........................	4,100,000	4,100,000
Miscellaneous noncurrent assets.................	659,139	247,866
TOTAL OTHER PROPERTY, INVESTMENTS, AND MISCELLANEOUS ASSETS......................	$ 45,683,277	$ 8,323,873
Current and Working Assets:		
Cash...	5,369,137	7,578,724
Temporary investments in U.S. government securities (at cost, which is approximate market value).....	5,175,087	5,995,858
TOTAL CASH AND TEMPORARY INVESTMENTS......	$ 10,544,224	$ 13,574,582
Accounts receivable (after deduction of $150,000 for estimated uncollectible accounts)..............	14,860,292	15,200,718
Estimated amount receivable for unbilled utility service.......................................	3,800,000	3,808,000
Inventories		
Fuel, at average cost.........................	13,960,392	11,385,257
Construction and maintenance materials, at average cost or less.............................	14,684,384	11,766,847
Merchandise for resale, at average cost.........	978,088	738,154
Pension appropriations, insurance, and other items paid in advance.............................	1,634,167	550,873
TOTAL CURRENT AND WORKING ASSETS.........	$ 60,461,547	$ 57,024,431
Unamortized Expense (less Premium) on Convertible Debentures....................................	112,338	184,872
Capital Stock Expense...........................	678,868	678,868
TOTAL ASSETS..............................	$667,193,005	$575,339,236

66

TABLE 4.2.—*(Continued)*

CAPITAL, LIABILITIES, AND RESERVES

	Dec. 31, 1951	Dec. 31, 1950
Capital Stock and Retained Income:		
Capital stock		
Authorized—15,000,000 shares of the par value of $20 a share of which 1,664,705 shares are reserved for conversion of debentures at Dec. 31, 1951		
Outstanding—9,174,858 shares at Dec. 31, 1951, 7,805,118 shares at Dec. 31, 1950	$183,497,160	$156,102,360
Premium on capital stock	864,186	825,801
Retained income appropriated for casualties and contingencies	———	3,258,236
Balance of retained income used in the business (in addition to $12,722,600 capitalized by stock dividend in 1947)	48,028,621	39,622,459
TOTAL CAPITAL STOCK AND RETAINED INCOME	$232,389,967	$199,808,856
Long-term Debt:		
General and refunding mortgage bonds		
Series H, 3%, due Dec. 1, 1970	50,000,000	50,000,000
Series I, 2¾%, due Sept. 1, 1982	60,000,000	60,000,000
Series J, 2¾%, due Mar. 1, 1985	35,000,000	35,000,000
Series K, 3⅜%, due Nov. 15, 1976	40,000,000	———
3% convertible debentures, due Dec. 1, 1958	33,294,100	44,482,500
Long-term notes (requiring various annual prepayments)		
2½% notes, due Oct. 1, 1959	10,000,000	10,000,000
3% notes, due Oct. 1, 1979	30,000,000	30,000,000
3¼% notes, due Aug. 1, 1959 (excluding amount due within one year)	24,000,000	———
TOTAL LONG-TERM DEBT	$282,294,100	$229,482,500
Current Liabilities:		
Long-term debt due within one year (see above)	1,000,000	———
Accounts payable	7,199,201	10,376,253
Payrolls (including estimated retroactive adjustments of $1,358,000 and $900,000 at Dec. 31, 1951 and 1950, respectively)	2,384,137	1,668,347
Dividend declared, payable in following January	3,210,535	2,339,669
Property and general taxes	7,314,330	6,742,774
Estimated federal taxes on income	14,580,608	13,464,205
Interest	2,509,603	1,910,895
Customer deposits	268,194	282,720
Miscellaneous	526,392	509,447
TOTAL CURRENT LIABILITIES	$ 38,993,000	$ 37,294,310
Deferred Credits:		
Unamortized premium (less expense) on mortgage bonds	772,448	483,371
Customer deposits for line extensions	46,407	58,486
Deposit in connection with sale of gas plant	———	100,000
TOTAL DEFERRED CREDITS	$ 818,855	$ 641,857
Retirement (Depreciation) Reserve	111,617,085	107,174,576
Contributions in Aid of Construction	1,079,998	937,137
TOTAL CAPITAL, LIABILITIES, AND RESERVES	$667,193,005	$575,339,236

TABLE 4.3. STATEMENT OF INCOME OF THE DETROIT EDISON
COMPANY AND SUBSIDIARY COMPANIES
Consolidated Income Statement

Gross Revenues from Utility Operations:	Year 1951	Year 1950
Electric		
Residential and farm service....................	$ 58,240,856	$ 52,222,934
Commercial and industrial service		
Low-voltage service at commercial rates.......	45,362,558	41,971,310
High-voltage service at industrial rates........	49,229,957	44,966,028
Other electric revenues........................	6,607,686	6,160,872
TOTAL ELECTRIC............................	$159,441,057	$145,321,144
Steam heating.................................	4,352,533	4,232,138
Gas (gas business sold Feb. 1, 1951)..............	180,887	892,328
Water...	25,133	25,272
	$163,999,610	$150,470,882
Deduct—Utility Expenses:		
Operating expenses		
Labor..	35,243,802	31,878,355
Fuel...	35,339,336	33,319,605
Materials, supplies, and other expenses............	15,564,933	13,443,992
Maintenance and repairs		
Labor..	8,948,352	7,748,849
Materials, supplies, and other expenses...........	5,242,835	4,762,448
Appropriations for employee pensions...............	3,248,292	2,712,979
Uncollectible accounts, less recoveries...............	214,225	238,469
Appropriations to retirement (depreciation) reserve...	11,400,000	10,110,000
Amortization of franchises.......................	48,207	2,663
Amortization of electric plant acquisition adjustments.	426,517	426,517
Taxes (other than income taxes)....................	14,583,722	12,781,047
Estimated federal income taxes		
Normal tax and surtax..........................	10,000,000	8,720,000
Excess profits tax.............................	None	None
	$140,260,221	$126,144,924
	$ 23,739,389	$ 24,325,958
Add—Other Income.............................	317,102	341,057
ANNUAL RETURN...........................	$ 24,056,491	$ 24,667,015

charges and reserves made, and finally the portion of the annual return
which is left in the business to be invested as management sees fit.

6. *Information* helpful to the appraiser in making estimates of the earning value and the service worth value of the enterprise.

A study of a series of annual statements of operation will show the
appraiser to what extent management has developed the markets available to the enterprise. A chart showing the ratio of the operation
expenses to income year by year can indicate something about the relative production efficiency of the enterprise. A chart showing the ratio of
total investment of the property to annual sales can indicate something

TABLE 4.3.—(Continued)

Deductions from Income:

Interest on long-term debt......................	$6,891,909	$6,241,853
Interest charged to construction—credit..........	—369,786	—137,956
Amortization of long-term debt expense less premium	39,405	26,083
Amortization of plant adjustments................	134,675	———
Loss on sales of real estate no longer useful in the business..	6,289	548,124
Loss on sale of gas business.....................	880,108	———
Other interest and miscellaneous deductions from income......................................	388,166	233,810
Portion of $5,804,500 appropriation to employees' retirement fund for past services (charged to Retained Income in 1946) which equals the reduction in the above provision for federal income taxes attributable thereto (see Statement of Retained Income).......................................	666,000	378,000
Portion of cost to redeem Series G bonds which equals the reduction in the above provision for federal income taxes attributable thereto...............	———	345,000
	$ 8,636,766	$ 7,634,914
NET INCOME................................	$ 15,419,725	$ 17,032,101

Consolidated Statement of Retained Income Used in the Business

Balance—Dec. 31, 1950...........................		$ 39,622,459
Add:		
Net income from income statement..................	$ 15,419,725	
Unused appropriations of prior years for casualties and contingencies..................................	3,258,236	
Portion of $5,804,500 appropriation to employees' retirement fund for past services (charged to Retained Income in 1946) which equals the reduction in federal income taxes charged to income account above.....	666,000	19,343,961
		$ 58,966,420
Deduct:		
Cash dividends...................................		10,937,799
Balance—Dec. 31, 1951...........................		$ 48,028,621

about the general type of business in which the enterprise is engaged.   If similar charts or statements from similar enterprises are available, the appraiser can pass judgment on the relative position of the particular enterprise within the industry.

Other studies to make may include the ratio of annual depreciation expense to the book cost of the physical property, a succession of charts showing the disposition of the sales dollar each year, and the ratio of annual return to the total investment year by year.   Table 4.3 is a typical statement of operations, modified to show the annual return of the enterprise.

4.4. Studies of the Property Ledger. Behind the summary item Plant and Equipment or Fixed Capital Physical Property which is found on the balance sheet (Tables 4.1 and 4.2) are numerous accounts and ledgers on which is recorded the cost of the property at the time of installation. These accounts and ledgers, in their entirety, constitute the property records discussed in Chap. 3. Before the appraiser can plan his valuation, he must determine whether or not the property ledger is adequate for his purpose. The adequacy of the property ledger may be tested by seeing whether or not it supplies the information enumerated in Sec. 3.1. For example, the appraiser might try to ascertain that the known installations in a given delimited area are currently shown in the appropriate sections of the property ledger. He may ascertain that property shown in the ledger is actually in existence in the field.

If such spot checks demonstrate that the property ledger is complete and accurate, the appraiser has some reason to trust it and use the information it contains as it is needed. If not, then the appraiser must prepare a complete inventory of the property of the enterprise by methods described in Sec. 4.13.

4.5. Studies of Records Subsidiary to the Property Ledger. As a part of the task of testing the adequacy of the property ledger, the careful appraiser will search for records which show the details of the installation of some unit of property or some project involving the installation of many units. The following list indicates the names and purposes of the several records which the appraiser is likely to find:

Construction Contracts.[1] The direct costs (contract costs) of the contractor-built property are to be found in the construction contracts and their accompanying vouchers. Many unit price data should be obtained from these sources.

Construction Work Orders. Work orders usually are issued in advance for the construction of property built directly by the owner. Such orders generally contain full and explicit instructions for the construction ordered, including references to detailed plans and specifications.

Invoices. The f.o.b. direct cost of purchased equipment and other construction materials required for the execution of work orders is usually found in invoices and their corresponding vouchers.

Requisitions. Formal requisitions for equipment and construction materials to be taken from stores to execute work orders often give the "stores cost" of such property.

Work-order Reports and Analyses. Copies of the original work orders are generally returned to the appropriate department, showing the

---

[1] Part of the property is likely to have been constructed by contract and part directly by the owner. In the latter case, records of the charges for construction material and equipment may be found in the "stores" records.

amount of materials used, number of hours of the various kinds of labor and machine time, and the unit prices.   Analyses of the completed construction generally reconcile the total cost of the construction with the fiscal accounts.   The disposition of the total cost to the various ledger accounts is also recorded.

Plans and Specifications.   Engineering records are of paramount importance in checking the construction performed.   Often estimated quantities of materials to be placed in the project are given, but these quantities may differ from those actually used.

Special Reports.   Special reports such as former appraisals, proposals relating to the purchase of equipment, and studies of the probable economic service life of property usually contain many cost data, some of which may be applicable to the present valuation.

By use of the foregoing records, it should be possible for the appraiser to check the total installed cost of a unit, or group of units, as shown in the property ledger.   If so, and if several other spot checks are similarly successful, the appraiser has reason to believe that he can trust the costs shown in the property ledger.   If not, the appraiser may find that his problem has been made much greater, for he will have to fall back on these detailed subsidiary records as his most important source of original cost data.

4.6. Used and Useful Property.   Frequently the appraiser finds that one of the problems encountered in the preliminary work is that of deciding whether or not to exclude some property on the basis of its lack of use or usefulness to the enterprise.

If the valuation involves the sale of the enterprise and the doubtful property is to be included in the transaction, such property should be included in the appraisal.   A similar decision applies to valuations for tax purposes, condemnations, adjustment of insurance claims, and financing.

On the other hand, if the problem involves the determination of a rate base for a public utility, the appraiser must screen the property carefully in order to exclude property not used or useful in the public service.   It is important, however, that the appraiser attempt to forecast whether or not these units may reasonably be expected to be useful in the public service in the near future before he excludes them from the valuation.

Again, the appraiser must not confuse "nonuse" with "lack of usefulness in the public service."   Consider the downtown parking lot, owned by a gas utility, adjacent to its central office, but which is used by the general public, who pay parking rates similar to those charged at other lots.   No concessions are made to the customers or employees of the gas company.   Undoubtedly, the lot should not be considered a property used and useful in the public service.   The lot is only a private subsidiary operation of the utility, and its value, as well as the income and expense incident to its operation, should be excluded from the appraisal for rate-making purposes.

However, consider a turbine in the generating room of an electric utility.   It has not generated a kilowatt-hour of energy in the past 6 months, though it has been warmed up on occasion.   Investigation discloses that it might be used some December or January when the peak loads come or when the main generating unit is taken off the line for more than week-end maintenance.   Such a unit is undoubtedly useful in the public service.

The above illustrations are fairly clear-cut.   Actual situations may be less clear-cut, but at all events the appraiser, by investigation and interview, should ascertain whether or not any significant portions of the property must be excluded on the basis of lack of use or usefulness.

4.7. Preliminary Examination, Summary.   The appraiser in his preliminary examination of the enterprise and its property studies the life history and circumstances of the organization in order to gain perspective of the valuation.   He analyzes the periodic financial reports so that he may obtain impressions of the general conduct of the enterprise.   He examines and tests the property ledger in order that he may see of how much aid these accounts will be in the determination of the original cost of the property.   He screens the property for any significant portion which may not be used or which is not useful.   This done, the appraiser is ready to plan the details of the procedure of valuation.

A word of caution may be necessary at this point.   Although complete and reliable accounting records are almost indispensable in making an engineering valuation of a particular property, the appraiser using them should keep in mind that their main use is to guide him in his conduct of the valuation and to supply him with certain factual information which he need not otherwise accumulate.   The value of the property which the appraiser is trying to determine cannot be found directly from the book records of the enterprise.   It must be arrived at by the exercise of judgment rendered only after a thorough study and checking of all of the company's records and on analysis of the circumstances incident to the past, present, and future operation of the enterprise.

PRELIMINARY INVENTORY OFFICE WORK

The second major step in the valuation process is the office work required before an inventory of the property can be obtained.   The amount of this office work depends on the following:

1. Whether or not there is a property ledger disclosing the information necessary to the establishment of valuation sections and inventory sections.

2. Whether or not the property ledger will disclose an acceptable breakdown of the property into identifiable and priceable cost units.

3. The nature and number of the forms required for the inventory field work.

Each of these subjects is discussed in the following sections.

4.8. Use of the Property Ledger in the Appraisal.   If, by the tests suggested in Sec. 4.4, the appraiser determines that the property ledger is complete and accurate, he can then prepare a tentative inventory of the entire physical property from these records.   At this point the reader may ask, "Why cannot the appraiser by-pass the preparation of the inventory completely, accept the original cost as stated in the property ledger, and go on to other things?"   The careful appraiser would answer, "If this valuation is to be done correctly, there will be an examination of the property to record its physical condition, which is needed later in the process of determining present value, and any discrepancies in the property ledger will be found and corrected.   Since the appraisal requires that the cost of replacing the property be obtained, the estimate of this cost must be determined item by item."

This situation is not as bad as it sounds.   By and large, about 25 percent of the number of units possessed by the enterprise represents about 75 percent of the investment in the property.   Special attention naturally will be given to these large units; the others will be handled on a mass basis as described in Sec. 4.10.

With a tentative inventory prepared, the appraiser can proceed to verify it by methods described in Sec. 4.14.

If, on the other hand, the appraiser determines that the existing property ledger will not be of much aid to him, he will of necessity be required to take a complete field inventory (Sec. 4.13).   Such a task is laborious and time-consuming.   The effort required to affix proper costs to the property items and groups is even greater, but no alternative exists in the absence of a property ledger if the appraiser desires to obtain a complete and accurate valuation.

4.9. Dividing the Property into Sections.   Normally it is necessary for the appraiser to divide the property into geographical sections. This division is required for two reasons: First, it may be necessary to have a complete appraisal on each of several parts of the enterprise. Second, for ease of checking (or preparing) the inventory of the property, it is desirable to divide the property into convenient, small areas.

A *valuation section* of an industrial property is a definitely delimited geographical subdivision for which a complete and separate valuation is desired.

In most appraisals the value of the entire enterprise is wanted, although in some appraisals main or secondary objectives may include the valuation of segments of the enterprise.

It is often necessary for tax purposes to ascertain the value of that portion of the property located in each tax district. Again, an enterprise may possess several manufacturing plants, each independent of the other. Far-flung enterprises may have several districts, and railway systems may cross a dozen states. In each of these situations, the purpose of the appraisal may require several valuation sections.

To prevent omissions and duplications, and to systematize the inventory work, the entire property to be valued should be divided into inventory sections.

An *inventory section* is a defined unit area of property, selected and delimited for convenience and accuracy of inventory work. The size, shape, and other features of inventory sections vary greatly and should always be those best adapted to the particular properties. A single building may often constitute an inventory section. A single inventory section in a telegraph system might readily be 100 miles long.

The careful appraiser should prepare written instructions describing the way inventory sections are to be delimited. He may require that pipe runs and wire services be included with the building (an inventory section) when these are inside but excluded when found outside the outer wall of the building. Care and uniformity in describing the boundaries of inventory sections will tend to hold down materially the errors and omissions.

An inventory section should always be confined within the limits of a single valuation section.

4.10. Property Units and Subunits. As a part of the planning preliminary to the checking (or taking) of the inventory of the physical property, the appraiser needs to provide for the proper designation of the separate items of property. Their correct description makes for a good inventory; careless work in this area leaves the inventory open to question.

A *property unit* is any item that may be treated as an entity in estimating construction costs and depreciation. It follows, therefore, that for valuation purposes the inventory property unit must be of such a character that it is identifiable, enumerable, and costable.

The separation of the inventory of the property into units by their ages is imperative if correct estimates of costs, values, operating expenses, and depreciation are to be obtained for the appraisal. Discretion is necessary in deciding which are separate units in any specific property. Buildings may be subdivided into units such as roof, structure, foundation, and mechanical and electrical services for purposes of final valuation or estimates of depreciation.   However, the inventory of buildings is more often recorded by an itemization of construction materials similar to that normally found in a contractor's bill of material.   Processing and fabricating equipment might be similarly treated.

It is not practicable to value small items of physical property (such as ties, rails, insulators, poles, wire, piping, meters, instruments, transformers, and furniture) as separate units because of the great number in

Form 401. XYZ Appraisal Company						
Field Inventory of General Property				Sheet____of____ Date_____		
Property_____				Inventory Section_____		
Address _____				Location _____		
Type of Property _____				Party Chief _____		
_____				Recorder_____		
Year Built	Mfrs No. or Model	Size	Quan- tity	Phys. Cond.	Description	Location & Remarks

FIG. 4.2. Form for field inventory of general property.

use.   Property of this type should be accounted for as groups of like units, segregated by ages when possible.

When sufficiently numerous, it may be practicable for appraisal purposes to combine large and costly units into vintage groups of like units. Machine tools, boilers, transformers, and even locomotives may be so treated.

By using the unit designations carried in the property ledger the appraiser can save much time and effort.   In addition, the records subsidiary to the property ledger (Sec. 4.5) usually carry the descriptions of the more important units, and the use of these records will reduce materially the descriptions which must be made during the field inventory.

4.11. Preparation of Field Inventory Forms. Surveyors' field books in which to record notes of inventory field data are used frequently; sometimes, sectional large-scale field maps may be used to advantage. Loose-leaf notebooks, with leaves ruled specially for inventory work, have many advantages for recording inventory field data. The $8\frac{1}{2}$- by 11-in. size is the best for most properties. The ruling shown in Fig. 4.2 may be used for general inventory work.

Form 402. XYZ Appraisal Company

Field Inventory of Pole Lines   Sheet ____ of ____ Date _____

Property _____   Inventory Section _____

Address _____   Location _____

Line: From _____   Party Chief _____

     To _____   Recorder _____

Poles					Cross Arms			Insulators	Racks	Brackets	Guys	Remarks
Pole No.	Year set	Physical cond.	Length, ft.	Top diameter, in.	2-Pin	4-Pin	6-Pin					

FIG. 4.3. Field inventory form for pole lines. An example of a special form for large numbers of similar property units.

Only the data of observations and measurements are to be recorded in the inventory field books and forms, leaving classifying and grouping of items for the office work, along with all computations and pricing.

Although the simple inventory field data form shown in Fig. 4.2 is well adapted to general inventory work, the use of additional, special forms may facilitate the work for certain properties. Figure 4.3 illustrates a special form for the inventory of pole lines.

Consulting valuation engineers, appraisal companies, utility commissions, and large enterprises usually have their own preferred forms.

4.12. Inventory Field Parties. The number of men required for a single inventory field party varies; usually it will range from one to enough to run survey lines or do cross-section work.

In much of the work of making inventories of industrial properties, two men are sufficient; often one of these need be only an assistant to help in making measurements.

At least one man on each inventory field party should be especially trained and otherwise qualified for inventory work. Employees in the engineering and property accounting departments of regulatory commissions, appraisal companies, consulting engineering firms, and industrial corporations are used for inventory work when available. Comparatively recent engineering graduates are readily trained for inventory work. Other employees of industrial plants make good assistants; so also do engineering students.

The appraiser must keep in mind the date the valuation report is to be completed so that he will allow sufficient time for the summarization, pricing, and costing of the inventory, the required calculations of value, and the compilation of the report itself. Normally, it is desirable to complete the inventory in a relatively short time in order that the maximum time will be available for the remaining phases of the valuation process. Consequently, a large number of field parties may be used to advantage.

INVENTORY FIELD WORK

During the preliminary office work, the plans for the field inventory are developed, and the field parties are organized. The success of the field inventory is dependent upon the advance planning and the thoroughness and correctness with which the field parties do their work. Thus, adequate instruction and training of the field personnel are essential.

4.13. Taking an Inventory. When it is necessary to take a complete inventory in the field, attention and effort should be centered upon the main objective—a complete, correct list of all the units of the property. Every care should be taken to ensure that all property units are listed, but only once.

Those in charge of field parties should avoid distraction of attention and effort by leaving for office work the operations of summarization and classification of the inventory. The taking of the inventory systematically throughout the entire project greatly aids the later office work. Care in planning each day's activities, even having a logical system of numbering the pages (or the field books), will save much time and effort.

The chief of each field party should be reminded of the importance of abiding strictly to the inventory section limits as previously determined (Sec. 4.9). It is easy to make absurd errors. For use in a highly controverted waterworks valuation case, the valuation engineer was once furnished an inventory agreed to by both the city and waterworks company. A standpipe, one of the most prominent units of the property, was omitted!

Prior to starting his work in any particular place or area, the leader of the inventory party should study all available pertinent material—maps, engineering drawings, and property ledgers. This study is especially necessary when many items may be concealed from view, as in the case of water mains and valves, pipe runs, or wiring.

A systematic plan of taking the inventory should be followed consistently. For example, say, take all rooms on a single floor in a clockwise order, starting with the one to the left of the main stairway. Again, record all items in each room in a similar order. Do not leave any units unrecorded for another party to pick up unless such units are outside the inventory section presently considered.

As noted in Sec. 4.12, at least one man on each field party should be especially trained and qualified. One of his duties is that of judging the present physical condition of the property units for their ages and the conditions under which they serve.

Finally, the inventory should be checked in the field after it is first completed. It is suggested that a competent engineer not on the original field party perform this check. He should examine every important, major unit in the inventory section and spot-check a number of those items to be handled as groups in the final summary.

When these procedures are followed, the result of taking the inventory will be a complete, thorough, and accurate listing of all the physical property possessed by the enterprise.

4.14. Checking a Tentative Inventory Prepared from the Property Ledger. When a tentative inventory has been prepared directly from the property ledger and other office records, the task before the chief of the field party is much simpler than that discussed in the previous section. However, the central objective still stands: to have a complete and correct list of all the units of property.

The inventory prepared in the office is normally placed on forms suitable for field use. The field man uses these forms on which to record the verification of the existence of the unit and its present physical service condition. He takes along extra blank forms to use if he finds property not listed. He attempts to examine each unit which will be handled in the valuation as a unit and spot-checks numbers of units which in the final appraisal will be considered in groups. His task is similar to that of the engineer who checks a field inventory.

4.15. Checking the Inventory of Materials and Supplies. Included in the appraisal is the item Working Capital. Significant items included in working capital are the materials and supplies composed of raw materials, goods-in-process, finished goods, fuel and similar operation materials, repair and maintenance parts, office materials and supplies, and the like.

Normally, accurate records of the receipts and disbursements of these materials are kept, but the careful appraiser will not accept these records without verification.   The method of appraisal of these items is discussed in Chap. 13; at this point, the determination of the amount of materials and supplies on hand will be discussed briefly.

The accounting department of the enterprise normally can provide a tentative inventory of materials and supplies as of any date, for it is customary and wise to have a continuous stores inventory.   Such a record should be broken down into major groups and by areas.   The field man can then make spot checks in several places until he is satisfied that the records have been verified.   It is wise to check the contents of isolated warehouses which the records show are stored with finished goods, "just to be sure."

Frequently, the same department purchases, stores, and issues construction materials and supplies as well as operation materials and supplies.   Both kinds of property are to be included in the valuation, but they should be separated.   The former will be shown in the final report as Construction Materials on Hand to be placed with the items of fixed-capital physical property, and the latter will be included as a part of working capital.

Finally, the appraiser needs to satisfy himself that the present existing stores system is adequate to provide him with the correct count of the materials and supplies on the day chosen as the official date of appraisal. Otherwise, he may need to take a complete count of the material and supplies as of a certain date and then have a means of correcting this count through records of purchases and requisitions.

INVENTORY CLASSIFICATION

The third step in the valuation process is the classification of the inventory.   It involves the separation of the units in each valuation section into valuation groups and subgroups, a summary of these groups, and the preparation of the material for the application of price and depreciation data on the basis of either original cost or replacement cost or both. Some of this work can start with the receipt of the first inventories obtained from the field.

4.16. Valuation Groups and Subgroups.   In order to facilitate the task of affixing the proper original cost or replacement cost to each unit (called *costing the unit*), the various units in each valuation section are classified into valuation groups and subgroups.

A *valuation group* is a subdivision of the property in a valuation section comprising all units of a particular general character or use. Examples are: land; structures; boiler-plant equipment; distribution mains; hydrants; general equipment; electric plant; overhead conductors; poles, towers, and fixtures; line transformers and devices; bridges, trestles, and

Form 403. XYZ Appraisal Company

Valuation of Property Groups and Subgroups   Sheet ____ of ____ Date _____

Property _____   Valuation Section _____

Address _____   Location _____

Type of Property _____   Analyst _____

_____   Checked by _____

| Item | Quan-tity | Age | Type Curve | Prob-able Life | Expect-ancy-Life Factor | Estimated Salvage Value | Cost | | Cost Adjusted for Decreased Usefulness | |
							Original	Reproduction or Replacement	Original	Reproduction or Replacement

Fig. 4.4. Form for the calculation of the evidence of the value of general property based on cost.

culverts; grading; ties; water stations. Note that the division is on the basis of use instead of location.

A *valuation subgroup* is a subdivision of a valuation group, restricted to property units so similar that grouping them on the same computation form facilitates the work of costing the units and computing their values. For instance, the valuation group, poles, towers, and fixtures, may be subdivided by types of materials, lengths, diameters, settings, and ages.

The best basis for the division of an industrial property into valuation groups is that system of property accounts used by the enterprise in conformity with the best practice in the industry or as prescribed for utility properties by regulatory agencies. Obviously the appraiser will save much time in the summary of the inventory if the grouping of the property and the classifications of the units are made to correspond with the classifications in the property ledger.

4.17. Forms Used in Classification Summaries. The ultimate objective of the inventory office work is the preparation of complete and correct summaries of the entire inventory by valuation groups and subgroups of the property, in the forms most convenient for the final pricing and costing and for the systematic computation of their present values.

Figure 4.4 is a general form for valuation of group and subgroup inventory summaries.

CHAPTER **5**

Cost Data, Price and Construction Cost Indexes

Following the completion and summarization of the inventory of the physical property, the appraiser is ready to proceed with the second major step of the valuation process as outlined in Sec. 2.22. This step is the estimation of those evidences of the value of the enterprise which are applicable considering the purpose of the appraisal. Included in this step are the determinations of both original cost and reproduction or replacement cost.

From the standpoint of the time and effort involved, the major task to be done is the pricing and costing of the inventory as explained in Chap. 6. However, before the details of the pricing and costing process are discussed, it is desirable that the reader become familiar with data useful to the appraiser in pricing and costing property. These data are unit prices and costs and price and construction cost indexes.

5.1. Pricing and Costing Procedure. Although dictionaries state that the words *price* and *cost* are synonyms, these words are used herein with a distinction. By *price* is meant that monetary sum at which a property or service is bought, sold, or offered for sale. By *cost* is meant the price paid plus any other charges incident to the acquirement of the property or service. Further, cost is used as applying to the monetary or other outlay required to assemble, construct, or bring into being a machine or structure which may be composed of several separate elements, each bought at a particular price and assembled into the final and completed machine or structure.

Pricing and *costing* are terms used to describe the act or procedure of determining the price and cost of specific items of property in an inventory.

When one is affixing original costs to the inventory, the recorded costs (Sec. 5.2) should be used whenever available. Actually, there will be many instances when original records cannot be obtained; the appraiser must supply the missing costs from some applicable source. He can use personal data (Sec. 5.3), prices, or estimates supplied by manufacturers or contractors to which proper installation costs and overheads are added (Sec. 5.4), or applicable published price data (Sec. 5.5). Under certain conditions, the appraiser can make use of indexes to supply the missing original costs.

If the problem is that of affixing estimated costs of reproduction or replacement to the units in the inventory, the appraiser still has recourse to the same sources of price data mentioned in the previous paragraph, but to a different degree.   Recorded book costs can be used only to a limited extent, for in costing on a reproduction cost basis the greatest need is for a large number of specific costs for specific units based on prices applicable to the date of appraisal.   Thus he may use his private collection of data or manufacturers' quotations for the bulk of the pricing and costing process.

An appraiser may obtain a satisfactory estimate of what the reproduction or replacement cost might be by determining a *trended original cost*, using appropriate indexes.   In this instance it is important to have complete records of book cost and a number of indexes which are related closely to the types of property considered.   Approximate or general indexes will not ensure that the trended costs will check reasonably well with an independent estimate of the cost of reproduction or replacement.

SOURCES OF COST DATA

Whether the costing is to be done on the basis of original cost, replacement cost, or reproduction cost, the appraiser has certain sources of his price and cost data to which he may turn.   He will be governed by the particular data he wants and the sources most appropriate for the occasion.

5.2. Construction Cost Data Possessed by the Enterprise.   The book records of the enterprise, discussed in Chap. 4, will provide much of the construction cost data.   When the property ledger is complete and accurate, not too much difficulty will be encountered in the use of these data in the pricing process.   However, the appraiser may find it necessary to look to the subsidiary records (Sec. 4.5) for his information if he determines that the property ledger is inadequate.

These records show the evidence of the original cost of the existing units, and they may be used to provide replacement cost data under certain conditions.   For example, an electric utility may purchase and install each year quantity lots of poles of several sizes, lengths, and types. If the immediate past recorded costs appear to be representative and applicable to the probable construction costs of the near future, the appraiser has at hand the data with which to determine the estimated cost of replacement of all poles of those sizes and types recently installed. Use of the past costs of property, however, is restricted to those property units in the inventory which are comparable with those recently installed.

5.3. Private Collections of Cost Data.   The valuator, or the appraisal firm which employs him, generally possesses a mass of cost data which can be applied to the particular task at hand.   These data usually have been collected over a period of years from other appraisals, published data, and information supplied by manufacturers and jobbers.

For many units such cost data can be broken down into parts, and trend lines can be made to show probable variations in cost. For example, the cost of poles for an electric distribution line may have a breakdown of total installed cost involving a few items of materials, the labor of installation, and the overhead costs of construction (Sec. 6.5). The *Engineering News-Record annual construction costs number* and other publications usually give representative costs of other units on which cost data have been collected:

Office buildings..... *Engineering News-Record*
Highway paving.... U.S. Bureau of Public Roads, California Highway Department
Hospitals.......... Veterans Administration
Dams............. Corps of Engineers
Housing........... New York City Housing Authority

Although these sources might come under published cost data, their use is not limited to the construction project reported upon. These data can be applied to other properties under appropriate conditions.

5.4. Data Supplied by Manufacturers. There exist many well-established firms who will, upon request, supply appraisers with price data. Such firms usually consider this routine a part of their maintenance of good will, though the wise appraiser will keep his requests within reason. The majority of such requests are probably for quotations on machinery and the like, obtainable by the manufacturer with no great difficulty. These price data are estimates and not cost data in the sense of recorded costs found in the property ledger of the enterprise. However, these data have their use in supplying missing records of original costs or in building up estimates of the costs of reproduction or replacement of property.

A similar source exists for buildings. Contractors (erectors rather than manufacturers) are in a position to give estimates of building costs. Although such data may be most useful, the estimate may have been made on a volumetric or area basis, not necessarily on a quantity survey (Secs. 6.12 to 6.14) basis. As a consequence, the analyst must ascertain whether or not estimates made on a volumetric or area basis are sufficiently precise for the appraisal at hand.

5.5. Published Cost and Price Data. Finally, the appraiser can look to many books, bulletins, professional periodicals, and trade journals as sources of cost data.

Attention is called to such standard works as:

Leon P. Alford, "Cost and Production Handbook," New York, The Ronald Press Company, 1934. (17th printing, 1943.)

E. H. Boeckh, "Boeckh's Manual of Appraisal," 4th ed., Indianapolis, The Rough Notes Company, Inc., 1945.

Charles F. Dingman, "Estimating Building Costs," 3d ed., New York, McGraw-Hill Book Company, Inc., 1944.

Harry E. Pulver, "Construction Estimates and Costs," 2d ed., New York, McGraw-Hill Book Company, Inc., 1947.

George Underwood, "Estimating Construction Costs," New York, McGraw-Hill Book Company, Inc., 1930.

Frank R. Walker, "The Building Estimator's Reference Book," 11th ed., Chicago, Frank R. Walker Company, 1950.

Although the numerical data published in these books indicate past rather than present costs, the appraiser can find in these books data to replace missing records and analyses and discussions helpful in the preparation of new cost data.

Current price data are carried in professional and trade journals such as *Iron Age, Railway Age, Electrical World*, and *Engineering News-Record*.

Tables 5.1 to 5.4 and Figs. 5.1 to 5.3 show samples of price data of selected materials and of construction wages.

TABLE 5.1.   BUILDING MATERIAL PRICES, NEW YORK CITY

Average yearly prices at New York, except in the case of steel, which is f.o.b. Pittsburgh mill.   Brick, wholesale f.o.b.   Portland cement, net delivered, cloth bags through 1948; 1949, paper bags.   Cast iron pipe price per ton f.o.b. Delaware River foundries, 6 in. and larger Class B or heavier bell and spigot.   Lumber, No. 1 common rough wholesale, LLYP 3 × 12 through 1945; 1946, 3 × 12 rough SLYP.   Source: *Engineering News-Record*.   Permission granted to reprint.

Year	Brick, common, per M	Cement, per bbl	Pine, per M fbm	Steel shapes, per cwt	Cast iron pipe, per ton
1900	$5.25	$2.16	$24.50	$1.95	
1901	5.77	1.89	17.50	1.60	
1902	5.39	1.95	21.00	1.60	$26.62
1903	5.91	2.03	23.50	1.70	27.56
1904	7.50	1.67½	21.50	1.60	22.92
1905	8.10	1.43	24.92	1.62	26.54
1906	8.55	1.55	29.33	1.60	30.12
1907	6.16	1.55	30.50	1.75	31.52
1908	5.10	1.46	30.50	1.76	24.69
1909	6.39	1.41	33.04	1.50	24.19
1910	5.70	1.07	24.00	1.46	22.99
1911	5.31	1.04	24.63	1.36	19.99
1912	6.75	0.97	24.92	1.33	21.22
1913	6.75	1.18	25.04	1.50	21.96
1914	5.50	1.17½	21.79	1.16	20.37

TABLE 5.1.　BUILDING MATERIAL PRICES, NEW YORK CITY.—
(*Continued*)

Year	Brick, common, per M	Cement, per bbl	Pine, per M fbm	Steel shapes, per cwt	Cast iron pipe, per ton
1915	$ 5.50	$1.00	$ 21.68	$1.28	$22.52
1916	8.00	1.32	27.60	2.45	30.25
1917	9.10	1.76	38.00	3.62	52.33
1918	10.98	2.48	46.68	3.00	58.68
1919	15.79	2.63	57.04	2.52	53.87
1920	18.00	3.52	71.17	2.45	71.77
1921	17.40	2.82	50.67	2.00	50.58
1922	16.91	2.43	49.41	1.70	46.42
1923	20.00	2.66	61.77	2.39	57.75
1924	18.00	2.50	55.17	2.19	54.33
1925	15.00	2.50	57.00	1.95	49.16
1926	17.00	2.50	60.33	1.93	48.50
1927	15.00	2.40	62.57	1.86	41.42
1928	14.00	2.30	63.33	1.87	35.92
1929	11.71	2.23	64.50	1.92	36.66
1930	10.88	2.19	64.33	1.71	37.00
1931	10.29	1.89	58.17	1.63	34.71
1932	9.75	1.62	39.91	1.56	30.58
1933	9.50	2.26	46.25	1.64	34.58
1934	10.87	2.48	57.17	1.78	41.00
1935	11.00	2.15	51.67	1.80	42.58
1936	12.00	2.26	56.75	1.84	43.00
1937	12.50	2.07	61.50	2.21	48.75
1938	13.10	2.12	59.33	2.18	48.33
1939	13.46	2.20	64.35	2.10	46.75
1940	13.50	2.20	67.39	2.10	49.00
1941	13.13	2.15	75.50	2.10	49.00
1942	14.17	2.20	85.61	2.10	49.00
1943	15.88	2.27	88.81	2.10	49.00
1944	17.46	2.42	89.92	2.10	49.00
1945	18.33	2.45	89.92	2.10	50.00
1946	23.04	2.71	93.58	2.29	60.08
1947	26.38	3.46	115.83	2.61	75.46
1948	30.33	4.05	114.38	2.98	91.83
1949	33.00	3.32	98.13	3.25	91.17
1950	33.50	3.52	131.88	3.42	
1951	37.92	3.78	154.79	3.65	

TABLE 5.2.   BUILDING MATERIAL PRICES—KANSAS CITY, MISSOURI
   Concrete, ready-mixed, 1:2:4 proportions, 25 cu yd or more delivered.   Sand, per
ton, carload lots until 1946, truck lots since 1946, f.o.b. city.   Reinforcing bars, per
cwt, ¾ in. base mill price, 20 tons or more, add switching and delivery charge.   Structural clay tile, partition, scored, 4 × 12 × 12 through 1933 and since 1934, 3 × 12
× 12 per M, 2,000 pieces or over, delivered.   Lumber, short leaf yellow pine, 2 × 4
s4s, No. 2 common.   Plywood, ¾ in., special concrete form, 4- by 8-ft panels, 5-ply
sanded 2 sides, water-resistant glue, delivered per M sq ft surface.   Ready-mixed
paint, ferric oxide, per gallon, 5-gal cans.   Roofing roll, slate-surfaced, 85 to 90 lb
per square.   Source: *Engineering News-Record.*   Permission granted to reprint.

Date July	Concrete ready-mixed, per cu yd	Sand, per ton	Reinforcing bars, per cwt	Structural clay tile per M	Lumber, per M fbm	Plywood, per M sq ft	Paint, per gal	Roofing roll, per square
1930	....	....	$2.46	$105.00				
1931	....	....	2.295	88.00				
1932	$ 7.50	$1.10	2.19	75.50				
1933	7.50	1.10	2.24	73.50	$ 32.00			
1934	7.00	1.15	2.53	63.50	.....	.....	$1.50	$1.75
1935	7.65	1.15	2.59	72.50	24.50	.....	1.00	2.05
1936	7.65	1.25	2.60	72.50	26.50	.....	1.10	1.78
1937	7.65	1.15	2.87	64.50	30.00	$ 93.97	1.21	1.93
1938	7.90	1.21	2.70	64.50	23.00	92.55	1.67	1.93
1939	7.90	1.00	2.51	64.50	28.00	96.45	1.67	1.93
1940	7.50	1.00	2.51	64.50	29.00	99.75	1.67	1.93
1941	7.25	1.00	2.51	64.50	37.00	110.25	1.82	1.93
1942	7.50	1.00	2.64	67.00	52.00	110.70	2.16	2.10
1943	7.50	1.00	2.61	67.00	52.00	120.25	2.16	2.10
1944	7.50	1.00	2.61	67.00	67.00	120.25	2.16	2.10
1945	7.50	1.00	2.61	67.00	67.00	120.25	2.16	2.19
1946	7.80	1.00	2.75	67.00	74.00	120.00	2.16	2.19
1947	8.50	1.40	3.35	115.00	75.60	199.30	3.16	3.00
1948	9.85	1.65	4.23	112.00	101.50	230.16	3.16	3.00
1949	10.40	1.30	4.80	115.50	90.00	167.16		
1950	10.40	1.50	5.50	115.50	125.00	224.16	....	2.095
1951	10.95	1.50	5.90	115.50	120.00	251.16	2.65	2.39

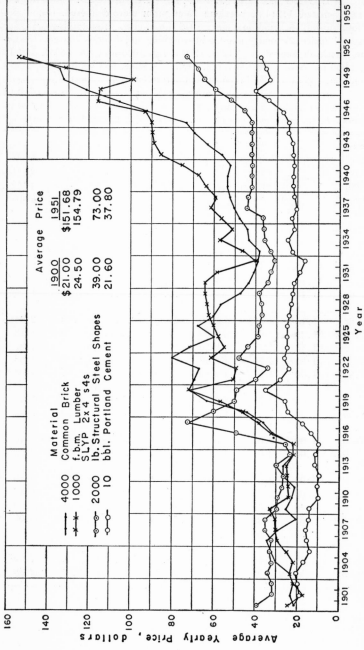

Fig. 5.1. Building material prices, New York City. Average yearly prices at New York, except in case of steel, which is Pittsburgh. Brick, wholesale, f.o.b. Portland cement, net delivered, cloth bags through 1948; paper bags since 1949. Lumber, Number 1 common rough wholesale, long leaf yellow pine 3 × 12 through 1945; since 1946 rough short leaf yellow pine 3 × 12. Structural steel shapes, f.o.b. Pittsburgh.   (*Source: Engineering News-Record, Annual Survey of Construction Costs.*)

TABLE 5.3. PRICES OF BASIC METALS

Electrolytic copper at New York City through 1930 and at Connecticut Valley since 1931. Straits tin, prompt price at New York City. Prime western zinc at New York City. Lead, common grade, at New York City. Aluminum, 99 percent plus, freight allowed. Iron ore per gross ton at lower lake ports, guaranteed maximum 0.045 percent dry phosphorus, 55 percent minimum natural iron through 1924 and 51.5 percent natural iron since 1925. Source: *Iron Age.* Permission granted to reprint.

Year	Copper, cents per lb	Tin, cents per lb	Zinc, cents per lb	Lead, cents per lb	Aluminum, cents per lb	Lake Superior iron ore, dollars per gross ton
1913	$15.7	$44.9	$5.8	$4.44		
1914	13.4	35.3	5.3	3.9	. . . . .	$3.50
1915	17.3	37.6	14.4	4.6	. . . . .	3.45
1916	27.5	43.3	14.0	6.8	. . . . .	4.20
1917	29.4	59.4	9.3	9.1	. . . . .	5.70
1918	24.7	85.2	8.3	7.4	. . . . .	6.15
1919	19.1	65.5	7.36	5.76	. . . . .	6.20
1920	18.0	50.3	8.08	8.07	. . . . .	7.20
1921	12.6	29.9	5.13	4.58	. . . . .	6.20
1922	13.48	32.51	6.09	5.79	$18.68	5.70
1923	14.47	42.68	7.00	7.39	25.41	6.20
1924	13.04	50.19	6.70	8.27	27.03	5.40
1925	14.05	57.90	7.96	9.10	27.19	4.40
1926	13.80	64.29	7.70	8.39	26.99	4.40
1927	12.93	64.32	6.60	6.75	25.41	4.40
1928	14.57	50.39	6.39	6.31	23.90	4.40
1929	18.11	45.16	6.87	6.83	23.90	4.65
1930	12.99	31.63	4.90	5.52	21.27	4.65
1931	8.37	24.43	3.98	4.24	19.71	4.65
1932	5.79	21.98	3.25	3.18	18.42	4.65
1933	7.28	39.12	4.40	3.87	19.38	4.65
1934	8.66	52.23	4.51	3.86	20.58	4.65
1935	8.88	50.39	4.70	4.06	20.50	4.65
1936	9.71	46.42	5.27	4.71	21.00	4.65
1937	13.39	54.29	6.90	6.02	21.00	5.10
1938	10.22	42.28	4.98	4.74	21.00	5.10
1939	11.20	49.11	5.51	5.05	21.00	5.10
1940	11.53	49.84	6.73	5.18	18.71	4.80
1941	12.00	52.03	7.88	5.79	16.50	4.60
1942	12.00	52.00	8.65	6.50	15.00	4.60

TABLE 5.3. PRICES OF BASIC METALS.—(*Continued*)

Year	Copper, cents per lb	Tin, cents per lb	Zinc, cents per lb	Lead, cents per lb	Aluminum, cents per lb	Lake Superior iron ore, dollars per gross ton
1943	12.00	52.00	8.65	6.50	15.00	4.60
1944	12.00	52.00	8.65	6.50	15.00	4.60
1945	12.00	52.00	8.65	6.50	15.00	4.70
1946	14.04	54.00	9.09	8.10	15.00	4.95
1947	21.30	77.95	11.02	14.69	15.00	5.70
1948	22.33	99.25	14.20	18.04	15.66	6.35
1949	19.51	99.22	12.85	15.37	17.00	7.35
1950	21.54	95.53	14.51	13.29	17.70	7.90
1951	24.50	127.00	18.75	17.49	19.00	8.45

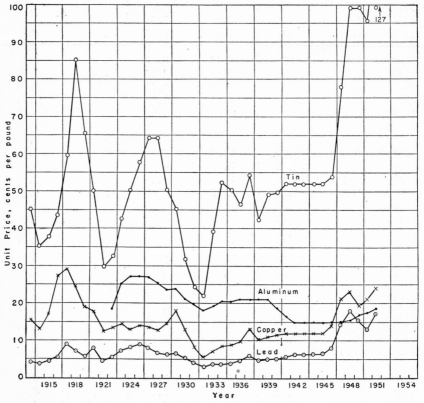

FIG. 5.2. Prices of basic metals.   All prices at New York City except copper, which is at Connecticut Valley since 1932.

TABLE 5.4. WAGE RATES PER HOUR, NEW YORK CITY
Common labor, 1900 to 1906, 9-hr day; 8-hr day 1907 to 1937; all other trades,
8-hr day 1900 to 1937.   Since 1938, all rates based on 7-hr day.   Source: *Engineering
News-Record*.   Permission granted to reprint.

Year	Carpenters	Bricklayers	Masons' laborers	Common laborers	Structural ironworkers
1900	$0.50	$0.56	$0.33	$0.14	
1901	0.50	0.59	0.33	0.19	
1902	0.51	0.65	0.36	0.17	
1903	0.56	0.65	0.36	0.16	
1904	0.53	0.65	0.36	0.19	
1905	0.54	0.70	0.36	0.20	
1906	0.58	0.70	0.38	0.21	
1907	0.625	0.70	0.375	0.22	$0.60
1908	0.625	0.70	0.375	0.22	0.60
1909	0.625	0.70	0.375	0.22	0.60
1910	0.625	0.70	0.375	0.22	0.625
1911	0.625	0.70	0.375	0.22	0.625
1912	0.625	0.70	0.375	0.23	0.625
1913	0.625	0.70	0.375	0.225	0.625
1914	0.625	0.75	0.375	0.225	0.625
1915	0.625	0.75	0.375	0.25	0.625
1916	0.625	0.75	0.375	0.25	0.66
1917	0.69	0.75	0.425	0.30	0.68
1918	0.69	0.81	0.47	0.405	0.80
1919	0.75	0.875	0.575	0.405	0.875
1920	1.125	1.25	0.775	0.75	1.125
1921	1.125	1.25	0.875	0.60	1.125
1922	1.125	1.25	0.875	0.60	1.125
1923	1.125	1.50	0.95	0.615	1.125
1924	1.3125	1.50	1.00	0.6875	1.29
1925	1.3125	1.50	1.00	0.6525	1.4675
1926	1.45	1.645	1.07	0.815	1.60
1927	1.50	1.75	1.125	0.90⅝	1.75
1928	1.50	1.75	1.125	0.90⅝	1.75
1929	1.55	1.84	1.15	0.985	1.81
1930	1.65	1.925	1.033	1.03⅛	1.925
1931	1.45	1.71¼	1.025	0.65⅝	1.925
1932	1.33	1.47	1.00	0.645	1.675
1933	1.375	1.575	0.91	0.725	1.65
1934	1.40	1.53	0.825	0.84¾	1.62

TABLE 5.4.   WAGE RATES PER HOUR, NEW YORK CITY.—*(Continued)*

Year	Carpenters	Bricklayers	Masons' laborers	Common laborers	Structural iron workers
1935	$1.40	$1.50	$0.825	$0.68	$1.65
1936	1.40	1.50	0.825	0.65	1.58
1937	1.60	1.73	0.91	0.76	1.79
1938	1.75	1.885	0.99⅔	0.91¼	1.925
1939	1.75	1.89¼	1.03⅛	0.91¼	1.925
1940	1.81	1.96	1.03⅛	0.91¼	1.96¼
1941	1.85	2.00	1.03⅛	0.93⁹⁄₁₆	2.00
1942	1.85	2.00	1.03⅛	0.95	2.00
1943	1.85	2.00	1.03⅛	0.95	2.00
1944	1.85	2.00	1.0885	0.954	2.00
1945	1.85	2.00	1.10	1.06	2.00
1946	2.10	2.25	1.23	1.20	2.25
1947	2.47	2.65	1.44	1.44	2.56
1948	2.73	2.94	1.62	1.63	2.98
1949	2.75	3.20	1.70	1.70	3.00
1950	2.88	3.30	1.78	1.78	3.14
1951	3.09	3.548	1.90	1.90	3.348

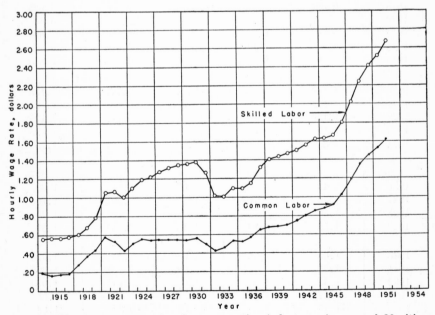

FIG. 5.3. Hourly wage rates for the construction industry.   Average of 20 cities.
(Source: Engineering News-Record, Annual Survey of Construction Costs.)

Two agencies of the United States government, the Department of Commerce and the Department of Labor, publish cost data in the form of indexes (see Sec. 5.6 for definition).   This information is contained in the monthly *Survey of Current Business* and its annual supplement.

The annual supplement of the *Survey of Current Business* and the annual construction cost numbers of the *Engineering News-Record* and other periodicals are comprehensive reviews of the existing price picture, and each should be of considerable aid to the appraiser in his task of pricing and in his predictions of prices and costs yet to come.

STANDARD PRICE AND CONSTRUCTION COST INDEXES

Price and cost data usually refer to a specific geographical location, commodity unit, and date; therefore, use of these data is somewhat restricted in their application to the prediction of future prices.   Recognizing this limitation, collectors of cost data often group these data and form price or cost indexes.

Apart from their usefulness in indicating probable trends in costs, indexes can be used to supply cost data under certain conditions.   These applications of price or cost indexes are discussed in Secs. 5.12 and 5.13.

5.6. Definition of Index.   An index, whether it be for price or cost, materials or wages, is a device for showing the relative changes in the price or cost of specific items or groups of items, over a period of time.

Of interest is the following brief description[1] of an early index:

About the middle of the eighteenth century an Italian named Carli wished to know the effect of the discovery of America upon the level of prices in Italy. To measure the price change which had taken place, he obtained a representative price of each of three commodities in the year 1500 and in the year 1750.   The three commodities chosen were grain, oil, and wine, which were considered to be representative of all Italian commodities.   These prices were then expressed as percentage relatives; that is, the prices in 1500 were each taken as 100 and the prices in 1750 were expressed relatively to their corresponding price for the year 1500.   Carli then averaged the three percentage relatives for the year 1750 arithmetically, and the resulting relative was his *index* of the change in prices between the years 1500 and 1750.

5.7. Process of Preparing an Index.   The process of making an index may be summarized into the following steps:

1. *Determine what the index is to show.*   For example, the *Engineering News-Record* building cost index is designed to indicate the relative nation-wide fluctuations of the costs of buildings in general.   On the other hand, the California highway construction cost index is designed to show relative costs for any year, based on the quantities and unit costs for

---

[1] John R. Riggleman and Ira N. Frisbee, "Business Statistics," p. 151, New York, McGraw-Hill Book Company, Inc., 1932.   Permission granted to reprint.

projects constructed in California during that year. Other examples showing this variation in the objective of the indexes are found in the description of the indexes in the following sections.

2. *Select a base period.* The base period may be one day, one year, or a series of years. However, to give significance to the current index as far as numbers are concerned, it is customary to use a period of time which is generally recognized as a significant price period. Usually the period is one of stable, representative prices (a price plateau) or a period just preceding a change of prices to new levels. The base period is usually chosen only after significant price changes are apparent. Examples of base periods are: average prices for 1910 to 1913; 1913; 1923 to 1926; 1926; 1935 to 1939; 1945.

3. *Decide what items will comprise the index.* One might decide to have an index of a single item or 3 items as Carli did. In the *Engineering News-Record* building cost index, 4 basic items are included, lumber, cement, structural steel, and skilled labor. The Boeckh index for various kinds of buildings uses 10 items.

4. *Determine the weight each item in the index should receive.* Many indexes are *simple indexes*, that is, each item receives equal weight. The computation process requires only the unit price of each item. It should be apparent that, for some studies, a simple index would be inappropriate. For example, in the computation of the index of construction cost of frame residences, one could not give equal weight to the unit prices of brick and lumber and still have an index which fairly reflects the influence of changes in the price of either brick or lumber.

In preparing indexes, two kinds of weighting are frequently used, (1) specific quantities and (2) percentages of total cost. These weighting factors are determined generally as averages of the items comprising an index. The *Engineering News-Record* building cost index and the United States Bureau of Public Roads construction cost index (Sec. 5.8) use specific quantities as weighting factors, while the Boeckh indexes of construction costs (Sec. 5.8) use percentages of total cost.

In each case the weighting factors indicate the relative importance of each item in the index to the total. Under fixed conditions, the two methods produce identical results.[1] The first method, specific quantities,

---

[1] To demonstrate that the two expressions are equal, let

U_i = the unit price of any item in the index at the date of appraisal
B_i = the unit price of any item in the index during the base period
Q_i = the specified quantity of any item in the index
W_i = the fraction of the total cost attributed to any item
    $= Q_i B_i / \Sigma Q_i B_i$

Then $Q_i U_i$ and $Q_i B_i$ are weight-price products.

Formula (5.1) is

is superior when specific quantities are more easily obtained; the second method of weighting is simpler when percentages of total cost are more readily available.   The method of specific quantities, however, lends itself a little more readily to revision in the size of the weighting factors. Tables 5.5 and 5.6, based on the items comprising the *Engineering News-*

TABLE 5.5.   CALCULATION OF A COST INDEX BY USING SPECIFIC QUANTITIES, FORMULA (5.1)

Based on the *Engineering News-Record* building cost index

Item	Assigned weight	Base period		Date of appraisal	
		Unit price	Weight-price product	Unit price	Weight-price product
Lumber, fbm...............	1,000	$0.05	$ 50	$0.10	$100
Cement, bbl...............	10	2.00	20	3.00	30
Structural steel, lb..........	2,500	0.02	50	0.048	120
Labor, man-hr.............	100	0.80	80	2.80	280
Total....................	.....	.....	$200	......	$530

$$\text{Index} = (100)^{530}\!/_{200} = 265$$

Record building cost index, illustrate the calculations required in each of the two methods.

5. *Collect periodic average unit prices.*   This step, while it sounds simple, requires the use of proper statistical methods to ensure that the result will be truly representative prices, seasonally corrected.   If a general, nation-wide index is desired, it is necessary that the important differences in the several price areas be accounted for properly.

$$
\begin{aligned}
\frac{\Sigma Q_i U_i}{\Sigma Q_i B_i} &= \frac{Q_1 U_1 + Q_2 U_2 + Q_3 U_3 + \cdots + Q_n U_n}{\text{total cost}} \\
&= \frac{Q_1 U_1 \dfrac{B_1}{B_1} + Q_2 U_2 \dfrac{B_2}{B_2} + Q_3 U_3 \dfrac{B_3}{B_3} + \cdots + Q_n U_n \dfrac{B_n}{B_n}}{\text{total cost}} \\
&= \frac{Q_1 B_1 \dfrac{U_1}{B_1}}{\text{total cost}} + \frac{Q_2 B_2 \dfrac{U_2}{B_2}}{\text{total cost}} + \frac{Q_3 B_3 \dfrac{U_3}{B_3}}{\text{total cost}} + \cdots + \frac{Q_n B_n \dfrac{U_n}{B_n}}{\text{total cost}} \\
&= W_1 \frac{U_1}{B_1} + W_2 \frac{U_2}{B_2} + W_3 \frac{U_3}{B_3} + \cdots + W_n \frac{U_n}{B_n} \\
&= \sum W_i \frac{U_i}{B_i}
\end{aligned}
$$

which is Formula (5.2).

TABLE 5.6.   CALCULATION OF A COST INDEX BY USING PERCENTAGES
OF TOTAL COST, FORMULA (5.2)

Data taken from Table 5.5

Item	Cost of item, percent of total cost	Ratio of present unit cost of item to that of the base period	Weight-ratio product
Lumber.............	25	2.00	50
Cement.............	10	1.50	15
Structural steel.......	25	2.40	60
Labor..............	40	3.50	140
Total.............	100	....	Index 265

6. *Calculate the index.*   If the weights are specific quantities, the formula used is

$$\text{Index for } x\text{th year} = (100) \frac{\sum_1^n (\text{weighting factor}) (\text{unit price in } x\text{th year})}{\sum_1^n (\text{weighting factor})(\text{unit price in base period})} \qquad (5.1)$$

where n is the number of different items considered in the index.   Note that the denominator is a constant and needs to be computed but once.

If the weights are percentages of the total cost in the base period, the formula is

$$\text{Index for } x\text{th year} = \sum_1^n \left(\begin{matrix} \text{weighting} \\ \text{factor in} \\ \text{percent} \end{matrix} \right) \frac{(\text{unit price in } x\text{th year})}{(\text{unit price in base period})} \qquad (5.2)$$

where n is again the number of different items comprising the index. Note that the ratio of the unit prices and not the prices themselves is the significant factor.

5.8. Description of Important General Indexes. The more important general indexes of interest to the appraiser are described in this section.   For the most part each index is computed monthly and reported monthly and annually in the *Survey of Current Business* and various periodicals.   The annual construction cost number of the *Engineering News-Record* is especially valuable to the appraiser since it reports most of these indexes for a long period of years.

The United States Bureau of Labor Statistics *consumer-price index*, reported frequently in newspapers and financial journals as well as in the *Survey of Current Business*, uses the average prices for the 1935–1939 period as a base.   The index is designed to show the effect of price changes on a selected fixed standard of living.   Six subindexes—clothing, food, fuel, electricity and ice, house furnishings, and rent and miscellaneous—are computed separately in addition to the combined index.

The United States Bureau of Labor Statistics *wholesale price of building materials index* (Fig. 5.4), reported in both the *Engineering News-Record* construction cost number and the *Survey of Current Business*, uses the average prices of 1926 as a base.   The index is designed to show the

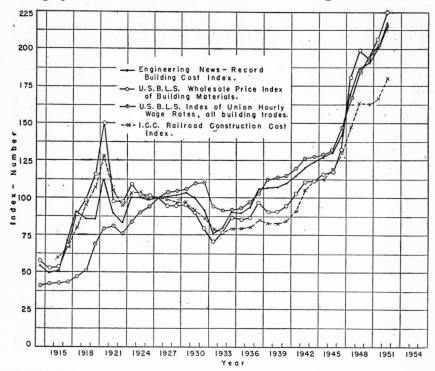

FIG. 5.4. Indexes of cost trends, 1926 = 100.   The U.S.B.L.S. index of union wage rates has been converted from its normal base period 1939 = 100 to the 1926 base. (*Source: Engineering News-Record, Annual Survey of Construction Costs.*)

change in prices, nationally, of items going into construction.   Seven subindexes—brick and tile, cement, lumber, paint and paint materials, plumbing and heating, structural steel, and other building materials—are computed separately in addition to the combined index.   Since 1948, a new index considering items which are important in housing has been reported.

The United States Bureau of Labor Statistics *index of union wage rates in the building trades* (Fig. 5.4), reported in many publications, uses 1939 as a base period.   The index shows the nation-wide variation of 17 trades; a subindex is computed for each.

The Marshall and Stevens, Los Angeles, Calif., *equipment cost index* (Table 5.7), reported by *Engineering News-Record,* uses average prices of 1926 as a base. The index shows variations in the cost installed of plant equipment as a whole. Machinery, furniture and fixtures, hand tools, and the like, are considered and appropriately weighted from studies made of 47 industries. Five major subindexes are computed—commercial, public utility, process, food, and general—representing 40 industries. Seven other subindexes are computed for the following industries: transportation (garage), metalworking, electrical equipment machinery and parts, textile, woodworking, cold storage–refrigerating, and contractors' equipment.

The *Engineering News-Record building cost index* (Table 5.7 and Fig. 5.4) has been previously described. Its companion, the *construction cost index,* differs only in the kind and amount of labor considered. The *Engineering News-Record,* in referring to these indexes, states:[1]

The *Engineering News-Record* Construction and Building Cost indexes reflect wage rate and material price trends. They do not adjust for labor efficiency, materials availability, competitive conditions, management, mechanization or other "intangibles" affecting construction costs.

A hypothetical cube of construction requiring 6 bbls. of cement, 1.088 M ft bm. of lumber, 2,500 lbs. of steel and 200 hours of common labor is used to measure the trend of the cost of heavy engineering construction.

The building cost index is based on a similar hypothetical cube using the same quantities of materials, but 68.38 hours of skilled labor.

This simple structure was adopted to facilitate prompt reporting of changes due to price and wage rate movements, both as to directions and degree.

Both indexes have proved, over the years, infallible as to the direction and in normal times remarkably accurate as to degree.

It may be noted that two of the components considered, labor and lumber, use the average prices of 20 key cities.

The *Aberthaw construction cost index,* reported annually by the *Engineering News-Record* and monthly by the *Survey of Current Business,* uses 1914 prices as a base. The index, a composite one, is designed to show the variation of costs of three typical multistory and two typical one-story industrial buildings in New England. Thirty-six major cost items are considered.

The *American Appraisal Company construction cost index* (Table 5.7), reported annually by the *Engineering News-Record,* monthly by the *Survey of Current Business,* and the company's publication, uses 1913 as a base period. It is designed to show cost trends of building construction only, excluding fixtures and decorations. It is a composite index utilizing

[1] *Engineering News-Record,* Annual Construction Costs Number, Vol. 142, No. 11, p. 160, Mar. 17, 1949.

TABLE 5.7. CONSTRUCTION, BUILDING, AND EQUIPMENT COST INDEXES

Source: *Engineering News-Record.* Reprinted by special permission of *Engineering News-Record,* American Appraisal Company of Milwaukee, Wis., and Marshall & Stevens of Los Angeles, Calif.

Year	Engineering News-Record building cost	American Appraisal Company building cost					Marshall & Stevens equipment	
		Average of 30 cities	Cincinnati	Chicago	Denver	Seattle	Plant	Construction
	1913 = 100	1913 = 100	1913 = 100	1913 = 100	1913 = 100	1913 = 100	1926 = 100	1926 = 100
1913	100.0	100	100	100	100	100	57.9	63.0
1914	91.9	98	99	97	100	96	54.1	59.2
1915	95.3	101	100	100	102	101	55.9	61.2
1916	130.9	116	115	116	118	115	62.8	67.5
1917	166.8	143	143	141	145	141	81.5	88.2
1918	159.1	177	173	170	171	176	109.7	122.6
1919	158.8	229	217	224	216	224	122.0	129.0
1920	207.2	283	276	294	262	268	153.3	154.4
1921	166.1	216	211	226	206	197	115.5	119.7
1922	154.9	200	194	202	191	186	85.5	83.5
1923	186.0	224	221	228	202	207	97.8	97.3
1924	185.8	222	221	225	206	206	105.3	107.2
1925	182.7	217	219	224	204	201	105.3	105.4
1926	184.9	217	217	219	204	199	100.0	100.0
1927	186.1	217	219	222	202	195	96.0	95.9
1928	188.0	217	219	222	205	194	96.5	96.8
1929	190.9	217	220	222	207	198	91.9	91.0
1930	185.4	200	202	205	189	184	87.0	86.1
1931	169.4	178	176	185	168	159	76.9	77.6
1932	140.9	155	157	162	149	141	66.1	71.9
1933	147.8	150	151	156	141	136	69.4	71.8
1934	166.7	161	161	166	150	150	74.6	76.0
1935	165.8	162	162	169	151	154	78.0	79.7
1936	172.2	170	174	179	157	161	81.6	83.0
1937	196.2	198	206	204	190	194	88.3	87.2
1938	196.8	199	209	205	193	193	84.4	82.9
1939	197.4	200	209	205	195	195	84.8	82.4
1940	202.8	204	213	207	199	200	86.6	83.4
1941	211.5	218	223	216	209	219	92.6	92.0
1942	222.4	241	242	235	226	244	99.6	100.8
1943	228.8	252	250	244	233	255	100.5	101.3
1944	234.7	261	266	250	237	267	102.4	101.6
1945	239.1	271	272	260	245	277	103.4	102.5
1946	262.4	322	317	303	297	324	123.2	124.2
1947	313.0	430	422	404	393	443	150.6	150.3
1948	344.5	490	483	456	443	506	162.8	161.1
1949	351.8	490	477	452	441	509	161.2	161.1
1950	375.2	500	480	467	453	518	167.9	166.2
1951	400.6	532	508	503	480	553	180.3	177.3

detailed analyses of material and labor costs required for the construction of all types of typical industrial buildings. Material costs are based on prices from 30 key cities.

The *Boeckh index of construction costs* (Table 5.8) reported annually in the *Engineering News-Record*, construction cost number, monthly by the *Survey of Current Business* and other publications, uses the average of 1926–1929 prices as a base. No composite average for all types of building construction is given; instead, a United States average for 10 types is presented under three major groupings: residences; apartments, hotels, and office buildings; commercial and factory buildings. In addition, the current index for four key cities is regularly published, Atlanta, New York, San Francisco, and St. Louis. At other times, the index for each building type is given for 16 other cities. This index utilizes current local prices paid by contractors for construction materials and the local unit wage rates. Five materials are considered—brick, lumber, steel, cement, and miscellaneous (plumbing, heating, iron and steel products)—and seven labor items are included: the hourly wages of common labor, brickmason, carpenter, plasterer, structural iron worker, plumbing and heating trades, and the average wage paid to painters, electricians, tinners, tile setters, and roofers. Additions for taxes and various overheads are included. The basis of building up the index permits the reflection of changes in labor efficiency and availability.

This index is important to the appraiser for two reasons: The manner of development makes it possible for an appraiser to compute a local index for any area, large or small, for specific building types, and it presents a pattern from which an appraiser can design a construction cost index for a specific item. Hence, the Boeckh index is discussed in more detail in Sec. 5.10.

The *Federal Home Loan Bank index* for a standard, six-room, two-story, one-family frame house, reported in the *Survey of Current Business*, uses 1935–1939 as the base period. Subindexes for materials and for labor, which enter into the total, are given in addition to the combined index. The standard residence, upon which this index is based, has a volume of 24,000 cu ft, wood siding, a one-car attached garage, unfinished cellar and attic, fireplace, plumbing, heating, wiring, and insulation. Excluded are such items as wallpaper or other interior finish, water heater, screens, and window shades. No allowance is made for the cost of land, surveying, architect's fees, financing, or sales cost. Average dealers' prices are used for the several basic materials.

The *highway construction index* of the United States Bureau of Public Roads, reported by many publications, uses the average of 1925–1929 prices as the base. Three subindexes, excavation, surfacing, and structures, are computed, as well as the composite index. Unit cost analyses

TABLE 5.8. BOECKH'S INDEX OF BUILDING COSTS

U.S. average for 1926–1929 = 100

Source: *Engineering News-Record.* Reprinted by special permission of E. H. Boeckh & Associates, Washington, D.C.

Year	Commercial and factory buildings of brick and steel				Apartments, hotels, and office buildings of brick and concrete			
	Atlanta area	New York area	San Francisco area	St. Louis area	Atlanta area	New York area	San Francisco area	St. Louis area
1926–1929	37.5	123.2	95.9	107.7	83.7	122.8	97.5	109.9
1913	44.3	53.2	64.4	54.7	43.3	53.9	63.8	56.7
1914	43.4	53.1	59.4	53.4	42.2	53.3	61.6	54.4
1915	43.7	51.8	59.8	55.1	43.3	52.5	62.5	56.9
1916	57.6	69.0	73.9	70.1	52.6	62.3	67.6	62.6
1917	74.4	83.9	94.6	81.3	63.7	73.2	77.2	71.7
1918	80.7	89.2	94.3	89.1	74.6	82.2	85.8	82.5
1919	90.9	93.6	102.2	93.8	87.0	92.0	96.7	91.4
1920	108.5	122.6	122.1	113.1	110.6	123.3	115.2	112.1
1921	76.8	100.1	103.8	103.2	81.9	101.3	102.3	105.0
1922	74.6	96.3	95.6	93.9	79.6	99.0	97.1	96.2
1923	86.1	112.7	103.1	109.4	88.9	112.3	103.1	110.2
1924	89.8	115.6	99.7	115.7	91.1	114.4	99.9	117.3
1925	83.4	110.3	98.0	114.4	88.6	111.4	99.5	116.3
1926	86.6	118.2	102.6	114.3	85.1	120.3	103.3	115.5
1927	85.5	115.6	100.5	112.5	83.2	117.2	102.1	113.5
1928	88.5	128.2	90.5	103.6	86.0	125.8	93.1	106.6
1929	89.4	130.8	90.0	100.4	80.5	127.9	91.9	104.0
1930	83.6	123.6	100.4	111.3	84.5	124.1	100.4	112.4
1931	80.4	122.8	94.8	107.8	80.4	119.7	94.6	108.0
1932	78.1	109.1	89.8	101.2	77.2	105.5	87.9	99.0
1933	79.0	97.6	85.3	99.6	77.9	101.1	84.7	97.9
1934	86.4	108.8	99.3	107.6	83.8	108.2	97.5	105.9
1935	85.6	105.3	99.8	105.7	83.9	103.6	96.5	104.2
1936	85.8	107.2	104.3	106.2	84.4	106.8	103.5	104.9
1937	93.7	120.6	113.3	117.0	92.7	119.6	112.2	113.1
1938	96.9	128.3	116.0	120.5	95.9	128.4	115.8	118.5
1939	94.6	130.0	116.5	119.2	95.1	130.6	117.4	118.7
1940	97.3	131.2	115.7	119.2	96.8	132.0	116.4	119.2
1941	100.7	134.4	123.4	122.1	99.6	135.0	120.1	121.1
1942	105.1	137.1	130.8	126.9	104.4	137.9	127.5	126.9
1943	108.7	139.0	136.3	130.3	108.5	140.2	133.2	131.2
1944	118.2	149.6	142.4	136.6	117.3	149.6	139.4	135.7
1945	123.3	155.4	147.9	145.6	123.2	156.3	144.5	146.2
1946	135.1	174.8	160.0	158.1	136.8	177.2	157.9	159.1
1947	158.0	203.8	203.9	184.0	158.1	207.6	183.7	183.9
1948	178.8	236.5	211.2	208.1	178.8	239.4	208.3	207.7
1949	177.5	240.0	216.1	213.6	180.6	242.8	214.0	212.8
1950	185.0	248.0	226.6	222.8	185.4	249.5	222.4	221.9
1951	205.0	262.2	243.1	239.0	204.2	263.7	239.6	238.5

TABLE 5.9.   PUBLIC UTILITY CONSTRUCTION COST INDEX FOR NORTH CENTRAL DIVISION

Source: *Engineering News-Record*, furnished by Whitman, Requardt, and Associates, Baltimore, Md.   Reprinted by special permission of Whitman, Requardt, and Associates, Baltimore, Md.

Date	Building		Gas plant		Electric power and light		
	Rein-forced concrete	Brick	Total construc-tion and equipment	Mechan-ical equip-ment (ex-cluding gas holders)	Total construc-tion and equipment	Accessory electric equipment	Sub-station equipment
	1911–14 = 100	1911–14 = 100	1911 = 100	1911 = 100	1911 = 100	1911 = 100	1911 = 100
1913	...	...	103	100			
1914	...	...	102	104	100	100	100
1915	...	...	109	108	105	102	102
1916	153	140	131	138	129	112	104
1917	230	189	180	195	154	123	122
1918	230	189	203	233	178	145	145
Jan. 1, 1919	220	199	210	219	184	163	155
July 1, 1920	270	272	257	241	214	188	180
Sept. 1, 1921	181	201	201	201	176	179	167
Feb. 1, 1922	163	181					
Jan. 1, 1923	193	206	206	194	179	171	162
July 1, 1924	214	218	224	218	189	185	179
July 1, 1925	208	215	217	213	192	189	184
1926	201	211	218	212	187	188	171
1927	194	208	211	211	182	185	168
1928	197	201	205	209	186	187	169
1929	203	205	206	221	199	202	177
1930	190	195	208	222	184	195	172
1931	177	186	203	217	187	199	179
1932	154	164	178	195	174	186	169
1933	162	170	185	199	179	189	171
1934	186	190	203	230	195	204	184
1935	182	184	203	234	194	202	184
1936	187	189	208	240	199	205	184
1937	209	207	235	277	224	227	204
1938	200	203	235	274	216	222	202
1939	200	203	232	278	218	223	202
1940	201	204	236	282	221	224	203
1941	225	220	245	295	232	229	206
1942	242	234	254	299	238	231	209
1943	243	235	261	298	239	231	207
1944	248	241	261	296	237	216	198
1945	253	250	269	301	243	218	200
1946	291	284	308	369	280	249	225
1947	339	324	367	395	324	289	257
1948	409	375	417	424	351	300	264
1949	418	390	434	481	374	307	280
1950	437	408	447	485	382	324	286
July 1, 1951	468	440	489	549	443	382	326

are made from contractors' bids. Quantities used in setting up the composite mile are 17,491 cu yd of excavation, 3,726 sq yd of surfacing, 16,000 lb of reinforcing steel, 4,325 lb of structural steel, and 68 cu yd of structural concrete. Fixed base prices established for each item are $0.135, $2.22, $0.052, $0.067, and $22.15, respectively.

The *railroad cost index* of the Interstate Commerce Commission (Fig. 5.4), reported by the Commission as well as by many publications, uses 1910–1914 as the base period. Data are secured from analyses of construction contracts and annual reports of the railroads. The country is divided into eight regions, and separate composite indexes are computed for each of the 46 fixed capital accounts such as engineering, grading, ties, rails, water stations, telephone and telegraph lines, signals and interlocks, shop and engine houses, shop machinery, and the like. Such an index is called the *road* index.

Three other indexes are computed: equipment (based on eight fixed capital accounts dealing with rolling stock); general expenditures; interest during construction. These four indexes are then combined to form the composite railroad cost index.

Other indexes which may be of use to the appraiser are the following: the Bradstreet index of wholesale prices, the Fruin-Colin industrial building index, Hurlin's index of commodity prices, the Turner building cost index, Tuttle's building cost index, and Whitman, Requardt, and Associates' (Baltimore, Md.) public utilities index (Table 5.9).

SPECIFIC CONSTRUCTION COST INDEXES

Although the price and cost data previously discussed are specific for the given conditions and localities, frequently it is desirable to develop indexes to use in cost studies under other specific conditions. For example, suppose an appraisal firm is determining the value for tax purposes of all the property in a county. The firm requires as data the estimated cost of replacement of the structures on the basis of 1941–1944 prices. An index for each type of structure, utilizing *local* conditions, would be most helpful because of the number of times it would be applied. Unfortunately, published general indexes are not too satisfactory for such a project, unless they happen to fit the local area, and such a circumstance may be hard to demonstrate.

It is not difficult to build up a proper local index. The process is a duplicate of that described in Sec. 5.7. The differences between a specific and a general index lie in two areas. First, in a specific index, one uses specific weights applying to a certain type of structure, using definite quantities of specific materials, instead of the general weights applying to a theoretical composite type of structure which is essentially mythical.

Second, the specific index is built upon exact unit prices for definite materials, while in a general index one uses the average price of the various sizes, shapes, and kinds of materials composing a class of materials. The following two sections describe the development of specific indexes, the first using physical quantities as weighting factors, and the second using factors of percentage of total cost.

5.9. Construction Cost Index for California Highways. The California Highway Department has developed an index of construction costs useful in predicting the probable costs of highways in the state. The specific data include the actual unit bid prices and the accompanying quantities on which the bids were made. Thus, the specific weighting factors, as well as the prices, change in size each year. The various items considered as quantities need not include all the items composing the projects, but they must be representative so that fluctuations in the index will reflect accurately changes in the estimated total cost of the projects. The average price for any item for any time is determined as the quotient

TABLE 5.10.   CALCULATION OF THE CALIFORNIA HIGHWAY
CONSTRUCTION COST INDEX

Method: Specific quantities and weight-price products
Source of basic data: *Engineering News-Record*, Vol. 146, No. 13, p. 131, Mar. 29, 1951

Item	Quantity ending Dec., 1950. (000 omitted)	Base period			
		1940		1950	
		Average unit price	Weight-price product	Average unit price*	Weight-price product
Roadway excavation, cu yd....	17,599	$ 0.22	$ 3,872	$ 0.392	$ 6,899
Crusher run base, tons.........	429	1.54	661	2.37	1,017
Plant mix, surfacing, tons......	1,982	2.19	4,341	4.25	8,424
Asphalt concrete, pavement, tons......................	120	2.97	356	4.40	528
Portland cement, concrete pavement, cu yd...............	308	7.68	2,365	11.44	3,524
Portland cement, concrete structures, cu yd...............	177	18.33	3,244	42.68	7,554
Bar reinforcing steel, lb........	28,881	0.040	1,155	0.087	2,513
Structural steel, lb............	17,772	0.083	1,475	0.109	1,937
Totals....................	......	....	$17,469	....	$32,396

$$\text{Index} = (100) \frac{32,396}{17,469} = 185.4$$

* Computed as the average of the quarterly reported prices.

of the total amount bid for the item divided by the total quantity to be installed.   Table 5.10 shows the calculation of this index for 1950, using 1940 prices as the base year.

5.10. Boeckh Construction Cost Index for Brick Residences in New York City.   The second method of development of a specific index uses the percentages of total cost as weighting factors.   The Boeckh construction cost index, described in this section, is an excellent illustration of this method.

Data required by the analyst are:

1. Local delivered unit price for each component construction material included in the index
2. Local wage rates for each trade which is included in the index
3. U.S. Bureau of Labor Statistics data on miscellaneous construction material and wages
4. Local average labor efficiency
5. Weighting factors for each component of the index obtained from fractional index tables[1]

Formula (5.2), Sec. 5.7, is required.   When modified for use with the Boeckh index, its form is

$$\text{Index} = \left(\begin{array}{c}\text{weighting factor}\\\text{in percent of}\\\text{total}\end{array}\right)\left(\frac{\begin{array}{c}\text{current unit price of each}\\\text{component}\end{array}}{\begin{array}{c}\text{U.S. average 1926–1929 price}\\\text{of each component}\end{array}}\right)$$

To save time and effort, Boeckh prepared tables[2] showing the results of the multiplication of each weighting factor by a large number of selected unit prices for each component included in each of his 10 types of building construction.   As a result, the analyst will find that the task of preparing the index is largely one of addition.

For example, it was determined by Boeckh that 12 percent of the cost of a typical brick residence during the 1926–1929 period was for brick. The United States average price for brick during that time was $16 per thousand on 10,000 common straight hard brick delivered to the job. When such brick sell in New York City for $38.50, the fractional index is 28.9, shown by the application of the index formula,

$$(12) \left(\frac{38.50}{16}\right) = 28.9$$

However, the Boeckh table gives the result of this computation directly.

[1] E. H. Boeckh, "Boeckh Index Calculator Tables," rev. ed., Washington, D.C., E. H. Boeckh & Associates, 1951.
[2] *Ibid.*

TABLE 5.11. CALCULATION OF LOCAL INDEX FOR BRICK RESIDENCES, NEW YORK CITY, MARCH, 1951

Item	Weighting factor, percent of total cost	Unit price		Unit price ratio	Weight-ratio product
		U.S. average for 1926–1929	New York, March, 1951		
Brick, M...............	12	$16.00	$ 38.50	2.41	28.9
Lumber, M fbm..........	28	40.00	116.25	2.91	81.5
Steel, cwt...............	0	3.50	3.67	1.05	
Cement, bbl..............	6	2.50	3.44	1.38	8.3
Common labor, hr........	9	0.50	1.90	3.80	34.2
Brickmason, hr...........	9	1.35	3.55	2.63	23.7
Carpenter, hr.............	12	1.25	3.09	2.47	29.6
Ironworker, hr............	4	1.75	3.35	1.91	7.6
Plasterer, hr.............	0	1.50	3.40	2.27	
Miscellaneous............	20	......	....	1.916	38.3
Local index, March, 1951	..	......	....	.....	252.1

TABLE 5.12. CALCULATION OF CONSTRUCTION COST INDEX FOR MISCELLANEOUS ITEMS, NEW YORK CITY, 1950

Boeckh construction cost index for brick residences, from E. H. Boeckh, "Boeckh Index Calculator Tables," rev. ed., pp. 63–64, Washington, D.C., E. H. Boeckh & Associates, 1951. Prices from *Engineering News-Record*, Annual Survey of Costs and Trends, Vol. 146, No. 13, Mar. 29, 1951

Item	Quoted U.S. Bureau of Labor Statistics index	Percent change for location*	Adjusted U.S. Bureau of Labor Statistics index	Fractional index
Plumbing and heating equipment, U.S. average......................	162.6	−5	154.5	52.6
Iron and steel products, U.S. average...	192.7	−5	183.0	31.1
Other building materials, U.S. average..	178.5	−5	169.6	25.5
Plumbing and heating trades, local hourly wage......................	3.18	...	.....	53.4
Painters, electricians, tinners, tile setters, roofers, local hourly wage...........	2.41	...	.....	25.1
State sales tax.......................	......	...	.....	.....
Social security payroll tax of 2¼%.....	......	...	.....	3.9
Total miscellaneous index...........	......	...	.....	191.6

* "Boeckh Index Calculator Tables," p. 22, gives 0 percent change for New York City; the −5 percent used here is for illustrative purposes only.

Table 5.11 shows the March, 1951, index for brick residences for New York City.

Table 5.12 shows the computations needed in the estimation of the final component of the Boeckh index.

USE OF INDEXES IN VALUATION

One of the more difficult problems which the appraiser encounters in the costing process is the placing of proper unit reproduction or replacement costs on the units composing the inventory.   This problem requires a forecasting of prices which will be reasonable and applicable in the near future, for which general and specific indexes are useful.   Further, indexes can be used to determine either original cost estimates or estimates of trended original costs indicative of what the replacement might be.   These three uses of indexes are discussed in the sections which follow.

5.11. Forecasting Prices.   When a price level is comparatively stable (a price plateau), the problem of forecasting is not too difficult.   Those forces which effected a stable level, if they are still operative, will tend to continue existing prices.   Such a situation, unfortunately, is not the usual case.   One plateau period was 1923–1929.   What can the appraiser do with changing prices to obtain proper representative prices for today and the near future?   He may use the average of the recent past and the present prices to give him a "period price" with the implication that these prices will be appropriate near future prices.   But there is no open-and-shut answer, because predictions are involved.   However, the appraiser does not want to have future events prove him completely wrong.

The problem is statistical and interpretive.   Movements in the price level may be attributed to (1) long-time trends, (2) cyclic variations, (3) seasonal changes, and (4) local influences.   The statistician can adjust data so as to eliminate the seasonal changes from the price picture; he can point to the long-time upward movement of prices and the variation attributable to changing business conditions.   Comparison of general and local indexes of the same construction unit over a given period of time will show the effect of certain local influences.   The analyst must try to discover what causes these price changes and then try to predict their future cumulative effect.

To go into details on the procedure of forecasting prices is beyond the scope of this text.   Such predictions are more properly made by cost analysts.   However, the appraiser will need to be able to discuss the causes of these fluctuations.   No answers are given to the questions which follow, but it is believed that each question bears on the problem of the future price level.

1. What does labor efficiency in construction do to prices?

2. How much will labor availability from other business areas tend to change construction costs?

3. Construction seasons are short in northern areas. Does this mean higher costs?

4. What do freight rates do to construction costs?

5. Of what economic importance is laborsaving machinery?

6. What happens to construction costs if materials costs go down and wages for construction labor remain at their present level or go higher?

7. What will happen to construction costs if in an area there appears to be "excess bidding capacity"?

5.12. Estimates of the Cost of Replacement.   When, in the costing process, the appraiser desires estimates of the cost of replacement, he generally builds up such costs by synthesis, using methods described in Chap. 6.   However, should he possess specific indexes, adapted to local conditions, he can determine a *trended original cost* using as basic data the recorded original cost of the unit.   The formula used is

$$\begin{pmatrix} \text{Trended original cost} \\ \text{of the specific unit} \\ \text{for the year } x \end{pmatrix} = \begin{pmatrix} \text{recorded original} \\ \text{cost of the} \\ \text{specific unit} \\ \text{installed year } y \end{pmatrix} \begin{pmatrix} \dfrac{\text{index number of specific unit for year } x}{\text{index number of specific unit for year } y} \end{pmatrix}$$

A trended original cost so obtained may give as good evidence of what the cost of replacement might be as one built up by synthesis, but it is repeated that the data used must be adequate.

Excerpts from *West et al. v. Chesapeake & Potomac Telephone Co. of Baltimore* (Case 64, Appendix A) indicate the result of the misuse of indexes.   The Supreme Court rejected the Commission's valuation because it was based on an empirically weighted average of some 16 construction cost indexes, although the Court felt that the proper use of price trends was not to be disregarded.

The Commission thought it found the answer in commodity indices, prepared to show price trends.   It selected sixteen of these, one covering as many as 784 commodities, falling into different classes, and weighted for averaging; others much less comprehensive; and its witness calculated by the use of each index the reduction in value of the company's assets considered as a conglomerate mass of dollar value from 1923, or subsequent date of acquisition, to 1932.   As might be expected, the results varied widely.   The lowest value found by the use of any index was $24,983,624; the highest $36,056,408—48 per cent higher.   The Commission then weighted these sixteen indices upon a principle not disclosed, giving them weights of from one to four, and thus got a divisor of thirty-one for the total obtained by adding the weighted results of all.   This gave what the Commission styled its "fair value index," which it applied to the 1923 value of the property then owned and to cost of all net additions in subsequent years, to obtain value as of 1932.   The result, after adding some $660,000 for working capital, was a rate base of $32,621,190. . . .

This method (the Commission's) is inappropriate for obtaining the value of a going telephone plant.   An obvious objection is that the indices which are its basis were not prepared as an aid to the appraisal of property.   They were intended merely to indicate price trends. . . .

Again, the wide variation of results of the employment of different indices, already mentioned, impugns their accuracy as implements of appraisal. . . .

To substitute for such factors as historical cost and cost of reproduction, a "translator" of dollar value obtained by the use of price-trend indices, serves only to confuse the problem and to increase its difficulty, and may well lead to results anything but accurate and fair.   This is not to suggest that price trends are to be disregarded; quite the contrary is true.   And evidence of such trends is to be considered with all other relevant factors.

A more fundamental defect in the Commission's method is that the result is affected by sudden shifts in price level.   It is true that any just valuation must take into account changes in the level of prices. . . .

We agree, therefore, with the view of the District Court that the method was inapt and improper, is not calculated to obtain a fair or accurate result, and should not be employed in the valuation of utility plants for rate-making purposes. . . . [1]

The reader is reminded that trended original cost estimates can be useful as an evidence of the cost of reproduction or replacement in such problems as appraisal for tax purposes, insurance adjustments, administrative purposes, or economic studies.

5.13. Estimates of Original Cost.   Often in the costing process, it is necessary for the appraiser to supply missing original costs.   He can do this by the use of specific indexes and cost data relating to the unit. The formula used is similar to the one given in Sec. 5.12, but the data are used differently.

$$\left. \begin{matrix} \text{Estimated original cost} \\ \text{of the unit installed} \\ \text{in year } x \end{matrix} \right\} = \left(\begin{matrix} \text{estimated cost} \\ \text{of install-} \\ \text{ing unit in} \\ \text{some year } y \end{matrix} \right) \left(\frac{\text{index number for}}{\text{unit for year } x} \bigg/ \frac{\text{index number for}}{\text{unit for year } y} \right)$$

Note that it is still necessary for the appraiser to have adequate cost data on the unit.   He obtains them from sources discussed in the first part of this chapter.   Possibly, his private collection of cost data may prove to be the most valuable source, although the records of the enterprise undergoing valuation may show the total cost of a similar or duplicate unit placed in service at some time other than the installation date of the unit in question.

[1] *West et al. v. Chesapeake & Potomac Telephone Co. of Baltimore* (No. 648), **295** U.S. 662, 672, 8 P.U.R. (N.S.) 433 (U.S. Sup. Ct. June 3, 1935).

CHAPTER 6

Costing the Inventory

The second major step in the valuation process is the determination of the various evidences of value of the enterprise. The replacement (or reproduction) cost and, in most cases, the original cost of the property included in the inventory will be the starting point in the determination.

The total estimated cost, on the basis of either replacement cost or original cost, is composed of two major parts: direct construction costs and overhead construction costs. Their definitions and processes of determination are discussed in the second portion of this chapter.

The final part of this chapter deals with a rather special costing process which has developed in the past few years, that of pricing buildings on a volumetric or area basis. Although such methods were formerly considered as only approximate, recently, through the collection and analysis of many data, unit price bases have been established by which reliable estimates of cost can be achieved. The use of these unit prices with the proper index, discussed in the previous chapter, enables the analyst to make excellent cost estimates.

6.1. Definitions. Reference is made to the previous chapters, where the terms which follow were discussed in a general way. In this section the terms are defined and delimited somewhat more precisely.

The *original cost* of a property is the amount which was required to procure and install it when new, using the prices and costs prevailing at the time of installation. Preferably, original cost should be the identifiable, recorded cost as shown on the property ledger, but when this cost is not recorded, it is necessary to estimate it either by synthesis or by use of an index. Note that the original cost of all the property of an enterprise is the sum of the original costs of many units installed at many different dates over a period of years.

The *replacement cost* of a property is the amount required to procure and install a similar or duplicate property, *supposing it to be new*, using the prices and costs prevailing at the date of valuation. This estimate can be determined by either of the two following methods, the selection depending on circumstances: (1) by finding the original cost of a similar or duplicate property installed in the recent past at prices which appear

110

to the appraiser to be proper; (2) by building up an estimate, using methods similar to those used by a contractor in preparing a bid on a construction project.

The *trended original cost* of a property is the amount obtained by translating the dollars of original cost to the dollars of the date of valuation. Such a translation is accomplished by use of proper specific indexes. The trended original cost of a property may be used separately to support an evidence of the value of the property or to check the reasonableness of an estimate of replacement or reproduction cost.

The *direct construction costs* of a property are those costs which can be determined exactly as being a definite part of the total cost of some one particular property unit. For example, the freight on a lathe, the materials and labor required to construct the foundation, and the labor of installation are direct construction costs.

The *overhead construction costs* of a property are those costs which must be allocated by some method to more than one property item, as distinguished from those costs whose exact quantity can be assigned directly to items of property. For example, the cost of building permits, the taxes and insurance during construction, and the wages of building inspectors are overhead construction costs, in the sense that they would be allocable to the several subclassifications of a building or to several buildings, should more than one be under construction at a time.

6.2. Concepts Attending the Cost of Replacement. Reference is made to Chaps. 1, 2, and 11 regarding the use of replacement cost adjusted for depreciation as an evidence of the value of a property. The following paragraphs describe briefly the conditions which the analyst assumes or infers in determining the replacement cost.

Two important considerations are involved, (1) the price basis and (2) the assumed conditions attending the theoretical replacement of the property.

The price basis used will be average or spot prices as of the date of valuation. In this regard, the replacement cost and the reproduction cost prices will be identical.

However, replacement cost and reproduction cost differ basically in the assumed conditions attending the theoretical replacement or reproduction of the property. To determine *replacement cost*, the analyst must estimate the cost of constructing a substitute new property having a capacity for service at least equal to that of the existing property if it were new, but not necessarily of the same design or process as that of the existing property. To determine *reproduction cost*, the analyst must estimate the cost of reconstructing the identical existing property in a new condition under current conditions and prices. When the analyst decides that there are no advantages in operating characteristics or in prices in choosing a substitute property over the existing property, the replacement cost will equal the reproduction cost.

The replacement cost of a warehouse now 30 years old would be the estimated cost of constructing a new warehouse of the same volume or floor space located in the same general area as the existing structure, using prices as of the date of valuation. Modern construction methods would be assumed. The theoretical structure should reflect the best design as of the specified date, using the most appropriate construction materials, in order that the resulting cost estimate may be as small as reasonably possible.

6.3. Concepts Attending the Cost of Reproduction. Reference is directed to Chaps. 1, 2, and 11 regarding the use of the cost of reproduction adjusted for depreciation as a measure of value. The paragraphs following describe briefly the conditions which the appraiser assumes or implies in determining the cost of reproduction.

Three important considerations are involved, (1) the price basis, (2) the assumed construction conditions attending the theoretical duplication or reproduction of the property, and (3) the reasonableness of the assumption of reproduction.

Suppose that it is desired to obtain the cost of reproduction of an electrical distribution system located in a subdivision of a city. The system was constructed in 1938, and additions and replacements have been made in each of the 14 years since. The cost of reproduction of the system is the estimated amount required to construct an identical distribution system, composed entirely of new units, using the present prevailing prices and including appropriate overhead construction costs. If it will help the reader, he may assume that the present existing installation is instantaneously wiped out and that at the date of valuation a contractor is ready and able to rebuild a system identical in size, quality, and performance to the one wiped out, but considering that it was new at the time of wiping out.

Second, it is generally assumed that the construction conditions attending the reproduction of the property are those prevailing at the date of appraisal. Suppose, in the case of the distribution system, that all the streets had been paved in 1940. Then, if any price advantage can be determined because of improved transportation facilities, this advantage should be reflected in the reproduction costs. The same is true of topography, materials, labor efficiency, business conditions, construction methods, construction equipment, and the like.

However, such assumptions must not be so fanciful and conjectural as to lead to obviously ridiculous estimates of the cost of reproduction. Suppose that a valuation required the cost of reproduction of some 50 distribution systems of various sizes, located in 50 different cities. It would not be reasonable to assume that one small contractor with two or three crews would construct such a large project requiring several years to complete the job. Instead, the analyst would realistically assume that there were enough contractors available to construct all of the systems concurrently, say in one year. He would be guided by the record of construction experienced by the enterprise.

One controversial point regarding the conditions of construction arose about 1918 [*City and County of Denver v. Denver Union Water Co.*, 246 U.S. 178, P.U.R. 1918C, 640 (U.S. Sup. Ct. Mar. 4, 1918)] regarding an allowance in a cost of reproduction estimate for the cost of cutting, breaking, and repaving pavement over water mains, when the evidence showed that the mains had been laid many years prior to the laying of the pavement. Logically, one should conclude that such an expense must be included in the estimate of the cost of reproduction, for the existence of the pavement at the date of appraisal is undeniable. However, in setting up a rate base, the courts have excluded this allowance for pavement laid over the mains when no such expense occurred. Such an allowance was large, sometimes enough to increase the cost of reproduction estimate by almost 50 percent, even when the original cost unit prices were comparable with prices prevailing at the date of appraisal. It would be interesting to surmise what would have been the attitude of the courts had the item been relatively small.

Third, the reasonableness of the assumption of reproduction should be studied. Consider an ancient wooden industrial building still used to capacity. If it were to be replaced, any manager would require a modern building of concrete and steel or other fire-resistant construction materials. Yet such a unit is reproducible, and fair estimates of its cost of reproduction could be obtained with little difficulty. On the other hand, consider an old steam engine, 25 hp, operating at 75 psi. Such a unit is probably not reproducible, because a fair estimate of the probable cost of manufacturing such a unit cannot be obtained through normal market channels. No doubt it has been some years since such an engine has been manufactured. A Model A Ford automobile also belongs in this category.

Finally, when the analyst decides that he cannot obtain the cost of reproduction of an item of property because he is unable to obtain the reasonable cost of its duplicate, his recourse is to determine the replacement cost of such a satisfactory substitute unit as described in the previous section.

The analyst when finding the reproduction cost of property for a public utility rate base study is not required to determine what is the most efficient substitute property which could duplicate the service of existing property; after all, the existing property is that which is being appraised.

As said by the United States Supreme Court,[1] "Save under exceptional circumstances, the court is not required to enter upon a comparison of the merits of different systems." The analyst, when finding reproduction cost, assumes that all property is reproducible (except, of course, land and depleting assets such as an oil well) if he can obtain present price data through the normal market or construction channels. If his judgment tells him that a reproduction cost estimate is ridiculously high, he rejects it in favor of the estimated cost of units which can duplicate the service, thus avoiding fanciful and conjectural assumptions.

6.4. Determining Direct Construction Costs.   Reference has been made (Sec. 4.4) to studies of the property ledger of an enterprise. Such investigations are made, among other things, to ascertain whether or not the costs reported therein are adequate and complete. If so, unit costs and quantities shown in the ledger can be used as found, provided the appraiser determines just how the overhead construction costs are handled in the accounts.

However, let it be supposed that some original costs are missing and that it is deemed necessary to build up an estimate of these costs by synthetic methods. This procedure is a duplicate of that involved in determining the cost of reproduction except for the difference of the unit prices and the difference of assumed conditions of construction. The process of building up this estimate of original costs may be described as follows.

Case 1.   *Project Constructed by Contract.*   Construction by contract can be assumed and used most advantageously when the cost estimate to be made is that for a project or property which was or could easily be done by contracting firms. The estimate of original cost would then be computed by the same procedure and on the same basis as a contractor would use in preparing his bid for the work in a competitive bidding.

The proper quantity of materials composing the project should come from the property ledger, records subsidiary to or supporting the ledger, or the summary of the field inventory. On some projects, it will be necessary to ascertain whether or not allowances have been made in the ledger quantities for such items as shrinkage of embankments, unavoidable losses of materials, such as nails, cement, and lumber, and miscellaneous breakage of glass and porcelain products. Although these losses could be accounted for by increases in the reported unit costs of materials or even as overhead construction cost allowances, it should be remembered that they are logically allowances on the reported *quantities* of materials. Thus when the analyst is using quantities obtained from his field inventory of materials, he will allow in these quantities the necessary amounts

---

[1] *McCardle et al. v. Indianapolis Water Co.* (No. 37), 272 U.S. 400, 418, P.U.R. 1927A, 15 (U.S. Sup. Ct. Nov. 22, 1926).

for shrinkage and losses during construction. When the analyst is using quantities taken from the property ledger, he should ascertain whether the allowances for shrinkage were made on the quantities of materials or through the adjustment of unit costs.

Another desirable procedure is to preserve the order of listing of the materials and their quantities as they should appear in the final report. Much time and effort of reclassification may be saved in this way. The analyst should also keep in mind that the detail shown in reporting the quantities must have accompanying unit costs of comparable detail.

The unit costs which are used should be either (1) cost delivered to the job site or (2) cost installed, the latter being the former cost plus the cost of installation. Cost of installation should include labor, plus a charge for the use of the equipment (usually estimated on a "use" basis, say hourly) needed in making the installation. These costs can include allowances for the various overheads incurred by the contractor. The experienced analyst can testify to their importance, both in magnitude and in number. Such items are bidding expense, permits, office expense, layout, guards, insurance, social security and workmen's compensation payments, taxes of all kinds, contractor's profit, and others too numerous to mention.

These latter items are items of overhead expense which a contractor would incur and thus would include in his bid on a construction project. However, these costs should not be confused with the overhead construction costs which the owner would incur and which will be described in the following sections.

The reader is referred to the several texts[1] which illustrate in great detail the process of making construction estimates. Much basic material, such as man-hours of labor required for the erection of some construction unit, is given in these excellent reference books, and the analyst may find these data to be most helpful.

Figure 6.1 illustrates a form which might be used in calculating the estimated cost of a building. Figure 6.2 shows a type of summary sheet, useful in making up estimates of building cost. Although this sheet is

[1] Leon P. Alford, "Cost and Production Handbook," New York, The Ronald Press Company, 1934 (17th printing, 1943).

E. H. Boeckh, "Boeckh's Manual of Appraisal," 4th ed., Indianapolis, The Rough Notes Company, Inc., 1945.

Charles F. Dingman, "Estimating Building Costs," 3d ed., New York, McGraw-Hill Book Company, Inc., 1944.

Harry E. Pulver, "Construction Estimates and Costs," 2d ed., New York, McGraw-Hill Book Company, Inc., 1947.

George Underwood, "Estimating Construction Costs," New York, McGraw-Hill Book Company, Inc., 1930.

Frank R. Walker, "The Building Estimator's Reference Book," 11th ed., Chicago, Frank R. Walker Company, 1950.

designed primarily by estimators preparing data for bids on construction projects, it is useful to an appraiser in making estimates of the original or reproduction cost of a building.

The reader may be surprised at the detail implied in Figs. 6.1 and 6.2, illustrating the method of building up the estimated cost of a structure. Although the final section of this chapter deals with a process of costing a structure on a unit cost per cubic foot basis, the reader is reminded here that such a method should be applied only to structures that are fairly

Form 601. XYZ Appraisal Company

Quantity and Pricing of Inventory

Property _____

Address _____

Job No. _____ Estimate No. _____

Classification _____

Sheet____ of____ Date_____

Section _____

Location _____

Estimator _____

Checked by _____

Description of Item	No. of Pieces	Dimensions			Materials				Labor			Total Cost Installed
					Unit	Quan-tity	Unit Price	Total Cost	Quan-tity	Unit Price	Total Cost	

Fig. 6.1. An estimate sheet for costing an inventory.

well standardized. The task of costing should be as detailed as possible consistent with the results desired. Good cost estimates generally are based on good quantity estimates. Walker points out:[1]

. . . A well prepared estimate has just as much to do with the success of a contractor as the manner in which he purchases his materials, lets his subcontracts or handles his work on the job. . . . Short cuts in estimating have probably "broke" more contractors than they have ever made money for, and with keen competition a difference of 5 to 10 per cent is the profit or loss on the job.

Such a caution applies equally to an analyst building up a cost estimate to be used in an appraisal.

[1] Walker, *op. cit.*, pp. 3–4.

Form 602. XYZ Company

Check Sheet and Summary of Cost Estimate   Date _____

Property _____   Section _____

Job No. _____ Estimate No. _____   Estimator _____

Classification _____   Checked By _____

1. Clearing old structures, trees, underbrush					
2. Excavating basement, piers, footings, areaways					
3. Backfilling, hauling away surplus dirt					
4. Rough and finish grading, seeding, sodding, adding top soil					
5. Wall, pier, and chimney footings					
6. Concrete, stone, block, brick, and tile walls; areaways					
7. Waterproofing and compounds, paint, plaster coats					
8. Drain tile, gravel backfill					
9. Masonry basement and garage floors					
10. Masonry sidewalks, driveways, terraces, areaways, retaining walls					
11. Reinforced concrete joists, beams, floors, stairs					
12. Common and face brick, backup tile, block					
13. Flue lining, fire brick, chimney caps, hearths, coping					
14. Stone trim, water tables, sills, lintels, steps, caps, mantels					
15. Pointing, cleaning brick and stone work					
16. Steel--columns, beams, lintels, windows, casements					
17. Framing lumber--posts, columns, joists, girders, plates, sills					
18. Lumber for rafters, studding, dormers, lintels, eaves, trim					
19. Sheathing, siding, subflooring, bridging, furring, porch material					
20. Insulating quilt, boards, dry fill, aluminum foil, building paper					
21. Iron bridging, dampers, clean outs, railings, coal chutes, gratings					
22. Interior wallboard, plywood, paneling, wall coverings					

FIG. 6.2. A check sheet and summary form for cost estimates. Listings are suggestive of the items that a complete list would include.

23. Wood flooring, floor tile, linoleum, brass, sanding and finishing								
24. Rough and finish stairs, well hole facing, mill work, handrail								
25. Misc. exterior carpentry, rafter ends, brackets, facia boards								
26. Misc. interior carpentry, chair rails, mouldings, hook strips								
27. Finish carpentry, mill work doors, windows, cabinets, casings								
28. Screens and storm windows and doors								
29. Shingles, roofing paper, ridge								
30. Sash weights, chain, nails, bolts, screws, garage door fittings								
31. Butts, locks, door holders, catches, hooks, door checks								
32. Sheet metal flashings, gutters, down spouts, decks, ducts, chutes								
33. Lathing and plastering, corner beads, metal casings, stucco								
34. Ceramic tile floors, wainscoting, hearths, mantels								
35. Weather stripping, caulking doors and windows, metal thresholds								
36. Glass and glazing, leaded glass, mirrors								
37. Curtain rods, blinds, dumb waiters, medicine cabinets, fans								
38. Painting and varnishing exterior and interior, paper hanging								
39. Water, sewer and gas services; floor drains, sill cocks								
40. Kitchen and bath fixtures								
41. Electrical service outlets, switches, control panels, bells								
42. Wall and ceiling fixtures and lamps								
43. Heating plant, distributing system, controls, piping, ducts								
44. Humidifying and air conditioning equipment								
45. Temporary buildings, winter protection, safeguards, scaffoldings								
46. Cleaning up, tools, equipment rentals, transportation								
47. Superintendence, overheads, permits, surveys, surety bond								
48. Insurance—fire, tornado, public liability, compensation								
49. Payroll taxes—social security, old age benefits, unemployment								
Total estimated cost								

FIG. 6.2.—(Continued.)

Case 2. Project Constructed by Owner. The assumption of owner construction can be used most advantageously when the cost estimate to be made is that for a project which was or could have been done by the construction crew or maintenance crew employed by the owner. Additions to existing facilities are frequently installed in this manner, such as the primary and secondary circuits required to bring electric power to a new subdivision or new equipment installed in an industrial building.

As previously mentioned, the analyst will obtain the list of materials from the property ledger or inventory summary. Generally the unit costs will be composed of the purchase price, transportation cost, and the direct cost of installing the property. However, since the owner is now the general contractor under this assumption, there is no allowance in the unit costs for the "contractor's overhead." Instead, the cost of these many items will appear as a part of overhead construction costs, and their determination will be discussed in the following sections.

The question may well be asked, "Do these two methods produce similar answers?" Suppose an analyst estimates the reproduction cost of a project by both methods. If the project is one which is frequently constructed in actual practice either by the owner or by contract, such a situation indicates that the difference in construction cost must not be great. When the cost difference between two methods is large, the analyst should use the construction method producing the lower cost when such cost estimate is known to be reliable and applicable.

OVERHEAD CONSTRUCTION COSTS

Overhead construction costs are those costs incurred by the owner in the construction of property which must be allocated by some method to more than one item of property, as distinguished from those costs whose exact quantity can be assigned directly to one inventory unit.[1]

Overhead construction costs can be classified into three groups, engineering, general, and interest during construction. Other items of cost which are sometimes considered as overhead construction costs but which the authors believe should be treated elsewhere in the appraisal are allowance for omissions and contingencies (Sec. 6.7) and the cost of organization, promotion, and financing the enterprise (Chap. 14).

The overhead construction costs are usually determined in dollars but often are expressed as a percentage of the direct construction costs. The use of percentages appears arbitrary, but it is a logical and a customary way of expressing these costs.

Interest during construction is a noncash cost, since the item represents return forgone on the investment in partially completed property not yet operative. For this reason, enterprises operating under a regulatory agency generally record this item in a separate account in order to enable them to report accurately the complete cash outlay for any single con-

---

[1] The contracting firm has the same condition to contend with when he carries on more than one contract within an accounting period. He must allocate his engineering, office, equipment, and other expenses to the various jobs contracted.

struction project. Other overhead costs of construction, however, are usually allocated to the several units comprising a project and shown in the property ledger as a part of the original cost.

Overhead construction costs may be estimated by three methods, (1) from the book records of the enterprise (the historical costs), (2) by estimated comparative percentages, and (3) by synthesis. The first method is appropriate for the determination of original costs when the book records are available, the others for estimates of the cost of replacement and reproduction.

6.5. Process of Allocation of Overheads. Overhead construction costs are allocated to each property unit or inventory group on a pro rata basis. For example, suppose that a project cost as follows:

Total paid to contractors for construction of building and equipment...	$1,000,000
Engineering costs incurred by owner................................	95,000
General overhead cost incurred by owner...........................	48,000
Interest during construction......................................	27,000
Total cost..	$1,170,000

Although the original cost of the entire project was $1,170,000, the cash outlay was $1,143,000.

Now suppose there is a unit of the project whose total materials and direct installation cost to the contractor, as shown by his records, was $5,000. The amount of the $170,000 overhead cost allocated to this unit will be determined by the ratio of its direct cost to that of the entire project. Thus, the overhead cost allocated to this unit would be

$$\left(\frac{\$5,000}{\$1,000,000}\right)(\$170,000) = \$850$$

The entire original cost of the unit would be $5,850.

A rearrangement of the expression demonstrates why overhead construction costs are so often shown as percentages of the direct cost.

$$\$850 = \$5,000\left(\frac{\$170,000}{\$1,000,000}\right)$$

The fraction indicates the relative size of the overhead costs compared with the total direct costs of the project. Thus, in this case, the overheads are 17 percent of the direct costs, the overhead charged to the specific unit is ($5,000)(0.17) = $850, and its original cost is ($5,000)(1.17) = $5,850. This procedure is somewhat more simple, and it is the easier way to allocate the indirect construction cost to property-ledger classifications of the units comprising a construction project.

6.6. Items of Construction Cost Usually Considered as Overheads. Examination of the records subsidiary to the property ledger, such as the completed work orders, should disclose the items which have been considered to be a part of overhead construction costs.   In addition, enterprises regulated by governmental agencies are generally required to keep separate accounts which will show the total overhead on any project. For example, the uniform system of accounts[1] prescribed by the Federal Power Commission for electric plants indicates that records should be made of:

(4) Transportation (of employees and work equipment to and from points of construction)

(5) Special machine service (cost of operation of construction equipment)

(6) Shop service (proportion of utility's shop department assignable to construction work)

(7) Protection (guarding against fire and theft)

(8) Injuries and damages (injuries to persons, damage to adjacent property, investigations relating thereto, defense against actions)

(9) Privileges and permits

(10) Rents (construction headquarters, office space)

(11) Engineering and supervision (portion of pay and expenses of engineers, surveyors, draftsmen, inspectors, superintendents, and their assistants assignable to construction work)

(12) General administration capitalized (portion of pay and expenses of the general officers and administrative and general expense applicable to construction work)

(13) Engineering services (amount paid to other firms or individuals for plans, designs, estimates, supervision, inspection, consulting advice, engineering reports)

(14) Insurance (against fire, theft, damages, but excluding workmen's compensation insurance)

(15) Law expenditures (other than those charged to items 7 and 8)

(16) Taxes (during construction against the property)

(17) Interest during construction (net cost of borrowed funds used for construction purposes, or a reasonable rate upon the utility's own funds when so used)

(18) Earnings and expenses during construction

Other enterprises not subject to similar regulation may record these costs under other headings, although the ones listed present a rather complete picture.

All the costs listed will generally be incurred specifically when the owner is his own contractor.   However, if a construction project is awarded to a contracting firm, items (4), (5), (6), (7), (8), (9), (10) and a part of items (11) and (13) will undoubtedly be included in the contract

---

[1] U.S. Federal Power Commission, "Uniform System of Accounts Prescribed for Public Utilities and Licensees, Subject to the Provisions of the Federal Power Act," p. 40, Washington, D.C., Government Printing Office, 1937.

price and thus they are buried in the direct costs. Such a situation produces but little difficulty in an analysis for original costs (Sec. 6.4); it is necessary only that the analyst determines what method was employed for any specific project.

The 15 items listed in this section may be grouped into the three classes proposed as follows:

Engineering—items (11) and (13)
Interest during construction—item (17)
General—all others

6.7. Items Not Properly Considered as Overhead Costs. Although it is true that the items discussed in this section are to be considered and provided for if necessary in a valuation, such items are not really overhead construction costs of the kind mentioned in Sec. 6.6. Nor should they be allocated by the proration method indicated in Sec. 6.5. Rather, each item should be treated separately as suggested in the paragraphs which follow.

An allowance for omissions is proper when the list of materials is derived solely from an inventory, because the enumeration in the field inventory is usually low. However, such an allowance, if needed, should be added to the inventory quantities, not to overhead costs. The quantities determined in the field inventory must always be increased to allow for the justifiable loss and wastage of materials during the process of construction. For example, the number of brick required to construct a finished wall exceeds the quantity in the finished wall by the number which were cut down to fit or were broken or lost.

An allowance for contingencies in replacement or reproduction cost estimates is often urged, because of the possibility that unforeseeable costs might be caused by strikes, wage increases, delays, and other uncontrollable factors. If every effort is made to have the proper and complete inventory priced at fair, appropriate prices, as of the date of valuation, no allowance for contingencies need be made.

Other items often suggested as overhead construction costs are the costs of organization, promotion, and the financing of the enterprise. Although it is true that the total cost of the physical property has a good deal to do with the requirements of the financing, yet the cost of financing more truly depends on the type of industry, the comparative risk of venturing into such an industry, and the character of the enterprise itself. Hence, these items should be considered as items of intangible property, with their costs attending the initiation of the enterprise rather than the construction of the physical property. They are discussed in Chap. 14.

6.8. Determining Overheads from Book Records. The basic problem which the analyst meets in his determination of the overhead construction costs by use of the book records of an enterprise is to discover just how the amounts indicated were really made up. Companies subject to the provisions of the Federal Power Act are required to comply with the following instructions:[1]

C. The records supporting the entries for overhead construction costs shall be so kept as to show the total amount of each overhead for each year, the nature and amount of each overhead expenditure charged to each construction work order and to each electric plant account, and the bases of the distribution of such costs.

Other enterprises may have similar instructions. But unless the book records show the data in the detail indicated, the analyst will have difficulty in verifying the overhead construction costs.

In order, therefore, to verify the recorded costs shown in the property ledger, the analyst looks for the accounts described in Sec. 6.6. A new set of accounts is opened at the beginning of each year. At the end of each year these accounts are closed into the proper accounts and the total overhead prorated into the cost of each property addition by the method described in Sec. 6.5.

There may be some instances when it is not necessary to prorate a construction cost. Such a case would be the inspection required on the erection of a simple structure which will end up as one property unit, such as a water tower. Although, in this situation, the cost of the inspection need not be prorated and thus the cost could be considered as a direct cost, yet it is customary to treat the inspection cost as an overhead.

When examining the ledger accounts for the proration of overhead construction costs, the analyst should satisfy himself that the overheads were allocated in a proper and reasonable manner. If he has reason to question the allocation as recorded in the ledger, he should make his own investigation to ascertain whether or not another method would be appropriate. If so, he should spread the overheads in accordance with his judgment rather than accepting the prorations shown in the ledger.

When the analyst discovers that no overhead construction costs have been allocated to the property ledger, he must proceed to build up the appropriate overhead construction costs. Usually he finds that the overhead costs, whether the construction was by contract or built by the owner, were absorbed by the company as charges to overhead operation expenses. In such a case, the analyst must estimate the total overhead construction cost for each period involved, as well as allocate these totals to the ledger classifications.

He may proceed by one of the following three methods: (1) make a test study of the company's operations for the past few months or for the

[1] *Ibid.*, p. 43.

next few months, whichever is appropriate, (2) apply the overhead experience of a similar type of company provided that he has access to such information, or (3) prorate such expenses on the basis of the relative dollar volume of the direct costs of materials and labor used in operations and in construction.

The third method may be expressed by the following formula:

$$
\left.\begin{array}{l}\text{Allocation of} \\ \text{expense of} \\ \text{engineering} \\ \text{department to} \\ \text{construction}\end{array}\right\} = \left[\begin{array}{l}\text{total annual} \\ \text{expense of} \\ \text{engineering} \\ \text{department}\end{array}\right]\left[\frac{\text{total annual direct construction cost}}{\left(\begin{array}{l}\text{total annual} \\ \text{direct con-} \\ \text{struction cost}\end{array}\right) + \left(\begin{array}{l}\text{total annual} \\ \text{direct oper-} \\ \text{ation expense}\end{array}\right)}\right]
$$

A similar expression could be written for that part of the expense of the engineering department which would be charged to operation.

TABLE 6.1. ANALYSIS OF OVERHEAD CONSTRUCTION COST
PERCENTAGES
Original Costs as Shown by Book Records

Proj-ect No.	Size of proj-ect, millions	Engi-neer-ing and super-vision	General overhead construction cost					Inter-est during con-struc-tion	Total over-head con-struc-tion costs
			Mis-cella-neous	Legal	Injuries and damages	Taxes during con-struc-tion	Total		
1	.....	3.6	....	....	....	....	1.93		
2	$17.5	5.80	....	....	....	....	1.57		
3	31.7	5.91	....	....	....	....	1.14		
4	46.1	4.71	....	....	....	....	0.83		
5	33.1	4.90	....	....	....	....	0.94		
6	34.2	4.59	....	....	....	....	0.87		
7	.....	4.24	....	....	0.11	0.06	5.98		
8	2.5	5.00	1.87	0.02	0.82	0.12	2.83	9.38	17.21
9	.....	4.26	4.11	0.07	1.19	0.03	5.40	3.74	13.40
10	15.1	5.51	2.03	0.46	0.84	0.28	3.61	4.43	13.55
11	8.8	5.42	3.40	0.62	0.65	0.46	5.13	3.86	14.41
12	3.2	15.50	....	....	....	....	3.20		
13	15.3	7.29	....	....	....	....	3.80		
14	11.3	6.23	....	....	....	....	7.93		
15	3.5	6.00	....	....	....	....	5.70		
16	0.2	4.00	1.00	0.50	1.00	....	2.50	2.17	8.67
17	0.2	3.20	1.50	0.50	1.20	....	3.20	2.20	8.60
18	30.6	5.00	2.50	2.50	1.00	0.50	6.50		
19	28.2	4.00	....	....	....	....	2.50		

To illustrate, suppose the analyst discovers these data:

Salaries and wages of engineering department................. $ 4,500
Other engineering department expenses...................... 1,312
Total annual direct construction costs of enterprise........... 40,939
Total annual direct operation expense of enterprise*........... 96,025

* Includes direct material and direct labor only which were used in the manufacturing process.

$$\left.\begin{array}{l}\text{Allocation of expense} \\ \text{of engineering department} \\ \text{to construction}\end{array}\right\} = (\$5{,}812)\left(\frac{40{,}939}{136{,}964}\right) = \$1{,}737$$

$$\left.\begin{array}{l}\text{Allocation of expense} \\ \text{of engineering department} \\ \text{to operation}\end{array}\right\} = (\$5{,}812)\left(\frac{96{,}025}{136{,}964}\right) = \$4{,}075$$

Table 6.1 summarizes data, accumulated from various sources, which show the relative size of the three main overhead construction costs. These estimates relate entirely to original costs, and for the most part were obtained from book records.

6.9. Estimating Interest during Construction. The analyst may need to verify the amount shown in the book records for interest during construction. To accomplish this, he needs to obtain a record of the amount and the date of payment for all direct construction costs (the record may be of vouchers made out to a contractor) incurred in the construction of the project. In addition he needs to know the amount of cash expenditures for overhead construction costs and their time of payment. The interest period is that length of time during which cash payments on the partially completed property are not earning a return because the property is not operating. The amount of interest is determined by the following formula:

$$\begin{array}{c}\text{Interest during} \\ \text{construction}\end{array} = \sum_{1}^{n}\left(\begin{array}{c}\text{each pay-} \\ \text{ment}\end{array}\right)\left(\begin{array}{c}\text{each inter-} \\ \text{est period} \\ \text{in months}\end{array}\right)\left(\frac{\text{annual interest rate}}{12}\right)$$

where n is the number of separate payments made on the construction.

The interest rate (rate of return) assumed should be a "reasonable rate," probably the going rate demanded by investors in this type of enterprise. It must be remembered that a standard warehouse constructed for an enterprise which operates at a high risk can be used for many purposes and can command a reasonable price if offered for sale. Thus, a rate not to exceed, say 5 percent, might be applicable for standard buildings, while at least 7 percent would be appropriate for a special-purpose structure built in some out-of-the-way place.

The money which is used to finance construction is obtained by industrial enterprises from three sources, (1) moneys on hand and not otherwise obligated, (2) the sale of those securities which will provide equity capital, and (3) the sale of those securities which will provide credit capital. It might appear that the calculation of interest during construction, which is to be capitalized as an investment, should be conditioned upon the source of the funds used to finance the construction. If a project is financed entirely by equity capital, there probably will be no interest or return actually paid in cash during the period of construction. In contrast, if the project is financed entirely by credit capital, interest on the bonds or other instruments would actually be paid or at least accrued for later payment. When it is considered that the interest during construction is an element to compensate the owners of the property for a return forgone during the construction period when it was not possible to derive any operating revenue, the conclusion is reached that the owner's risk began at the time he made his first payments for the construction work. He would therefore be entitled to consider that his return forgone or his interest during construction was at a rate equal to the acceptable rate of return for that particular enterprise.

The concept of the allowance for interest during construction as a capital investment is illustrated by the following hypothetical situation: Suppose a contractor was asked to submit two bids for the construction of a large building wherein the only difference in his two bids was the manner of the payments on the contract. The first bid was to be on the basis that one lump sum would be paid to the contractor upon completion and acceptance of the job; under the second bid, the contractor would be paid in full at the end of each month for the work and materials put into the job during the month. The dollar difference in the two bids would be an estimate of the amount of interest during construction. The contractor, were he to accept the job on the basis of one lump-sum payment, would be required to finance the entire construction to its completion and would include in his contract price a sufficient amount to compensate him for the money he had temporarily invested in the construction.

Table 6.2 indicates what a typical computation might be for interest during construction. The total cash outlay of the project, $123,234, is composed of $12,000 of overheads (plans and specifications of $5,000, and overheads of $7,000) and $111,234 of direct costs. The total interest during construction, $1,460, can be expressed in percentage of the direct costs by use of the method suggested in Sec. 6.5:

$$\left(\frac{1,460}{111,234} \right) (100) = 1.31 \text{ percent}$$

6.10. Estimating Overheads by Synthesis. The second method used to determine overhead construction costs, that of synthesis, is most

TABLE 6.2. COMPUTATION OF INTEREST DURING CONSTRUCTION

Project accepted and placed in operation November 1. Annual interest rate 5 percent. Monthly interest rate $\frac{5}{12}$ percent

Payment item	Amount of payment	Date of payment	Interest period, months	Interest during construction
First payment to architectural firm for detailed plans......................	$ 2,500	Feb. 28	8	$ 83
Overhead construction costs allocated for January........................	512	Jan. 31	9	19
Overhead cost allocated for February......	357	Feb. 28	8	12
Second payment to architect.............	1,500	Mar. 31	7	44
Overhead cost allocated for March........	622	Mar. 31	7	18
Overhead cost allocated for April.........	515	Apr. 30	6	13
First payment to contractor (80% of materials and labor invested by him in project to Apr. 30).....................	7,212	Apr. 30	6	180
Overhead cost allocated for May.........	859	May 31	5	18
May estimate to contractor..............	18,711	May 31	5	390
Overhead cost allocated for June.........	1,207	June 30	4	20
June estimate to contractor..............	23,923	July 10	$3\frac{2}{3}$	366
Overhead cost allocated for July..........	725	July 31	3	9
July estimate to contractor..............	13,594	July 31	3	170
Overhead cost allocated for August.......	836	Aug. 31	2	7
August estimate to contractor............	9,413	Aug. 31	2	78
Overhead cost allocated for September.....	691	Sept. 30	1	3
September estimate to contractor..........	7,147	Sept. 30	1	30
Overhead cost allocated for October.......	676	Oct. 31	0	0
Final payment to architect..............	1,000	Oct. 31	0	0
Extras put in by contractor..............	9,234	Oct. 31	0	0
Final payment to contractor..............	22,000	Oct. 31	0	0
Totals.............................	$123,234	....	...	$1,460

adaptable to estimates of the cost of replacement or reproduction of property. In brief, the method requires setting up an assumed construction program in sufficient detail so that the analyst may work up the amount of each main group of overheads. The analyst can assume that the project is to be constructed either by contract or by the owner's construction employees.

In either case, a construction organization will be assumed. Obviously, the recorded history of the construction of the property will prove useful in determining what to set up in theory. However, the analyst will take advantage of conditions prevailing at the date of appraisal, using current standards for organization and construction methods. With this organization determined, the analyst then is ready to estimate what costs will be incurred by the organization in carrying out the assumed construction program.

The list of accounts presented in Sec. 6.6 provides a guide to the analyst which should show what the detailed items of overhead costs may be. When the theoretical construction program assumes an organization and method of payment similar to that followed when the original construction took place, the synthetic overhead costs would be estimated by the same procedure as used in the original construction.

The unit costs involved in this process are the salaries, wages, and office expenses prevailing for the assumed construction period. When this study is (as it is generally) a cost of replacement or reproduction estimate, the current salaries, wages, and office expenses of the enterprise will provide useful data.

The analyst is reminded that fanciful and conjectural assumptions have no place in the determination of overhead costs by the synthetic method, any more than in determining direct construction costs. The construction organization must be realistic. The analyst must not assume "high-powered" and expensive talent as consultants, adding and pyramiding costs.

Since it will be assumed that the construction program will progress smoothly, it may be possible to determine an adequate estimate of interest during construction with much less detail than that shown in Sec. 6.9. For example, the assumption can be made that the expenditures for construction are made at a uniform rate. Then the interest during construction can be computed by the formula

$$
\begin{pmatrix} \text{Interest dur-} \\ \text{ing con-} \\ \text{struction} \end{pmatrix} = \begin{pmatrix} \text{total direct} \\ \text{construc-} \\ \text{tion costs} + \begin{matrix} \text{engineering and} \\ \text{general overhead} \\ \text{construction costs} \end{matrix} \end{pmatrix} \begin{pmatrix} \dfrac{\text{construction}}{\text{period in years}} \\ 2 \end{pmatrix} \begin{pmatrix} \text{annual} \\ \text{inter-} \\ \text{est rate} \end{pmatrix}
$$

A diagram showing the amount invested in idle property as the construction period progresses (a straight line) will indicate the correctness of this formula.

Another assumption might be that a certain portion of the total construction expenditures will be incurred in each of several subperiods of the entire construction program. This method usually requires that it be assumed that funds spent during each subperiod are expended at a uniform rate. Table 6.3 illustrates the application of this assumption.

Generally, the synthetic method of determining the overhead construction cost estimates produces satisfactory results. After all, the analyst is following a procedure similar to that used in estimating the direct costs of construction, a procedure which a contractor frequently uses in preparing his bid on proposed construction. In costing units for appraisal,

TABLE 6.3.   CALCULATION OF INTEREST DURING CONSTRUCTION
(APPROXIMATE METHOD)

Direct construction cost $1,500,000.   Engineering overhead 7%.   General overhead 5%.   Total outlay for construction $1,680,000.   Length of each construction subperiod 3 months.   Number of subperiods in construction program 3.   Annual interest rate 6%; monthly interest rate $\frac{1}{2}$%

Subperiod No.	Costs incurred in subperiod		Interest period, months	Interest during construction
	Portion	Amount		
1	$\frac{1}{16}$	$ 105,000	7.5	$ 3,938
2	$\frac{7}{16}$	735,000	4.5	16,537
3	$\frac{8}{16}$	840,000	1.5	6,300
Total......	...	$1,680,000	...	$26,775

Interest during construction in percent of

$$\text{overhead base} = \left(\frac{26,775}{1,500,000} \right) (100) = 1.79\%$$

the analyst has no reason to be less accurate than the estimator who prepares bids.

6.11. Estimating Overheads by Comparative Percentages.   Estimating overheads by comparative percentages is a simple process, but to produce good results, there should be a maximum of historical data and good judgment available.   When this method is employed, the analyst makes direct estimates of each of the three main overhead construction costs, usually in percent.   Each estimate is determined by use of data collected from many similar past projects.   After careful examination of these data, the analyst decides on appropriate overhead percentages suitable to the appraisal being studied.

This process is not without value.   In fact, for bidding purposes, estimators employed by contractors use this method most frequently, and there is nothing wrong with their estimates.   However, the appraiser or his analyst should not afford the luxury of a "guess-timate," when more precise data and methods are available.

PRICING BUILDINGS ON A VOLUMETRIC OR AREA BASIS

For many years appraisal firms have estimated the replacement cost (and original cost as well) of buildings on a volumetric or area basis, using information gathered by the firm on the recorded cost of similar buildings. Such estimates were most commonly used in appraisals for insurance, tax, or sale purposes, and the phrases "This building would cost $0.55 per cubic foot if erected today" or "I doubt if this building could be put up today for less than $12 per square foot" were often heard. Recently such data have been compiled for general use and published. One such book is "Boeckh's Manual of Appraisals,"[1] and the authors acknowledge the permission received to extract parts of the manual for use in the sections which follow.

Boeckh's manual contains general instructions relating to the procedure of appraisal of buildings and, of particular interest to the reader at this point, specifications and unit costs of three general types of buildings. Since these costs are based on nation-wide average prices for the period from 1926 to 1929, the manual includes instructions which enable the analyst by means of the Boeckh Index Calculator Tables (Sec. 5.10) to translate average costs to a specific location and a specific time.

Such information is of much benefit to the analyst because he need not be his own collecting agency of the vast number of data required to make such costs representative. Furthermore, the procedures outlined suggest that an appraisal firm desiring such information may collect cost data on other structures such as bridges, dams, or pavements and use them in a similar way.

The sections which follow contain a discussion of the data provided by Boeckh's manual, the field and office work required, and an example illustrating the procedure of estimating the 1950 cost of a factory building located in New York City.

6.12. Data Needed for Cost Estimates Based on Volume or Area. An analyst accustomed to the use of a detailed quantity analysis of the materials and labor comprising a building (wood, steel, brick, plaster, plumbing, heating, wiring, etc.) may consider that the methods described in these sections are but approximations of the real situation. It may be true that, if one does not apply the corrective factors, pricing on a volume or area basis results only in approximations. Boeckh's manual, however, provides for these modifications.

First, there is the type of structure. Three general groups are given: (a) residences; (b) apartments, hotels, and office buildings; (c) commercial and factory buildings. Obviously each general group has many varieties, and so a further classification is made. For example, the first group is broken down into frame and brick, each of which is subclassified into one-story dwelling, two-family one-story dwelling, two-family two-story dwelling, and two-story flats and terraces (a total of 12 different residence categories). A similar breakdown of the remaining two general groups is made; for the apartments, hotels, and office buildings, 50 types are described, and the commercial and factory group contains 25 items. An added section is used for miscellaneous buildings and farm structures of 16 types.

[1] Boeckh, *op. cit.*

The second selectivity factor is that of the quality of construction. Generally, four categories are given, cheap, average, good, and expensive. Where applicable, the category fireproof is given. For each type of structure and quality of construction, a brief set of specifications is presented, generally covering the following items: excavation, foundation, walls, floor, roof, interior finish, and service improvements. Further, a base unit cost (per cubic foot or square foot as the case may be) is given for each structure described. At this stage, therefore, the problem of estimating the cost of a structure is reduced to two elements: (a) finding the dimensions of the building and (b) describing it properly so that its counterpart may be selected from the manual.

Two modifications are used. The first deals with the variation in unit cost occasioned by differences in ground floor area. For example, two small stores may have equal volumes, but one will be slightly more expensive to build because it has a higher ceiling, even though its ground area is smaller than that of the other store. Tables showing this unit cost variation are given for each structure where applicable.

The second modification deals with "individual costs." Frequently a structure does not fit any set of specifications exactly. A residence has an extra porch or bathroom; an apartment otherwise of good construction has a cheap heating unit or perhaps finished apartments other than janitor's quarters below ground level. These differences are shown as "flat charges" per installation, or as specific additions to the base unit cost.

It should be apparent to the analyst that the manual described in the preceding paragraphs contains literally thousands of items of cost data, and so it does. Obviously, these data can relate only to a specific location and to a specific time. As stated previously, all these prices are in terms of the nation-wide average construction costs for the period from 1926 to 1929. However, the data will not be out of date until the descriptions of the various structures become inapplicable, because these unit costs can be translated to a specific location and to a specific time by use of the Boeckh Index Calculator Tables (Sec. 5.10).

These data, the type of structure, quality of construction, individual costs, base unit prices, and the local translating index, are necessary prerequisites for acceptable estimates of the cost of buildings on a volume or area basis.

6.13. Field and Office Work Procedures. The necessary field work for appraisal of structures by volume or area differs from those procedures described for unit or item appraisal (Secs. 4.8 to 4.15) because in the case at hand the problem is one of inspection rather than one of making an exact quantity survey. The field work can be facilitated by the use of an appraisal work sheet as illustrated by Figs. 6.3 and 6.4 from "Boeckh's Manual of Appraisals."

For Use with BOECKH'S MANUAL OF APPRAISALS

APPRAISAL REPORT

Owner..Location: No................Street................................

City..Inspector.. Date........................

GRADE						CORECTION TO BASE UNIT COST — CENTS —	FLAT CHARGES

Key: 1—Expensive; 2—Good; 3—Average; 4—Cheap

1	2	3	4		

A. EXTERIOR
ARCHITECTURE
GENERAL PLAN
LANDSCAPING
EXPOSURE

B. Type of Building: Cottage — Bungalow — 2-Story Dwelling — Duplex Dwg. — Terrace — Apartments — Store — Dept. Store — Hotel — Hospital — Office Bldg. — Theatre — Church — Factory — Shop or Storage — Warehouse — Public Bldg. — Public Garage — School — Club — Bank — Filling Station.

C. Construction: Height, Stories................. .. Stores .... Rooms.................
Apts.............. Baths............ F. P. .... Semi-F. P. .... Ord...............
Frame — Brick — Steel — Concrete — Metal — Stone — Veneer.

D. BASIC EXTERIOR CONSTRUCTION

FOUNDATION *Material:* Concrete — Concrete Block — Brick — Stone — Cut Stone — Piers.
    Excavation: ... . % of Area ... .% of Depth

WALLS *Type:* Wood Frame — Steel Frame — Concrete Frame — Solid Masonry
  Face Material: Face Brick — Common Brick — Terra Cotta — Siding — Shingles — Stucco — Concrete — Concrete Block — Marble — Granite — Stone — Cut Stone — Metal.
  Bearing Wall............... ft. Curtain Wall. .... ft. Party Wall........... ...... ft. Division Walls. ... ... ft.

WINDOW SASH Wood — Metal   Plain — Casement   *Glass:* Plain — Plate — Leaded

EXTERIOR TRIM *Style:* Plain — Ornamental.
    Material: Wood — Tile — Stone — Plastic — Metal — Terra Cotta — Marble — Granite.

ROOF *Type:* Flat — Gable — Hip — Gambrel — Monitor — Saw Tooth
  Material: Shingles, Wood — Composition — Concrete — Gypsum — Slate — Tile — Asbestos — Copper — Tin — Built Up — Rolled.
  Dormers........ ....   Finished Rooms in Attic.. .. ..

E. BASIC INTERIOR CONSTRUCTION

BASEMENT *Finish:* Open   Plastered Wall — Ceiling   No. Finished Rooms. ....
    Floors: Wood — Cement — Earth   Built-in Garage No Cars. . .. . Sub-Cellar.

HEATING *System:* Steam — Hot Water — Vapor — Hot Air — Stoves   Concealed Radiation — .. ..%
    Plant: Stoker — Gas — Oil Burner   Temperature Control

FLOORS *Material:* Pine—Oak—Maple—Cement—Tile—Marble—Cork—Terrazzo—Linoleum—Composition.
  Type: Reinf Concrete — Steel & Concr — Steel & Tile — Steel & Wood — Joisted — Mill Type.

INTERIOR FINISH *Material:* Pine — Oak — Gum — Birch — Poplar — Metal — Formica — Steel.
    Fireplaces: No.   — Colonial — Stone — Brick — Ash Pit.

PARTITIONS *Material:* Wood Lath — Metal Lath — Plaster Board — Shiplap — Gypsum Tile — Hollow Tile.
    Finish: Painted — Papered — Craftex — Canvassed — Travertine.

ELECTRIC SYSTEM *Fixtures:* Modern — Old — Suitable to Type   House Phones
    Type: Conduit — BX — Knob and Tube

PLUMBING Baths. .... Showers .... Toilets. .. ... . Lavatories..........
  Laundry Trays. .. .. Sinks .... Slop Sinks . .. . Sewer — Water — Gas
  Tile Floors. ... . x .. .... Tile Walls. x

F. EQUIPMENT AND ACCESSORY SCHEDULE

				Mech. Refrig.	PRICE	1	2	3	4		PRICE
				Concealed Beds						Screens	
				Wardrobes						Ironing Boards	
				Breakfast Sets						Service Cabinets	
				Dressing Tables						Mail Boxes	
				Stoves—Elec.						Mail Chute	
				Stoves—Gas						Telephone Cabs	
				Incinerator						Weather Strips	
				Kitchen Cabinets						Awnings	
				Dish Closets						EXTRAS	
				Pass. Elevator							
				Frt. Elevator							
				Fire Escape							
				Automatic Sprinklers							
				TOTAL						TOTAL	

G. PORCHES—Memo.

Size	Height	Cubage	Found.	Floor	Columns	Roof
... x	.. x ...	=				
..... x	..... x	=				
... x	... x	=				

H. DEPRECIATION   Base Rate. ....%
Date Built·   Remodeled:
Condition, Exterior: Excellent—Good—Normal—Fair—Poor
Condition, Interior Excellent—Good—Normal—Fair—Poor
∓ for Condition ... . %
∓ for Obsolescence .... %
TOTAL DEPRECIATION RATE ....%

I. Sound Value of Building

I-1 Total Corrections	
I-2. Base Unit Price for Type and Class (Ch. IV) .	
I-3. Total Base Unit Price @ Index 100 (1 plus 2) .	
I-4 Total Flat Charges	$
I-5. Cu. Ft (Sec. J.)...........x Base Price (Line 3) .....=	$
I-6. Total Value, @ Index 100	$
I-7. Local Index .... x Value (Line 6) $...............	
= Reproduction Costs	$
I-8 Depr (See H) % .....x Repr. Costs (Line 7) $............	$
I-9. SOUND VALUE OF BUILDING	$

(For Sketch and Measurements of Building, Land Valuation, and Summary of Appraisal, See Other Side.)

FIG. 6.3. Appraisal report form. (*Courtesy of E. H. Boeckh and Associates, Inc., Washington, D.C.*)

J. BUILDING
(Include here Porches (Sec. G))

SIZE	Height	Cubage
x		
x		
x		
x		
x		
x		
x		
x		
x		
x		

REMARKS

K. Other Buildings	CONSTRUCTION						Size	Height	Cubage	Base Rate	Depreciation	Base Value	Local Index	Sound Value
	Foundation	Walls	Floors	Roof	Equipment	Condition								
Private Garages							x							
Barns and Sheds							x							
Green Houses							x							
							x			*				
							x							

*See Chapter VI, Individual Costs.

L. LAND VALUATION

Unit Percentage Factor	100	—	+	Unit Percentage Factor (Continued)	—	+
Depth				Schools		
Width				Churches		
Shape				Neighborhood Shopping		
Topography				Main Shopping		
Street Width						
Alley						
Corner Lot						
Street Paving				Zoning Laws		
Side Walks				% Developed		
Street Lights				Classification		
Telephone				Exposure		
Sewer—Water				Filled Ground		
Gas—Electric						
Transportation						
Fire Protection				Total Factors		
Total Factors				Net Total Factors		
Net Total Factors						

Sale or Rental Analysis of Neighborhood   Converted Index

No	Date	Price	

Frontage   ft.
Unit Value $
Unit Percentage   %
Actual Unit Value $

LAND IMPROVEMENTS
Grading and Sodding $
Walks $
Driveways $
Shrubbery $
Total 100 Index $
    ∓   % $
Current Price $

SUMMARY
Lot Value $
Lot Improvements $
Total Land Value $

M. Insurance Exclusions

M-1. Value, Building Structure (Line I-5) $ ....
(Not Including Flat Charges)

M-2. Multiplied by Local Index (...........) $ ....

M-3. Less Depreciation (Sect. H) @.. ...% $ ....

M-4. Present Sound Value of Structure.. ...$ ....

M-5. Insurance Exclusions, @...... ., ...% $ ....

N. SUMMARY OF APPRAISAL

N-10. Sound Value of Building (Line I-9)... .. ..$ ....

N-11. Other Improvements—Sound Value (Sect. K)... .. ..$.....................

N-12 Land Value—Including Improvements (Sect L) $ ....

N-13 Less Unpaid Taxes and Assessments .. ...., ...$.... ....

N-14. Sound Land Value (Lines 12 minus 13).....................$.... .. ...

N-15. Total Sound Economic Value .. ..$...........

© Rough Notes Co. Inc., Indianapolis, Ind.

FIG. 6.4. Appraisal report form, reverse side. (*Courtesy of E. H. Boeckh and Associates, Inc., Washington, D.C.*)

In the field, the appraiser should accomplish the following:

1. *Obtain (or check) building dimensions.* Measure the exterior perimeter at the ground level. Show each bay or porch or projection. Vertical dimensions start at the top of the basement floor or top of exterior wall footings. Vertical dimensions end at the exterior roof surface. Since roof design varies widely, it is well to measure up to the eaves, considering the building as a rectangular solid; then add the volume of the roof's space, using those solid mensuration formulas which apply.

2. *Inspect the building.* Grade each of the seven major specification items on quality of construction. Note percentage of area excavated to basement depth. Note variations in foundation walls, quality of basement floors, drainage, etc. Note kind of exterior surface. Note type and extent of insulation. Note basement piers, columns, girders, spacing of joists, presence of fire stops. Note kinds of flooring and each amount. Indicate roof style, and record special features. Note type of partitions, interior finish, type of plaster base, quality of interior carpentry and hardware. Pay particular attention to items which are not in keeping with the general level of construction quality indicated.

3. *Check the type of structure and construction quality level.*[1] Determine whether or not there are any significant omissions or added features which must be handled either as a correction to the base cost or as a flat charge.

In the office the following should be accomplished:

1. Calculate the perimeter, area, and volume of the structure as applicable.

2. Use the field report as a guide to determine the type, size, and grade of structure, and obtain a base unit cost per cubic foot (or square foot if applicable). Note that this base cost is determined from average prices and for some past date.

3. Compare the field report with the standard specifications given for the type, size, and grade of structure, and determine if any special items require an addition to or subtraction from the base unit price.

4. Compare the field report with the standard specifications given for the type, size, and grade of structure, and determine if any special items require additions to the cost by way of flat charges.

---

[1] During the course of inspecting the building and checking the quality of construction, the inspector would record his estimate of the physical condition of the property to be used in estimating depreciation. However, since this step is a valuation problem, not a pricing problem, no discussion of this step is given here.

5. Calculate the estimated cost new of the structure for a specific location and time. If the base cost is in dollars per cubic foot,

$$
\begin{Bmatrix} \text{Estimated} \\ \text{cost} \end{Bmatrix} = \left[\begin{pmatrix} \text{volume of} \\ \text{building} \end{pmatrix} \begin{pmatrix} \text{modified} \\ \text{base unit} \\ \text{cost per} \\ \text{cu ft} \end{pmatrix} + \begin{pmatrix} \text{extras on a} \\ \text{flat charge} \\ \text{basis} \end{pmatrix} \right] \begin{pmatrix} \text{translating index} \\ \text{for a specific} \\ \text{location and time} \end{pmatrix}
$$

When the base cost is in dollars per square foot,

$$
\begin{Bmatrix} \text{Estimated} \\ \text{cost} \end{Bmatrix} =
$$

$$
\left[\begin{pmatrix} \text{ground floor} \\ \text{area, main} \\ \text{structure} \end{pmatrix} \begin{pmatrix} \text{modified} \\ \text{base unit} \\ \text{cost per} \\ \text{sq ft} \end{pmatrix} + \begin{pmatrix} \text{addi-} \\ \text{tional} \\ \text{areas} \end{pmatrix} \begin{pmatrix} \text{unit cost} \\ \text{per sq ft} \end{pmatrix} + \begin{pmatrix} \text{extras} \\ \text{on a flat} \\ \text{charge} \\ \text{basis} \end{pmatrix} \right] \begin{pmatrix} \text{translating} \\ \text{index for a} \\ \text{specific loca-} \\ \text{tion and time} \end{pmatrix}
$$

6.14. Example—Costing a One-story Brick and Steel Factory Building. Suppose the problem is to cost a building used as a garage. From the field report the following information will be obtained from the forms illustrated by Figs. 6.3 and 6.4:

1. One-story brick and steel light-duty factory building. Size 50 by 125 ft, rectangular, no projections. Height, top of footings to exterior of roof, 21 ft.

2. Reinforced concrete footings, no basement walls, 12 in., face brick exterior, structural tile backing about 25 percent wall area in glass. Standard steel pivot-type windows with double-strength glass. Five-inch reinforced concrete floor, well drained. Average wall height 16 ft. Flat roof, gravel on composition, carried by structural steel frame strong enough to carry small hoists. Low-pressure heating, supplied from outside source.

3. Good construction, no added individual costs.

The office work shows:

1. Perimeter 350 ft; area 6,250 sq ft.

2. Use specifications and costs for one-story brick and steel factory building, light duty, type 3 (pages 214 and 215 of Boeckh's manual, shown here as Figs. 6.5 and 6.6). For given perimeter and area, base cost is $3.28 per square foot.

3. Since building is of type E in this category, the specifications call for a multiplier of 1.03 to take care of face brick exterior. Since average wall height is 1 ft more than indicated in specifications, 1.5 percent is added to base cost. Since roof is carried on structural steel frame, add 0.25 to base cost. The modified base unit cost per square foot, therefore, is $(3.28)(1.03)(1.015) + 0.25 = \$3.68$.

ONE-STORY BRICK AND STEEL FACTORY BUILDING—LIGHT-DUTY— TYPE NO. 3

One-story brick and steel; average wall height, 15 feet; average roof height, 20 feet. A type of industrial building commonly used for manufacturing the lighter type of commodities, especially in the metalworking groupings.

Specifications

FOUNDATIONS: Steel reinforced concrete, footings and foundation of sufficient depth to run below frost line. No basement.

WALLS:

Type A: 12-in. common brick curtain between pilasters; pivot commercial type steel sash windows with D. S. glass 50% of wall area; unfinished interior; no parapets; average wall height 15 feet. (*Use* 100% *of base price table and convert by Brick-Steel Industrial Index.*)

Type B: 12-in. common brick curtain between pilasters; pivot commercial type steel sash windows with D. S. glass 25% of wall area; no parapets; average wall height 15 feet. (*Use* 96% *of base price table and convert by Brick-Steel Industrial Index.*)

Type C: 12-in. common brick curtain between pilasters; blank or solid wall construction; unfinished interior; no parapets; average wall height 15 feet. (*Use* 92% *of base price table and convert by Brick-Steel Industrial Index.*)

Type D: 12-in. wall, face brick exterior with common brick or structural tile backing; pivot commercial type steel sash windows with D. S. glass 50% of wall area; unfinished interior; no parapets; average wall height 15 feet. (*Use* 105% *of base price table and convert by Brick-Steel Industrial Index.*)

Type E: 12-in. wall, face brick exterior with common brick or structural tile backing; pivot commercial type steel windows with D. S. glass 25% of wall area; unfinished interior; no parapets; average wall height 15 feet. (*Use* 103% *of base price table and convert by Brick-Steel Industrial Index.*)

ROOF: Built-up 5-ply gravel covered composition on hy-rib cement plaster slab, supported by lightweight steel columns and girders. Skylights or other roof openings to be charged for extra.

FLOORS: 5-in. reinforced concrete on cinder fill; all floors well drained to sewers.

INTERIOR FINISH: Open finish ceiling and wall throughout. Partitions to be added extra.

SERVICE IMPROVEMENTS:

Electricity: Conduit wiring, drop cord metal reflector lights.

Heating: Low pressure, 1 pipe system.

Plumbing: Sewer and drain connections only; add additional charges for fixtures.

FIRE PROTECTION: Automatic sprinkler, if any, to be added extra—see Individual Costs section of this manual.

FIG. 6.5. Specifications to use as a basis for pricing a one-story brick and steel factory building, light-duty, Type No. 3. (*From "Boeckh's Manual of Appraisals," page 214, by permission.*)

(1-STORY BRICK-STEEL LIGHT-DUTY FACTORY—TYPE 3—Cont'd.)

Base Price Per Square Foot of Ground Area
(At Boeckh Index No. 100)

SQ. FT. GROUND AREA	\multicolumn{12}{c}{PERIMETER OF EXTERIOR WALLS}											
	150'	200'	250'	300'	350'	400'	450'	500'	550'	600'	650'	700'
1,600	4.31	5.00	5.69									
2,000	3.70	4.25	4.81	5.36								
2,500	3.36	3.81	4.25	4.70	5.14							
3,000	....	3.50	3.87	4.24	4.61	4.98						
3,500	....	3.30	3.62	3.93	4.25	4.60	4.89					
4,000	....	3.14	3.41	3.70	3.97	4.25	4.53	4.81				
4,500	....	....	3.26	3.51	3.76	4.00	4.25	4.50	4.74			
5,000	....	....	3.14	3.36	3.58	3.76	4.03	4.25	4.47	4.69		
6,000	....	....	2.95	3.14	3.33	3.51	3.70	3.88	4.07	4.25	4.44	
7,000	....	....	....	2.98	3.14	3.30	3.46	3.62	3.77	3.93	4.10	4.25
8,000	....	....	....	2.86	3.00	3.14	3.28	3.42	3.56	3.70	3.83	3.97
10,000	....	....	....	2.70	2.81	2.92	3.03	3.14	3.25	3.36	3.47	3.58
12,000	....	....	....	....	2.75	2.81	2.86	2.92	2.97	3.03	3.08	3.14
15,000	....	....	....	....	2.55	2.63	2.70	2.77	2.85	2.92	3.00	3.07
20,000	....	....	....	....	2.42	2.47	2.53	2.59	2.64	2.70	2.75	2.81

Corrective Factors for Structural Deviations

	FLAT CHARGES	CENTS CHANGE IN BASE PRICE
FOUNDATIONS: Boiler pits or other open pits with concrete retaining walls all around, *add* per lineal foot of perimeter for each foot of depth (plus excavation at $1.00 per yard)..............	$ .60	
WALLS: Base price contemplates an average wall height of 15 feet—top of foundation to eaves. For each foot differential in height *add* to or *deduct* from base price 1½%.........................		
Wired glass window lights where windows are 50% of wall area, *add* 2.7% to base price...		
25% of wall area, *add* 1.4% to base price...		
Parapets with tile coping, *add* per lineal foot of wall		
12-in. parapets.........................	1.15	
24-in. parapets.........................	1.79	
36-in. parapets.........................	2.43	
ROOF AND SUPPORTS: Steel structural framework for carrying machinery, *add* to base price........		$ .25
Sawtooth construction with same basic specifications, *add* to base price..................		.34
All steel monitor construction, no craneway, *add* to base price...........................		.28
With light craneway, *add* to base price.......		.48
FLOORS: Reinforced concrete floors, *add* to base price...		.10
Earth floors, *deduct* from base price..........		−.25
Maple floor on sleepers embedded in concrete, *add* to base price...........................		.16
SERVICE IMPROVEMENTS: If no heating, *deduct* from base price................................		−.30

FIG. 6.6. Base prices and corrective factors for pricing a one-story brick and steel factory building, light-duty, Type No. 3. (*From "Boeckh's Manual of Appraisals," page 215, by permission.*)

4. Since steam is supplied from an outside source, deduct $275 for omitted boiler.

5. Estimated 1950 cost of building,

$$\text{Estimated cost} = [(6\ 250)(3.68) - 275](2.48)^* = \$56,358$$

* 1950 construction cost index for brick and steel commercial and factory buildings in New York.   See Table 5.8 for index.

CHAPTER 7

Methods of Estimating Service Lives

The pricing and costing of the property in the inventory as described in Chap. 6, whether on an original cost, replacement cost, or reproduction cost basis, is followed by a procedure of adjusting for depreciation. Property which has been used is not generally worth as much as the identical property if new. Property in service has given up some of its potential usefulness; therefore, in appraising such property consideration is given to the fact that the potential useful service of the property has been decreased.

The factor almost universally used in measuring the consumption of the usefulness of a depreciable asset is the potential total usefulness of the asset. The unit most frequently used for this purpose is the time unit of one year. Other units of use such as hour, mile, ton, items, products, or services rendered are used occasionally.

Because of the importance of the service life in appraisal of property, this chapter is devoted to the methods of estimating the probable service life of unit properties and the probable average service life of group properties. The four chapters which follow are on the subject of depreciation, to which the service life is an all-important factor. The best procedure in estimating service lives is to study past experience, and then to adjust the results when informed judgment indicates that the probable future experience will produce estimates of service lives significantly different from those arrived at by analysis of experience.

7.1. Property Retirements. Retirements of property are the withdrawals from useful service of the property. At this time the original cost of the property retired is written out of the investment account. The useful service life of the property ends with its retirement. Property may be retired by removal physically or by being left in place intact but unused. Generally, however, the property is not considered to have been retired until the accounting department credits the retirement in the property asset account. In order to handle the accounting entries, a policy on what constitutes a retirement must be adopted (see Sec. 3.5).

With the exception of complete destruction by accident or catastrophe, property is retired by decision of management. Thus, personal opinion as a power of management usually is the controlling force determining

139

when property is to be retired from useful service. In many instances the property is retired for a combination of reasons. For instance, a milling machine already somewhat worn would be likely to be retired after meeting with a serious accident, while if it were new it would be repaired and restored to service. Retirement ends the service life in the particular service at the time, but the property may be reinstalled in another service.

The conditions which lead to the retirement of property include the following:

A. Physical condition
  1. Accident
  2. Catastrophe
  3. Deterioration from time
  4. Wear and tear from use
B. Functional situations
  5. Inadequacy
  6. Obsolescence
    a. Economic
    b. Style and mode
C. Situations unrelated to the property
  7. Termination of the need
  8. Abandonment of the enterprise
  9. Requirement of public authority

To isolate the one cause why a given property was retired is often difficult; yet an understanding of the general classification of the causes of retirement of property is helpful in the prediction of useful service life.

A. The physical conditions of a property which are causes of its retirement may be described as follows:

1. Sudden physical damage may be caused by miscellaneous accidents, such as explosions, collisions, falls, failures of buildings and other structures, or the breaking of machinery by extraneous forces.

2. When sudden damage from disasters, such as fires, storms, floods, or earthquakes, amounts to destruction, the property is retired thereby. When the damage is partial, the cost of repairs or reconstruction is weighed against cost of replacement in deciding whether or not to retire the property.

3. Physical decrepitude is that physical disablement of property which develops and increases during service in spite of expenditures for repairs and other maintenance. Physical decrepitude may be caused by physical deterioration from rusting and other chemical processes, the mechanical effects of freezing and thawing, other temperature variations, or gradual decay as in timber and other materials of organic origin. Examples are a

wooden bridge unsafe because of decay or a steel bridge weakened by corrosion. Physical deterioration increases with age and extent of exposure to destructive elements rather than with use.

4. Wear and tear from friction, impact, vibration, stress, and fatigue of materials is caused by normal use. Examples are an engine, a lathe, or a concrete mixer worn out by use. Wear and tear are proportional to use rather than to age.

B. Industrial property is functionally inefficient whenever its services could be rendered more efficiently or economically by other units of the same or different design. Functional inefficiency may result from:

5. Inadequacy or insufficient capacity for the service required. An example is a 50,000-lb per hr steam generator when a 100,000-lb per hr generator is required.

6. Obsolescence, another characteristic of functional undesirability, is usually brought on by the invention and development of improved devices of the same general character. An example is using steam generators for 300 psi steam pressure in large power plants where new 1,000 psi steam generators would effect great savings.

6a, 6b. Style changes and supersession cause obsolescence when the same service can be rendered with greater economic efficiency by a different kind of structure or equipment. An example would be the substitution of electric motors or internal combustion engines for steam generator engines in plants where the two former would be more economical.

C. Management is sometimes called upon to retire property which is wholly satisfactory. Its business may change in such a way that there is no further need for the property. These classifications may be:

7. No further need of the property because of termination of a phase of the business. For example, a company which gives up its manufacture of heating specialties in order to devote its full resources to the production of oil and gas furnaces would retire certain tools and equipment because of having no further need for them.

8. Retirement of property because of abandonment of the entire enterprise, such as the moving of an entire cement manufacturing plant to a new location nearer a new rock deposit.

9. Retirement of underground services to make way for a municipal transit authority subway or the removal of structures from land which is to be flooded for a water storage reservoir.

7.2. Replacements. Property retired may be renewed or replaced (Sec. 7.4). A replacement is a substitution for property retired at the end of its useful service life, usually because it is damaged, worn out, or obsolete. A replacement may or may not substantially duplicate the property retired or its service. Replacements include renewals (which duplicate the old property) but are not limited to renewals. Improvement in machinery, for example, may make it advisable to replace a machine by one considerably different in character and which may cost more or cost less than the original machine.

Not all retirements are replaced. Prevailing conditions at the time of decision to retire property form the basis of whether or not new property is to replace that retired.

7.3. Significance of the Action of Retirement. The cause of retirement is relatively unimportant, except that such knowledge may be used in selecting new properties, supposedly of greater usefulness than the property retired, or knowledge of the causes of retirement may be helpful in forecasting the service life of existing property. Retirements are important to all industry because the act of retirement signifies the end of service usefulness of that property as determined by the judgment of management.

The aim of management is to retire property at the end of its *economical service life,* that is, when it is more profitable to use other property or at least is no longer profitable to use that particular property. In practice, however, property is sometimes used beyond the point of economical use or is retired before it has reached the end of its economic usefulness. Service life ends, nevertheless, with the act of retirement. This is the important fact in cost accounting and in valuation because the date of ending the service life is that date which controls certain aspects of depreciation accounting and is the date of minimum value of the property to the owner.

INDUSTRIAL PROPERTY SURVIVOR CURVES

The statistical method of arranging and studying human births and deaths has been in use a long time by insurance actuaries to determine human life expectancy and corresponding insurance premium rates; the method is now coming into use by valuation engineers and accountants to assist in determining the service lives of physical properties. Survivor curves of human beings have been used for determining insurance rates for some 200 years. Such curves show the number of persons who survive the various ages of life.

The compilation of similar curves for physical properties should have been just as natural a development, but this was not the case. Only since 1902 have any such curves been compiled; the number now available is still limited when compared with the multitudes of items and classes of property in service. But the actuarial analysis of the service lives of depreciable properties is now an established practice in industry, both regulated and nonregulated.

7.4. Nomenclature of Survivor and Derived Curves. Terms used in the following discussion of service lives and their determination are defined as follows:

1. *Original data* refers to the records showing the property installed, including number of items, dollars cost, ages, dates of placement in service, dates of retirement, and other facts necessary to a complete understanding of the life history of the property during the period covered by the data.

2. A property group is composed of a number of *individual units*, each unit distinct from a physical or accounting consideration.

3. A *property group* is any collection of similar units comprising a property or section of a property, regardless of the ages of the units included.

4. An *original group*, or *vintage group*, is a collection of units installed in service at the same time, or at least during the same accounting interval.

5. In certain statistical treatments, a property group is observed over a period of years called the *observation*, or *experience*, *period*. An experience period of several years is frequently chosen in using the retirement rate method of calculating a survivor curve.

6. The *age* of a property is the lapsed time from the date of its installation to the date of observation. For a property group the *average age* is the average of the ages of the separate units. For convenience, the age is usually designated to the nearest whole year or to January 1, which would age property on the half year when measured from an average installation date of July 1.

7. An *age interval* is measured from the beginning of one age period (usually a year or other similar unit) to the beginning of the next consecutive period. The terms *at the beginning of the age interval* and *at the end of the age interval* are usually employed to avoid confusion in calculations. For calculation purposes, the units installed during an age interval are assumed to have been installed simultaneously at the middle of the interval and thus to have an age dating from the middle of the interval during which they were placed in service.

8. The *service life* of a property is that period of time (or service) extending from the date of its installation to the date of its retirement from service. While the service life of physical property is usually expressed in years, it may also be expressed in terms of units produced (screws, wheels, cars, pounds, miles, car-miles), time units of less than a year (months, hours, minutes), or combinations of physical units or service and time (lamp-hours, ton-years).

9. The *probable service life* of a unit is that period of time extending from its date of installation to the forecasted date when it probably will be retired from service.

10. The *expectancy* of life of a unit is that period of time extending from the observation age (usually the present) to the forecasted date when the unit probably will be retired from service. Age plus expectancy always equals probable life.

11. The *average service life* of a group of units is the quotient obtained by dividing the sum of the service lives of all the units by the number of units. The average service life (in years) is equal to the area under the survivor curve in percent-years (or unit-years) divided by 100 percent (or the total number of units).

12. The *probable average service life* of a group of units is the average of the probable service lives of the units of the group.

13. The *average expectancy* of life of a group of units is that period of time extending from the observation age (usually the present) to the average of the forecasted dates when the units probably will be retired. The observation age plus the expectancy always equals the probable average service life.

NOTE: Service life and average service life are always known quantities since they represent completed service life; probable service life and probable average service life always must be estimated since they are forecasts of uncompleted service.

14. *Maximum life* or *maximum age* is the age of the last unit of a given group to be retired from service; it is also the age at which the survivor curve has a zero ordinate, or zero percent, surviving.

15. A *retirement* is any property removed from service for any reason whatsoever. Retirements may include original units (units of the initial installation) as well as "subsequent generation" units, that is, replacements (or renewals) which were installed to take the place of units removed.

16. A *replacement* is the property put into service to replace a retirement.

17. *Renewals* are replacements "in kind" which have the same life characteristics as the retirements.

18. All renewals, replacements, and installations are *placements*.

19. *Survivor curves* show the property surviving in service at successive ages. The ordinates to the curve give at any particular age the percentage (or the actual number) surviving in service. The abscissa is measured in years or other suitable measure of service. The *original survivor curve* is the curve drawn through the points calculated from the original data without adjustment. Since this original survivor curve is

generally irregular, it is smoothed to produce a *smoothed survivor curve*, sometimes referred to as an *adjusted curve*.

Survivor curves have in some publications been referred to as "mortality curves." However, the term survivor curve is used in this book because the curves referred to show the percentage surviving, not the percentage retired, and because the term mortality suggests human beings and not inanimate objects.

20. A *stub survivor curve* is an incomplete survivor curve, that is, one which does not extend to zero percent surviving because of a lack of retirement data.

21. A *probable-life curve* shows the probable average life of the survivors at any age from zero to maximum life.

22. When the percent surviving is read at the beginning of each successive age interval and the differences in these successive readings plotted at ages corresponding to the mid-points of the intervals, the resulting points form a *frequency curve*, or *distribution curve*.

23. The point on the frequency curve having the greatest ordinate is called the *mode*. The year in which the mode occurs is the *modal year*.

24. A *maximum-life cycle* is a period of time corresponding in length to the maximum life of the units. An industrial property may continue to be operated through several maximum-life cycles of some of the units of which it is composed.

25. An *average-life cycle* is a period of time corresponding in length to the average service life.

26. When a property is continued in service for a long time and maintained with a constant number of like units of substantially the same potential average service life, it will reach a *normal condition* or *stabilized condition*, after which the average age of the units in service and the annual renewals will be constant year after year.

27. *Normal renewals* are the annual renewals after the property has reached a stabilized condition. Normal renewals, in percentage of the original number of units, are equal to 100 percent divided by the average life.

28. *Generalized curves* are those curves whose ordinates are expressed in percentage of the total number of units and whose abscissas (ages) are expressed in percentage of average service life.

29. *Type curves* depict typical survivor curves and frequency curves. Original survivor curves are compared with type survivor curves in the process of determining probable average service lives.

7.5. Survivor Curves. For the purpose of gaining an understanding of the survivor curve, Table 7.1 and Fig. 7.1 are presented ahead of the

TABLE 7.1. SURVIVOR, FREQUENCY, AND PROBABLE LIFE CURVES
The percentages surviving in column (2) are assumed for purposes of this illustration of the basic curves.

Age interval, years	Percent surviving at beginning of age interval	Percent retired during the age interval	Interval area under survivor curve, %-years	Remaining area under survivor curve to right of beginning of age interval, %-years	Expectancy of survivors at beginning of age interval, years	Probable average service life of survivors at beginning of age interval, years
(1)	(2)	(3)	(4)	(5)	(6)	(7)
0 –0½	100.00	0.00	50.00	1,249.98	12.50	12.50
0½–1½	100.00	0.00	100.00	1,199.98	12.00	12.50
1½–2½	100.00	0.08	99.96	1,099.98	11.00	12.50
2½–3½	99.92	0.33	99.76	1,000.02	10.01	12.51
3½–4½	99.59	0.76	99.21	900.26	9.04	12.54
4½–5½	98.83	1.38	98.14	801.05	8.11	12.61
5½–6½	97.45	2.32	96.29	702.91	7.21	12.71
6½–7½	95.13	3.92	93.17	606.62	6.38	12.88
7½–8½	91.21	6.27	88.07	513.45	5.63	13.13
8½–9½	84.94	8.83	80.53	425.38	5.01	13.51
9½–10½	76.11	10.68	70.77	344.85	4.53	14.03
10½–11½	65.43	11.20	59.83	274.08	4.19	14.69
11½–12½	54.23	10.42	49.02	214.25	3.95	15.45
12½–13½	43.81	8.89	39.36	165.23	3.77	16.27
13½–14½	34.92	7.24	31.30	125.87	3.60	17.10
14½–15½	27.68	5.83	24.77	94.57	3.42	17.92
15½–16½	21.85	4.78	19.46	69.80	3.19	18.69
16½–17½	17.07	3.97	15.08	50.34	2.95	19.45
17½–18½	13.10	3.32	11.44	35.26	2.69	20.19
18½–19½	9.78	2.74	8.41	23.82	2.44	20.94
19½–20½	7.04	2.19	5.95	15.41	2.19	21.69
20½–21½	4.85	1.69	4.00	9.46	1.95	22.45
21½–22½	3.16	1.23	2.55	5.46	1.73	23.23
22½–23½	1.93	0.85	1.50	2.91	1.51	24.01
23½–24½	1.08	0.54	0.81	1.41	1.31	24.81
24½–25½	0.54	0.31	0.39	0.60	1.11	25.61
25½–26½	0.23	0.15	0.15	0.21	0.91	26.41
26½–27½	0.08	0.06	0.05	0.06	0.75	27.25
27½–28½	0.02	0.02	0.01	0.01	0.50	28.00
28½–29½	0.00	......	....	0.00	0.00	.....
Total	1,349.98	100.00	1,249.98	....	.....	.....

methods of calculating survivor curves from retirement experience (see Secs. 7.9 to 7.12).

A survivor curve indicates the percentage of the property (physical units or dollars) which survives in service at ages from zero to maximum life. The surviving property could be expressed in number of physical units rather than in percentage for certain types of analyses, but per-

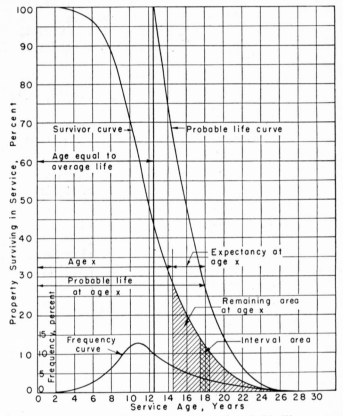

FIG. 7.1. The survivor curve, frequency curve, and probable life curve and their nomenclature.

centage is preferred because curves so expressed have general rather than specific application. The age is usually expressed in years, although any other chosen unit of service or of production may be used.

Column (1) of Table 7.1 is expressed on the ½-year basis because the information received on inventory or in the analysis of a company's retirement experience is generally dated by the calendar year. The year of installation or construction of property is usually obtainable. Retirements are usually given for the calendar years. The assumption is made that the installations of a given calendar year were made somewhat uniformly throughout the year; therefore, the assumption that all the units were zero years old on July 1 of the year of installation is appropriate. The average age of retirements would then always be the integral years 1, 2, 3, etc. But retirements having an average age of, say 3 years, must be composed of units having specific ages varying from $2\frac{1}{2}$ to $3\frac{1}{2}$ years. Ages for specific reference in the calculation of the survivor curve or for a January 1 inventory date must be expressed on the $\frac{1}{2}$-year basis. The integral intervals of 0–1, 1–2, 2–3, etc., may be used when the original data are so given; further, smoothed curves may be read at the integral ages when desired.

Another customary assumption is that property retired during the same calendar year as it was installed is retired during the age interval of 0–$0\frac{1}{2}$, or at an average age of $0\frac{1}{4}$ year.

The percents surviving in column (2) of Table 7.1 are the main objective of the methods of calculating survivor curves illustrated in Secs. 7.9 to 7.11. For the purpose of this illustration these surviving percentages have been assumed such as to form the smooth survivor curve of Fig. 7.1.

For ordinary investigations of the service lives of physical properties, the frequencies shown in column (3), Table 7.1, need not be computed. They are obtained by successive subtraction of the percents surviving in column (2). These frequencies are the percentages of the 100 percent base at zero age which are retired during the several age intervals. The frequencies total 100 percent. The frequency curve is plotted in Fig. 7.1.

An examination of the survivor curve of Fig. 7.1 discloses the fact that the total service which the property renders from age zero to maximum life is a direct function of the area enclosed between the survivor curve and the two axes. This service area would be expressed in percent-years, the two units of measurement used. Since the total amount of property considered is 100 percent, the total area in percent-years divided by 100 percent would give the average service life of the property. The service area may be closely approximated by the method illustrated in columns (4) and (5) of Table 7.1.

The interval areas of column (4) are the vertical strips of area for each 1 year of age, except for the age interval of 0–$0\frac{1}{2}$ years. The interval areas are calculated assuming that the survivor curve is a straight line across the age interval. The percents surviving at the beginning and ending of the age interval are averaged and the result multiplied by the strip width of 1 year. This procedure results in interval areas that are slightly greater than the correct areas for all intervals to the right of the modal age and interval areas that are less than the correct area for all intervals to the left of the modal age. The total area is exact for symmetrical frequency curves and close to correct for all other shapes. The total area of the survivor curve in Fig. 7.1 is 1,249.98 percent-years [column (5), Table 7.1], which corresponds to an average life of 12.50 years.

Column (4) is summed from the bottom upward to produce the entries of remaining areas in column (5). The total area divided by the percent (100 percent) surviving at age zero gives the average service life at age zero—identical to the expectancy of the survivors at age zero. Therefore, the area remaining at any service age divided by the percent surviving at that age results in the average expectancy of the surviving property at that age. See results of this calculation in column (6) of Table 7.1. The probable service life of the survivors at each age is equal to their age plus their expectancy. Column (7) and Fig. 7.1 show these probable service lives for each age.

When the series of remaining areas for each age [column (5), Table 7.1] is not wanted, the total area may be obtained by direct addition of the percents surviving in column (2), but including only three-fourths of the percent surviving at age $\frac{1}{2}$ year and one-fourth of the percent surviving at age 0 years. The percent surviving at age $\frac{1}{2}$ year is generally 100 percent or close to 100 percent. Therefore, only an insignificant error is introduced in the calculated area by summing all the percents surviving, starting with the maximum life at 0 percent surviving and ending with the percent surviving at age $\frac{1}{2}$ year.

7.6. Generalized Survivor Curves. The survivor curve of Fig. 7.1 is for the specific average service life of 12.50 years. The curve is generalized to apply to any amount of property by expressing the survivors in percent; the age may be likewise generalized by expressing it in percent of average service life. Table 7.2 and Fig. 7.2 illustrate the survivor curve, frequency curve, and probable life curve when so generalized.

Survivor curves and their derived curves expressing the service age in percent of average service life are useful in classifying curves by their shapes, in using standard or type curves for extending and smoothing original data curves, and in predicting the probable service life of a particular unit by use of group experience. When the average service life is the sole objective of the study, there is no need to express the survivor curve in percent of average life; in fact the curve cannot be so expressed until the average service life is obtained.

7.7. Classification of Survivor Curves by Their Shape. The process of generalization of survivor curves makes possible the comparison of any number of curves regardless of their average service life. The basic mathematical shape of survivor and frequency curves is important in the process of smoothing the original data and in extending stub curves to zero percent surviving. These fundamental shapes are apparent when many generalized curves are plotted to the same set of scales.

The upper sets of curves in Fig. 7.3 plotted to an age scale in years

TABLE 7.2.   GENERALIZATION TO AGE EXPRESSED IN PERCENT OF
AVERAGE LIFE OF THE CURVE IN TABLE 7.1

Age interval,* percent of average life	Percent surviving at beginning of age interval	Percent retired during the age interval	Interval area under survivor curve, %–%	Remaining area under survivor curve to right of beginning of age interval, %–%	Expectancy of survivors at beginning of age interval, percent of average life	Probable average service life of survivors at beginning of age interval, percent of average life
(1)	(2)	(3)	(4)	(5)	(6)	(7)
0–4	100.00	0.00	400.00	9,999.84	100.00	100.00
4–12	100.00	0.00	800.00	9,599.84	96.00	100.00
12–20	100.00	0.08	799.68	8,799.84	88.00	100.00
20–28	99.92	0.33	798.04	8,000.16	80.07	100.07
28–36	99.59	0.76	793.68	7,202.12	72.32	100.32
36–44	98.83	1.38	785.12	6,408.44	64.84	100.84
44–52	97.45	2.32	770.32	5,623.32	57.70	101.70
52–60	95.13	3.92	745.36	4,853.00	51.01	103.01
60–68	91.21	6.27	704.60	4,107.64	45.03	105.03
68–76	84.94	8.83	644.20	3,403.04	40.06	108.06
76–84	76.11	10.68	566.16	2,758.84	36.25	112.25
84–92	65.43	11.20	478.64	2,192.68	33.51	117.51
92–100	54.23	10.42	392.16	1,714.04	31.61	123.61
100–108	43.81	8.89	314.92	1,321.88	30.17	130.17
108–116	34.92	7.24	250.40	1,006.96	28.84	136.84
116–124	27.68	5.83	198.12	756.56	27.33	143.33
124–132	21.85	4.78	155.68	558.44	25.56	149.56
132–140	17.07	3.97	120.68	402.76	23.59	155.59
140–148	13.10	3.32	91.52	282.08	21.53	161.53
148–156	9.78	2.74	67.28	190.56	19.48	167.48
156–164	7.04	2.19	47.56	123.28	17.51	173.51
164–172	4.85	1.69	32.04	75.72	15.61	179.61
172–180	3.16	1.23	20.36	43.68	13.82	185.82
180–188	1.93	0.85	12.04	23.32	12.08	192.08
188–196	1.08	0.54	6.48	11.28	10.44	198.44
196–204	0.54	0.31	3.08	4.80	8.89	204.89
204–212	0.23	0.15	1.24	1.72	7.48	211.48
212–220	0.08	0.06	0.40	0.48	6.00	218.00
220–228	0.02	0.02	0.08	0.08	4.00	224.00
228–236	0.00	......	....	0.00	......	228.00
Total	1,349.98	100.00	9,999.84	....	......	......

* Any interval, in percent of average life, may be used, such as 5% or 10%.   In
this curve 8% (corresponding to an average life of 12.5 years) is used to show the correspondence with the same curve expressed in years which is shown in Table 7.1 and
Fig. 7.1.

appear to differ more widely than they do.   A range in average service lives separates a group of survivor curves horizontally but disperses the frequency curves more vertically than horizontally.   These apparent differences are minimized when the curves are plotted to a service age scale in percent of average service life as shown in the lower set of curves

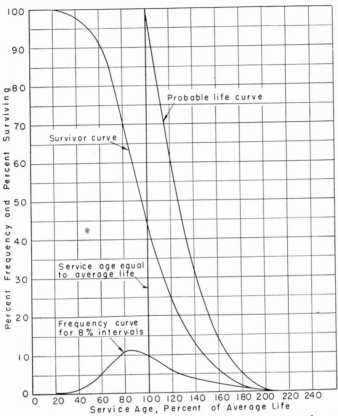

FIG. 7.2. Generalized curve of Fig. 7.1.   The plot of age is in percent of average service life.   The frequency curve may be plotted for any chosen age interval.   An interval of 8 percent of average life is used here.

of Fig. 7.3.   Curves A and D are found to be identical in shape; the modal frequencies of curves B and D (and A) are of about the same magnitude, but the B mode occurs to the left and the D mode to the right of the age equal to average service life.   The mode of curve C comes exactly at the average service life age of 100 percent; this frequency curve is symmetrical about the average-life age.

The modal age and modal frequency of survivor curves are important characteristics which distinguish curves one from another.   The fre-

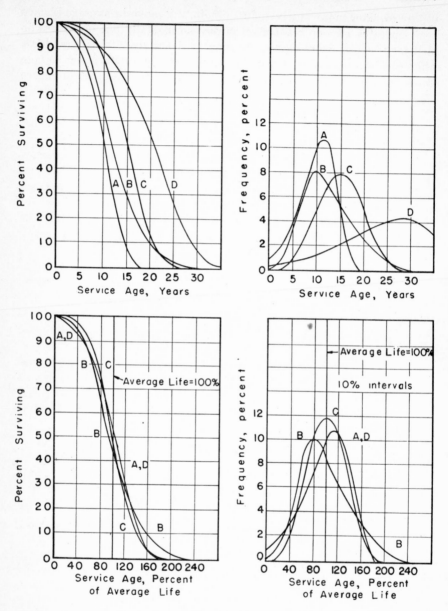

FIG. 7.3. Comparison of survivor and frequency curves with the service age plotted in years and plotted in percent of average life.

quency curve, as is seen from Fig. 7.3, shows the retirement dispersion more plainly than can be judged from the survivor curve. Classification of curves can be achieved by comparison of the modal characteristics. This classification may be made on the basis of whether the mode occurs at an age before, at, or after the age equivalent to the average service life and by the modal frequency. These characteristics are plainly shown by the generalized frequency curves in Fig. 7.3. They are the basis of the development of the families of type curves discussed in the following section.

7.8. Iowa Type Survivor Curves. When survivor or frequency curves are plotted to an age scale in percent of average service life, an excellent basis is at hand of classifying the curves by their basic mathematical shape. One such classification resulted in 18 type curves[1] divided among three families, the left modal group of 6 curves, the symmetrical group of 7 curves, and the right modal group of 5 curves. These type curves, now commonly referred to as the *Iowa type curves*, are reproduced in Appendix B, Figs. B.1, B.2, and B.3. A greater number of type curves could have been developed by spacing the curves of a family closer together. Experience with these 18 curves since their publication in 1935 has shown some need for curves interpolated between the established types, particularly among the types of low modal frequencies.

The Iowa 18 type curves resulted from a study of 176 curves of many types of properties. Therefore, these curves have resulted from experience; their applications since have proved the original selection sound and adequate. However, other type curve systems could be developed,[2] but there can be no great difference in the curves because experience has shown that the physical properties of industries develop survivor curves which, in the main, follow closely the shapes of the Iowa 18 type curves.

The primary uses of type survivor curves are three in number: (1) as a device for smoothing original survivor curves and extending stub curves, (2) as an aid in determining the probable life of single units, and

---

[1] Robley Winfrey, "Statistical Analyses of Industrial Property Retirements," Iowa State College, Engineering Experiment Station, Bulletin 125, 1935.

[2] See the following:

Joseph B. Jeming, Estimates of Average Service Life and Life Expectancies and the Standard Deviation of Such Estimates, *Econometrica*, Vol. 11, No. 2, pp. 141–150, April, 1943.

National Association of Railroad and Utilities Commissioners, "Report of Special Committee on Depreciation," pp. 61–65, New York, State Law Reporting Co., 1938.

See also, National Association of Railroad and Utilities Commissioners, "Report of Committee on Depreciation," pp. 253–257 (curves by Lawrence S. Patterson), Washington, D.C., National Association of Railroad and Utilities Commissioners, 1943.

Bradford F. Kimball, A System of Life Tables for Physical Property Based on the Truncated Normal Distribution, *Econometrica*, Vol. 15, No. 4, pp. 342–360, October, 1947.

(3) as a means of checking the adequacy of the depreciation reserve balance or in obtaining an adjustment factor in appraisal procedure.

The process of smoothing and extending stub survivor curves by use of type curves is explained in Sec. 7.15; the procedure for estimating the probable life of a single unit by use of a type survivor curve is given in Secs. 7.21 and 7.22; and the use of type survivor curves and expectancy-life ratios is presented in Secs. 11.6 and 11.7.

METHODS OF CALCULATING SURVIVOR CURVES

Three systematic actuarial methods for calculating property survivor curves are discussed, the *annual rate*, or *retirement rate*, method, the *original group* method, and the *individual unit* method. Of these, the retirement rate method is much the best, because it is based on the collection and compilation of the data of all property in service during a period of recent years, both property retired and that still in service. The original group method uses only the data of one vintage installation. The individual unit method is a last-resort method because it uses only the data of property which has been retired.

7.9. Retirement Rate Method. The retirement data collected for use in the retirement rate method should be those for a recent normal period of, say 3 to 30 years, which will give retirement rates fairly representative of present and probable future policies and service conditions. The ideal period is one so short that it reflects only present policies and standards; yet it is long enough for sufficient retirements to have been made at each age to give reliable average retirement rates over a period that averages the ups and downs of the enterprise.

For any type of industrial property, the steps in the retirement rate method of compiling a survivor curve are as follows:

1. Determine the numbers of units, or their total costs, and the ages of the property retired each year of the experience band of years chosen for study. Table 7.3 illustrates the compilation of this information for the retirements from 1940 through 1950 for centrifugal gas pumps.

2. Determine the numbers of units, or their total costs, and ages of the property in service at the beginning of each year of the experience band. Table 7.4 illustrates the compilation of this information on exposures for the same property for which the retirements are given in Table 7.3. The experience band is 1940 to 1950, although the placement band is 1919 to 1950.

3. By using the retirements for each experience year from each vintage group as obtained in step 1, determine the total retirements during each age interval. Column (3) of Table 7.5 illustrates the result of this step. The total retirements at each age are obtained by adding the retirements

from Table 7.3 on the diagonal stair-step line. Retirements on all such diagonals were made at the same average integral age. The line illustrated is for the retirements at an average age of 11 years or for the age interval of $10\frac{1}{2}$–$11\frac{1}{2}$. The two retirements at this age are 689 from the 1939 vintage in 1950 and 10,609 from the 1935 vintage in 1946. The total retirements for the age interval are 11,298. Only one retirement, 618, was made during the age interval 0–$0\frac{1}{2}$ years.

4. From the property in service each year as obtained in step 2, determine the total number of units exposed to retirement at the beginning of each age interval. Column (2) of Table 7.5 illustrates the result of this step. The total exposures at each age are obtained by adding the property in service from Table 7.4 on the diagonal stair-step line in the same manner as for the retirements. For the age interval of $10\frac{1}{2}$–$11\frac{1}{2}$ this sum is the total of 3,199, 962, 0, 996, . . . , 58,690, and 70,812, or 244,448. The exposure at the beginning of the age interval 0–$0\frac{1}{2}$ is the sum of the installations for each year of the experience band. For the example, this sum is obtained from column (2) of Table 7.4 by adding the installations from 1950 back to and including 1940, which are 90,676, 102,434, 180,111, . . . , 20,606, and 15,215. The total is 546,214.

5. Using the retirements at each age, as determined in step 3, and the amounts of property of each age in service determined as in step 4, calculate the retirement rate of the property at each age. These rates are illustrated in column (4) of Table 7.5 and result from the division of column (3) by column (2).

6. Calculate the percentage surviving at the beginning of each age interval by multiplying the retirement rate for each age interval by the percentage surviving at the beginning of that age interval and subtracting this product from the percentage surviving at the beginning of the same interval. Thus, using the retirement rate for the age interval of $10\frac{1}{2}$–$11\frac{1}{2}$, the percent surviving for age $11\frac{1}{2}$ is calculated as follows: $93.37 - (93.37)(0.046218) = 89.05$. These surviving percentages are illustrated in column (5) of Table 7.5.

7. Plot the survivor curve from the survivor percentages found in step (6), as far as they extend. These percentages are illustrated in column (5) of Table 7.5 and plotted in Fig. 7.4. In Fig. 7.5 this curve is compared with survivor curves calculated by the original group and individual unit methods.

8. Determine the average service life from the area under the survivor curve. When the original survivor curve is not reasonably smooth or when it is a stub curve, the curve should be first smoothed and extended as explained in Secs. 7.12 to 7.15.

7.10. Original Group Method. The original group method of calculating survivor curves is applicable to vintage groups. When applied

TABLE 7.3. DOLLAR COST OF CENTRIFUGAL GAS PUMPS RETIRED EACH YEAR 1940 TO 1950

Arrangement of Retirements for Calculation of Average Service Life by the Retirement Rate Method

Dollars original cost retired during the calendar year (columns 1940–1950)

Year	Dollars cost installed during year	1940	1941	1942	1943	1944	1945	1946	1947	1948	1949	1950
(1)	(2)	(3)	(4)	(5)	(6)	(7)	(8)	(9)	(10)	(11)	(12)	(13)
1919	1,578											
1920	3,260		1,512	202								
1921	5,980											
1922	61,930	10,604					316		2,115			
1923	24,888						812		23,411			
1924	54,680	365										11,712
1925	60,980								8,612			
1926	50,600	8,206		24,116		19,100						
1927	129,612	6,055		412				8,200		8,412	19,815	
1928				5,812		7,381		17,000	17,641	12,200	24,452	
1929	86,412		4,612									
1930	60,812						24,280		2,792			17,601
1931	8,916											
1932	22,102						2,402					
1933									7,465		9,224	6,129
1934												
1935	80,916						2,016	10,609				
1936	3,012											
1937	901								901			
1938	1,206			244								
1939	3,600											689
1940	15,215		401					1,261				
1941	20,606							1,060				
1942	712					877						2,141
1943												712
1944												
1945	44,900											
1946	91,560											
1947	180,111								916			
1948												
1949	102,434										618	
1950	90,676											
Total	1,207,599	25,230	6,525	30,786	0	27,358	29,826	38,130	63,853	20,612	54,109	38,984

TABLE 7.4. DOLLAR COST OF CENTRIFUGAL GAS PUMPS IN SERVICE JAN. 1, 1940, TO JAN. 1, 1950

Arrangement of Property in Service for Calculation of Average Service Life by the Retirement Rate Method

Year	Dollars cost installed during year	Dollars remaining in service Jan. 1 of year										
		1940	1941	1942	1943	1944	1945	1946	1947	1948	1949	1950*
(1)	(2)	(3)	(4)	(5)	(6)	(7)	(8)	(9)	(10)	(11)	(12)	(13)
1919	1,578	1,578	1,578	1,578	1,578	1,578	1,578	1,262	1,262	1,262	1,262	1,262
1920	3,260	3,260	3,260	1,748	1,546	1,546	1,546	734	734	734	734	734
1921	5,980	5,980	5,980	5,980	5,980	5,980	5,980	5,980	5,980	3,865	3,865	3,865
1922	61,930	24,989	14,385	14,385	14,385	14,385	14,385	14,385	14,385	14,385	14,385	14,385
1923	24,888	24,888	24,888	24,888	24,888	24,888	24,888	24,888	24,888	1,477	1,477	1,477
1924	54,680	20,689	20,324	20,324	20,324	20,324	20,324	20,324	20,324	11,712	11,712	11,712
1925												
1926	60,980	51,416	51,416	51,416	27,300	27,300	8,200	8,200				
1927	50,600	50,600	42,394	42,394	41,982	41,982	41,982	41,982	41,982	41,982	33,570	13,755
1928	129,612	118,855	112,800	112,800	106,988	106,988	99,607	99,607	82,607	64,966	52,766	28,314
1929	86,412	70,812	70,812	66,200	66,200	66,200	66,200	66,200	66,200	63,408	63,408	63,408
1930	60,812	58,690	58,690	58,690	58,690	58,690	58,690	34,410	34,410	34,410	34,410	34,410
1931	8,916	8,916	8,916	8,916	8,916	8,916	8,916	8,916	8,916	8,916	8,916	8,916
1932	22,102	20,467	20,467	20,467	20,467	20,467	20,467	18,065	18,065	10,600	10,600	1,376
1933												
1934												
1935	80,916	80,406	80,406	80,406	80,406	80,406	80,406	80,406	69,797	69,797	69,797	69,797
1936	3,012	3,012	3,012	3,012	3,012	3,012	3,012	996	996	996	996	996
1937	901	901	901	901	901	901	901	901	901			
1938	1,206	1,206	1,206	1,206	962	962	962	962	962	962	962	962
1939	3,600	3,600	3,600	3,199	3,199	3,199	3,199	3,199	3,199	3,199	3,199	3,199
1940	15,215		15,215	15,215	15,215	15,215	15,215	15,215	13,954	13,954	13,954	13,954
1941	20,606			20,606	20,606	20,606	19,729	19,729	18,669	18,669	18,669	18,669
1942	712				712	712	712	712	712	712	712	712
1943												
1944												
1945												
1946	44,900								44,900	43,984	43,984	43,984
1947	91,560									91,560	91,560	91,560
1948	180,111										180,111	180,111
1949	102,434											101,816
1950	90,676											
Total	1,207,599	550,265	540,250	554,331	524,257	524,257	496,899	467,073	473,843	501,550	661,049	709,374

* Since 1950 is the last year for which the retirements are used in the experience band, the property in service Jan. 1, 1951, is not used in the retirement rate analysis for the experience band of 1940–1950.

TABLE 7.5.   CALCULATION OF SURVIVOR CURVE FOR CENTRIFUGAL
GAS PUMPS BY RETIREMENT RATE METHOD

Placement band: 1919–1950.   Experience band: 1940–1950

Age interval, years	Dollars exposed to retirement at beginning of age interval	Dollars retired during age interval	Retirement rate	Percent surviving at beginning of age interval
(1)	(2)	(3)	(4)	(5)
0 –0½	546,214	618	0.001131	100.00
0½–1½	458,520	916	0.001998	99.89
1½–2½	356,994	401	0.001123	99.69
2½–3½	177,383	877	0.004944	99.58
3½–4½	87,958	244	0.002774	99.09
4½–5½	124,136	1,060	0.008539	98.82
5½–6½	123,076	1,261	0.010246	97.98
6½–7½	121,815	0	0.000000	96.98
7½–8½	142,282	712	0.005004	96.98
8½–9½	150,486	4,157	0.027624	96.49
9½–10½	188,491	901	0.004780	93.82
10½–11½	244,448	11,298	0.046218	93.37
11½–12½	349,495	10,667	0.030521	89.05
12½–13½	388,466	10,608	0.027307	86.33
13½–14½	429,274	5,812	0.013539	83.97
14½–15½	422,466	38,286	0.090625	82.83
15½–16½	341,201	31,862	0.093382	75.32
16½–17½	334,227	9,224	0.027598	68.29
17½–18½	349,992	49,496	0.141420	66.41
18½–19½	305,100	17,641	0.057820	57.02
19½–20½	281,803	38,001	0.134850	53.72
20½–21½	228,571	34,376	0.150395	46.48
21½–22½	130,787	20,017	0.153050	39.49
22½–23½	82,456	8,612	0.104444	33.45
23½–24½	60,089	23,411	0.389605	29.96
24½–25½	36,678	812	0.022139	18.29
25½–26½	35,866	14,143	0.394329	17.89
26½–27½	21,723	0	....	10.84
27½–28½	20,246	0	....	
28½–29½	5,861	0	....	
29½–30½	1,996	0	....	
30½–31½	1,262	0	....	
Total..........	6,549,362	335,413	....	......

to a single group, the 100 percent base for calculation of the entire curve is the property installed during the zero year.   Two or more consecutive vintages may be grouped to form a multiple group analysis.   The method consists in calculating the percentage of the original group of units (or dollars) which survives in service at yearly intervals, usually as of January 1 each year following the year of installation.

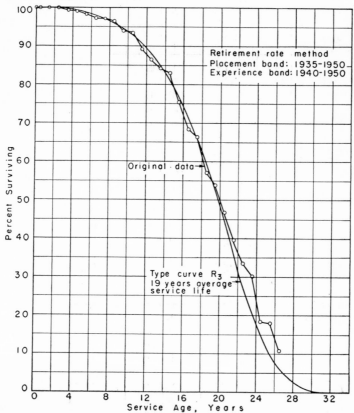

FIG. 7.4. Survivor curve of centrifugal gas pumps as calculated by the retirement rate method illustrated in Tables 7.3, 7.4, and 7.5.

The original group method is particularly adapted to developing a series of survivor curves showing the trend in average service life of the vintages over a period of years.   The results should show the effect of changing design, styles, models, and conditions of service on the useful service life.   An analysis for this purpose, however, may not always be achieved because of a deficiency in number of units or dollars in the several vintages.   The method is easily applicable, when the records disclose the information, to a study of the average service lives of motor vehicles

TABLE 7.6.   ORIGINAL GROUP METHOD OF CALCULATING A SURVIVOR CURVE

These data for centrifugal gas pumps are for the 1928 vintage group from Table 7.4. Surviving dollars prior to 1940 have been supplied from original sources.

Year	Age of survivors Jan. 1, years	Dollars surviving Jan. 1 [also at age of col. (2)]	Percent of original group surviving at age of col. (2)
(1)	(2)	(3)	(4)
1928*	0*	129,612*	100.00
1929	0½	128,952	99.49
1930	1½	128,760	99.34
1931	2½	128,760	99.34
1932	3½	128,760	99.34
1933	4½	126,372	97.50
1934	5½	126,307	97.45
1935	6½	123,779	95.50
1936	7½	123,779	95.50
1937	8½	122,120	94.22
1938	9½	121,200	93.51
1939	10½	121,200	93.51
1940	11½	118,855	91.70
1941	12½	112,800	87.03
1942	13½	112,800	87.03
1943	14½	106,988	82.54
1944	15½	106,988	82.54
1945	16½	99,607	76.85
1946	17½	99,607	76.85
1947	18½	82,607	63.73
1948	19½	64,966	50.12
1949	20½	52,766	40.71
1950	21½	28,314	21.85
1951	22½	28,314	21.85

* This vintage group was installed during the calendar year 1928; therefore, the property is assumed to be zero years old July 1, 1928, at which date 100 percent would survive.

by year models on a state or national basis, of the yearly construction of highway pavements, of the types and locations of telephone or power poles, and of other mass properties.

Table 7.6 and Fig. 7.5 show the calculation of the survivor curve for the 1928 additions of centrifugal gas pumps included in Table 7.4 for illustrating the retirement rate method.   A stub curve frequently results from the original group method; in fact, when the curve is plotted yearly as retirements are made from the vintage group, the curve will be a stub until the last of the property is retired.

7.11. Individual Unit Method.   In the individual unit method, data of retired property only are used in compiling the survivor curve.

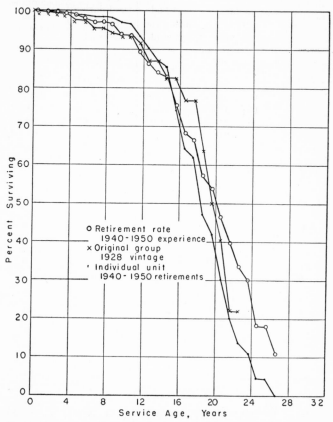

FIG. 7.5. Comparison of survivor curves calculated by the retirement rate, original group, and individual unit methods.   Basic data from Tables 7.3 and 7.4; calculations given in Tables 7.5, 7.6, and 7.7.

The retirements are organized so as to group the units or dollars cost by ages at retirement.   Actually, the property in each such age group may have been retired in different years.   The property is grouped by the nearest full year of age, so that the range is from ½ year before to ½ year after the given average age of retirement for each age grouping.

For convenience in the use of the survivor curve, it is customary to reduce the number of retirements in the different age intervals to per-

TABLE 7.7. INDIVIDUAL UNIT METHOD OF CALCULATING A SURVIVOR CURVE

These retirements are identical with those in Table 7.4 for centrifugal gas pumps for the retirement rate method for the experience band of 1940 to 1950.

Average age of dollars retired, years	Age interval during which the retirements occurred, years	Dollars retired at the average age and during the interval	Percent of total retirements retired during the age interval	Percent surviving at beginning of age interval
(1)	(2)	(3)	(4)	(5)
0	0 – 0½	618	0.18	100.00
1	0½– 1½	916	0.27	99.82
2	1½– 2½	401	0.12	99.55
3	2½– 3½	877	0.26	99.43
4	3½– 4½	244	0.07	99.17
5	4½– 5½	1,060	0.32	99.10
6	5½– 6½	1,261	0.38	98.78
7	6½– 7½	0	0.00	98.40
8	7½– 8½	712	0.21	98.40
9	8½– 9½	4,157	1.24	98.19
10	9½–10½	901	0.27	96.95
11	10½–11½	11,298	3.37	96.68
12	11½–12½	10,667	3.18	93.31
13	12½–13½	10,608	3.16	90.13
14	13½–14½	5,812	1.73	86.97
15	14½–15½	38,286	11.41	85.24
16	15½–16½	31,862	9.50	73.83
17	16½–17½	9,224	2.75	64.33
18	17½–18½	49,496	14.76	61.58
19	18½–19½	17,641	5.26	46.82
20	19½–20½	38,001	11.33	41.56
21	20½–21½	34,376	10.25	30.23
22	21½–22½	20,017	5.97	19.98
23	22½–23½	8,612	2.57	14.01
24	23½–24½	23,411	6.98	11.44
25	24½–25½	812	0.24	4.46
26	25½–26½	14,143	4.22	4.22
27	26½–27½	0	0	0.00
Total......	....	335,413	100.00	1,912.58

centages of the total retirements at all ages; the percentage surviving at the beginning of each age interval is then readily computed. The retirement data may be assembled in the form shown in Table 7.7, columns (1), (2), and (3).

The individual unit method of computing a survivor curve is generally not to be recommended, though in certain instances the data available limit the analysis to the individual unit method. The fact that the method utilizes only retired property means that the resulting *average service life* is the *average age at retirement.* In a comparatively young

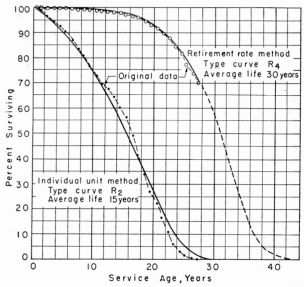

FIG. 7.6. Comparison of survivor curves of watt-hour meters computed by the retirement rate and the individual unit methods. Since the oldest unit observed was 27½ years old, the maximum life of the individual units curve cannot be greater than 27½ years, thus producing an indicated life much less than the correct average service life.

property the average age of the units retired in a year or over a period of years is less than the true average service life of the property. The true average service life can be calculated only by giving proper weight to the surviving units as well as to the retired units, except, of course, when all of the property in question is retired.

Column (5) of Table 7.7 is plotted in Fig. 7.5. The average service life of about 18 years compares favorably with the result obtained by the retirement rate method. Such close agreement of the results obtained by the two methods is usually not to be expected, however, particularly for property accounts which are young, growing, or declining, as indicated in Fig. 7.6.

Figure 7.6 shows the retirement rate and individual unit survivor curves for the alternating-current watt-hour meters in a large utility plant. Retirement data were obtained for each of 8 years; a total of about 44,000 meters served during all or part of the 8 years; of these meters, 1,043 were retired during the 8 years.

The retirement rate curve data, from the entire 44,000 meters, closely fit an R_4 type survivor curve with an average service life of 30 years. This curve gives the best indication obtainable of the probable future of the 43,000 meters still in service unless new inventions or some material change of policy intervene.

On the other hand, the individual unit curve from the data of only the 1,043 meters retired indicates an average service life of only 15 years, obviously a life unreasonably short.   If retirement data are kept of the 43,000 meters yet in service until the last one is retired, there is every reason to expect that the then resulting individual unit curve would not differ greatly from the retirement rate curve in Fig. 7.6, but by then the retirement data are likely to be only of historical interest.

7.12. Estimating Average Service Life from Survivor Curves. The average service life of a property is determined by the area beneath its complete survivor curve.   In practice, the retirement rate and the original group methods frequently result in stub survivor curves, that is, curves that end at a percent surviving greater than zero.   Further, many original data survivor curves, complete or stub, are irregular in shape to the extent that they exhibit sharp angles or horizontal segments.

The stub curve must be extended to zero percent surviving and the irregular curve should be smoothed before the average service life is computed.   The objective is to obtain the most probable average service life. Such probability is indicated by a smooth complete survivor curve because such a smooth curve is the type most likely to result from observation at regular yearly intervals of large numbers of exposures to retirement.   Further, decisions of management and accidents which produce sharp angles in survivor curves are unlikely to occur again at the same ages.

The extension and smoothing of survivor curves is a procedure necessary to the proper use of survivor curves in determining average service life.   Three methods of extending and smoothing are next discussed.

7.13. Extension of Survivor Curves by Judgment.   When a stub survivor curve is reasonably smooth and extends below about 40 percent surviving, it may be extended by eye by a person experienced enough in the characteristics of survivor curves to be capable of exercising good judgment.   Shorter curves and irregularly shaped curves are difficult to extend solely by relying on sight.   A good analyst will employ other aids. The smoothing of complete or nearly complete curves by sight and judgment of what the most probable curve should be can be accomplished reasonably satisfactorily.

There is no need to balance the areas of departure between the original curve and the smooth curve.   The objective is to smooth the curve along the most probable path.   In so doing, reference should be made to the calculations to determine the relative size of the exposures at each age so that desirable weights can be accorded the plotted points.

7.14. Extension of Survivor Curves by Statistical Curve Fitting. The smoothing of observed data and the fitting of equations to data have long been practices of the statistician.   Many detailed procedures[1] may be employed to smooth or to extend survivor curves with some success. The large number of hours required and the uncertainty of what type of curve equation to try make the method of curve fitting undesirable in practical analyses for average service lives.   By most mathematical procedures difficulty is experienced in according desirable weights to the several observed values.   At the lower end of the survivor curve a process of weighting the points is especially desirable.   The simple process of matching original data curves with type survivor curves is a process of much less work than mathematical curve fitting and a procedure that produces results equally as reliable.

7.15. Extension of Survivor Curves by Matching. The third method that may be used to extend (and to smooth) original survivor curves is to match them to type or standard curves.   The process involves the use of a set of type curves, previously established, which are known to be representative in shape of those curves likely to be encountered within the field at hand.

These type curves may be developed by the investigator himself or by the enterprise whose property is being studied, or the type curves may be chosen from other sources.   Section 7.8 and Appendix B describe the development of the Iowa type curves.

Figure 7.7 illustrates the matching method of extending stub survivor curves.   Each of the type survivor curves is drawn on a transparent sheet of paper to a range of average service lives, say from 5 to 50 years by 3- or

---

[1] See the following sources:

Winfrey, *op. cit.*, pp. 110–140.

National Association of Railroad and Utilities Commissioners, "Report of Special Committee on Depreciation," *op. cit.*, pp. 78–83.

National Association of Railroad and Utilities Commissioners, "Report of Committee on Depreciation," *op. cit.*, pp. 238–250.

R. A. Fisher, "Statistical Methods for Research Workers," 11th ed. rev., pp. 147–174, New York, Hafner Publishing Company, 1950.

Edison Electric Institute and American Gas Association, "An Appraisal of Methods for Estimating Service Lives of Utility Properties," pp. 27–31 or E4–E25, New York, February, 1942.   (Prepared under direction of cooperating committees on depreciation of these two organizations.)

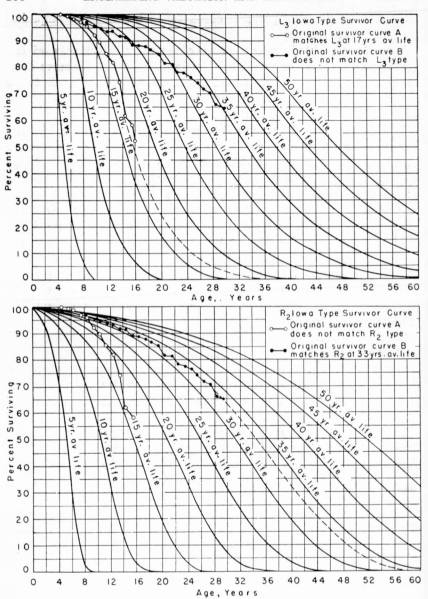

FIG. 7.7. The L_3 and R_2 Iowa type survivor curves drawn to specific average service lives to illustrate the matching method of smoothing and extending original survivor curves.

5-year intervals. The original data stub survivor curve may be then matched in turn to the several types until the best match or fit to the stub curve is chosen. The stub curve is then extended to 0 percent surviving along the path followed by the chosen type curve. The area of the extended curve may then be determined and the average life established. Usually, it is sufficient to read the average service life directly from the type curve matched, rather than arithmetically calculating the area beneath the extended curve.

Of the three methods of smoothing and extending stub survivor curves, the method of matching to type curves is easily and quickly applied and is one that has proved as reliable as statistical curve-fitting methods. The matching method is recommended for all ordinary applications to establish average service lives.

OTHER STATISTICAL METHODS OF ESTIMATING SERVICE LIVES

The actuarial methods described, or variations of them, are preferred to the various turnover methods for estimating service life. The actuarial methods require that the ages of the retirements be known. The retirement rate and the original group methods require, also, that the ages of the surviving property be known. The turnover methods employ ratios of annual retirements to plant balances without regard to ages. A brief explanation is given of three turnover methods and the simulated plant balance method.

7.16. Turnover Period Method. The turnover period method requires the annual additions, annual retirements, and the beginning balance. These data may be expressed in physical units or dollar units. The method determines the period of time required to "turn over" the plant balance from any given date. A plant account having 7,500 units in service January 1, 1930, and cumulated retirements of 7,500 units up to December 31, 1950, would have a turnover period of 20 years. One of three procedures may be used to determine the turnover period:

1. From a complete record of gross additions and gross retirements their cumulative curves are plotted from the beginning of the account. The turnover period is the horizontal distance between the two curves measured backward from any chosen date (usually the most recent) on the curve of the cumulative retirements.

2. The yearly account, or plant, balance may be plotted. A curve of the retirements accumulated backward from the chosen date is then plotted until it intersects the curve of the plant balance. The turnover period is the number of years between the date from which the retirements are accumulated backward and the date corresponding to the point of intersection of the curves.

3. Instead of accumulating the retirements backward as in procedure 2, the gross additions may be accumulated backward until they equal the plant in service at the date the backward accumulation was begun.

The turnover period would be equivalent to the years of average service life in a stabilized nongrowing account, a situation that is not often found. The turnover period is affected by the growth and decline of the account balance and the cyclic behavior of retirements and additions. Therefore, the turnover period is not to be considered the average service life of the property, but only an indication thereof. By adjusting the turnover period for the rate of growth and for the normal retirement dispersion (age distribution of the retirements), the average service life can be approximated. An appropriate survivor curve has to be assumed for the property in order to get the retirement dispersion.

Although the rate of growth will vary from year to year, it is assumed to be a uniform rate for purposes of adjusting the turnover period. Because of these assumptions, the adjusted turnover period is regarded only as an approximation of the average service life.[1]

7.17. Half-cycle Ratio Method. Jeynes developed a half-cycle ratio method[2] which can be applied to the turnover data when they cover a period of years as short as about one-half the average service life. The turnover period method requires a period at least equal to the period of turnover.

The half-cycle method is solved by successive trials. A year is chosen for which the retirements are known. Next a turnover period for the property is assumed. The plant balance is determined at the prior date exactly one-half cycle (a period of years equal to one-half the assumed turnover period) earlier than the end of the year for which the retirements were selected. This plant balance is divided by the total retirements for the chosen year to get the turnover period. The trial is repeated until an approximate agreement is achieved between the assumed period and the calculated period. As with the turnover period method, this half-cycle ratio method likewise results in a turnover period which has to be adjusted for growth and retirement dispersion in order to get an approximation of the average service life.

7.18. Asymptotic Method. The asymptotic method developed by

---

[1] For a more detailed discussion of the turnover period method and procedures for making the adjustments see National Association of Railroad and Utilities Commissioners, "Report of Committee on Depreciation," *op. cit.*, pp. 250–263.

[2] Paul H. Jeynes, Determination and Forecast of Average Service Life (a paper presented at the fourth National Accounting Conference, American Gas Association and Edison Electric Institute, Detroit, Mich., Dec. 2–4, 1940), Edison Electric Institute Bulletin 9, pp. 9–13, 33, January, 1941. See also, National Association of Railroad and Utilities Commissioners, "Report of Committee on Depreciation," *op. cit.*, pp. 265–267.

Jeming[1] is based upon the fact that a continuous property group kept replaced to full operating level will ultimately reach a limiting ratio of both annual additions and retirements to plant balance. The average service life is equal to the reciprocal of the geometric mean of the additions and retirement ratios.

The asymptotes may be determined by plotting curves of the two ratios and fitting them to a curve of the form

$$y = a + \frac{b}{x} + \frac{c}{x^2}$$

where y is the addition or retirement ratio, x the year or age scale, and a, b, and c are constants to be determined.

The asymptotic method is excellent in theory, but in practice it is difficult to fit the ratio curves. Additions and retirements so frequently vary over wide percentages of the plant balances that the determination of the curve of these ratios requires the exercise of considerable judgment.

For old plant accounts somewhat stabilized the addition and retirement ratios will become constant and a straight line from year to year. In this condition the curve is not asymptotic. No ratio curve need be fitted, and the method becomes what Jeming has called the "method of geometric mean."

7.19. Summary of Turnover Methods. The actuarial methods are to be preferred to the turnover methods of establishing average service lives. But when the ages of the property are not available, the turnover methods must of necessity be used in the analysis.

The turnover methods do not give information as to the retirement dispersion or the existing age distribution, both of which factors are important in depreciation studies. The answers obtained by the turnover period and half-cycle methods require adjustment to arrive at an estimate of average service life. For older accounts containing large numbers of retirement units the annual activity involving additions and retirements may be sufficiently uniform so that the turnover methods will give reliable estimates of average service life. The turnover methods are not suitable for young accounts, accounts in which the retirement units are large, and accounts in which the additions and retirements are not reasonably uniform.

7.20. Simulated Plant Balance Method. The simulated plant balance method of analyzing an account to determine average service life

[1] Joseph Jeming, An Asymptotic Method of Determining Annual and Accrued Depreciation, in Maurice R. Scharff, Franklin J. Leerburger, and Joseph Jeming, "Depreciation of Public Utility Property," pp. 97–128, New York, Burstein and Chappe, 1941. See also, Proceedings of the National Accounting Conference, Edison Electric Institute, Chicago, December, 1939.

and dispersion is another method using successive trials. Bauhan,[1] who developed the method into a workable procedure, uses the record of annual gross additions and the yearly plant balances as his basic information. An average service life and a dispersion are assumed. The Iowa type curves are suggested as suitable dispersion patterns.

The process consists in applying the survival ratios of the assumed curve to the plant additions in order to produce the plant balances of each vintage over a period of years. The total of these vintage balances is compared with the actual plant balances over the chosen band of years. Successive trials are made until that type curve and average service life are found which produce the best agreement with the actual plant balances.

This method requires a considerable number of calculations but is otherwise desirable. A survivor curve is developed, the resulting average service life requires no further adjustment, and the method is applicable to both growing and declining accounts.

SERVICE LIVES OF SPECIFIC UNITS AND PUBLISHED TABLES OF SERVICE LIVES

In the introduction to this chapter it is stated that the measurement of the consumption of the usefulness of a depreciable asset is based primarily on the age and probable service life of the asset. If a property group is being considered, the probable average service life is required; if a unit of property is being considered, its probable service life is required. These data are necessary to both valuation and accounting.

The survivor curve for a property group can be used to estimate the probable average life of the group and in addition will serve as the starting point in the prediction of the probable service life of a unit of the group if that is desired.

The following two sections discuss the details of the estimations. A third section discusses the use of published tables of service lives which are useful when data are not available with which to calculate survivor curves.

7.21. Use of Type Survivor Curves in Estimating Probable Lives. Sections 7.13 to 7.15 describe methods of extending stub survivor curves in order that the average service life of the stub curve can be estimated. Another use of type survivor curves is in predicting the probable life of a surviving unit of property for which its type curve is known or can be

---

[1] Alex E. Bauhan, The Simulated Plant Record Method of Determining Past Life and Mortality Dispersion from Plant Records. Proceedings of the National Conference of Electric and Gas Utility Accountants, American Gas Association and Edison Electric Institute, Buffalo, Apr. 8, 1947. See also, Alex E. Bauhan, Simulated Plant-record Method of Life Analysis of Utility Plant for Depreciation-accounting Purposes, *Land Economics*, Vol. 24, No. 2, pp. 129–136, May, 1948.

assumed.   Estimating the probable service lives of separate physical units of an industrial enterprise requires examinations of the property by well-qualified persons, who ascertain the physical condition and service conditions of the property.   The steps in estimating the probable lives of the units or of vintage groups of units should be about as follows:

1. Make an on-the-spot examination of each unit or vintage group. With the aid of operating personnel, book records, and personal judgment, determine and record:

   a. Year of installation of the property
   b. Past service conditions
   c. Probable future service conditions
   d. Present physical condition of the property for its age

Rating scales.   In deciding and in recording the physical condition and the service condition, the following rating scales may be used:

Physical condition: Excellent, good, average, poor, bad
Service condition: Mild, favorable, average, unfavorable, severe

In addition, generally it will be necessary to make a numerical estimate of the service factor (see Sec. 11.5) to compensate for any lowered operating efficiency or lessened value of the service caused by service conditions and not compensated for by the estimated probable service life.   This service factor, however, is used in the computation of appraised value, not in the estimation of the service life.

2. Determine the average service life of similar units under similar general service conditions.   One object of estimating this average service life is to permit the use of the type survivor curves in Figs. B.1, B.2, and B.3 of Appendix B whose ages are plotted in percent of average service life.   When possible, this average service life should be determined by a retirement analysis of the particular property being studied.

3. Select the survivor type curve which best fits the characteristics of the property.   When survivor curves are calculated for the particular property, their type may be ascertained by the matching process described in Sec. 7.15.   When no specific survivor curves are available, the type curve is selected by judgment, giving consideration to the probable retirement dispersion of the particular class of property.

4. Estimate the probable service life of an average surviving unit or vintage group having the age of the unit or group whose service life is being estimated.   Use the survivor and probable life curves selected in step 3 in making this estimate.   The estimate may be made in percent of average life or in years, depending upon whether type curves or specific curves are used.

5. Adjust the estimate of the probable service life of the average survivor obtained in step 4 as necessary to compensate for factors of physical condition and service conditions which appear to make the given unit or vintage group of different expectancy from that of the average surviving unit of that age.

6. Calculate the probable life and expectancy of the particular unit or vintage group. Check this final estimate of probable life and expectancy for reasonableness in view of what is known about management policies and future operations.

7.22. Estimating the Probable Service Life of a Gas Pump. The method described in Sec. 7.21 for estimating the probable service life of a property unit now in service, will be applied to a gas pump, centrifugal type, as follows:

A survivor curve for the gas pumps owned by the company has already been compiled by the retirement rate method in Sec. 7.9; the resulting curve is shown in Fig. 7.4. The process of estimating the probable life of the particular gas pump in question would work out about as follows:

1. By personal examination the data of this gas pump are found to be (a) service age, 24 *years;* (b) physical condition, *good* for its age; (c) past service condition, *average;* (d) probable future service conditions, *favorable.*

2. The average service life of gas pumps, centrifugal, in this company was calculated in Sec. 7.9 by the retirement rate method and found to be about 19 years (Fig. 7.4).

3. The selection of the type curve is determined by the matching process described in Sec. 7.15. The fit is found to be R_3.

4. To estimate the probable service life of this particular gas pump, it is found by reference to type curve R_3 and its probable life curve (Fig. B.3, Appendix B) that the average gas pump surviving at age 24 years would have a probable life of 137 percent of the average service life of gas pumps in this company and, further, that only 0.56 percent of the pumps are likely to have service lives greater than 155 percent of average service life.

The estimate of 137 percent as the estimated probable service life of the average survivor at age 24 years is obtained as follows: The age of 24 years is 126 percent of the average service life of 19 years. From the plot of the R_3 type survivor and probable life curves in Fig. B.3, the probable average life of 137 percent is found by the up-over-down process; up vertically from service age 126 percent to the survivor curve, over horizontally to the probable life curve, and down vertically to the base line, where 137 percent is read.

5. This particular pump has a better physical condition and will serve

under better probable future service conditions than the average surviving pump 24 years old. Its probable life is evidently somewhere
between 137 and 155 percent of average service life and may reasonably
be estimated at 150 percent of average life.

The range of probable service life for a unit or vintage group is from
the present age to the probable service life of the average survivor when
the physical condition and service conditions are such that the expectancy
of service is judged to be less than that of the average survivor at that
age.

6. The probable service life of this gas pump is (19)(1.50) = 28 years.
Its expectancy of future service is 28 − 24 = 4 years. Before accepting
the probable service life of 28 years as final, consideration should be
given to the reasonableness of the 4 years expectancy in view of the
current outlook for the enterprise and this gas pump in particular.

7.23. Published Tables of Useful Service Lives. For many years
in depreciation cost accounting, in valuation practice, and in studies of
engineering economy, estimates of service lives of the innumerable classes
of industrial properties have been used. Although tables of service lives
and isolated reports are available in the literature,[1] their use is not generally recommended when more specific information may be obtained.

Critical study of the various published tables of service lives indicates
that to a considerable degree they have been compiled from each other
and that originally they represented opinions of valuators and accountants rather than analysis of retirement experience. Further, recent
experience of the authors of this book shows that the service life of a single
class of property, for instance, freight train cars, varies widely under the
conditions of use, ownership, design, and geography. Full examination,
study, and analysis of the property of the company for which the service
lives are wanted should be made in each case if reliable service lives are
wanted.

The U.S. Bureau of Internal Revenue has published Bulletin F[2] as a
guide to service lives for estimating cost depreciation for income tax
returns. Currently this compilation of average service lives is no doubt
the best one available. But there is no evidence to show that Bulletin F
is not also largely a compilation of opinion and practice rather than of
service lives calculated from retirement experience.

[1] Anson Marston and Thomas R. Agg, "Engineering Valuation," 1st ed., pp. 497–
514, New York, McGraw-Hill Book Company, Inc., 1936. This reference lists service
lives of about 1,600 items and gives the source of the information. U.S. Treasury
Department, Bureau of Internal Revenue, Bulletin F, is now considered a superior
reference.

[2] U.S. Treasury Department, Bureau of Internal Revenue, "Income Tax Depreciation and Obsolescence, Estimated Useful Lives and Depreciation Rates," Bulletin F
(revised January, 1942), Washington, D.C., Government Printing Office, 1942.

The following is quoted from the inside title page of Bulletin F:

The estimated useful lives and rates of depreciation indicated in this bulletin are based on averages and are not prescribed for use in any particular case. They are set forth solely as a guide or starting point from which correct rates may be determined in the light of the experience of the property under consideration and all other pertinent evidence.

More and more utilities and manufacturers are applying statistical analyses to their own exposure and retirement experience in order to arrive at useful service lives for cost depreciation and valuation purposes.

CHAPTER 8

Depreciation Principles and Relations

In endeavoring to determine the value of property, an appraiser usually must also make estimates of depreciation. He is concerned with the annual charge to production expense for the consumption of the useful service of long-lived properties and with the remaining useful service related to the total useful service for the entire life span. Furthermore, in approaching the value of a property through a study of either repro- duction cost or replacement cost, it is desirable that the appraiser adjust these estimates which apply to new properties to bring them into line with the existing property which has given up a portion of its original service usefulness. An appraiser thus needs a sound working knowledge of the theory, concepts, and practices in accounting for depreciation costs and of the effect of age, use, and other factors on the values of old property compared with new property.

When the inventories are costed, the next step in the appraisal process is to adjust these costs for the decrease in usefulness of the property. Chapters 8 to 11 discuss depreciation from the several aspects relating to the engineering valuation of industrial property.

HISTORY, CONCEPTS, AND DEFINITION OF DEPRECIATION

Depreciation is a word well known to all businessmen, men of many other walks of life, and to the accountant, lawyer, and engineer. Yet in spite of its widespread usage the word depreciation is often applied loosely and in several meanings. Before depreciation is discussed as a factor in valuation, it is well to examine its development and meaning.

8.1. Three Meanings of Depreciation. Currently, the word depreciation is used in three distinct meanings, though such usages are frequently those of persons who do not take care to be exact in their expression. Depreciation may refer to (1) decrease in value, (2) a cost of operation, and (3) physical condition. These three meanings will be discussed in connection with a short review of the historical development of accounting. The word depreciation first appeared in the accounting literature about 1835 in England and 1838 in the United States.

8.2. Accounting Evolution. The early works on bookkeeping are the best sources through which to trace the development of depreciation as a cost element.[1]

There was little need for bookkeeping by the early civilizations until commerce and individual ownership developed. Even in the early days of bookkeeping, depreciation as a cost was not involved because there was but little long-lived property in commercial usage. Joint ownership, however, did raise the question of change in value with age. To quote from a manuscript of about 27 B.C.:[2]

He, therefore, who is desirous of producing a lasting structure, is enabled, by what I have laid down, to choose the sort of wall that will suit his purpose. Those walls which are built of soft and smooth-looking stone, will not last long. Hence, when valuations are made of external walls, we must not put them at their original cost; but having found, from the register, the number of lettings they have gone through, we must deduct for every year of their age an eightieth part of such cost, and set down the remainder or balance as their value, inasmuch as they are not calculated to last more than eighty years. This is not the practice in the case of brick walls, which whilst they stand upright, are always valued at their first cost.

Although the Romans of the period A.D. 0–500 are reputed to have had some method of bookkeeping which resembled the double-entry method, there is little evidence that it contained any organized system of double-entry accounts.

There is little of importance to note "From the Fall of the Western Empire until the Norman Conquest of England, when the English Exchequer, with its elaborate system of finance and its famous Pipe-Rolls, first comes to notice."[3]

In 1494, a monk, Luca Pacioli,[4] produced what is probably the first treatise on double-entry bookkeeping as a part of his work on mathe-

---

[1] See the following:

Ananias C. Littleton, "Accounting Evolution to 1900," New York, American Institute Publishing Co., Inc., 1933.

Perry Mason, Illustrations of the Early Treatment of Depreciation, *Accounting Review*, Vol. 8, pp. 209–218, September, 1933.

Earl A. Saliers, "Depreciation; Principles and Applications," 3d ed., pp. 8–36, New York, The Ronald Press Company, 1939.

W. Chester Fitch, "Fundamental Aspects of Depreciation Theory," unpublished Ph.D. thesis, Library, Iowa State College, Ames, Iowa, 1950.

[2] Marcus Vitruvius Pollio, "The Architecture of Marcus Vitruvius Pollio in Ten Books Translated from the Latin by Joseph Gwilt, F.S.A., F.R.A.S.," Book II, Chap. VIII, p. 47 (from manuscripts dated 1552, 1649, and later), London, Lockwood & Co., 1874.

[3] Arthur H. Woolf, "A Short History of Accountants and Accountancy," p. 54, London, Gee and Co., Ltd., 1912.

[4] Luca Pacioli, "Summa de arithmetica geometria, proportioni et proportionalita," Venice, 1494.

matics. Although depreciation allowance, based either on the concept of decrease in value or on the concept of it being an operating cost, is not mentioned by Pacioli, his work led to many later books on bookkeeping in which the equivalent of cost depreciation was mentioned.

In 1588 John Mellis wrote the following in his textbook[1] on book-keeping:

Implements of householde here against is due to have xl.xs. and is for so much as I doe finde at this day to be consumed and worn, which said xl.xs. for the decay of the said household stuffe is borne to profit and losse in Debitor (15). 10 10 0

The profit-and-loss account was debited as follows:

More xl.xs. for so much lost by decay householde stuffe as in Creditor (06) 10 10 0

Stephen Monteague in his "Debtor and Creditor Made Easie" in 1683 allowed for deterioration of bulls by valuing the unsold ones at the end of the accounting period at 15 shillings less than at the beginning of the period.[2]

Other mentions of wear and tear and decreases in value appear between 1683 and 1833, when the Baltimore and Ohio Railroad in its annual report mentioned the establishment of an annuity for 12 years at 5 percent to provide funds for the renewal of oak sills and sleepers and yellow pine stringpieces.[3]

The term *annual depreciation* was used in 1835 by a committee reporting on the prospects of a company in London to conduct inland navigation in India with steamships.[4] The committee used 5 percent annual depreciation on the vessels and engines and 20 percent on the boilers.

In 1836 the *American Railroad Journal* in an analysis of cost of the Reading Railroad referred to "repairs and depreciation of engine and tender."

The use of the word depreciation steadily increased after 1835 along with an increased importance of long-lived assets as stock corporations became numerous and as governments became interested in the affairs of private business, particularly the railroads.

This brief review of the early development of the use of the word depreciation and of allocating the cost (or value) of long-lived assets to expense shows that before the word depreciation was introduced both

---

[1] John Mellis, "A Briefe Instruction and Manner How to Keepe Bookes of Accompts after the Order of Debitor and Creditor," London, John Windet, 1588 (text of the bookkeeping portion adapted by Hugh Oldcastle from L. Pacioli). Title from Institute of Chartered Accountants, Library Catalogue, Vol. II, "The Bibliography of Bookkeeping," London, Gee and Co., Ltd., 1937.

[2] Littleton, *op. cit.*, p. 224.

[3] Mason, *op. cit.*, p. 211.

[4] *Ibid.*

cost and value were used in estimating the charge for consumption of long-lived assets. Further, there existed a tendency to confuse repairs and maintenance and replacement with a charge for depreciation.

8.3. Concept of Physical Condition. Along with the development of the use of the term depreciation in 1835 there also developed a practice of relating depreciation to the physical condition of the property. The "good as new" concept developed. Many persons believed that property which was maintained in a state of high efficiency and good physical condition could not have suffered much depreciation. These ideas led to findings of 90 or higher percent condition[1] in valuation cases, because, upon inspection, the property was found not to be handicapped by wear and tear.

The concept of depreciation as a state of physical condition measured by wear and tear continues today. One hears or reads frequently the statement that a badly run-down and worn property is highly depreciated. However, such outward physical appearance is not a reliable index of the useful service possessed by the property or of the amount of service that has been rendered to date.

8.4. Definitions of Depreciation. From these early beginnings of what is now called depreciation there have been thousands of articles and chapters written about the subject by lawyers, economists, accountants, businessmen, tax officials, and engineers. Before many of these writings can be appreciated fully, the reader needs to gain an understanding of the three concepts commonly applied to the word depreciation.

Since 1934 literature often quotes the following definition from the *Lindheimer v. Illinois Bell Telephone* case:[2]

Broadly speaking, depreciation is the loss, not restored by current maintenance, which is due to all the factors causing the ultimate retirement of the property. These factors embrace wear and tear, decay, inadequacy, and obsolescence.

But this Lindheimer definition fails to state what is lost. In the use of this definition the words *in value* have been frequently supplied by others, thus making the definition apply to depreciation in the sense of value. Also, the phrase *in service capacity* has been supplied following the word *loss*.

An inconsistency in the Lindheimer decision itself is apparent when the above definition is studied in the light of the few sentences which immediately follow, namely:

[1] *Percent condition* is a phrase referring to the amount of observable wear and tear in a property relative to the property new.

[2] *Lindheimer et al. v. Illinois Bell Telephone Co.* (No. 440), 292 U.S. 151, 167, 3 P.U.R. (N.S.) 337 (U.S. Sup. Ct. Apr. 30, 1934).

Annual depreciation is the loss which takes place in a year. In determining reasonable rates for supplying public service, it is proper to include in the operating expenses, that is, in the cost of producing the service, an allowance for consumption of capital in order to maintain the integrity of the investment in the service rendered. The amount necessary to be provided annually for this purpose is the subject of estimate and computation. In this instance, the company has used the "straight line" method of computation, a method approved by the Interstate Commerce Commission. 177 I.C.C. pp. 408, 413. . . . According to the principle of this accounting practice, the loss is computed upon the actual cost of the property as entered upon the books, less the expected salvage, and the amount charged each year is one year's pro rata share of the total amount. . . . The Company employs averages, that is, average service life, average salvage of poles, of telephones, etc.

While property remains in the plant, the estimated depreciation rate is applied to the book cost and the resulting amounts are charged currently as expenses of operation. The same amounts are credited to the account for depreciation reserve, the "Reserve for Accrued Depreciation."

The phrase, "an allowance for consumption of capital," can hardly be considered a loss, though it could be a decrease, but a decrease of what is not stated. The Court could not have had in mind in this definition a loss in value because in the above extract the depreciation referred to is clearly based on "cost of the property as entered upon the books." This definition then is clearly one of cost depreciation as used in the cost accounting process. Value is not involved, and apparently neither is physical condition of the property.

The Federal Communications Commission has defined depreciation as follows:[1]

Depreciation, as applied to depreciable telephone plant, means the loss in service value not restored by current maintenance, incurred in connection with the consumption or prospective retirement of telephone plant in the course of service from causes which are known to be in current operation, against which the company is not protected by insurance, and the effect of which can be forecast with a reasonable approach to accuracy. Among the causes to be given consideration are wear and tear, decay, action of the elements, inadequacy, obsolescence, changes in the art, changes in demand and requirements of public authorities.

This definition bears a striking resemblance to the Lindheimer definition. The phrase "in service value" has been inserted to state what it is that is lost. Omitted, however, is any explanation of whether service value means productive capacity, measured in some unit of service, or whether service value means a dollar valuation of the property's service.

[1] U.S. Federal Communications Commission, "Uniform System of Accounts for Telephone Companies," p. 4, Washington, D.C., Government Printing Office, 1935.

In 1943 the National Association of Railroad and Utilities Commissioners Committee on Depreciation stated:[1]

Depreciation is the expiration or consumption, in whole or in part, of service life, or utility of property resulting from the action of one or more of the forces operating to bring about the retirement of such property from service; the forces so operating include wear and tear, decay, action of the elements, inadequacy, obsolescence, and public requirements; depreciation results in a cost of service.

Here is a definition that omits all reference to loss, to value, and to cost, except the statement that depreciation results in a cost. Perhaps this definition is more in line with the current practice and objective of depreciation accounting than prior definitions. The definition has merit in that it defines depreciation not in terms of a cost or value but in terms of the fundamental characteristics of the property—its ability to render useful service—for which its cost was incurred and from which its value emanates.

The American Institute of Accountants in speaking of depreciation accounting seems to give support to the National Association of Railroad and Utilities Commissioners definition of depreciation:[2]

Depreciation accounting is a system of accounting which aims to distribute the cost or other basic value of tangible capital assets, less salvage (if any), over the estimated useful life of the unit (which may be a group of assets) in a systematic and rational manner. It is a process of allocation, not of valuation. Depreciation for the year is the true portion of the total charge under such a system that is allocated to the year. Although the allocation may properly take into account occurrences during the year, it is not intended to be a measurement of the effect of all such occurrences.

The United States Treasury Department has the following to say:[3]

The term "depreciation" is often loosely used. For income tax purposes it has a well-defined meaning. Depreciation is loss which is due to factors that cause ultimate retirement of the property, and which is not restored by current maintenance. These factors include wear and tear, decay, inadequacy, and obsolescence.

The purpose underlying allowances for depreciation is to permit the taxpayer to recover *over the useful life of the property the capital he has invested in it*. Such allowances are permitted only where the property is used in a trade or business or is used for earning nonbusiness income, such as rents and royalties.

[1] National Association of Railroad and Utilities Commissioners, "Report of Committee on Depreciation," p. 30, Washington, D.C., National Association of Railroad and Utilities Commissioners, 1943.

[2] American Institute of Accountants, *Bulletin* 22 (*Special*), May, 1944. See also, *Journal of Accountancy*, Vol. 76, p. 484, 1943.

[3] U.S. Treasury Department, Office of Internal Revenue, "Your Federal Income Tax," p. 49, Washington, D.C., Government Printing Office, 1950.

In spite of the popular conception of depreciation to be loss or fall in value, which idea is expressed in numerous text- and reference books, its application in accounting, engineering economy studies, tax studies, and rate cases is almost always based on cost, not value.

The literature since 1900 contains many discussions of depreciation and its concepts.[1] And these many concepts and applications have given rise to controversial literature, much of which could have been avoided had each writer and each speaker clearly stated whether he was using the word (1) to mean an allocation of cost, (2) to mean a change in value, or (3) as an indication of the state of physical condition of the property.

While depreciation does not seem to be defined in terms of the physical condition of the property, the layman's impression is often that a property which shows a high degree of wear and tear or lack of maintenance care is highly depreciated. Such expression of thought frequently appears in print and not always from those who would be called laymen.

On the other hand, appraisers have long used physical condition as a direct index of value of property. Utility rate cases are filled with testimony of experts regarding the "observed depreciation" and "percent condition" of property. Obviously, cost depreciation or value depreciation cannot be observed; what is observed is physical condition from which one may gain evidence bearing upon a proper allowance for cost depreciation or upon the value of the property. However, physical condition to the extent that it can be observed and compared with the physical condition of new property is not the sole measure of the consumption of the useful service or utility. The so-called "observed depreciation" or "percent condition" may be related to the state of wear and tear and physical unfitness of the property, but a reliable estimate of the cost allocation for depreciation or the present value of property should be based upon age, inadequacy, obsolescence, usefulness, and other factors as well as the physical state. *Physical condition alone is neither depreciation nor the sole measure of depreciation, in the sense of either cost or value.*

8.5. A Measure of the Decrease in Value of Property. The decrease in value[2] of property from age zero to any service age results from a reduction, since it was first put into service new, in the present worth of its probable future services. Physical property decreases in value with age and use because it thereby suffers a decrease in the amount and character of the future service it can render before it will be retired.

---

[1] For other definitions and concepts see Edison Electric Institute, General Accounting Committee, "Summary of Definitions Covering Depreciation and Related Terms," New York, Edison Electric Institute, 1939.

[2] For the purpose of this discussion a constant price level is assumed. During periods of rapidly increasing prices, some properties in use experience increasing values rather than decreasing values.

The *basic measure* of the amount of this decrease in value at any date is not the amount of service the unit has rendered, although it is during the rendering of service that it has lessened in value. The basic measure, on the contrary, is the decrease in the present worth of the service remaining in the unit, the amount of which is the difference between the value new and the present worth of the future service remaining in the unit, allowing for salvage value, if any.

Since the remaining service lies in the future, it cannot be foretold with certainty; but the future service life of the property can be re-estimated from time to time, and as the property approaches retirement, such estimates can be made with increasing accuracy. The service life is never known with certainty until the property is finally retired.

In general, a decrease in value because of use is inevitable (assuming no change in price level). No amount of wise expenditure for maintenance can accomplish more than to ensure that the date of retirement is only postponed somewhat.

The main cause of the decrease in value is the decrease in the number of future annual returns resulting from a decrease in expectancy of future service life. An additional cause of decrease in value is a decrease in the future annual value of the annual returns caused by lowered efficiency of the property, lowered output capacity, increased cost of maintenance, increased running costs, intermittent (stand-by) service, and operation at less than normal capacity.

Depreciation in the sense of value as applied in valuations is discussed more thoroughly in Chap. 11.

8.6. Depreciation and Replacement. In the sense of cost, depreciation is unaffected by the replacement policy of the owner of a property, except as replacement policy may control the average or probable service life of the property. The sole purpose of depreciation cost accounting is to recover the depreciable cost of the property through charges to production cost. Obviously, such an objective is totally unrelated to replacement cost as well as to replacement. Depreciation cost accounting is not for the purpose of building up a fund for replacement of property (see Secs. 10.1 and 10.7).

In the sense of value, depreciation is related to replacement cost. If the cost of replacing a property for continuation of the same or similar function tends to increase, a higher value of the existing property can be expected, except when its value is only scrap value. In this application an existing property may be valued by estimating the cost of replacement, then adjusting for depreciation to compensate for the difference in utility between the property if it were new and as it is at date of valuation.

8.7. Depreciation and Preservation of Investment. Associated with the misconception that depreciation cost allocations are for the purpose of accumulating funds for the replacement of the property is the idea that the purpose of depreciation accounting is to "preserve the integrity of the investment." Although the capital invested in depreciable assets may be recovered, it is not necessarily preserved in the business. After the cost of an asset is recovered, management has the responsibility and freedom to use the funds in accordance with its best judgment.

Furthermore, regardless of the amount of the depreciation charge or how it is made, unless the company can earn this charge plus all other expenses through sales income, the investment cost will not be recovered in full.

RELATION BETWEEN DEPRECIATION AND MAINTENANCE

Maintenance work and maintenance cost are often confused with depreciation expense. The cost of maintenance is a direct charge to operating expense, but the depreciation charges are allocations from a prior expenditure. Good maintenance can prolong the useful life of certain depreciable property, but maintenance operations do not entirely overcome the forces that ultimately cause the retirement of physical property.

8.8. Maintenance and Repairs. The term *maintenance* conveys the idea of constantly keeping up the good condition of the property. The maintenance costs thereby incurred constitute one important class of operation costs. Some examples of maintenance are the inspection, painting, adjustment, and repair of structures and machines.

The term *repairs* conveys the idea of mending or replacing broken or worn parts by overhauling to restore run-down units of property to as good physical condition as is economical or practicable. Repair costs are a part of the maintenance costs and include both labor and materials. Repairs sometimes become extraordinarily large, but nevertheless the costs are directly chargeable to operation, except for additions or betterments, which are considered to be new investment (Sec. 3.5.).

Deferred maintenance is maintenance work which has been postponed beyond the date when it should have been performed and which still remains to be done and paid for. The ultimate cost of deferred maintenance sometimes becomes a large amount, as in the case of failure to keep roadbeds, ties, rails, structures, highways, machines, and mobile equipment in first-class condition in times of wars or severe business depressions.

8.9. Maintenance Cost Contrasted with Depreciation Cost. Maintenance costs and depreciation costs are really quite different in character and treatment. Maintenance costs are operation expenses, paid from current income as they are incurred; depreciation costs stem from the inevitable write-off of the cost new of the property at the end of its useful life. Depreciation cost represents the original cost of the property allocated to operation expense regardless of the state of maintenance.

To a certain extent, however, annual depreciation cost (but not total depreciation cost) may be controlled by maintenance work. Property which is regularly and adequately maintained may last a greater number of years or perform a greater number of services than similar property not so well maintained. The annual depreciation cost allocation would normally be less for the well-maintained property than for the under-maintained property because of the longer useful service life.

Deferred maintenance is an accumulation of work that when eventually performed results in current operating charges somewhat larger than normal; likewise, the operating charges for the years during which the deferred maintenance accumulated were perhaps less than normal. When deferred maintenance exists, the property has a value less than it would have if it were in first-class operating condition. The value of the property may be increased upon performance of the deferred maintenance work, but in no sense is the cost of this work a depreciation charge. The state of maintenance of the property is an item for consideration in valuing property because physical condition of the property has a bearing upon expectancy of life, operating costs, and production output. However, no property can be made "good as new" by maintenance.

TERMS USED IN DEPRECIATION CALCULATIONS

In the sections which follow, the terms used in this book in depreciation calculations are defined and discussed. Many of the terms are in common use although some will be defined and delimited in meaning more precisely than has been the custom in the literature.

8.10. Salvage Value. The salvage value of industrial property is the net sum (actual or estimated), over and above the cost of removal and sale, realized for it when it is disposed of by its owner or the value of the property retired for use in a different location or for a different purpose.

Sometimes the highest salvage value may be realized when the property is sold for further service, as when an electric motor is retired and then sold for use elsewhere. Often the retired property may be reused in an entirely different function, as, for example, a railway boxcar converted to an equipment storage building. Salvage value often is zero and sometimes may be negative; it is not necessarily the same as scrap value or junk value, though for many properties these values are the same.

Scrap, or *junk, value* is the net value realized when the unit of industrial property is sold for use again as manufacturing raw material. It may be sold intact, or it may be cut or broken into pieces convenient for removal.

Salvage value in depreciation accounting is usually an estimated value because the salvage value is required to be estimated before the annual accounting depreciation costs can be determined. The expected salvage recovery is not to be allocated as a depreciation cost. As with the probable life of the property, salvage value should be re-estimated from time to time during the service life of the property. Salvage value is a value, not a cost, because it is the value of the property realized at the time of retirement or the probable value realized at the forecasted date of retirement.

8.11. Depreciation Base and Depreciable Base. The term *depreciation base* is the original cost, the replacement cost, the value, or any similar amount which is to be allocated or adjusted for depreciation. The depreciation base is inclusive of salvage value.

The term *depreciable base* is employed to designate the depreciation base less salvage value. This term is used rather than the older term *wearing value* because it is more descriptive of that quality of the property the term is to designate. The depreciable base corresponds to the useful service in the property. The depreciable portion of a property is that part of the depreciation base which is to be recovered through allocations of depreciation cost rather than by sale or reuse of the property when it is retired. The depreciable base often equals the entire depreciation base because no net amount is receivable as salvage when the property is retired.

8.12. Accrued Depreciation. The term *accrued depreciation* has been used by many authors in three rather distinct applications, and not always has the context made clear the meaning intended by the author. In all uses, however, the intent is to measure a total depreciation from a given base from date new to the date of valuation or inquiry.

First, in estimating present value from the evidence of replacement cost, accrued depreciation is assumed to be the difference between the estimated replacement cost new and the determined present value of the existing property.

Second, when original cost is used as the starting point, accrued depreciation is assumed to be the difference between the original cost and the present value. Accrued depreciation in this second case frequently has little significance (except at date of retirement of the property) because the cost is on one price basis and the value is on another. Actually, the accrued depreciation, in some situations, could be a negative amount.

Finally, in the accounting sense, accrued depreciation is the summation of the annual (or other periodic) depreciation allocations recorded in the books of account to date for the property in question. The accounting accrued depreciation at a particular time may not agree with what management then feels should be the book accrued depreciation as based upon a current analysis of the physical condition, the probable service life, and the salvage value of the property. Thus, the accounting accrued depreciation might be either of two amounts, (1) that actually recorded on the books and (2) that which management feels should have been recorded on the books. Numerically, these three accrued depreciations may differ, and their applications may differ; hence the desirability of careful usage of the term.

8.13. Annual Depreciation. The annual depreciation of a property is the depreciation during a year of its service life. In accounting, the annual depreciation is the amount of the cost which is allocated to operating expense during the year; in the sense of value, annual depreciation is the decrease in value during the year.

8.14. Present Value. The present value of an industrial property is its value in its existing condition at the date of valuation, correct adjustments having been made for depreciation and other factors.

8.15. Theoretical Depreciation. Theoretical depreciation is depreciation estimated without giving reasonable consideration to the several factors which affect the depreciation of the property. Such factors as age, physical condition, conditions of past service, probable future service conditions, and technological developments have an influence upon the value and future usefulness of properties, and if a reliable estimate of depreciation is to be made, these and other factors are to be considered. The term may be applied to either value depreciation or cost accounting depreciation.

8.16. Actual Depreciation. In opposition to theoretical depreciation is actual depreciation—that estimate of depreciation made by competent authority after giving just consideration to all factors influencing the depreciation of the property. Actual depreciation cannot be estimated without accurate knowledge of the physical condition and condition of service of the property. The term may be applied to either depreciation of value or depreciation in accounting.

8.17. Accelerated Depreciation. Wear and tear of many items of depreciable property is recognized as one of the chief causes of their ultimate retirement and therefore of their lessening of value. For accounting purposes, the cost of the property is usually allocated to expense on a basis of annual rates determined after consideration of the probable service life and salvage value of the property. In times of heavy use of the property such as during wars or periods of continuous 24-hr use, the usefulness of the property may be consumed faster than anticipated when the accounting depreciation rates were set. An enterprise for internal purposes can change depreciation rates at will to meet these changing conditions, but it cannot do so for federal income tax purposes. Regulated utilities need to obtain approval from their regulatory commissions. Consumption of useful service which occurs under periods of extraordinarily heavy production is sometimes referred to as accelerated depreciation or added depreciation resulting from added use.

Another application of the term accelerated depreciation refers to a rapid write-off of the cost of a depreciable asset at a rate unrelated to the rate at which the useful service is consumed. A rapid write-off of 20 percent a year for income tax purposes was authorized by Congress for application to capital improvements made in connection with national defense activities starting in 1941.

8.18. Depletion. The word depreciation has been applied in the foregoing discussion to that class of property which is man-built and which can be replaced. *Depletion* is the word applied to the consumption of the natural resources, another important class of physical assets, the cost of which is chargeable to expense. Typical examples include the reserves of natural gas, oil, coal, timber, and ores of all kinds and the deposits of building materials such as rocks and gravels. These resources are not replaceable; further, they are quantitatively consumed during use and are not subject to wear and tear, physical deterioration, inadequacy, and obsolescence in the normal sense as applied to depreciable man-built assets. The prepaid expense (the investment cost or other basis) of these natural resource assets is allocated to production expense by a charge for depletion. The contra account, the reserve for depletion, takes the credit entry.

Depreciation and depletion as terms of cost accounting refer to the same principle and objective, but depletion is applied only to irreplaceable natural resource assets. The determination of depletion rates for cost accounting is not discussed herein.[1] For appraisal methods applicable to natural resources and limited-life enterprises see Chap. 18.

---

[1] For a useful discussion of depletion see Eugene L. Grant and Paul T. Norton, Jr., "Depreciation," New York, The Ronald Press Company, 1949. Also, U.S. Treasury Department, Office of Internal Revenue, "Regulations III Relating to the Income Tax under the Internal Revenue Code," . . . Washington, D.C., Government Printing Office, 1943.

CHAPTER 9

Methods of Estimating Depreciation

Much of the controversy over methods of estimating depreciation has come about because the purpose of estimating it has been confused—whether for cost accounting or for valuation. Likewise, additional controversy is caused because the theories and assumptions on which certain methods are based are realistic when applied to single units of property but inapplicable to groups of units.

In Secs. 9.3 to 9.16 depreciation methods are explained as applied to single units of property and, with the exception of the present worth method (Sec. 9.13), mainly from the cost accounting concept. By restricting these discussions in this manner the several methods are more easily compared and differentiated in their basic differences. In Secs. 9.17 and 9.18 the methods are discussed from the standpoint of their applicability to group accounting for depreciation expense. Chapters 10 and 11 present the methods again as applied to depreciation accounting and valuation processes, respectively.

9.1. Nature of the Estimates of Depreciation. In general, the many well-known methods of estimating depreciation may be classified into two groups, (1) those not involving considerations of interest or time discounts and (2) those involving the theory of compound interest. Another classification would place in one group those methods which are solely schemes of allocating the cost of depreciable property to operating expense and in a second group those methods which are for valuation purposes.

Another application of depreciation methods which the choice of method affects is whether annual cost depreciation, accrued cost depreciation, or accrued decrease in value is desired. Again, depreciation is a capital cost that is considered in engineering economy studies in which the objective is to determine the most economical design or process or to compare alternate possibilities.

Whether for cost or value, annual depreciation must be an estimated quantity. Depreciation, while a tangible characteristic of physical property, is an estimated quantity the way it is ordinarily used because it depends largely upon the future. Except for a retired property, salvage value lies in the future, and the remaining service to be got from the property lies in the future. Both these quantities are essential to a determination of cost accounting depreciation. Since the future cannot be known with certainty, depreciation, in cost allocations and in valuation, is an estimated dollar quantity.

In the last analysis the total cost accounting depreciation for a specific property is the same regardless of the method by which it is estimated from year to year because it must be equal to the depreciation base minus the realized salvage value at retirement. The methods differ only in the way they distribute the depreciable base over the period of usefulness of the property.

9.2. Review of the Development of Depreciation Methods. Probably the first depreciation method developed was the simple straight line method. However, when knowledge of depreciation increased sufficiently to make clear that the straight line assumption did not take any account whatsoever of interest, it was natural that someone should develop a sinking fund depreciation method. The sinking fund method was partially developed on the erroneous replacement concept of depreciation in order to build up a sinking fund which could be used for the purchase of a replacement property. Further, the sinking fund method has a closer relationship to the concept of value than does the straight line method.

Although practically all the references on depreciation for accounting procedures speak of the lessening of value of the property and of the resultant need of making a charge to production cost, the depreciation procedures used in accounting do not attempt to allocate depreciation costs in accordance with the changes in values. A depreciable property may be valued on the basis of its market value were it to be removed and sold, or ownership value were it retained in place and continued to be productive. The former basis would produce the secondhand value and the latter basis the present worth of the future returns from its continued use. A possible third basis is to consider the value of the present property in comparison with the purchase of new property to produce the same service. Obviously, accounting processes of allocating depreciation cost do not follow any of these valuation methods. If they did, depreciation charges would fluctuate widely from year to year.

Should the accountant use valuation methods to obtain estimates of depreciation cost allocations, such results would not be worth the effort needed to make the valuation. What is used, then, is either a process which is expedient from the viewpoint of business judgment or one which is to a certain extent correlated with the rate that the potential service usefulness of the property is consumed.

NONINTEREST METHODS OF ESTIMATING DEPRECIATION
FOR SINGLE UNITS OF PROPERTY

Several allocation systems have been developed in accounting procedures for systematically allocating the original cost of depreciable property, less salvage value, to production cost. Some of these methods are arbitrary; others are based on theory. Certain of these methods are next discussed as they apply to one unit of property.

9.3. Good-as-new Depreciation Assumption. The erroneous good-as-new assumption may be stated as follows:

Property units so well maintained that their service efficiency and daily output capacity are practically undiminished are as good as new.

That this assumption is entirely erroneous is made clear by the fact that the difference between the future services which an *old* property is yet to render and the future services which the same property would *render if still new* is equal to the entire services rendered to date by the old property. Thus, this assumption was developed as a basis of value of property more than as a method of allocating depreciation expense.

The good-as-new assumption is not only erroneous but absurd when applied to property due for early retirement. This good-as-new assumption has its parallel in the depreciation accounting system (now practically abandoned) that makes no charge for the consumption of the service usefulness of the property until it is retired.

9.4. Direct Appraisal Method. The direct appraisal depreciation method, which is unwarranted but formerly common, may be stated as follows:

It is sometimes assumed that a competent valuator by expert intuition can decide arbitrarily, by merely inspecting a property, how much it is depreciated in value without applying any particular process of reasoning or analysis or without reference to any cost data applying to the property.

For simple short-lived property perhaps a competent valuator by inspecting the property can determine the approximate accrued depreciation percentage based on usefulness or on value, without formal calculations. His reasoning process may be so short and so informal as to be accomplished almost unconsciously. In the majority of cases, however, attempts to determine depreciation by direct appraisal are apt to lead to arbitrary estimates, often not entirely free from unconscious influence by some bias of the estimator.

The accrued depreciation for valuation purposes of many properties has been estimated by inspection of the property to observe its physical state of wear and deterioration. By relating the observed physical state of wear to condition new, a so-called "percent condition" is determined.

The accrued depreciation (in percent) in such methods is assumed to be equal to 100 percent minus the percent condition. Obviously, such appraisal methods result in high property values and low accrued depreciation because neither present value nor remaining useful service is necessarily proportional to the state of observed wear and tear; other factors of age, obsolescence, company policy, and state of business are also relevant. Any method which consists solely in observing the physical condition of the property has no application whatever in cost depreciation accounting; neither is it a sound method for estimating depreciation (consumed usefulness) in appraisals.

9.5. Arbitrary Lump Sum Method. Although now practically abandoned, many enterprises prior to restrictions on depreciation deductions imposed by the U.S. Bureau of Internal Revenue made arbitrary lump sum allocations to expense for depreciation. These allocations were generally made for the business as a whole rather than for a particular property group or unit. The inclination of management was to make large allocations in years of large gross revenue and small allocations for depreciation when revenue was low.

The arbitrary lump sum depreciation method is based on no particular theory, is not related to the probable useful service life of the property, and is a method lacking in consistency year to year. For these reasons the method is now of only historical interest.

9.6. Depreciation as a Percentage of Revenue. Estimating cost depreciation as a percentage of revenue involves the same motive as found in the arbitrary lump sum method. Management, when allocating depreciation expense as a percentage of gross revenue, is endeavoring to stabilize net profit, rather than to make a charge to production proportionate to the utilization of the usefulness of the depreciable property. On the other hand, there may be some direct relationship between gross revenue and consumption of useful service of the property. This method bears some resemblance to the production or use basis discussed in Sec. 9.9 under the straight line method.

The percentage of gross revenue method seems not to have been used much except several years ago by public utilities. Utility commissions no longer encourage the method, and it is now only of historical interest. The method is not applicable to specific units or to groups of property because there is no adequate or provable method of allocating the revenue of an enterprise to the separate physical properties.

9.7. Sum of the Digits Method. In the sum of the years digits method, the sum of the arithmetic series of numbers from 1 to n is used, where n represents the probable life of the unit, as the denominator of a series of fractions, n in number. The numerator of the fraction for any specific year is the expectancy of life as of that year. If 6 years is the estimated probable service life of the unit, the denominator of the fractions is $1 + 2 + 3 + 4 + 5 + 6$, or 21.   The depreciation allocations for the first through the sixth years are found by multiplying the depreciable cost by the series of fractions: $\frac{6}{21}$, $\frac{5}{21}$, $\frac{4}{21}$, $\frac{3}{21}$, $\frac{2}{21}$, and $\frac{1}{21}$.

The sum of the years digits method is an arbitrary method of allocation in which the depreciation base is held constant and the yearly rate decreased.   As with the declining balance method, the result is to allocate the larger amount of depreciation to the first year and to decrease the amount each succeeding year.   The method has not been used to any great extent, partially because it is difficult to apply to groups of units, and because the declining balance method achieves similar results with greater ease and flexibility.

9.8. Declining Balance Method.   The declining balance method is a variation of the fixed percentage depreciation idea, in which the fixed percentage is applied to the unallocated balance of the base instead of to the cost new base.   In results, the declining balance method closely parallels the sum of the digits method.

When the declining balance method is applied to a single property unit, the annual depreciation is always a fixed percentage of the unit's unallocated base at the beginning of the year.   The formula for the unallocated base of the unit at any age by the declining balance method is

$$B_x = B(1 - f)^x \qquad (9.1)$$

where B = depreciation base, including the salvage value V_s

B_x = unallocated base at age x

f = the period (annual) rate of depreciation

Although the expression $(1 - f)^x$ is always less than unity and decreases as the age x increases, it does not equal zero until x equals infinity. Hence, the accrued book depreciation of a property unit by the declining balance method theoretically would never reach 100 percent of the base.

A finite ending of B_x can be achieved by use of a salvage value.   That is, Eq. (9.1) may be written in terms of the salvage value and the service life n,

$$V_s = B(1 - f)^n \qquad (9.2)$$

When B_x becomes equal to V_s, the depreciable portion of the base B would have become fully allocated.

By use of the salvage value V_s and a probable life n of the unit, it is possible to determine f.   For this case Eq. (9.2) reduces to

$$f = 1 - \sqrt[n]{\frac{V_s}{B}} \qquad (9.3)$$

from which it is seen that the fixed rate of depreciation to be applied to the declining balance is dependent upon the service life period and the ratio of salvage value to the depreciation base.   Equation (9.3) is not fully desirable because the declining balance rate f is made to depend upon the salvage value. The salvage value should affect the amount of the base to be allocated, but there is no logic in having the rate of allocation controlled by the amount of salvage. Perhaps the better method of establishing f is to arbitrarily fix it at 1.5 to 3.0 times the reciprocal of the service life n.

The curve of $B_x = B(1 - f)^x$ is concave upward, similar to the curve of secondhand values. Although useful in representing the law of second-hand values under a stable price level, the declining balance method has no particular basis other than that it is a scheme which produces heavier depreciation allocations in the early life of the unit than in the later life. The method has an advantage when applied to a unit for which the operating costs increase with age. Further, with decreasing annual allocations of depreciation cost combined with increasing annual operating expense or when new property is used heavily, there is a tendency to equalize annual stated profits. The method, as applied to a unit or to a vintage group, has the desirable merit of conservative business judgment because the rate f can be chosen so as to recoup the cost at a greater rate in early service periods than that which results from the straight line method applied to the full period of service.

9.9. Straight Line Depreciation Method. The declining balance and sum of the digits methods distribute the depreciation base to expense accounts more heavily in the early periods of use of the unit than in the latter periods. The straight line depreciation method allocates the depreciable base of a property unit uniformly throughout its service life except when the estimate of service life is changed.

This fixed percentage depreciation method is more widely used in depreciation calculations than any other. It is the one method most generally used for determining depreciation for tax purposes and for profit and loss financial statements. It is the method prescribed by the Interstate Commerce Commission, Federal Power Commission, and many other regulatory agencies.

The basic concept of the straight line method is that as long as the service period and salvage value on which the depreciation allocation is based remain unchanged, the depreciation provision remains the same for each unit of service rendered. However, when the probable life of a property unit is changed, say to 14 years after having been used at 10 years for the past 7 years, the graph representing accrued accounting depreciation between zero age and age of retirement is two straight line segments, each with a different slope, but joined at age 7. Nevertheless, the method is still regarded as the straight line method.

A variation of the straight line method is the multiple straight line. A multiple straight line (when considered for one unit of property) results when there is a change in the estimated probable life or salvage value from that used the first year. This change in factors could result from a planned program or from a re-estimate of the factors. Under a planned program, a shorter service life and smaller salvage value would be used in the period of early service than would be used following a planned change in these factors. The intent of such planning is to achieve depreciation allocations in early life greater than would result from using the final service life throughout all service periods. By frequent increases in the estimated probable service life, the multiple straight line method would produce results somewhat similar to those obtained by use of the declining balance method.

The straight line method may be applied to units of production as well as to years. The mile, ton-mile, gallon, ton, unit pieces fabricated, or other measure of service may be used. This so-called "use basis," or "production method," as distinguished from the "year basis," has advantages for properties whose useful life is more dependent upon the number of operations performed than on calendar time.

The straight line method is equally applicable to single units, a group of units all of the same age (a vintage group), or groups of units of mixed ages. This general applicability of the straight line method is another of its characteristics that has caused it to be widely used and accepted.

9.10. Mathematics of the Straight Line Method. The basic formulas of the straight line method are developed in this section. The following notations are used in this development and also in the development of formulas of the sinking fund and present worth methods:

B = depreciation base, including salvage value; this base may be original cost, other cost, or a value which is to be allocated

B_d = depreciable base, which is the quantity to be allocated; the depreciation base less the estimated salvage value

$\quad = B - V_s$

B_x = unallocated portion of the depreciation base which is unallocated to age x

D = annual depreciation allocation

$\sum_0^x D$ = total accrued depreciation allocation to age x

$\quad = B - B_x$

x = age of property, years

n = probable service life of property unit; average service life of a group; number of year-end payments in the sinking fund method

e = expectancy of service life; $e = n - x$

f = depreciation rate per year

V_s = salvage value at end of service life n; sale income or inventory value less cost of removal

By definition of the straight line method, the annual allocation is

$$D = \frac{B - V_s}{n} = \frac{B_d}{n} \tag{9.4}$$

and the total allocation to age x is $x(B_d/n)$.

The expression for the unallocated base B_x is developed as follows:

$$B_x = B - x\frac{B_d}{n} \tag{9.5}$$

$$B_x = (B_d + V_s) - x\frac{B_d}{n}$$

$$B_x = B_d\left(1 - \frac{x}{n}\right) + V_s$$

$$B_x = B_d\left(\frac{n - x}{n}\right) + V_s \tag{9.6}$$

The $n - x$ is the expectancy of service life at age x. The expectancy-life factor is $(n - x)/n$, the ratio at age x of the unallocated portion of B_d to B_d.

DEPRECIATION METHODS BASED ON INTEREST THEORIES

The foregoing depreciation methods, which do not involve the theory of interest, have their application primarily in cost allocations, but also in certain valuation applications and approximations in engineering economy studies. The sinking fund and present worth theories, as applied to single units, are discussed next. Each method uses the concept of interest.

9.11. Sinking Fund Depreciation Method. The sinking fund theory of depreciation is now used in cost accounting by only a few enterprises, although some years ago it did enjoy a certain popularity in the public utility field. The method is still used extensively in engineering economy studies as a basis of selection of alternate proposals.

In the sinking fund depreciation method, the total allocation of the base to any date is equal to the corresponding accumulation (of annual payments to the sinking fund and compound interest thereon) in a hypothetical equal-annual-year-end-payment sinking fund, in which the total accumulation at the end of the service life of the unit would be just equal to the depreciable base of the unit. The sinking fund method, although based upon a well-established principle of compound interest, is not based upon a premise related to the consumption of usefulness of the property.

The sinking fund depreciation method may be understood better by considering the following:

1. The depreciation sinking fund is merely a mathematical concept used to develop formulas by which to compute depreciation allocations by the sinking fund method.

2. It is not practicable, nor if practicable would it be wise, to invest all or even a considerable part of the annual depreciation allocation of an industrial enterprise in any kind of sinking fund.

3. The total accrued depreciation at each service age is assumed to be equal to the corresponding accumulation in the hypothetical depreciation sinking fund.

4. The depreciation allocation for a specific year is the equal annual deposit plus that year's interest on the accumulation. Thus, the annual depreciation allocation is ever increasing to the last year of service of the property unit.

5. The annual depreciation annuity, set aside out of current annual income, is not the full annual depreciation allocation but only the equal-annual-year-end payment to the sinking fund.

6. The annual payments to the sinking fund do not sum up to the total depreciable base, the difference being made up by the compound interest earnings on the sinking fund. Therefore, the owner must depend upon earning a return on his depreciation return for the purpose of recovery of part of his investment in depreciable property.

From these observations it is easily seen why the sinking fund method is somewhat impractical to use in cost accounting procedures, although the method does have some application in valuation since it includes a time-interest factor. This concept is. better brought out, however, in the present worth method, discussed in Secs. 9.13 and 9.14.

The sinking fund method, developed for a single unit of property, is applicable to group accounting, but with some indirectness.

9.12. Mathematical Development of the Sinking Fund Method. Derivation of the formulas pertaining to the sinking fund method may be accomplished by use of the following notations in addition to those given in Sec. 9.10:

i = interest rate per period
R = end-of-period annuity; in this derivation, the equal-annual-year-end payment
S_n = accumulation in the sinking fund in n years
S_x = accumulation in the sinking fund in x years

The accumulation in the fictitious sinking fund is:

At end of 1st year: $S_1 = R$
At end of 2d year: $S_2 = R + R(1 + i)$

At end of 3d year: $S_3 = R + R(1 + i) + R(1 + i)^2$
At end of nth year:

$$S_n = R + R(1 + i) + R(1 + i)^2 + \cdots + R(1 + i)^{n-1} \qquad (9.7)$$

Multiplying Eq. (9.7) by $(1 + i)$,

$$S_n(1 + i) = R(1 + i) + R(1 + i)^2 + R(1 + i)^3 + \cdots + R(1 + i)^n$$
$$(9.8)$$

Subtracting Eq. (9.8) from Eq. (9.7),

$$S_n - S_n(1 + i) = R - R(1 + i)^n$$

$$S_n = R \frac{(1 + i)^n - 1}{i} \qquad (9.9)$$

and

$$R = S_n \frac{i}{(1 + i)^n - 1} \qquad (9.10)$$

For any age x instead of age n, Eq. (9.9) may be written

$$S_x = R \frac{(1 + i)^x - 1}{i} \qquad (9.11)$$

For a unit of property, $S_n = B_d$, or the depreciable base to which the fund must accumulate in n years; therefore,

$$R = B_d \frac{i}{(1 + i)^n - 1} \qquad (9.12)$$

which gives the amount of the equal-annual-year-end payment to the sinking fund for a depreciable base of B_d. The accumulation in the fund at any year end is represented by S_x, which is found by substituting in Eq. (9.11) the expression for R as given by Eq. (9.12),

$$S_x = B_d \left[\frac{i}{(1 + i)^n - 1} \right] \left[\frac{(1 + i)^x - 1}{i} \right] = B_d \left[\frac{(1 + i)^x - 1}{(1 + i)^n - 1} \right] \qquad (9.13)$$

The unallocated base B_x is equal to the depreciable base new, minus the accumulation in the sinking fund (accrued depreciation), plus the salvage value, or

$$B_x = B_d - S_x + V_s$$

$$B_x = B_d - B_d \left[\frac{(1 + i)^x - 1}{(1 + i)^n - 1} \right] + V_s \qquad (9.14)$$

$$B_x = B_d \left[\frac{(1 + i)^n - (1 + i)^x}{(1 + i)^n - 1} \right] + V_s \qquad (9.15)$$

The unallocated base of a unit of property at age x depreciated by the sinking fund method is given by Eq. (9.15). Later it will be shown that the present worth method results in this same expression when r, the rate of return, is substituted for i, the rate of sinking fund interest.

9.13. Present Worth Depreciation Principle. The sinking fund method is an arbitrary one based wholly upon a scheme of accumulating through payments and compound interest thereon the depreciable base of the unit by its forecasted retirement date. The present worth method is a similar method, in fact identical in result when the same interest rate is used, but one based on the fundamental concept of value. It seems evident that one principle by which to determine the decrease in value of a property unit during its service life is to measure the decrease in the value of its future usefulness. The fundamental basis of value of a property is the present worth of its probable future services.

This present worth principle is that the value of a property, at any date during its service life is the present worth at that date of the probable future operation returns yet to be earned through its probable future services. This principle correctly takes into account the fact that the present value of a future service is less than that of a present service—in fact, much less when the future service is remote.

For a property to justify its economic existence, its annual operation return should be at least sufficient to repay its yearly depreciation allocation and, in addition, pay each year a fair return on the unallocated base of the unit at the beginning of the year. In many cases, except those in which the annual unit service costs increase materially during the service life of the property, it is convenient (though not mathematically the same) to estimate the future operation returns as a uniform annual sum, made up of the sum of an increasing annual depreciation component and a decreasing annual return on the unallocated portion of the base.

The derivation of the present worth formula of value is simply a process of developing an expression for the present value of a series of annual incomes yet to be received. If these incomes can be evaluated as of the present date, the means are then available for calculating depreciation as a decrease in value of the probable future services with increasing age of the property.

9.14. Mathematical Derivation of the Present Worth Formulas. In addition to the notations in Secs. 9.10 and 9.12 the following are used in the derivation of formulas for the present worth method:

r = rate of return

R = annual operation return

R_1, R_2, R_n = annual operation return for year indicated

The value of a property by the present worth theory is equal to the present worth of the probable future annual operation returns throughout its service life, plus the present worth of the probable salvage value receivable at retirement.   The annual operation returns $R_1, R_2, R_3, \ldots ,$ R_n will vary, but they may be represented by an equivalent uniform annual operation return R of such magnitude that the sum of the present worths of all the R's receivable during the life of the property is equal to the sum of the present worths of the actual annual operation returns during the same life period.   By definition, operation return includes annual depreciation and annual return on the depreciated base, including salvage value.

The derivation of the formulas proceeds on the basis of finding the present worth B of the probable future operation returns R:

$$B = B_d + V_s = \frac{R_1}{1 + r} + \frac{R_2}{(1 + r)^2} + \frac{R_3}{(1 + r)^3} + \cdots$$
$$+ \frac{R_n}{(1 + r)^n} + \frac{V_s}{(1 + r)^n} \quad (9.16)$$

Substituting[1] R for $R_1, R_2, R_3, \ldots , R_n$, so that Eq. (9.16) may be summed,

$$B_d + V_s = \frac{R}{(1 + r)^1} + \frac{R}{(1 + r)^2} + \frac{R}{(1 + r)^3} + \cdots$$
$$+ \frac{R}{(1 + r)^n} + \frac{V_s}{(1 + r)^n} \quad (9.17)$$

Multiplying by $(1 + r)$,

$$(B_d + V_s)(1 + r) = \frac{R}{1} + \frac{R}{(1 + r)^1} + \frac{R}{(1 + r)^2} + \cdots$$
$$+ \frac{R}{(1 + r)^{n-1}} + \frac{V_s}{(1 + r)^{n-1}} \quad (9.18)$$

Subtracting Eq. (9.17) from Eq. (9.18) and solving for R,

$$(B_d + V_s)(1 + r) - (B_d + V_s) = \frac{R}{1} - \frac{R}{(1 + r)^n}$$
$$+ \frac{V_s}{(1 + r)^{n-1}} - \frac{V_s}{(1 + r)^n} \quad (9.19)$$

[1] In making the substitution of R for $R_1, R_2, \ldots , R_n$, recognition is given to the fact that the series of operation returns for n years will vary in amount, perhaps widely.   The resulting equation (9.24) in the sense of exactness is good only when R is uniform throughout n years.   Even though R was chosen at that specific amount which would produce the same present worth as obtained by using $R_1, R_2, \ldots , R_n$, the resulting curve of present worth from age 0 to n would be unlike that obtained using $R_1, R_2, \ldots , R_n$.   Nevertheless, the concept of decrease in present worth of the probable future operation returns has an application in any study of depreciation methods.

$$r(B_d + V_s) = R\left[\frac{(1 + r)^n - 1}{(1 + r)^n}\right] + \frac{V_s(1 + r) - V_s}{(1 + r)^n} \qquad (9.20)$$

$$R\left[\frac{(1 + r)^n - 1}{(1 + r)^n}\right] = rB_d + rV_s - \frac{rV_s}{(1 + r)^n}$$

$$R = B_d\left[\frac{r(1 + r)^n}{(1 + r)^n - 1}\right] + rV_s\left[\frac{(1 + r)^n - 1}{(1 + r)^n}\right]\left[\frac{(1 + r)^n}{(1 + r)^n - 1}\right]$$

$$R = B_d\left[\frac{r(1 + r)^n}{(1 + r)^n - 1}\right] + rV_s \qquad (9.21)$$

Equation (9.21) is an expression for the equivalent uniform annual operation return in terms of the depreciable base and salvage value.

The expression $\dfrac{r(1 + r)^n}{(1 + r)^n - 1}$ is designated by Grant as the capital recovery factor.[1] This factor is in fact the capital recovery with interest, or the return *on* the investment plus the allocated return *of* the investment. The equation for the depreciation base may be written from Eq. (9.20),

$$B = B_d + V_s = R\left[\frac{(1 + r)^n - 1}{r(1 + r)^n}\right] + \frac{V_s}{(1 + r)^n} \qquad (9.22)$$

At age x the present value is the present worth of the remaining annual operation returns plus the present worth of the salvage value, or

$$B_x = R\left[\frac{(1 + r)^{n-x} - 1}{r(1 + r)^{n-x}}\right] + \frac{V_s}{(1 + r)^{n-x}} \qquad (9.23)$$

Substituting the value of R from Eq. (9.21) in Eq. (9.23), the result is

$$B_x = \left[B_d\frac{r(1 + r)^n}{(1 + r)^n - 1} + rV_s\right]\left[\frac{(1 + r)^{n-x} - 1}{r(1 + r)^{n-x}}\right] + \frac{V_s}{(1 + r)^{n-x}}$$

$$B_x = B_d\left[\frac{(1 + r)^{2n-x} - (1 + r)^n}{(1 + r)^{2n-x} - (1 + r)^{n-x}}\right] + V_s\left[\frac{(1 + r)^{n-x} - 1 + 1}{(1 + r)^{n-x}}\right]$$

$$B_x = B_d\left[\frac{(1 + r)^n - (1 + r)^x}{(1 + r)^n - 1}\right] + V_s \qquad (9.24)$$

That is, the present value of a unit property at age x years and of probable total service life of n years is equal to the depreciable base times the expression in the brackets, plus the salvage value. The expression

---

[1] Eugene L. Grant, "Principles of Engineering Economy," 3d ed., p. 44, New York, The Ronald Press Company, 1950. Grant's formula for annual cost of capital recovery with interest is identical with Eq. (9.21) for R. See Eugene L. Grant, Depreciation Problems: Relationship to Competitive Industry, *Proceedings of the American Society of Civil Engineers*, Vol. 67, p. 1620, November, 1941.

in the brackets of Eq. (9.24) may be called the expectancy-life factor which is defined in Sec. 11.5 and discussed in Secs. 11.6 and 11.7.

The foregoing development of the present worth depreciation method was accomplished by using the concept of value, rather than the concept of a cost allocation.   However, recognizing that cost is not value, from Eq. (9.24) factors may be calculated and applied to a cost base for purposes of determining allocations.   The present worth and sinking fund methods each presents practical difficulties when applied to the accounting allocation of depreciation expense, but both methods, which are identical in final result, are easily applied to valuation procedures when expectancy-life ratio tables (Sec. 11.6 and Appendix C) are available.

COMPARISON OF THE SEVERAL DEPRECIATION METHODS APPLIED TO SINGLE PROPERTY UNITS

The several depreciation methods presented in Secs. 9.3 to 9.14 need to be compared to bring out their desirability for cost accounting or appraisal purposes.   Some of the methods are wholly arbitrary, some are based on mathematical theory, and others are a combination of dogmatic decision and theory.   At this point the methods are being considered only as they apply to single units of property; Secs. 9.17 and 9.18 discuss applications to group properties.

9.15. Comparison of the Methods of Estimating Depreciation When Applied to Single Units of Property.   A comparison of the several depreciation methods as applied to single property units will reveal that the declining balance and sum of the digits methods give similar results; that the straight line, sinking fund, and present worth methods are equivalent except for consideration of the interest rate; and that the direct appraisal, arbitrary lump sum, percentage of revenue, and good-as-new methods are wholly unlike the other methods and also that they are methods no longer of any importance in accounting or valuation procedures.

For a property unit of 10 years service life, Fig. 9.1 shows curves of the unallocated portion of the base when the annual depreciation is estimated by several of the methods discussed.   The annual allocations are shown in Fig. 9.2.   The arbitrary lump sum method produces any number of distributions of the annual allocation because the allocations are arbitrarily determined.   The good-as-new method would also result in different allocations, but practically 100 percent of the base, less salvage value, would be allocated in the last year of service.

The annual allocation by the sum of the digits method decreases uniformly; by the declining balance method the decrease in the size of the annual allocation is at a decreasing rate.   The results obtained by the declining balance method are controllable by the rate chosen to apply to the declining balance. The curve in Fig. 9.1 for the declining balance method will never reach zero unallocated balance, which characteristic is one of the objectional features of this method.

A similarity is noted in the straight line, sinking fund, and present worth methods, especially for the short service life of 10 years. The

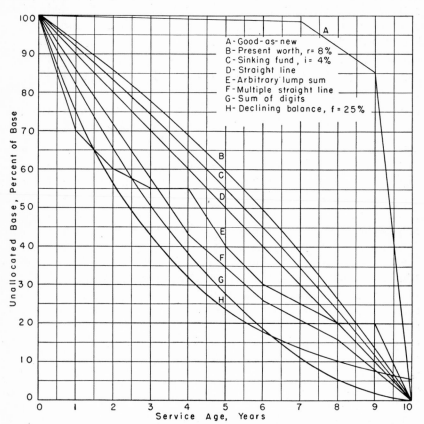

FIG. 9.1. Unallocated depreciation base in percent applicable to several depreciation methods. Illustration is for one property unit of 10 years service life and zero net salvage.

annual allocations by the sinking fund and present worth methods increase with age; longer life and higher interest rates would result in more pronounced increases of the annual allocation with age. In conformity with the general theory of sinking funds, a low interest rate would be used in this method because the hypothetical fund would be invested in high-grade securities of minimum risk. On the other hand, when the method is used, the annual deposit to the sinking fund is not placed in an actual sinking fund but is used for the current needs of the enterprise. The rate used in the present worth method should be that rate of return likely to be earned by the owner of the property. The straight line method results in equal annual allocations as long as the

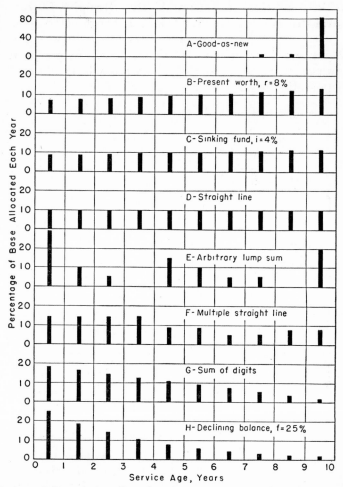

Fig. 9.2. Annual depreciation allocations for one property unit with zero salvage as calculated by eight methods.

service life or salvage value estimates remain unchanged. These three methods, as demonstrated in the next section, give identical results when the interest rate is zero. The straight line method is that special case of the interest methods when the rate is 0 percent.

Figures 9.1 and 9.2 illustrate the straight line method with no change in the service life. The multiple straight line method would result when the service life or salvage value is changed. The curve for the multiple straight line is dependent upon the changes in the service life. The curve for the arbitrary lump sum method is entirely dependent upon the arbitrary allocation year to year.

9.16. Mathematical Relation of the Straight Line, Sinking Fund, and Present Worth Methods. Although based upon entirely different concepts, there is a mathematical similarity between the straight line, sinking fund, and present worth methods. In previous sections the following formulas were developed to express the unallocated portion of the depreciation base:

For the straight line method:

$$B_x = B_d \left(\frac{n - x}{n} \right) + V_s \tag{9.6}$$

For the sinking fund method:

$$B_x = B_d \left[\frac{(1 + i)^n - (1 + i)^x}{(1 + i)^n - 1} \right] + V_s \tag{9.15}$$

For the present worth method:

$$B_x = B_d \left[\frac{(1 + r)^n - (1 + r)^x}{(1 + r)^n - 1} \right] + V_s \tag{9.24}$$

Equations (9.15) and (9.24) are seen to be identical in form and identical in value when $i = r$. Thus, when the sinking fund interest is equal to the rate of return, the sinking fund and present worth methods result in identical annual allocations and unallocated balances.

When the rate of interest or rate of return is 0 percent, Eqs. (9.15) and (9.24) will reduce to Eq. (9.6) for the straight line method. Thus, the straight line method is the special case of the sinking fund or present worth method at zero interest or zero rate of return.

A substitution of $i = 0$ in Eq. (9.15) results in an indeterminate expression of the form of 0/0. Evaluation may be accomplished by differentiating the numerator and denominator separately with respect to i. The resulting expression can be evaluated when i tends toward zero.

$$\lim_{i \to 0} \frac{(1 + i)^n - (1 + i)^x}{(1 + i)^n - 1} = \lim_{i \to 0} \frac{n(1 + i)^{n-1} - x(1 + i)^{x-1}}{n(1 + i)^{n-1}} = \frac{n - x}{n}$$

Therefore, when $i = 0$, Eq. (9.15) becomes identical to Eq. (9.6).

The fact that the straight line, sinking fund, and present worth methods are equivalent except for the interest rate reduces the matter of choice between these three methods to one of selection of interest rate. For most accounting procedures the zero interest rate is selected. In appraisals, when an interest rate is desired, the rate of return is usually chosen rather than a sinking fund interest rate.

ANALYSIS OF DEPRECIATION METHODS WHEN
APPLIED TO GROUPS OF UNITS

The discussion of depreciation methods in Secs. 9.3 to 9.16 is restricted to their application to single units of property.   In both cost accounting and appraisal procedures, annual allocations of depreciation and their accruals are handled on a group basis more frequently than they are by single units of property.   The several depreciation methods are next examined as they apply to group properties, including vintage groups in which all units are of the same age, and continuous groups in which the units are not of the same age, that is, groups of several vintages.

9.17. Comparison of Depreciation Methods as Applied to Vintage Groups.   When property records are maintained so as to reflect the dollar investment in mass or composite properties for each year's addition or vintage, there may be a desire to determine the depreciation allocations separately for each vintage.   A discussion of the various methods as applied to a vintage group is presented.   The curves in Fig. 9.3 apply to a vintage group of 5 years average service life, 10 years maximum life, and zero salvage.   The survivor curve shows the survival pattern of the group.   The unallocated percentage of the depreciation base applies to the surviving units, not to the original 100 percent group.

The *good-as-new* method would result in an unallocated percentage curve holding close to 100 percent until near the date of retirement of the last surviving unit.   Annual allocations of cost depreciation, however, would be required in an amount equal to the net cost of the units retired.   The shape of the curve of unallocated percentage depends entirely upon the amount of allocation thought to be applicable.

The *direct appraisal* method is more of a valuation method than it is a means of allocating depreciation cost.   The discussion in Sec. 9.4 applies to vintage groups as well as to single units.   The method is even less desirable for groups, because of the difficulty in getting an accurate appraisal of the units on an average basis.

The *arbitrary lump sum* method, being wholly an arbitrary method, would produce whatever curve happened to result from the arbitrary annual allocations.   No exact comparison with the results of the other methods can be stated.

The *sum of the digits* method is not applicable to vintage groups in the manner developed for single units because there would be several series of ages to be summed for the vintage group.   The assumption could be made that the retirements for each year were the equivalent of one unit. A combination rate could then be developed to apply to the survivors. Such a procedure, however, is not worth developing because the results would not vary enough from what could be achieved by more direct methods.

The *declining balance* method, for which the depreciation rate is arbitrarily selected, may be applied to a vintage group once the rate is

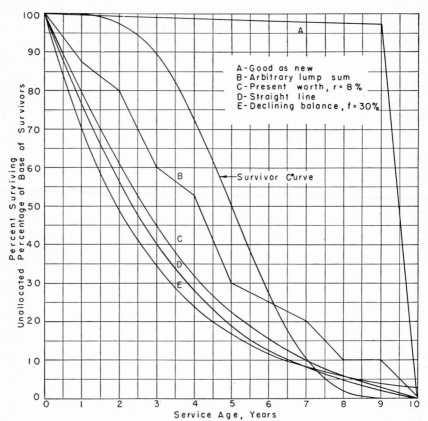

Fig. 9.3. Comparison of unallocated base of survivors for a vintage group of units by different methods of allocation. Salvage value assumed to be zero.

selected, but with some uncertainty of result. Because of the uncontrolled retirements, which reduce the depreciation reserve balance as well as the depreciation base, selection of the depreciation rate would need to be by trial for an assumed retirement distribution. Unless the depreciation rate is changed during the life of the group, the depreciation reserve balance may become negative. The application of the declining balance method to vintage groups can be achieved with some inconvenience and by making periodic adjustments, but the results as adjusted are not likely to vary much from those obtained by the straight line method, except for the few early years. Unless the declining balance rate is adjusted, the unallocated balance may become greater than it would be by use of the ordinary accountant's straight line method.

The *declining balance* method may be objected to when applied to a vintage group because the annual allocation rate is not directly controlled in any manner by the surviving units. Thus, the relative results would be quite different for two or more vintage groups, identical in average service life, but varying in retirement dispersion.

The *straight line* method is applied to a vintage group in the same manner as to a single unit. The depreciation rate is the reciprocal of the average service life of the group of units. The depreciation base decreases throughout the life of the vintage group in accordance with the retirements from the group. The curve in Fig. 9.3 for the straight line method is not a straight line when applied to a vintage group. The allotment during the first year is greater than the allotment for any other year. The straight line method may be considered a reasonable and appropriate method because it does attempt to allocate the depreciation base in conformity with a plausible assumption as to the rate at which the useful service is utilized. The soundness of this assumption is more apparent when the factor of service life by which the allocation is determined is thought of as a production unit. The production unit may be a factor of time or of material items produced.

The *sinking fund* and *present worth* methods are applicable to a vintage group, but with less ease than for the straight line method. Because of the compounding effect of the interest rate the depreciation rate changes somewhat for each age throughout the life of the group. The annuity rate in the sinking fund method would be calculated for the anticipated schedule of retirements. The year-end sinking fund deposit would be the product of the annuity rate times the dollar base of the units surviving each year. The reserve account balance times the interest rate would give the theoretical compound interest earning for the year. The sum of the annuity deposit and the compound interest would give the total annual allocation. Figure 9.3 shows the comparison of the sinking fund and present worth methods with the straight line method. The straight line method results in a slightly higher rate of allocation during the earlier years than does an interest method.

The foregoing discussions may be summarized by stating that (1) the direct appraisal, good-as-new, and arbitrary lump sum methods are as applicable to vintage groups as they are to single units, though such application is to be avoided, (2) the declining balance and sum of digits methods are applicable to vintage groups only indirectly through additional calculations, (3) the straight line method is equally applicable to vintage groups and single units, and (4) the sinking fund and present worth methods are directly applicable to vintage groups, but with the requirement of increased calculations because the depreciation rate varies with the age of the group and retirement dispersion. For cost accounting purposes the straight line method is more direct, the easiest to apply, and a method that results in allocations which are as reasonable as those obtained by any other method.

9.18. Comparison of Depreciation Methods as Applied to Property Groups of Mixed Ages. In both accounting and appraisal procedures, depreciation methods may be applied to groups of units of properties which consist of a collection of several vintage groups. For accounting purposes, particularly, it is important to know how the several depreciation methods apply to groups of units of mixed ages, or continuous groups, as they are sometimes called. Continuous property groups are the usual type found in the accountant's investment accounts, because these accounts usually do not separate the property by vintages. The depreciation base is therefore composed of the dollar amounts for units of many ages.

The *good-as-new* method would be applied to a continuous group account in exactly the same manner as to a single unit or to a vintage group. The assumption in each application is that the units in service are essentially as good as new and, therefore, no depreciation need be allocated. For the units retired, however, the minimum allocation would be the net cost of the units retired. For the units in service, the unallocated portion of the base would remain near to 100 percent.

The *direct appraisal* method is of even greater difficulty in application to continuous groups than to vintage groups. Inspection of the property as a basis of appraisal would become a laborious task. Without using some statistical basis, the appraisal of a group property of mixed ages would be subject to a high degree of uncertainty.

Under the *arbitrary lump sum* method the allocation would be more or less than the dollar retirements each year in accordance with the dictum. The unallocated cost percentage would vary between whatever minimum and maximum limits were desired. The percentages would be controlled by the additions, the retirements, and the cost allocations. The allocations, the additions, and the retirements each would be controlled by business decisions made currently each year.

The *sum of the digits* method is not applicable to continuous groups because there is no way to establish a sum of digits.

The *declining balance* method would have no application to a continuous group within the concept of the method. An arbitrary rate could be applied to the unallocated portion of the base to produce an annual allocation, but such procedure would result in no advantage over applying a similar arbitrary rate to the 100 percent base.   Any arbitrary rate would require adjustment in order to maintain the reserve account at the proper level.   The arbitrary rate could be chosen so that the result would be identical with that produced by the straight line method.

The *straight line* method is applied to continuous groups in exactly the same manner as it is to vintage groups.   The amount of the annual allocation will vary in accordance with the depreciation base, which varies up and down in accordance with the relative amounts of annual additions and retirements.

The *sinking fund* and *present worth* methods are not directly applicable to continuous groups.   But at considerable expense an application could be made by determining the annuity deposit for each vintage group separately and summing the several amounts.   Interest on the reserve account balance added to the total annuity deposit would produce the total annual allocation.   But such a method is so cumbersome that the interest methods are not applied to continuous property groups within the true concept of the methods.

Applications of the depreciation methods to continuous groups (accounts) may be summarized by stating that (1) the good-as-new and arbitrary lump sum methods are as applicable to continuous groups as they are to single units or vintage groups, though not recommended, (2) the declining balance and sum of the digits methods are not applicable, (3) the straight line method is directly applicable and easily applied, and (4) the sinking fund and present worth methods apply in concept but are applicable only with greatly added calculations.   For cost accounting purposes the straight line method is by far the preferred choice.

When the straight line, sinking fund, and present worth methods are applied to a continuous group of stable average age and stable depreciation base, the annual allocation by all three methods is exactly the same in amount.   Should the three methods be applied correctly from the date of installation of the first vintage group, the depreciation reserve account will stabilize at a different level for each interest rate.   The straight line (zero interest) method will maintain the largest reserve balance.   Above the zero interest rate, the depreciation reserve balance will stabilize at decreasing levels with increasing interest rates, but at levels also controlled by the retirement dispersion of the property.

SUMMARY OF DEPRECIATION METHODS

The foregoing explanation of the several depreciation methods is presented mainly from the viewpoint of their applicability to cost accounting.   Their adaptability to accounting purposes, however, is generally the same for appraisal purposes, because the basic considerations are similar even though the procedures may differ. Nevertheless, this chapter will be concluded with brief evaluations of the depreciation methods as they apply to cost accounting (Chap. 10) and to valuation (Chap. 11).

9.19. Evaluation of Depreciation Methods as Related to Cost Accounting. As stated in Sec. 10.1, the main objective of accounting procedures for depreciable property is to allocate the cost of the property to production expense. An allocation equal to the full cost of the property is not made at the time of purchase of the property for three reasons: (1) The practice could result in extreme fluctuations in the profit and loss statement, (2) all depreciable property would be immediately credited off the investment account, thus leaving no such assets on the balance sheet account, and (3) the usefulness of the property would not have been consumed by the date of its charge to expense.

Charging the entire cost of the depreciable property to expense at the time of its retirement is not the preferred practice either because (1) the result could be extreme fluctuation in the statement of profit and loss or because (2) the series of balance sheet statements of physical assets prior to retirement of the property would not reflect any reduction from cost to account for the partial consumption of usefulness of the property yet in service.

The desirable accounting procedure, then, is to follow an allocation method that tends to equalize the charge per unit of service for depreciation year to year but at the same time makes the allocation in conformity with the consumption of the useful service of the property. If these two objectives are to be achieved, the *direct appraisal, good-as-new,* and *arbitrary lump sum* methods are not usable as devices for allocating depreciation expense. The arbitrary lump sum method is ruled out, also, because it follows no certain system which could be followed by another person or which could be depended upon for consistency from year to year.

The *sum of digits* method when applied to a single unit of property has the merit of a positive scheme of allocation, subject only to the judgment of its probable service life. For group property, however, the sum of the digits method is not usable, because there is no single logical basis of arriving at the fractions which determine each year's allocation.

The *declining balance* method has considerable merit when applied to single units of property but is not practical for groups of units. For purposes of financial protection, a heavier charge for depreciation of property in early life than in later life is sound; further, from a production viewpoint, a property probably gives up its usefulness more rapidly in its early life than it does during its latter years.

The *straight line* method has found universal acceptance for depreciation cost accounting. No other method results in a distribution of the cost attributable to the consumption of useful service of the property by a procedure so easily applied and understood. Further, the method is related to a reasonable assumption as to the rate of usage of the useful service of the property. Also, the method is equally applicable to unit or group accounting. The method is objected to only because it does not allocate a greater portion of the base to early years than it does to latter years. In group accounting, however, which is the most frequent application, this objection loses most of its significance because of the wide range of ages of the units making up the account.

The *sinking fund* and *present worth* methods are somewhat troublesome in their application to accounting and are further objected to because they allocate more heavily to the latter years of service of a unit than to the early years. The methods are more appropriately used in valuation and economy studies than in cost accounting.

The foregoing discussions lead to the conclusion that, for day-to-day cost accounting in industry and business, the straight line depreciation method is superior to all other methods yet proposed. Although the year is the service unit of allocation most frequently used, any other suitable production or service unit may also be used.

9.20. Evaluation of Depreciation Methods Applied to Appraisal Procedures. Although this chapter on depreciation methods is presented largely in consideration of depreciation for purposes of accounting, a brief evaluation of the methods as applied to appraisal procedures will terminate the chapter.

In appraising property, the value thereof is the objective. Depreciation may not be a factor at all in the process of arriving at the value. However, when the approach to value of old property is made by first determining replacement cost new or reproduction cost new, some adjustment of these costs is required in order to obtain an evidence of present value of the existing property. This adjustment is frequently a deduction for depreciation—a measurement of the consumed usefulness of the property as compared with a new similar property. The amount of adjustment is usually determined by use of one or more of the depreciation methods.

The *good-as-new* method is not applicable in appraisal procedures because no property in a partially consumed state can render in the future as much service as it could if it were new. In view of this fact there *is need* to adjust the replacement or reproduction cost new to arrive at an evidence of present value.

The *direct appraisal* method of arriving at the amount of adjustment for depreciation in appraising property could be used in applications to certain simple unit properties when the appraiser is thoroughly familiar with the specific property as well as with the general experience with such types of properties. Such factors as age, expectancy, service conditions, and physical condition should be weighed in arriving at the amount of depreciation adjustment. But when such complete information is used, the process becomes an age-life or straight line method rather than one of direct appraisal. Group properties and large complicated unit properties require a greater detail of analysis and computation than would be applied under the direct appraisal method.

Obviously, the *arbitrary lump sum* and the *percentage of revenue* methods are not applicable to appraisal procedures because neither method is related to those factors which affect value.

Neither the *sum of the digits* method nor the *declining balance* method is recommended for appraisal work. Even for single units these methods do not necessarily measure the amount of usefulness the property has given up. This statement applies particularly to the declining balance method in which an arbitrary depreciation rate is chosen in the first place. These two methods are allocation methods designed to distribute the depreciation base of a single unit in decreasing amounts with increasing age; as such they are not satisfactory measures of the amount of consumed usefulness of property.

The *straight line* method is a useful method in appraisal work by which to estimate adjustments for depreciation. When the property age and probable service life (or average service life) can be established, the computation of the amount of depreciation adjustment is easily calculated. By using tables of expectancy-life factors (Appendix C) the replacement cost or reproduction cost can be adjusted to present value by multiplying the estimated cost by the expectancy-life factor. The straight line method makes no allowance for a difference in value because of time, as does the present worth method.

The *sinking fund* and *present worth* methods are applied in appraisals exactly as is the straight line method. Higher values will be found for the reason that an interest factor above zero produces higher unallocated portions of the base—higher expectancy-life factors—than does the straight line method. When value based on the present worth of the probable future services is desired, the present worth method should be used for adjusting estimated replacement and reproduction costs from a new basis to the basis comparable with the existing property whose value is sought.

CHAPTER 10

Depreciation Accounting

The accountant's responsibility for depreciation is one of making the proper allocations of the cost of fixed capital properties to operation expense in order that the profit and loss statement and the balance sheet will reflect correct results. Depreciation in this sense is not a matter of valuation, although depreciation accounting is a necessary procedure in the conduct of business with which the valuator needs to be familiar. Chapter 10 is devoted to a consideration of depreciation accounting about which the literature is voluminous but yet controversial.

DEFINITION AND OBJECTIVES OF DEPRECIATION ACCOUNTING

Depreciation as an element of cost in the production of goods and services has long been known to accountants, although the true concepts and objectives of depreciation have not been well understood. Appraisers, no less than accountants, need to have the correct understanding of the principles and methods of accounting for depreciation—for the consumption of the productive usefulness of physical plant.

10.1. Concept of Depreciation Accounting. By far the majority of references to depreciation deal with it in connection with cost accounting. Even though the United States Supreme Court[1] did not recognize depreciation as an inescapable cost in the production of goods or services by public utilities until 1909, it has been so recognized by accountants and others in the fields of business and industry since at least 1588 in England and 1833 in the United States (see Chap. 8).

Textbooks and other literature still refer to depreciation in accounting in the sense of loss or decrease in value, rather than in the sense of a cost allocation. Although experience indicates that depreciable property usually does decrease in value in time, depreciation charges to production costs do not, however, stem from this fact. These charges come from the fact that a consumable property has been purchased, and unless its cost is included in the operating expense, a correct statement of profit and loss cannot be rendered.

[1] *City of Knoxville v. Knoxville Water Co.* (No. 17), 212 U.S. 1 (U.S. Sup. Ct. Jan. 4, 1909).

Depreciation accounting, then, is a process of allocating a prepaid expense to accounting periods during which there are benefits realized from the depreciable property, the cost of which is a proper form of prepaid expense. As explained in Chap. 9, several methods have been developed for making these allocations. They are arbitrary. They must be arbitrary because there is no theoretical proof or practical proof of the manner or rate of consumption of the economic productive usefulness of depreciable property. Steam generators, telephone poles, office buildings, and printing presses alike ultimately reach the time when management no longer sees fit to continue them in productive service. When this time is reached, the depreciation allocations should have accumulated to the original cost of the property less salvage value realized upon retirement of the property. The accountant's responsibility is to distribute this cost to the productive periods in a rational and equitable manner.

10.2. Confusion of Value and Cost. Practically all the books and references on accounting indicate that depreciation accounting arises because of a decrease in value of the physical property with time and use. Yet these same references usually set out on a method of allocating the cost of the property to operation expense without any attempt to determine a value of the property by methods using current price of product or service, replacement cost, market price for the property, competitive price, or present worth of the future services from the property. The method of allocation usually used is the so-called "straight line method," which (for a single unit) allocates the depreciation in equal periodic amounts over the assumed service life.

The accounting procedure is simply a method of allocating a prepaid cost to the periods of operation during which the serviceability of the property is consumed in rendering service. In this determination by the accountant there is no regard for the monetary rate of any decrease in value of the property, but rather he attempts to allocate the cost of the property, less salvage value, on some equitable basis related to production time or production units other than time. It could be that such a determination might bear a reasonable relationship to value because the monetary value, among other elements which affect value, is dependent upon the future productive capacity of the property. During long periods of economic stability, the consideration of depreciation accounting as a decrease in value could be relatively sound. Primarily, however, the accounting objective is the distribution of a prepaid investment cost to production expense.

Engineers and accountants alike are agreed that the depreciable base should be allocated to production expense over the period of productive service of the property. Whether the straight line method based on years or production units, the declining balance method, or some interest theory method is used is a matter of personal choice. Nevertheless, in commercial, industrial, and public utility enterprises the standard method almost universally used is the straight line method in one variation or another.

Accounting procedures are designed to achieve an equitable distribution of depreciation cost, although there is far from unanimous agreement as to how these objectives are to be obtained. General practice and basic concepts are well established, however.

10.3. Objectives of Depreciation Accounting. The ultimate objectives of depreciation accounting are:

A. To account correctly and currently for all depreciation production expenses by
1. Keeping proper accounts of the current annual depreciation costs of the various plant operations and units of equipment
2. Making proper current depreciation allowances in determining fair rates and prices for the various services rendered and commodities produced by the plant
3. Providing for the maintenance of a proper depreciation reserve account
B. To furnish at call all current depreciation data needed by the management of the enterprise as a basis of
1. Determining the operating profits each year, after making annual depreciation charges
2. Determining the relative economy of various types of properties and processes

Business management and taxing authorities agree that production expense should be charged with a cost representing the consumption of the useful service of physical properties, although in years past this universal agreement did not exist. The following quotation[1] from the many which could be cited is indicative of the agreement which now prevails on this once controversial item. There remains, however, in controversy the system of allocating the depreciation expense and the base which is to be allocated.

Depreciation is one of the most important of all the overhead expenses, because it is generally the largest. . . . It is universally admitted, however, that depreciation does exist, that it is an element of cost just as much as labor or material, and that any system which does not provide for including it is faulty and one that will not give true costs.

Accounting for the proper depreciation on a monthly or similar current basis is one of the major essentials in attaining the objective of deprecia-

[1] U.S. Federal Trade Commission, "Fundamentals of a Cost System for Manufacturers," p. 12 (64th Cong., 1st sess., H.Doc. 1356), Washington, D.C., Government Printing Office, 1916.

tion accounting. Depreciation is just as real a cost of production as is money paid for labor, fuel, materials, and supplies. Moreover, depreciation is one of the major costs of production. Inaccuracies in estimating and recording depreciation expense are as serious and objectionable as are inaccuracies of like amounts in bills of all kinds for labor, fuel, materials, supplies, equipment, buildings, and plant.

Although inaccuracies in estimating and accounting for depreciation are serious and objectionable, the not unknown practice of manipulating depreciation accounts to conceal either profits or losses is reprehensible. Unless depreciation is correctly accounted for currently, the accounts will be false accounts. It is not permissible to charge off less than the normal depreciation in years of depression or more than the normal depreciation in years of unusual prosperity.

GENERAL PRINCIPLES OF DEPRECIATION ACCOUNTING

There are a number of general practices and methods of depreciation accounting which still are subjects of difference of opinion and of active discussion. These are described in the following sections.

10.4. Current Depreciation Accounting. In current depreciation accounting, effort is made to estimate the correct total annual depreciation each year or for each production order or group; all the current estimated annual depreciation is charged to the current production expenses and credited to the depreciation reserve account. The reserve account is charged with the book cost new, less actual salvage, of the property at the date of retirement; thus, the balance in the reserve account shows at all times the accounting depreciation which has been allocated on the property still in service. If the depreciation allocations have been estimated correctly, the expense accounts will then show the correct depreciation production costs; also, the depreciation reserve accounts will always show the proper estimate of the consumption of service capacity of the depreciable property.

Objections are sometimes made to the maintenance of current depreciation accounting systems because of the work and expense required. The same objections might be raised to all kinds of accounts; accounting of every kind is costly. The real question is whether or not the expense is necessary; if so, depreciation accounting is justified if the enterprise is sound. The practically unanimous opinion of those best qualified to judge is that depreciation accounting is not only necessary but feasible, and not only feasible but profitable.

The Interstate Commerce Commission has said,[1] referring to the con-

---

[1] *Depreciation Charges of Telephone Companies* (No. 14,700), *Depreciation Charges of Steam Railroad Companies* (No. 15,100), 118 I.C.C., 317, 318 (Nov. 2, 1926).

tention by steam railway representatives that complete depreciation accounting will be so expensive as to require an increase in railway rates:

This contention, after all, begs the question. If depreciation accounting is a method by which the facts with respect to the cost of operating railroad and telephone companies are recorded with approximate accuracy, then that method should be adopted regardless of its effect on rates. Nothing is to be gained by refusal to face facts or by deferring to some future date burdens which ought to be borne now. As we have seen, however, there are substantial reasons for believing that no additional burdens upon patrons will result.

The Federal Trade Commission has said[1] of cost systems, of which depreciation accounting records are an important essential feature:

A system will not run itself; neither will it in itself reduce costs nor increase efficiency. This is strictly up to the manufacturer himself. A system will give him the information, and if this information is properly used, he will unquestionably find that his system is not an item of expense, but a very valuable asset.

Current depreciation accounting is advocated by the great majority of accountants, business and manufacturing associations, valuation authorities, and governmental agencies. It is strongly favored by the Interstate Commerce Commission, Federal Power Commission, Bureau of Internal Revenue, and industrial accountants in general. The authors of this book are convinced, first, that it is the only method which permits of proper depreciation expense accounts; and, second, that its use is to the best interests of both producers and consumers and of both owners and the public.

10.5. Retirement Accounting. In retirement accounting, the only depreciation charged to production expense each year is the cost less salvage value of the property retired that year. This expense is termed *retirement expense.* The depreciation accruing on property still in service remains unprovided and unaccounted for.

Instead of allocating a depreciation charge just equal to the net cost of the property retired during the year, one of two variations has been used, (1) the average of past or of anticipated future retirements, or, (2) the average of past or of anticipated future retirements plus an arbitrary lump sum amount.

The retirement accounting procedure is not recommended for use in production expense accounts, because (1) the accruing depreciation expenses on property still in service are omitted, (2) the cost of retired property is charged wholly to the year in which the retirements happened to be made, instead of to the years in which the usefulness of the property was consumed, and (3) the plant accounts show no deductions from the

[1] U.S. Federal Trade Commission, *op. cit.*, p. 31.

investment cost new of property on account of consumed usefulness, even when it is known that such property is to be retired in the near future.

A retirement reserve account may be provided for in the retirement accounting system. The main purpose of such a reserve account is to provide in advance for extra large retirement demands in any one year. The reserve may be established and maintained by reserves from income, from surplus, or from both. The amount of the reserve is subject to the discretion of management.

Although retirement accounting is fairly equitable for matured accounts or properties wherein the cost of the property retired is about the same year after year, such a system of accounting fails to protect the owners against unusually large retirements in a single accounting period or from increased cost of the newer property not likely to be retired for some years. Further, the balance sheet statement would overstate the net plant investment by the amount of depreciation which would be shown had current depreciation accounting been used.

When the sale price of the services or goods produced by the property is being determined, the production costs would be over- or understated under retirement accounting except for old properties which had reached a stabilized condition under a constant price level.

One of the main arguments for retirement accounting by its supporters is that it permits using business judgment to reduce retirement expense in years of poor business. Opponents of the system object to this practice as it tends to mislead the stock- and bondholders.

10.6. Replacement Expense Accounting. A system of accounting somewhat similar to retirement accounting is that which makes no charge to production for depreciation or for retirement of property but charges production with the cost of the property purchased to replace that retired. Obviously, such a system is not wisely applicable to properties which may be retired without replacement or to replaceable properties wherein replacements may not be reasonably uniform year to year.

Railroad ties, railroad rail, and railroad ballast are handled under this system of accounting under provisions of the Interstate Commerce Commission. Until 1944 roadway property was similarly handled, when it was placed under current depreciation accounting. In the replacement method, the cost of new units purchased to replace the ones retired is charged directly to expense, the capital accounts being left unaltered. Under this system, the stated book cost of the property becomes grossly understated as compared with the cost of the existing property after periods of rising prices. Similarly, operating expense is overstated as compared with what it would be under a system of current depreciation accounting. Under railway practice the extra weight of rail over what was retired is chargeable to capital expenditure, as are certain other betterments effected by replacements.

Although this method of replacement accounting has been in practice for years with the railroads, the Interstate Commerce Commission has under advisement the matter of placing the roadbed property under current depreciation accounting, or on a basis similar to that applied to roadway property and equipment.

10.7. Depreciation Base. For cost accounting purposes the original cost of the depreciable property is the widely used depreciation base for both the unit and group methods. The depreciation rate is usually adjusted for the estimated salvage value when the straight line method is used:

$$\text{Depreciation rate} = \frac{1.00 - \dfrac{\text{estimated salvage value}}{\text{original cost}}}{\text{probable life or average life}} \tag{10.1}$$

In some applications the full cost, including salvage value, is recovered through depreciation charges, and then the salvage value recovered and the costs of retiring the property are cleared through the current operating accounts.

Although the cost adjusted for the anticipated salvage value could be considered to be the depreciation base, it is more convenient and in conformity with accounting practice to use the cost unadjusted for the salvage value as the base. The required adjustment in the amount of the annual depreciation charge to provide for the anticipated salvage value is accomplished by setting the depreciation rate as indicated in Eq. (10.1).

The cost less salvage value would be the convenient depreciation base to use with the sum of the digits method; however, the rate could be adjusted for salvage if desired and then applied to the full cost. The declining balance method adapts itself to the full 100 percent cost base because this method inherently never reduces the depreciation base to zero.

For cost accounting purposes, the cost is ordinarily used as the depreciation base rather than an appraised value. However, for federal income tax returns, the U.S. Bureau of Internal Revenue permits fair market value or cost, whichever is greater, for property acquired prior to March 1, 1913. For property acquired after February 28, 1913, the base is, in general, the cost of such property. Exceptions are property acquired by gift, transfer, inheritance, exchange, involuntary conversion, reorganization, and liquidation, for which cost or the fair market value is permitted depending on the specific circumstances.[1]

---

[1] For more detail on the bases and methods of accounting for depreciation for federal income tax purposes, see U.S. Bureau of Internal Revenue, Bulletin F (revised

The United States Supreme Court ruled January 6, 1930, that the legal depreciation base for regulated utilities was the fair present value. To quote: ". . . It is the settled rule of this court that the rate base is present value, and it would be wholly illogical to adopt a different rule for depreciation."[1] Despite this ruling of the Court, the fair value of the property was never used as the depreciation base by utilities, and in 1944 in *Federal Power Commission v. Hope Natural Gas Co.* the Court rescinded its Baltimore Street Railway statement relative to the depreciation base. Thus, the United States Supreme Court now recognizes that cost is a proper depreciation base for cost accounting purposes in utility rate-making procedures.

Replacement cost also has been proposed as the base for allocating depreciation. Just after the First World War and again just after the Second World War, inflation caused prices to soar to high levels as compared with the prices paid for the then depreciable property on the books. Businessmen and industrialists then became concerned about financing replacements and extensions. Because of the inflated prices, a change from the practice of basing depreciation charges on original cost to basing them on replacement cost was thought by the management of many business concerns to be logical and desirable.[2] Such practice would have had two immediate results: (1) Increased depreciation charges would have reduced the stated book profits and made it easier to pay less dividends to stockholders, and (2) the cash available for other corporate purposes would have been increased in accordance with any decrease in dividends.

In the early 1920's and again in the mid-1940's the prevailing opinions were against the practice of basing depreciation charges on anything but the book costs. Many concerns, however, eased the financing problem to some extent by making a special charge against income for replacements and extensions, thus reducing their stated profits to stockholders, but not reducing the amount of income tax payable. Other corporations simply retained a higher percentage of profits in surplus or directly appropriated profits to replacement of depreciable property or to plant extensions.

In the accounting procedures followed by business, cost depreciation is that element of expense entered into the production cost statements to account for the consumption of the usefulness of physical properties which

---

January, 1942), "Income Tax Depreciation and Obsolescence, Estimated Useful Lives and Depreciation Rates," Washington, D.C., Government Printing Office, 1942.

[1] *United Railways & Electric Co. of Baltimore v. West, Chairman et al.* (No. 55), 280 U.S. 234, 254, P.U.R. 1930A 225 (U.S. Sup. Ct. Jan. 6, 1930).

[2] The Depreciation Dilemma, *Fortune*, Vol. 39, pp. 66–68, January, 1949.

Shorts and Faces ($1 Is $1—or Is It?), *Fortune*, Vol. 36, p. 136, December, 1947.

Lewis H. Kimmel, "Depreciation Policy and Postwar Expansion," Washington, D.C., Brookings Institution, 1946.

normally last more than one year. The books of accounts, therefore, reflect the cost of this depreciable property in the investment accounts and the amount of this cost which has been allocated to production expense. To handle the entries incident to depreciation cost accounting on any basis other than actual cost of the depreciable property would result in utter confusion for the accountant.

Consider, for a moment, that replacement cost was used as the depreciation base and that the accounting procedure was designed to recover replacement cost rather than original cost. To follow this procedure would require frequent re-estimates of the replacement cost which may vary up or down from previous estimates. Over a period of rising costs, not only would the depreciation base increase from year to year, but the depreciation rate would likewise need to be increased in order to gain the amount of the increase in the base not applicable to past years. Such a changing base, changing rate, and changing balance sheet would ultimately result in full confusion of management and stockholders alike. Original cost is the only base that can be successfully used in the book accounts of the company for the purpose of depreciation cost accounting.

There is reason, nevertheless, why management, immediately following periods of heavy increase in prices, may wish to make a supplementary charge for replacement of property in excess of that allocated on the original cost depreciation base. When retired property is replaced or when plant extensions are made in periods of high prices as compared with the cost of the plant in use, new capital is necessary. This new capital may come from (1) the sale of new securities, (2) earned surplus, (3) the normal annual depreciation return, (4) a special provision from revenue set aside before stated profits to stockholders, or (5) a stepped-up depreciation charge. Methods 4 and 5 would reduce the amount of stated profits from what they would be without these provisions. Income tax authorities, however, would not allow such provisions ahead of the stated profits. Should an extra allowance be made for annual depreciation, as indicated in method 5, by using replacement cost as the depreciation base, the additional depreciation expense over that computed on the original cost base should be credited to a special capital account and not to the regularly established depreciation reserve account.

Although the accountant should be restricted to use of original cost for his computation of the normal annual depreciation expense for the regular books, management does have the right to make such additional allocations of revenue as it may decide are in the best interests of the enterprise.

Depreciation accounting seeks to allocate the cost of property to the costs of production for the same reason that the cost of labor and supplies are charged to production expense. In view of this purpose there can hardly be any base for normal cost depreciation other than original cost. Adopting market value, replacement cost, or fair value as the depreciation base would call also for a restatement of the balance sheet value of assets, which again would cause confusion to anyone endeavoring to make a comparative study of financial reports.

10.8. Selection of Depreciation Method. Because the allocation of the prepaid investment cost of depreciable property to current production expense does not involve the estimation of the value of the property, there is no justification for using a method in depreciation cost accounting involving an interest rate, or discount factor. The straight line method is ordinarily used by all forms of enterprise—commercial, business, farming, manufacturing, and public utility. Further, as between an interest method and a noninterest method, there is little difference for old enterprises with many units of widely varying ages. In these properties the interest factor will make only a slight change in the annual total depreciation allocations for the entire property as compared with the total depreciation by the straight line method. For a property group having a stabilized average age, the annual depreciation is exactly the same when computed on the age-life basis by the present worth method at any rate of interest and by the straight line method. The depreciation reserve account balance accumulated by the different methods, however, will stabilize at different levels by the several depreciation methods.[1]

For a newly formed enterprise, there is a distinct advantage in recouping investment in depreciable property in its early years rather than in late years. This fact lends point to the argument for the appropriateness of the declining balance or sum of digits methods. For machines which tend to increase in operating and maintenance costs with age or use, a depreciation accounting method which allocates successively decreasing depreciation charges will tend to develop equal annual total production costs when depreciation and operation costs are combined.

For cost accounting purposes, the arbitrary lump sum and percentage of income are not recommended, for the reasons mentioned in Chap. 9. The multiple straight line method is a wise choice for management when a short life is first used, followed by longer lives, and when applied to a single unit. The method, however, has little significance when applied to group accounting, for the effect of the multiple of straight lines is lost.

In cost accounting the procedure for determining the annual depreciation allocation should start with the cost of the depreciable property. In the usual accounting system, the investment accounts reflect the cost of the property in use. This cost sum is always directly available. The entry of concern to the accountant is the amount to charge to deprecia-

[1] See Robley Winfrey, "Depreciation of Group Properties," Iowa State College, Engineering Experiment Station, Bulletin 155, 1942.

tion expense for the accounting period. Therefore, the procedure of determining the allocation for cost depreciation usually starts with the book original cost of the property and proceeds directly to the sum to be allocated. Normally, the accountant prefers to accomplish this step by multiplying the depreciation base by a depreciation rate. Such a procedure is simple, easy to understand, direct, and economical in execution.

Any method that requires additional procedures is not welcomed by the accountant. Further, the accountant desires that the depreciation rate be one not required to be redetermined or reselected at each application. The declining balance method is not desired because it requires that the unallocated cost be determined upon each occasion of applying the depreciation rate. This unallocated cost would be determined by obtaining the cost new from the property asset account and the accrued allocation from the depreciation reserve account. The difference between the original cost and the reserve account would be the declining balance to which the declining balance rate would be applied.

Although the probable service life or average service life measured in years is the factor used universally in allocating depreciation charges, service life may be measured in other units of use. Units of hours, miles, ton-miles, production items, or services may be used. This "use basis" or "production basis" (other than years) has gained some support in recent years. For certain types of properties, a production service unit (other than years) tends to equalize costs and profits as between different accounting periods. The use basis gains favor in times of excessive employment of equipment as during the Second World War. Its application is permitted for federal income tax purposes under certain conditions.

The objective of any method of accounting for cost depreciation, however, should be to spread the cost of the depreciable property to the production statements in accordance with the consumption of the economic service usefulness of the property. The difficult determination is that of finding an accurate measure of consumption. Certain types of properties wear out with use, others deteriorate with time, others become inadequate, and many become uneconomical because of the availability of improved types. These forces which ultimately cause management to retire property from use are ever variable in both magnitude and direction; thus, management is forced to adopt methods of allocating depreciation expense which are practicable, reasonable, and equitable, all based largely upon judgment rather than a rigid mathematical analysis or theoretical concept.

In general, all industry uses the straight line method based upon age-life relationships in years. In special cases the use, or production, basis is applied by the straight line method. Since the risks of the future cannot be determined exactly, the service life chosen for accounting purposes should be the shortest reasonable one. Such practice in choosing the service life will in effect, for both unit and group methods, simulate the results obtained by the declining balance method.

10.9. Unit and Group Systems of Depreciation Accounting. Two systems of depreciation accounting are in use, the unit system and the group system.

1. In the unit system, the depreciation is determined and recorded for each unit separately. In general, this is the most desirable system, because (1) it furnishes the depreciation data in complete detail, permitting classifications and summations to meet all the needs of valuation and cost accounting; and (2) the depreciation can be definitely checked for each unit at retirement. However, the unit system is not practicable for numerous and comparatively small units, such as poles, transformers, freight train cars, and machines, or for heavy complicated production assemblies like gas plants, oil refineries, and steel mills.

Unit accounting is used for large special-function types of property wherein there is little convenience to be gained in grouping or wherein there are no other similar units with which to form a group. Large bridges, dams, reservoirs, special production equipment, and the like, may be handled on the unit basis.

2. In the group system, the depreciation is accounted for and determined by groups of units of the same general class.

Group accounting is used almost exclusively by large corporations because of its ease of application and reasonable accuracy when applied to large group accounts. Typical group accounts are those composed (1) of large numbers of identifiable small units of property, (2) of large numbers of small units which are difficult of identification, (3) of reasonably large numbers of large units, or (4) of large properties, such as a building or a factory, which may be rebuilt, altered, or replaced in part from time to time.

When the depreciation rates are chosen with proper attention to the service lives of the property and when the rates are changed as the life experience deviates from the originally anticipated experience, there is little difference in results between the unit and group systems of depreciation accounting other than that arising from errors of judgment in the service lives.

10.10. Selection of Average and Probable Lives. Regardless of the method adopted for allocating depreciation expense some estimate of useful productive life is necessary. Experience with the same or similar type of property offers the best guide to this estimate. Chapter 7 is devoted to statistical methods of analyzing retirements as a basis of estimating probable service lives.

Although the property now in use is not that which was previously retired and which was used in the statistical analyses, past experience offers the best possible starting point for assignment of probable service lives to existing property. Once the lives of past property are known, judgment can be applied to such lives to correct for possible differences in inherent physical qualities, management policies, conditions of use, and obsolescence which may alter future service lives from those of the past.

In choosing the probable service life of a unit of property or the average service life of group properties for depreciation accounting purposes, conservative business judgment would tend to the selection of service lives on the low side, rather than on the high. The future is unknown; the further in the future the prospective retirement is, the more uncertain is the retirement date. The risk of business is therefore greater; this risk can be partially insured against or lessened by the choice of the shortest service life which is reasonable.

Whenever evidence is at hand that the probable future service life is to be different from that corresponding to the currently used depreciation rate, the rate should be adjusted accordingly. The advantage of starting with the shorter service life is that recoupment of the cost is more certain and that when an adjustment in depreciation rate is desirable it will be to a lower rather than to a higher rate. Good accounting practice includes frequent checks of the depreciation rates, service lives, salvage values, and the size of the depreciation reserve balance relative to the unexpired service life of the property.

Good practice in accounting calls for adjustment in depreciation rates whenever it becomes apparent that the property will be retained in service for more or less time than was estimated when the currently used depreciation rate was adopted.

10.11. Salvage Value. Depreciable assets, such as power machinery, automotive equipment, machine tools, and similar types, usually have a salable or usable value upon retirement, either for reuse as is, or for scrap. The amount of this value as salvage is not usually recovered as a depreciation allocation, but through sale or transfer.

Many properties produce no salvage value upon retirement because either they are abandoned in place or the cost of dismantling and removal is about equal to the value of the salvaged material. When the cost of removal exceeds the value of the retired property, after its removal, the result is a negative salvage value.

When the straight line method is used, common practice is to determine the depreciation rate to be applied to the depreciation base as indicated by Eq. (10.1). Adjusting the rate rather than the base is a procedure more convenient for handling salvage value because the books of account customarily show only the full cost.

Regulatory commissions for utilities and the U.S. Bureau of Internal Revenue are careful to see that any appreciable salvage value is taken into account in determining the depreciation allocation. When the salvage is negative, the numerator of Eq. (10.1) becomes greater than unity, which permits the recovery of more than the original cost by the amount of the estimated negative salvage value. Under income tax regulations, however, the depreciation charges cannot exceed the cost. Negative salvage is charged as a current operating cost.

Industrial accountants frequently assume that the salvage value will be zero, and then they charge all costs of removal to operating expense and credit salvage income to operating revenue. This procedure has the advantage of not requiring an estimate of salvage value and eliminates adjustments in the reserve account because of salvage. In the long run there is no adverse effect upon the statement of profit and loss, although if salvage value is a material positive amount in a single accounting period, the profits might be somewhat higher than in previous years. When excessive removal costs occur in one accounting year, the reverse effect on the profit and loss statement would prevail.

10.12. Adjusting Depreciation Accounts Maintained under the Unit System. The estimated service life of a unit of property usually differs from the actual service life; hence, the total of the annual accounting allocations will agree with the true depreciation of the unit (cost new minus salvage value, if any) at the date of its retirement only when the final adjustment is made. Various arbitrary accounting devices become necessary to adjust for the difference between the book accrued allocations at the date of retirement and the cost new less salvage realized.

Not always are depreciation estimates continually checked and corrected when necessary in accordance with the retirement experience of the properties. Nevertheless, care should be taken to compare the results with retirement experience, using every reasonable effort to secure as close an agreement between depreciation allocations and consumption of service usefulness as is practicable.

Likewise, salvage value also may not materialize as originally estimated. Adjustments for failure of either salvage value or retirement date to agree with that estimated for accounting purposes must be made. These adjustments may be made (and should be) during the course of the life of the property by changing the rates of depreciation frequently enough so that the book accrued depreciation at the retirement date is in approximate agreement with the cost new less realized salvage value.

In certain situations it is desirable to estimate the remaining life and then to spread the remaining depreciable cost over the remaining life, which is equivalent to starting with a new depreciation base and a new service life. This practice is provided for in the federal income tax regulations.

When the property is retired following conditions which did not permit of accruing the exact total of depreciable cost by the date of retirement, the difference may be handled in one of three ways: (1) The difference between the book accrued depreciation and the final depreciation at retirement may be charged or credited to the current period's accounts, (2) the difference may be adjusted through the surplus account, and (3) the difference when large enough to disturb the current financial status may be carried on the books under a provision of amortization during a reasonable future period.

The choice of method of adjusting the difference between book accrued depreciation and the final depreciation cost at retirement is controlled by the accounting policy for private industries and to a certain extent by tax regulations. For utility properties the accounting provisions applicable under regulation may determine the procedure.

10.13. Adjusting Depreciation Accounts Maintained under the Group System. In group accounting procedures applied to a continuous account, the only check on the adequacy of annual depreciation allocations is to compare the size of the depreciation reserve credit balance with what the reserve balance should be for the ages of the existing units (or dollars) and the appropriate average service life. This check requires the following determinations:

1. The age distribution of the dollar cost of property in service as of the date of the check
2. The service life of the property as indicated by an analysis of the retirements
3. The shape of the survivor curve pertaining to the dispersion of the retirements of group accounts
4. The probable salvage value of the existing property
5. The depreciation reserve balance pertaining to the property account being investigated

The reserve balance for a surviving group of units all of the same age whose allocated costs have been made by the straight line age-life method should be as follows:

$$\left.\begin{array}{l}\text{Depreciation reserve}\\ \text{credit balance}\end{array}\right\} = \left(\begin{array}{l}\text{cost less salvage}\\ \text{value}\end{array}\right)\left(1 - \frac{\text{expectancy}}{\text{average life}}\right) \qquad (10.2)$$

The expectancy is a function of the shape of the survivor curve (Secs. 7.4 to 7.6) and average life. The above equation is applied to each vintage group separately and the several results summed to get the required reserve balance for the entire account which corresponds to the chosen service life, survivor curve, and salvage value. Average expectancies of groups of different ages or expectancies applicable to average ages will produce incorrect results because the reserve requirement for a vintage group varies on a curved line with age.

When materially too small or too large estimated service lives are used for a lengthy period, the depreciation reserve account balance will become so excessive or so deficient that major revisions will be necessary to bring it back to a proper level. The necessary adjustments may be made as follows:

1. The depreciation rate may be changed such that within a reasonable future time the reserve balance will be at the desired level.

2. The depreciation rate may be changed and the reserve balance adjusted for the full discrepancy, with concurrent adjustment to the earned surplus account.

3. The depreciation reserve and the earned surplus accounts may be adjusted to bring the reserve balance to the desired level without altering the depreciation rate.

Which method is used to adjust the depreciation reserve account balance for deficiencies or excesses from past allocations is dependent largely upon what factors caused it to be out of line with present ages, average service life, and estimated salvage value. Income tax authorities will have an interest in such adjustment if depreciation rates are changed; regulatory commissions will have much to say concerning such adjustments for utilities.

ACCOUNTING PROCEDURES RELATED TO DEPRECIATION RETURNS

Regardless of the method adopted for making the annual depreciation allocation, the company undertakes certain obligations with respect to the depreciation returns (allocations). These obligations and the ultimate effect on the balance sheet statement are discussed next.

10.14. Depreciation Returns and Their Disposition. By making each year a depreciation allocation to expense before net profits, the owners of an industrial property can assure the return of the investment in the property concurrently with the utilization of its useful service, provided, of course, that the depreciation charges are earned through income.

The obligation to recoup the investment in an industrial property by depreciation charges rests entirely upon its management. All depreciation charges against income should be treated as obligated to the purpose of returning to the business the total cost of the property by the date of retirement (that is, the cost less the salvage realized).

Once the investment in depreciable property has been recovered through depreciation returns, these returns may be handled as follows:

1. *Current replacement costs.* Pay each year out of the current annual depreciation return, so far as it is sufficient, the cost of replacement property.

2. *Improvements and enlargements of the physical property of the enterprise.* Annual depreciation return should be invested in improvements and enlargements of plant if possible. Such investments are in lieu of new capital, which it otherwise would be necessary to procure.

3. *Working capital.* Depreciation returns may be used to increase the working capital of the enterprise by retaining them in cash or by the purchase of supplies, raw materials, or other current assets.

4. *Depreciation fund.* To the extent a sinking fund is really needed, limited fractions of the depreciation return may be invested in a depreciation fund. Such funds are for the purpose of guarding against occasional excessive demands for cash with which to make replacements.

5. *Reduce the funded debt.* Depreciation returns may be used, when desirable, to reduce the funded debt of the enterprise through the purchase of outstanding bonds.

6. *Buying back from stockholders part of their equity.* Depreciation returns left after wise investments of the character described in (1), (2), (3), and (4) may be returned to the stockholders of the enterprise. Whether so admitted at the time or not, such payments to the stockholders have the effect of decreasing the stockholders' true equity in the concern's property; this should be made clear at the time, both to the stockholders and to the public, in the regular financial statements of the enterprise.

10.15. Depreciation Reserve Account. The depreciation reserve account is a balance sheet book account to which all depreciation allocations charged to production expense accounts are credited and to which the book costs new of the retirements are debited at the dates of retirement. Other entries relating to the salvage value realized are made in accordance with the specific accounting policies of the enterprise. Thus, the depreciation reserve account balance shows the total accounting accrued depreciation allocations on the existing property. This total accrued accounting depreciation is that which was charged in the past to production expense as an allocation for the consumption of the service usefulness of the existing property. The depreciation reserve account is merely a book account, not a cash reserve at all.

10.16. Illustration of Current Depreciation Accounting. The results of current depreciation accounting procedure as it is related to depreciation expense, the depreciation reserve account, and a depreciation fund are illustrated in Tables 10.1 and 10.2.

Assume:

1. That the original cost of a certain property X, on January 1, the first year of its operation, was $1,000,000.

2. That no additions or improvements were made with newly contributed capital during the first 5 years of operation.

3. That the yearly depreciation allocations from income, the yearly investments in depreciable property, and the yearly additions to the depreciation reserve account were as shown in Table 10.1 during the first 5 years of operation.

It should be noted, in connection with Table 10.1, that all differences between the cost of the property retired and added the same year are added algebraically to the investment.

It was found to be wise to allocate $13,000 during the first 5 years to establish a small depreciation fund. The depreciation fund interest

TABLE 10.1. DEPRECIATION ACCOUNTING DATA FOR PROPERTY X

	Depreciation reserve account			Disposition of depreciation return			
Year	Depreciation allocations (credits)	Retirement of property at cost (debits)	Net accruals to depreciation reserve account	Original cost of replacements, betterments, and other additions to property	Payments to actual depreciation fund	Added to working capital	Net increase in capital investment
(1)	(2)	(3)	(4)	(5)	(6)	(7)	(8)
First..........	$15,000	$ 1,000	$14,000	$ 8,000	$ 1,000	$ 6,000	$ 7,000
Second........	16,000	3,000	13,000	11,000	2,000	3,000	8,000
Third..........	18,000	4,000	14,000	19,000	4,000	−5,000	15,000
Fourth........	21,000	6,000	15,000	16,000	1,000	4,000	10,000
Fifth..........	25,000	3,000	22,000	18,000	5,000	2,000	15,000
Total........	$95,000	$17,000	$78,000	$72,000	$13,000	$10,000	$55,000

earned was turned into the general income, instead of being kept in the fund accumulating at compound interest.

The yearly depreciation returns not required for increasing the depreciation fund were invested in additions to the property or in improvement of existing units or retained as working capital. The depreciation reserve is fully balanced at all times by property assets (including the depreciation fund); and the investment in the enterprise is maintained within the business.

TABLE 10.2. CAPITAL ACCOUNTANCY DATA FOR PROPERTY X

Beginning of year	Working capital, accrued change	Depreciation fund balance	Capital investment account balance	Accrued accounting depreciation	Net remaining investment in physical plant	Total investment, plant plus working capital plus depreciation fund
(1)	(2)	(3)	(4)	(5)	(6)	(7)
First........	$ 0	$ 0	$1,000,000	$ 0	$1,000,000	$1,000,000
Second......	6,000	1,000	1,007,000	14,000	993,000	1,000,000
Third.......	9,000	3,000	1,015,000	27,000	988,000	1,000,000
Fourth......	4,000	7,000	1,030,000	41,000	989,000	1,000,000
Fifth........	8,000	8,000	1,040,000	56,000	984,000	1,000,000
Sixth.......	10,000	13,000	1,055,000	78,000	977,000	1,000,000

From the yearly depreciation accounting data in Table 10.1 starting with a cost new of the entire property of $1,000,000, Table 10.2 has been prepared, showing the resulting book capital accounts of the property each year, to the beginning of the sixth year of operation.

The cost new of the existing property increases each year owing to the additions and improvements. In spite of these increases the unallocated cost decreases, in the case of this property, owing to the increase in the accumulated yearly net allocations.

CHAPTER 11

Depreciation in Valuation

Depreciation as a cost is discussed in Chaps. 8 and 10. Of the three concepts of depreciation—cost, value, and physical condition—cost accounting is by far the most frequently referred to. In valuation procedure there is some uncertainty of the proper role of value depreciation, because its application to valuation is confused with its application to accounting. In this chapter depreciation methods are considered as they relate to valuation work. Further clarification of cost depreciation and value depreciation is made.

11.1. Depreciation as a Factor in Value. Despite the popular concept that depreciation is a loss, a decrease, or a lessening in value, depreciation is only infrequently measured in terms of value. When value of a particular property is sought, such value may be determined directly without estimating value depreciation. For example, a real estate appraiser establishes value, usually market value, directly by judging the worth of the property at the time and for the specific purpose at hand. He does not estimate depreciation and then subtract this estimate from another value to get present value. The decrease in value in this instance would be of only academic interest. However, value is frequently arrived at by finding replacement cost, then adjusting this cost for depreciation.

There is no logic in starting with original cost, subtracting an allowance for depreciation, and supposedly getting value as a remainder. When the allowance for the depreciation subtracted is on a cost basis, the answer is unallocated cost, not value. Should the appraiser attempt to estimate value depreciation and subtract this estimate from original cost to get present value, his answer would have little significance for the reason that cost less value is an anomaly—somewhat similar to subtracting francs from dollars without introducing a conversion factor.

A third scheme is to estimate the present value and subtract this value from original cost to get depreciation. The difference would be another abstract quantity of no significance, except in two special applications. In determining the depreciable cost of a property, an estimated salvage value is subtracted from original cost to obtain that portion of original cost which is to be or which should have been recovered through cost depreciation allocations. In this application, the salvage value is that remaining portion of original cost recoverable at retirement date through sale of the property or by transfer to another use. The second special application of subtracting value from cost is in engineering economy studies.   A machine now in use is being compared with a prospective new machine.   The present value (usually market value as a secondhand machine) is used as the base for setting up the annual depreciation cost of the existing machine.

To a lesser or greater degree the value of property fluctuates from day to day, certainly from year to year.   Annual value depreciation, therefore, also is a changing factor.   It may become appreciation, or negative depreciation, should the value of the property increase from one year to the next.   In the period starting at the close of the Second World War in 1945, many properties rose in dollar value, thus experiencing a negative value depreciation as compared with prior years.   In appraising property, however, in the years since 1945, the appraiser has not specifically estimated the increase in value and added this increase (negative depreciation) onto a value established at a prior time to get present value. Neither did he in the depression era of the 1930's estimate the decrease in value (positive depreciation) and subtract the decrease from a value previously established to get the present value.

Depreciation can be used correctly in the sense of value, but in the ordinary practice of estimating value, seldom is value depreciation estimated as such; rather, value depreciation is simply a quantity obtainable after the value sought has been determined for at least two conditions.

Recognition is due the common practice of estimating the value, usually at market price, of a property, say a machine tool, and then subtracting this value from the original cost of the property to get depreciation.   Such practice is proper in cost accounting and in economy studies. The depreciation so found, even though value is subtracted from cost, is in reality strictly a cost depreciation for the reason that the value subtracted is that portion of the original cost which need not be allocated as a production expense but which is recoverable directly through an exchange of property.

In estimating the value of simple properties there seems to be no need for estimating depreciation in the sense of a decrease in value.   In rate base determinations of public utilities a somewhat similar analysis, though more complicated, may be made.   Depreciation as a factor in value will be discussed in the next sections, beginning with a consideration of depreciation methods.

DEPRECIATION METHODS AND PROCEDURES APPLICABLE TO VALUATION

Chapter 9 presents several depreciation methods, mainly as they apply to cost allocations.   Chapter 9 includes reference to the application of depreciation methods to valuation procedures, but additional explanation is desirable, particularly for those methods based on service age and service life.

11.2. Good-as-new Method. Regardless of how well an old property performs its function and how little evidence it shows of wear and tear, such property cannot have a value as great as it would have if it were new. Every item of depreciable property in service is giving up part of its potential total service with every service it performs. Its capacity for rendering service is what gave it value in the first place. As this service usefulness is consumed, the property becomes worth less and less of what it would be worth if new. For example, a 5-hp motor, 8 years old, now operating at near its original efficiency, properly cannot be judged to be worth as much as an identical motor in new condition. The good-as-new theory is not tenable for the valuation process or for accounting purposes.

11.3. Direct Appraisal Method. For marketable goods and properties, a competent appraiser can, by shrewd judgment, determine fair values directly without the aid of recorded data, calculations, and comparisons. In fact, residential real estate, commercial buildings, industrial machinery, and automotive equipment are usually appraised in this manner. The appraiser, however, usually does not estimate depreciation separately, although he may be guided in his judgment by his estimate of what the replacement cost new would be. For appraisal purposes of properties not highly complicated, the direct appraisal method applied by skilled persons has a rightful place; where applicable, the depreciation adjustment for value may also be made by judgment without the aid of extensive recorded data.

11.4. Declining Balance and Sum of Digits Methods. Neither the declining balance nor the sum of the digits method has enough merit to warrant its use in valuation procedure. They are difficult of application to group properties, and the judgments and calculations required for application to single unit properties are such that these methods offer no advantage over the straight line and interest methods.

11.5. Straight Line and Interest Methods. Because the straight line, sinking fund, and present worth methods (Sec. 9.16) are identical, for the zero interest rate, they are considered together as applied to appraisals. In Secs. 9.10, 9.12, and 9.14 the following expressions were developed for the straight line, sinking fund, and present worth methods, respectively:

$$B_x = B_d \left(\frac{n - x}{n} \right) + V_s \tag{11.1}$$

$$B_x = B_d \left(\frac{(1 + i)^n - (1 + i)^x}{(1 + i)^n - 1} \right) + V_s \tag{11.2}$$

$$B_x = B_d \left(\frac{(1 + r)^n - (1 + r)^x}{(1 + r)^n - 1} \right) + V_s \qquad (11.3)$$

In Sec. 9.16, Eqs. (11.2) and (11.3) were shown to be equivalent to (11.1) when i and r were 0 percent rates. The factor

$$\frac{n - x}{n} \quad \text{or} \quad \frac{(1 + r)^n - (1 + r)^x}{(1 + r)^n - 1}$$

may be isolated and dealt with separately, because this factor controls the adjustment of B_d in accordance with n, x, and r or i. This factor may be called the *expectancy-life factor*[1] because it is the ratio of expectancy to service life when r and $i = 0$.

The basic equation may then be written

$$B_x = B_d \text{ (expectancy-life factor)} + V_s \qquad (11.4)$$

In Eq. (11.4), B_x is more realistically considered to be the unconsumed service than it is the unallocated service because, in the present valuation considerations, annual allocations are not made.

One other factor may be introduced in Eq. (11.4) for appraisal purposes. When Eq. (11.3) was derived in Sec. 9.14, a factor R was introduced in the derivation as the equivalent uniform annual operation return to replace the unequal annual operation returns R_1, R_2, and R_3, . . . , R_n. Although R drops out in the mathematical procedure, the final equation must be considered to be one applicable in a true mathematical sense only to an equal annual operation return. Perhaps, more often than otherwise, the services of a property may be worth less in its latter periods of use than in the periods of its early service. Especially is this true of operative machinery, which reduces in operating efficiency and increases in operating costs (exclusive of depreciation cost) with age.

The expectancy-life factor measures the reduction in usefulness only on a time or service unit basis, but not with regard to the *quality*, or *value*, of that service. This quality, or value, of the service may need recognition in appraisals and is in effect, when so recognized, an adjustment of the assumed R in the derivation to compensate for the fact that operation returns may not be uniform during the entire service life.

This adjustment factor may be termed the *service factor*, and, as such, the service factor is one of judgment to be introduced as the appraiser

[1] The term *condition percent* previously has been given to this factor, but *expectancy-life factor* is preferred because it is more descriptive of the ratio, it can be published in decimal form, and it is not so easily confused with the term percent condition used by some valuators to express a state of observed physical wear and tear. For prior use of the term condition percent see Robley Winfrey, "Condition-percent Tables for Depreciation of Unit and Group Properties," pp. 26–105, Iowa State College, Engineering Experiment Station, Bulletin 156, 1942.

may see need for its use.   The service factor may be less than unity or greater than unity; its main function is to compensate, when necessary, for failure of the expectancy-life factor to produce the desired adjustment of the base new to current conditions.   Equation (11.4) may be further modified as follows:

$$B_x = B_d \text{ (expectancy-life factor) (service factor)} + V_s \qquad (11.5)$$

Equation (11.5) may be considered as a valuation formula by which an estimated replacement cost or a reproduction cost on a new basis can be adjusted to the condition of the existing property to compensate for reduced usefulness of the existing property as compared with the usefulness of the property if new.

11.6. Expectancy-life Factors for Single Units.   The factor $(n - x)/n$ in Eq. (11.1) when applied to single units of property may be easily calculated from the estimated probable life of the unit n and its age x.   When use of interest rates is desirable, the factor

$$\frac{(1 + r)^n - (1 + r)^x}{(1 + r)^n - 1}$$

must be solved.   For single units these two factors have been solved and published[1] for all probable lives from 1 to 100.   Appendix C.1 gives these solutions in decimal form for probable lives of 1 to 100 and interest rates of 0, 2, 5, and 8 percent.

11.7. Expectancy-life Factors for Property Groups.   Although the factors $\dfrac{n - x}{n}$ and $\dfrac{(1 + r)^n - (1 + r)^x}{(1 + r)^n - 1}$ are solved directly and used in Eq. (11.5) for single units of property, their solution for groups of units is arithmetically more involved.   The factors may be solved in such a way that they are applicable to units all of the same age—a vintage group—but not to a group of mixed ages.   Two procedures are available, but the results are not identical.   The unit summation procedure gives factors somewhat less than the average life procedure.

The unit summation procedure results in a factor at any chosen age of the vintage group which is the weighted average expectancy-life factor for the units surviving at that age.   By this method any continuous property group in a nongrowing constant condition of stability (a matured condition of the group wherein the number of units in service and the average age of those units are both constant year to year) will have a composite factor of exactly 0.50 for the zero interest rate.   This procedure

[1] For complete tables of these factors in percent see:
  Anson Marston and Thomas R. Agg, "Engineering Valuation," 1st ed., pp. 536–615, New York, McGraw-Hill Book Company, Inc., 1936.
  Winfrey, *loc. cit.*

gives full weight to the units of the group on the basis that each unit is evaluated separately in accordance with its specific expectancy.

The average life procedure results in a factor at any chosen age of the vintage group which is the expectancy-life factor for the average survivor at that age.   By this procedure any continuous property group in a nongrowing constant condition of stability will have a composite factor of more than 0.50 at zero interest, the amount being dependent upon the shape of the survivor curve applying to the group.   The average life procedure at zero interest is identical in result with what is obtained in the ordinary accounting procedure with the straight line method when the depreciation rate, $1/n$, is applied to the average survivors during each year.   The average life procedure valuates the vintage group on the basis of the unit-years of service of the group without regard to a specific unit.   It allocates equal cost to each unit of service.

When examined in the light of depreciation accounting, the unit summation method provides that each unit of the group build up its own reserve credit to 100 percent by its retirement date; the average life method depends upon the units surviving past average life to build up greater than a 100 percent reserve to compensate for the failure of the earlier than average life retirements to build up their full reserve.

Tables 11.1 and 11.2 illustrate the two calculation procedures for zero interest when applied to a 10-year average service life group.

Tables of the unit summation factors for the 18 Iowa type survivor curves at interest rates of 0, 2, 4, 6, and 8 percent and average service lives of 10, 20, 25, 30, 40, and 50 years have been published.[1]   Similar tables for the average life method have not been published, though the zero interest tables have been computed.[2]

Specimen tables for the unit summation procedure are in Appendix C.2 and for the average life method in Appendix C.3.

11.8. Interest Methods of Finding Depreciation in Valuation. The fundamental basis of value is the present worth of the future returns, benefits, or satisfactions, and in placing a value on a property or service, an interest discount factor is applied in order to get the present worth of values that lie in the future.   But if depreciation is defined as a decrease in value, there is reason to expect that such decrease should be measured by the difference in values established for two different calendar times or under two different service conditions.

As explained in Sec. 11.1, value depreciation need not be determined in the process of finding the value of a property.   Therefore, the sinking fund or other interest method of estimating depreciation need not be applied in the valuation process, because value of the property is estab-

---

[1] Winfrey, *op. cit.*, pp. 107–177.
[2] Robley Winfrey, unpublished work.

TABLE 11.1.   CALCULATION OF EXPECTANCY-LIFE FACTORS FOR IOWA TYPE CURVE R_3, 10 YEARS AVERAGE SERVICE LIFE, 0 PERCENT INTEREST RATE, AND UNIT SUMMATION PROCEDURE

Age interval, years	Probable life of retirements during age interval,* years	Retirements during age interval, percent	Expectancy-life factor for each retirement group remaining in service at age x							
			$x=1$	$x=2$	$x=3$	$x=4$	$x=5$	$x=6$	$x=7$	$x=8$
(1)	(2)	(3)	(4)	(5)	(6)	(7)	(8)	(9)	(10)	(11)
0–1	0.56436	0.22845	0.000000							
1–2	1.55541	0.47264	0.357083	0.000000						
2–3	2.54789	0.88416	0.607518	0.215037	0.000000					
3–4	3.54147	1.51920	0.717631	0.435263	0.152894	0.000000				
4–5	4.53611	2.42948	0.779547	0.559094	0.338640	0.118187	0.000000			
5–6	5.53196	3.66659	0.819232	0.638464	0.457697	0.276929	0.096161	0.000000		
6–7	6.52917	5.30665	0.846841	0.693682	0.540524	0.387365	0.234206	0.081047	0.000000	
7–8	7.52709	7.46469	0.867147	0.734293	0.601440	0.468586	0.335733	0.202879	0.070026	0.000000
8–9	8.52387	10.18444	0.882682	0.765365	0.648047	0.530730	0.413412	0.296094	0.178777	0.061459
9–10	9.51724	13.10162	0.894928	0.789855	0.684783	0.579710	0.474638	0.369565	0.264493	0.159420
10–11	10.50597	15.12407	0.904816	0.809632	0.714448	0.619264	0.524080	0.428896	0.333712	0.238528
11–12	11.49034	14.83774	0.912970	0.825941	0.738911	0.651881	0.564852	0.477822	0.390793	0.303763
12–13	12.47209	11.85630	0.919821	0.839642	0.759463	0.679284	0.599105	0.518926	0.438747	0.358568
13–14	13.45391	7.59101	0.925672	0.851344	0.777016	0.702689	0.628361	0.554033	0.479705	0.405377
14–15	14.43284	3.86502	0.930714	0.861427	0.792141	0.722854	0.653568	0.584281	0.514995	0.445709
15–16	15.38167	1.33156	0.934988	0.869975	0.804963	0.739950	0.674938	0.609925	0.544913	0.479900
16–17	16.21569	0.13638	0.938331	0.876663	0.814994	0.753325	0.691657	0.629988	0.568319	0.506651
A. Σ[col. (3) $\times$ col. (4)]; Σ[col. (3) $\times$ col. (5)]; etc.			88.50884	77.38136	66.579415	56.164324	46.229986	36.892960	28.291241	20.588554
B. Percent surviving at age x			99.77155	99.29891	98.41475	96.89555	94.46607	90.79948	85.49283	78.02814
C. Expectancy-life factor at age $x = A \div B$			0.887115	0.779277	0.676519	0.579638	0.489382	0.406312	0.330919	0.263861

* Probable life of each retirement group for each age interval was determined by weighting the mid-point of the interval by frequencies for each 1 percent of average life, for the type curve at 100 years average service life.

TABLE 11.1. CALCULATION OF EXPECTANCY-LIFE FACTORS FOR IOWA TYPE CURVE R_3, 10 YEARS AVERAGE SERVICE LIFE, 0 PERCENT INTEREST RATE, AND UNIT SUMMATION PROCEDURE.—(Continued)

Expectancy-life factor for each retirement group remaining in service at age x

Age interval, years	$x = 9$	$x = 10$	$x = 11$	$x = 12$	$x = 13$	$x = 14$	$x = 15$	$x = 16$
(1)	(12)	(13)	(14)	(15)	(16)	(17)	(18)	(19)
0–1								
1–2								
2–3								
3–4								
4–5								
5–6								
6–7								
7–8								
8–9	0.000000							
9–10	0.054348	0.000000						
10–11	0.143344	0.048160	0.000000					
11–12	0.216733	0.129704	0.042674	0.000000				
12–13	0.278389	0.198210	0.118031	0.037852	0.000000			
13–14	0.331049	0.256722	0.182394	0.108066	0.033738	0.000000		
14–15	0.376422	0.307136	0.237849	0.168563	0.099276	0.029990	0.000000	
15–16	0.414888	0.349876	0.284863	0.219851	0.154838	0.089826	0.024813	0.000000
16–17	0.444982	0.383313	0.321645	0.259976	0.198307	0.136639	0.074970	0.013301
A	13.977493	8.656950	4.759621	2.248814	0.8730304	0.2541554	0.0432644	0.00181399
B	67.84370	54.74208	39.61801	24.78027	12.92397	5.33296	1.46794	0.13638
C	0.206025	0.158141	0.120138	0.090750	0.067551	0.047657	0.029473	0.013301

lished in a procedure not requiring that value depreciation be first established.

In rate base determination as a phase of public utility regulation, the depreciation adjustment on reproduction cost is usually made on the

TABLE 11.2. CALCULATION OF EXPECTANCY-LIFE FACTORS FOR IOWA TYPE CURVE R_3, 10 YEARS AVERAGE SERVICE LIFE, 0 PERCENT INTEREST RATE AND AVERAGE LIFE PROCEDURE

Age, years	Percent surviving at age	Interval area 1 year to right of age,* %-years	Remaining area under curve to right of age, %-years $\Sigma(3)$	Expectancy of survivors at age, years $(4) \div (2)$	Expectancy-life factor $(5) \div 10$
(1)	(2)	(3)	(4)	(5)	(6)
0	100.00000	99.90048	1000.00000	10.0000	1.00000
1	99.77155	99.56142	900.09952	9.0216	0.90216
2	99.29891	98.89917	800.53810	8.0619	0.80619
3	98.41475	97.71815	701.63893	7.1294	0.71294
4	96.89555	95.76854	603.92078	6.2327	0.62327
5	94.46607	92.74996	508.15224	5.3792	0.53792
6	90.79948	88.30095	415.40228	4.5749	0.45749
7	85.49283	81.96270	327.10133	3.8261	0.38261
8	78.02814	73.17902	245.13863	3.1417	0.31417
9	67.84370	61.51876	171.95961	2.5346	0.25346
10	54.74208	47.27033	110.44085	2.0175	0.20175
11	39.61801	32.05581	63.17052	1.5945	0.15945
12	24.78027	18.52121	31.11471	1.2556	0.12556
13	12.92397	8.77860	12.59350	0.9744	0.09744
14	5.33296	3.14088	3.81490	0.7153	0.07153
15	1.46794	0.64460	0.67402	0.4592	0.04592
16	0.13638	0.02942	0.02942	0.2157	0.02157

* Interval areas calculated from the probable lives given in column (2) of Table 11.1, which procedure is more accurate than assuming that the average percent surviving between two ages is the simple average of the two percents surviving.

zero interest method. The objective is to find the proportional part of the reproduction cost new which would not have been recovered in the accounting process had the depreciation base been reproduction cost. The concept here is still one of cost, not one of value. But if value were the objective, rather than merely finding an adjustment equivalent to the accounting depreciation, the use of the present worth theory would be appropriate. The expectancy-life factor to use in Eq. (11.5) would then be chosen for the proper rate of fair return.

On the other hand, when other than a rate base is being determined, value may be the objective. For certain types of properties or enterprises, the earning value may be established as one of the evidences of value. To be comparable evidence, the value of the physical property on a replacement cost base also should be made on a present worth basis.

Whether to use a zero interest basis or a fair rate of return basis in the selection of the expectancy-life factor [Eq. (11.5)] depends on the purpose of the appraisal. The important factor is whether present value to the owner is sought or whether the present investment (depreciation base less an allowance for consumed usefulness) in the property is wanted on the basis of what it would be had the present replacement cost new been the depreciation base in the accounting process. The replacement cost concept is that most frequently used, and so interest rates as a factor in depreciation are seldom needed.

11.9. Procedure for Finding the Adjusted Cost. Regardless of whether original cost, replacement cost, or reproduction cost is to be adjusted for depreciation, the same basic information is needed, and the procedure of calculation is the same. The following outlines a step-by-step procedure (see also Sec. 7.21 for methods of estimating service life).

1. From an examination of the book records, discussion with the operating personnel, and inspection of the property unit or vintage group, determine and make a record of the following information:

   a. Year of installation of the unit or vintage group
   b. Past service conditions—mild, favorable, average, unfavorable, or severe
   c. Probable future service conditions—mild, favorable, average, unfavorable, or severe
   d. Physical condition of the property for its age—excellent, good, average, poor, or bad
   e. Probable future service factor
   f. Salvage value in percentage of the base or in dollars

2. Determine the average life of the vintage group and the appropriate type survivor curve; for a single unit determine its probable service life and type survivor curve applicable to property of its type (see the 6-step process in Sec. 7.21).

NOTE: The average service life of the vintage group should be determined when possible from an analysis of the retirement experience of the company in accordance with the methods described in Chap. 7. When the data for such analysis are not available, recourse is to other similar experience or to judgment.

3. Determine the dollar base which is to be adjusted for depreciation—original cost new, replacement cost new, reproduction cost new, or other basis.

4. Determine the expectancy-life factor by solution of $\dfrac{n - x}{n}$ or $\dfrac{(1 + r)^n - (1 + r)^x}{(1 + r)^n - 1}$, or select the factors from appropriate tables.

5. Find the adjusted cost B_x by solution of the equation

$$B_x = (B - V_s) \text{ (expectancy-life factor) (service factor)} + V_s$$

DEPRECIATION IN RATE BASE DETERMINATIONS

Of all the controversial factors that have entered rate base determinations in public utility regulation, depreciation is one of the foremost. Regardless of whether original cost, reproduction cost, or fair value becomes the main evidence in establishing the rate base, depreciation is an important factor.

11.10. Original Cost Depreciation. When original cost is to be the rate base, there follows the need of estimating the depreciation to be deducted. Three possibilities prevail: the deduction from original cost may be (1) the depreciation reserve account credit balance, (2) what the depreciation reserve balance would be under a carefully conducted age-life study to arrive at the depreciation costs which appropriately could have been allocated to the date of valuation, and (3) an allowance based on the so-called "observed depreciation." The following discussion is based entirely upon the straight line zero interest method of estimating depreciation.

Whether or not the depreciation reserve account credit balance should be deducted from original cost to arrive at an original cost rate base is conditioned by the past regulations under which the utility was permitted to build up the reserve. Certainly it would be unfair to the company to deduct its reserve should it on its own initiative have allocated more annual depreciation than that stipulated by the commission in its prior orders. The goal desired is to subtract from original cost only that amount of original cost recovered by the company through depreciation returns paid by the customers under regulated rates. These depreciation returns lessen the company's investment used for benefit of the customers, and therefore the customers should not be required to pay a return on that investment which they have already liquidated. Thus, this first case reduces itself to a determination of the amount of depreciation return provided by the customers under rates stipulated by the commission.

The second possibility would be to deduct from original cost an allowance for depreciation, based on the ages of the properties and their service lives. Should age-life depreciation be deducted on the basis of the ages of the properties at date of valuation and the service lives then estimated, the amount of deduction would be realistic in so far as it would be an accurate estimate of the correct cost depreciation which should have been allocated; but such deduction may not be fair to either the customers or the company. The amount of depreciation credited to the reserve on the date of valuation could be more or less than the amount then determined by the age-life study. If the estimated amount was more than that permitted under regulation, the company would be penalized, and if the age-life estimate of depreciation was less than the accrual permitted by the commission (and realized by the company), the deduction would be unfair to the customers.

Under the third possibility, the "observed depreciation," so called, would have no significance whatsoever. Observed depreciation as a measure of consumed service usefulness is inadequate unless the factors of life, age, obsolescence, company policies, and other factors not physically observable are considered along with the observed state of wear and tear.

In this analysis of original cost depreciation in an original cost rate base determination there has been no mention of value. Value is not a factor here. The objective is solely one of determining how much of the original cost of the property remains as a present investment used and useful in rendering the service purchased by the customers. The cost depreciation to be deducted is determined by study of the past depreciation rates used by the company, whether or not prescribed by regulatory authority, currently allowed annual depreciation, the age-life consumption of useful service to date, and other factors.

11.11. Reproduction Cost Depreciation. Reproduction cost adjusted for depreciation is one of the evidences of value (Chap. 2). Under the *Smyth v. Ames* fair value doctrine, reproduction cost less depreciation has been accorded great weight in establishing the rate base for regulated utilities. The depreciation to deduct in such reproduction cost rate base determinations could be estimated by using (1) the identical age-life relationships applied in estimating original cost depreciation, (2) the same percentage of the reproduction cost new as was found for original cost depreciation, or (3) observed depreciation on the existing property.

In dealing with reproduction cost, the conditions of the existing property are assumed throughout in the application of the reproduction cost concept (see Sec. 6.3). Therefore, the age-life relationships of the existing property are the logical ones to apply to the reproduction cost study in finding the depreciation adjustment.

In a rate base study, the original cost depreciation deduction might not be decided on a strict age-life basis because of other pertinent factors.

When the age-life relationship is not used in the original cost depreciation study, a proper procedure in the reproduction cost study would be to deduct the same percentage as found in the original cost study.

Observed depreciation in reproduction cost studies is just as unreal as it is in original cost and, therefore, not applicable.

In a reproduction cost study for a rate base determination, a depreciation adjustment in the sense of value does not enter the considerations. There is no attempt to estimate a value as a value. The emphasis is entirely upon estimating a cost which may be used as an evidence of value to be established or as an evidence of what the rate base should be, without relating it to value of the property. This conclusion is the same as reached in the discussion of the original cost rate base.

11.12. Depreciation Adjustment in Determining a Fair Value Rate Base. When fair value is established as the rate base, it is to be presumed that all the evidences of value were accorded their just and right weight in arriving at the fair value. The original cost of the property and the reproduction cost of the property, each separately adjusted for consumed usefulness, were necessarily considered as evidences of value. Therefore, in this process of establishing a fair value rate base, a separate adjustment of the fair value for depreciation is not a necessary or logical step.

Since fair value of the property is being sought, it follows that the adjustment of original cost for depreciation should be consistent in amount with the existing consumed usefulness of the property. As explained in the previous section, the adjustment of reproduction cost for depreciation should be at the same percentage as found in the age-life analysis applied to the original cost study. However, as stated in Sec. 11.10, proper consideration is to be given to any excess or deficiency in the depreciation reserve account and to the actions, orders, and practices that caused such excess or deficiency.

11.13. Annual Depreciation, Accrued Depreciation, and Reserve Balance Relationships. The total depreciation to date of valuation (accrued depreciation) deducted from the original cost or reproduction cost should be in harmony with the cost depreciation found for the annual depreciation allocation.[1] As explained in Chaps. 9 and 10, the unconsumed usefulness of a property and its depreciation reserve ratio at any time bear a definite relationship to the ages of the properties and the annual depreciation rate, or rates, used in cost accounting during the past accounting periods. Consider a water tower now 30 years old for which a probable life of 40 years and a cost depreciation rate of 2.5

---

[1] See National Association of Railroad and Utilities Commissioners, "Report of Committee on Depreciation," pp. 154–170, Washington, D.C., National Association of Railroad and Utilities Commissioners, 1943.

percent has been used. The depreciation reserve account balance would be 75 percent of the cost base, corresponding to an expectancy-life factor of 0.25. In rate cases, valuators have reported a percent condition of 50 to 90 percent for property corresponding to this water tower. Yet at the same time they found that the annual depreciation for this water tower should be at the rate of 2.5 percent. No consistency was maintained in the relationship between annual depreciation rate for operating cost purposes and accrued depreciation for rate base purposes. Yet for rate base purposes the depreciation deducted to arrive at a rate basis should be in harmony with the annual allocation of cost for depreciation. The same factor in each case is being measured.

No doubt the many rate cases heard by the commissions and courts in which wide variances existed between annual depreciation expense and accrued depreciation to be deducted in the rate base determination led to the use of age-life factors and abandonment of observed depreciation.

Consistency in annual depreciation and in depreciation adjustment in arriving at the rate base is highly desirable; likewise, the same consistency is desirable between the annual cost depreciation allocation and the depreciation reserve account balance. Although depreciation rates of necessity are based on forecasted service lives and salvage values, there is no reason why these rates should not be adjusted whenever there is evidence that experience is departing from forecasts.

What the depreciation reserve account balance should be at any time can be estimated within reasonable limits of error by an age-life analysis using expectancy-life factors as calculated by the methods explained in Secs. 11.5 to 11.7. Should the existing depreciation reserve balance be found excessive or deficient, an investigation should be made to discover whether past depreciation rates, average service lives, or salvage values were out of accord with current estimates of these factors.

The procedure of adjusting the rates or adjusting the depreciation reserve account balance to correct for past excesses or deficiencies is not discussed here because it is an accounting matter within a given company or a policy for utility commissions to handle in each separate case (see Secs. 10.12 and 10.13). The depreciation reserve account balance and the annual cost depreciation allocation should always be held to a consistent relationship. When this consistency is maintained, consistency between the annual depreciation provision and the rate base adjustment for depreciation can be achieved easily.

DEPRECIATION IN APPRAISALS

Many appraisals of property are conducted by the process of adjusting replacement cost new for the consumed usefulness of the property being appraised.   Especially is this process followed when the market price for the used, or nonnew, property is not established by frequent current sales.   An age-life factor is ordinarily used in making the adjustments.

11.14. Depreciation in Insurance, Estates, Condemnations, and Assessments.   The establishment of the value of property in the settlement of insurance, estates, condemnations, and assessments is usually a process of estimating the value on a market basis.   To arrive at such value, replacement cost of either new or used property may be first established.   When the replacement cost new is established, some allowance for the consumption of the service usefulness of the old property is desirable.   A depreciation factor is here applied to the cost of replacement new to arrive at the present value of the property whose value is sought.

Insurance claim adjusters allow in this way for the service in property which has been utilized from the date of original purchase to the date of damage.   The ordinary age-life straight line method is applied in computing the depreciation factor, mainly because of established custom, but also because the concept is one of "What percentage of his original cost should the owner have written off to expense in the past?"

11.15. Depreciation in Valuation—Summary.   This chapter endeavors to show that although the word depreciation is popularly defined as a decrease in value, it is seldom employed in valuation procedures in the strict sense of value.   On the contrary, cost depreciation is employed, or depreciation is measured in terms of the useful service consumed. Value is established through exercise of judgment applied to all the factors and evidences that pertain to value.   In this process, depreciation as a value in itself is not often determined.   *Value depreciation is therefore only an end by-product of the valuation procedure, not a factor within the procedure.*

CHAPTER 12

Valuation of Land

Frequently, in connection with the appraisal of a utility or manufacturing establishment or building, it is necessary that the value of a plot of land be established, exclusive of buildings or other construction. In many such instances it is convenient and economical to employ specialists in land appraisal, but there are cases where the engineer himself desires to make or check the valuation. For this reason a brief summary of the principles and procedure of land valuation, particularly business and industrial lands, is presented.

Special problems related to the value of land are often encountered, such as the taxable value of land, the value of land used as right of way (or abandoned as right of way), or the value of discarded lands. A brief discussion of each of these problems is included.

12.1. Basis of Appraisal of Land. The art of appraisal of land has developed materially in the past quarter century, and much has been written[1] on the subject. In general the value of land can be estimated correctly from but two bases: first, and most important, the fair market value of similar adjacent land; second, the value based on the reasonably anticipated earnings to be derived from the land.

Fortunately, of all the properties which are freely exchanged, probably no item is more often bought and sold than land. As a result, the appraiser should have abundant data at hand from which he can estimate what should be a fair market price for the land at hand. Two pressing questions, however, must be answered in order that he may be sure of his estimate:

1. How optimistic or pessimistic is the present level of market prices which have been used as a basis of the estimate (Sec. 12.2)?

[1] J. M. Cleminshaw Company, "The Revaluation of Municipalities," New York, J. M. Cleminshaw Company, 1938.

National Association of Assessing Officers, "Urban Land Appraisal," Chicago, National Association of Assessing Officers, 1940.

William G. Murray, "Farm Appraisal," 2d ed. rev., Ames, Iowa, The Iowa State College Press, 1950.

Winfred L. Prouty, Clem W. Collins, and Frank H. Prouty, "Appraisers and Assessors Manual," 1st ed., New York, McGraw-Hill Book Company, Inc., 1930.

2. How representative of the specific land being appraised are those lands whose prices are to form the basis of the estimate (Sec. 12.3)?

If these questions are answered so that the appraiser is confident that his prices are fair and that his price data relate to similar lands, he has a reliable estimate of the value of the land.

The second basis of value, the present worth of the anticipated earnings, is applicable under certain conditions. It is undoubtedly applicable when the land itself produces the earnings, such as a farm (where the improvements, such as fences and buildings, are relatively minor), a truck garden or grove of fruit, or a lot used for the parking of automobiles. It is also applicable when the land is leased to another to serve as the site of an income-producing structure. But the value of land based on anticipated earnings cannot be fairly estimated when the business or factory building and the land are owned as a unit because there are no data available to show just what portion of the total return can be attributed solely to the land. Of course, an analyst can estimate what might be a fair rental for the land, but such a figure would undoubtedly be based on what similar lands can command as rent, which in turn is based on market value!

Generally, the original cost of land has little relation to its value at some materially later date. The change (either an increase or a decrease) in the value of a parcel of land since its acquisition can be determined only by comparison with the present market price of similar lands; thus, no additional evidence of value has been presented. The cost of replacement or of reproduction as an evidence of value of land is not appropriate for the reason that land is not reproducible. The appraiser will, for the most part, use the fair market price of similar land as the basis for his appraisal of land.

12.2. Estimating a Fair Price Level for Land. What is a *fair* price level? Information indicating the relative price levels prevailing at the date of valuation is most appropriate. Has the real estate market been brisk? It may be that lands are being sold at speculative prices as a natural consequence of overoptimism on the part of buyers in a period of prosperity; it may be that the demand for lands in the particular area appears to be a continuing one and that an increased general price level is warranted and probably permanent. However, the reverse may be the situation. In either case, the existing price level of land could be significantly different from a fair average price level. Thus, the appraiser should study his data thoroughly and avoid giving too much weight to the accumulated "hunches" of the buying public.

Another danger to be avoided is that of attempting to establish a fair price level at the date of valuation on the basis of inadequate data. The valuator should attempt to obtain the results of as many recent sales of similar lands as is consistent with the probable value of the property being appraised.   The enlightened opinion of qualified men who are willing to indicate what "a certain parcel of land might sell for" is useful, but generally information pertaining to recent sales is to be preferred.

In setting a fair price level at the date of valuation the valuator must take into consideration the long-time trend of prices, not only as these prices reflect fluctuations in the value of money, but also as these prices reflect the history of real estate values in the particular area.   Experience shows that land prices reflect considerably the general location of the land and its proximity to major streets, parks, schools, churches, transportation lines, business, and industrial districts.   The major business district, wherein are found the lands of highest value, frequently develops around some transportation nucleus and contains areas devoted to wholesale and retail business, theaters, hotels, and public properties of various types.   As cities have grown, this main business district has gradually expanded and around its boundaries (which are never clearly defined) is a fringe in which the properties are changing from a residential to a business use.   In the inner areas of the fringe, the prices of land may be increasing; on the other hand, the outer areas of the fringe probably will not be converted into a business district for some time (and at present are not desirable residential districts), and hence the prices of land may be stationary or decreasing.

Answering the question, "Is the price level which is proposed a *fair* one?" requires unbiased judgment, adequate price data, an understanding of the history and circumstances of the long-time variations of land prices in the specific area, and some knowledge of the probable immediate or long-time development of the area.

12.3. Tests of the Similarity of Land.   The answer to the question, "How representative of the specific land being appraised are those lands whose prices are to form the basis of the estimate?" requires the exercise of much judgment.   In this section a few of the procedures by which the answer is obtained are discussed.

Appraisal firms have developed ways to standardize the tests of similarity and thus reduce the probable range of errors of estimate.   One such firm[1] first classifies land into (1) business, (2) industrial, (3) residential, and (4) farm properties.   For each land classification, a list of pertinent factors affecting values has been prepared; for example, for residential urban land, values may differ from normal because of the following factors:

---

[1] E. H. Boeckh, "Boeckh's Manual of Appraisals," 4th ed., pp. 339–341, Indianapolis, The Rough Notes Company, Inc., 1945.

Land	Service	Distance to	Conditions
1. Depth	1. Paving	1. Schools	1. Zoning
2. Width	2. Sidewalks	2. Churches	2. Area development
3. Shape	3. Street lighting	3. Transportation	3. Classification
4. Topography	4. Telephone	4. Neighborhood shopping	4. Exposure
5. Street width	5. Sewers	5. Main shopping	5. Filled ground
6. Alley location	6. Water	6. Recreation	
7. Corner lot	7. Gas	7. Industrial establishments	
8. Elevation	8. Electricity		
	9. Transportation		
	10. Fire protection		

Thus, residential urban lands located in the same kind of zoned district, in areas developed to the same degree, having community services equally available, and with similar topographical features should most certainly be similar lands. Undoubtedly, if the data are at hand, the market values of the lands should check; even if the lands are not exactly similar, the appraiser's experience may indicate how much differential will exist for any specific dissimilarity.

A second example is taken from the appraisal of farm lands. Basically the farm has value because of its capacity to produce; therefore, the tests of similarity of land should be based on the soil productivity. A farm appraiser[1] examines the area carefully and divides up the farm by soil types, topography, drainage, depth of surface soil, and the like. A summary of these data for any two farms provides the appraiser with the information needed to test the similarity of the two areas.

Industrial land can be compared by analysis of such factors[2] as

Utility	Labor
1. Size	1. Proximity of labor
2. Shape	2. Wage rates
3. Topography	3. Labor supply
4. Accessibility	*Community*
a. Streets	1. Insurance rates
b. Railroads	2. Property tax rates
c. Waterways	3. Public attitudes
d. Material markets	*Public utilities*
e. Product markets	1. Available power
5. Advertising possibilities	2. Cost of power
	3. Water supply
	4. Drainage systems

"How closely do the price data obtained from general sources represent fair prices of the specific land being appraised?" is a question requiring tests of comparison for an answer. These tests are peculiar to the use of

---

[1] Murray, *op. cit.*, Chap. 1.
[2] Boeckh, *op. cit.*, pp. 359–360.

the land. Judgment and experience are important in the proper analyses of these tests.

12.4. Estimating the Value of Land Based on Earnings. Mention has been made of the fact that land produces earnings separate from the improvements thereon only in certain cases. The appraisal of farms and similar properties, one of these exceptions, is discussed in Sec. 12.6. Other cases are presented in this section.

Estimating the earning value of land is fundamentally the same as finding any other required estimate of value based on anticipated earnings (Chap. 16). The appraiser first predicts what the returns may reasonably be for the appropriate future period, and, second, he determines their present worth, using a discounting factor commensurate with the character and risks of the enterprise.

Suppose that the plot of land to be appraised is owned by an individual and leased to a corporation which has erected a warehouse on the land. The lease, which will expire in 25 years, provides for a specified annual rental on the land and contains an agreement for the renewal of the lease or the disposition of the building.

One might say that the value of land based on earnings is the present value of an annuity certain, or

$$P = (\text{annual rent} - \text{expenses}) \left[\frac{1.06^{25} - 1}{(0.06)(1.06^{25})} \right]$$

where 0.06 is a reasonable rate of return and the "expenses" are the property and income taxes on the land, plus any necessary management costs. This calculation, however, neglects the fact that the land has a capacity for producing returns for an indefinitely long period. Hence, consideration must be given to the probability that the existing returns can be continued beyond the 25-year period of the lease.

A second consideration is one relating to the size of the existing earnings. In addition, however, the appraiser needs data to indicate whether or not the land is developed to the most lucrative use possible in view of its location, for only on such a basis can he estimate the maximum value of the land. The existing warehouse may not permit such a development; perhaps an office building is justifiable. Thus, the appraiser needs to have studies at hand which may indicate these possibilities. Fortunately, most cities now are zoned into various types of districts, and city planning commissions have made the studies which the appraiser needs to examine. From such studies, he can view the potentialities of the location and can translate them into reasonable estimates of the highest probable returns to be expected from the land. He then is able to develop an estimate of the value of the land based on the most probable earnings.

This latter consideration is most appropriate when one is studying the value of a plot of land located in the main business district of a city and which is at present used as a parking lot for automobiles. It may be that an office building or a multistory garage erected on the land is a reasonable possibility, and one which should increase tremendously the anticipated earnings from the location.

The reader is reminded, however, of the opening statement of this section, namely, that land seldom produces earnings separate from the improvements thereon. Too often attempts are made to determine the value of land based on earnings when there is no way to determine just what portion of the total returns of the enterprise is attributable solely to the land. If one arbitrarily makes such a division, it is possible to calculate the value of the land separately from that of the construction upon it. Little is accomplished, however, for the sum of the two estimates thus determined will add up to the total calculated figure had there been no apportioning of the total earnings at all.

For example, assume that a house and lot is rented at a price which nets the owner $500 annually. The replacement cost of the house adjusted for depreciation is $7,000. Assume that the house has an expectancy of 50 years and that the fair rate of return is 0.05.

METHOD 1.   ANNUAL RETURN DIVIDED

Annual return after taxes		$500
Return at 5 percent on depreciated cost of house	$350	
Annuity at 5 percent required to amortize house cost in 50 years		
(7,000)(0.00478)	33	383
Remainder (assumed annual return attributed to the lot)		$117
Assumed capitalized value of land, 117/0.05	$2,340	
Depreciated cost of house	7,000	
Total	$9,340	

METHOD 2.   ANNUAL RETURN UNDIVIDED

Annual return after taxes	$500
Less annuity required to amortize house cost	33
Remainder	$467
Value of house and lot based on anticipated earnings, 467/0.05	$9,340

Summarizing, the appraiser can determine the value of land based on anticipated earnings provided that

1. He can obtain adequate data showing just what the land itself is producing in the way of an annual return.

2. He investigates the possibilities of the earnings of the land when it is put to its highest and best use.

3. He predicts these annual returns for as long a period as is reasonable.

12.5. Appraisal of Lands Owned by a Public Utility. The principles of appraisal of land mentioned in previous sections generally apply to public utility land as well as to other lands.

Legally, the basis of value of utility lands is the fair market value of abutting and adjacent lands of similar character. The United States Supreme Court stated this dictum in the *Consolidated Gas Case* and the *Minnesota Rate Cases*.[1] Subsequent decisions have indicated that additional allowances over and above market value, for possible severance damages to the land when the properties were purchased, will be excluded. Similarly, allowances for additional "plottage value"—an increase of value because several areas have been gathered together into one plot— must be excluded.[2]

In rate cases, however, the value of land is not always used as the allowance for land in the rate base. Of late there has arisen the practice of using the amount expended for the land at the time the land was first "dedicated to public use." It should be clear to the appraiser that such a figure may not be even close to the value of the land at the date of appraisal. However, as pointed out in Chap. 2, a rate base determination can be, and often is, based on factors which in themselves are not necessarily evidences of value, nor does the rate base necessarily have to be "fair value."

Thus, the value of lands owned by public utilities will be determined by the same methods as for lands owned by other agencies, though for rate-making purposes estimates other than valuation estimates may be used.

12.6. Appraisal of Farm Land. In his widely read text, Murray has developed a valuation procedure for the appraisal of farm land.[3] Basically, Murray obtains a value of the farm from the capitalization of the anticipated earnings of the land and next obtains a fair market value of the farm by comparison. With these two evidences of value at hand, the appraiser estimates the present value of the property. The following outline shows the essential detail of the procedure:

1. *Procure appraisal map.* This map should show the soil survey, kind of soil, slope, and depth of surface soil. An aerial photograph is a material aid in the whole process of farm valuation.

---

[1] *Willcox et al., Constituting The Public Service Commission of New York v. Consolidated Gas Co.* (No. 396), *City of New York v. Consolidated Gas Co. of New York* (No. 397), *Jackson, Attorney General of the State of New York v. Consolidated Gas Co.* (No. 398), 212 U.S. 19 (U.S. Sup. Ct. Jan. 4, 1909).

The Minnesota Rate Cases. Simpson et al., Constituting the Railroad and Warehouse Commission of the State of Minnesota v. Shepard (No. 291), *Same v. Kennedy* (No. 292), *Same v. Shillaber* (No. 293), 230 U.S. 352 (U.S. Sup. Ct. June 9, 1913).

[2] Claims for plottage value occur frequently in appraising land used as right of way for highways or railroads, dams, reservoir sites, and large industrial sites.

[3] Murray, *op. cit.*, Chap. 1.

2. *Estimate yield and select a rotation system.* The rotation system selected should maintain the present productivity of the farm. From yield data and rotation plan calculate the expected average annual yields—bushels of grain, tons of forage, etc.—over a period of years.

3. *Inventory and analyze the farm improvements.* Estimate the probable life of improvements or their probable annual substitute improvements.

4. *Translate yield of various areas into annual dollar income.* Use a properly weighted local average unit price for each crop produced. Consider the land to be rented on a crop-sharing basis, and determine the probable landlord income. Subtract the landlord's expenses (taxes, maintenance, crop expense, seed, insurance, etc.).

5. *Determine the earning value of the farm.* Capitalize the landlord's estimated return at an average fair rate of return (often 5 percent). Deduct any deferred maintenance on the improvements or any difference between the normal depreciated cost of the improvements and the present value of the most efficient substitute improvements.

6. *Compare the sale price of similar farms with the one being appraised.* Consider the significance of location with respect to permanent roads, communities, churches, schools, and markets.

7. *Estimate the value of the farm.* Give appropriate weight to the evidences of value obtained in steps 5 and 6.

12.7. Appraisal of Business and Industrial Land. The previous sections 12.1 to 12.6 include the principles applicable to the appraisal of all kinds of lands. In this section some of the problems peculiar to business and industrial lands are presented. The task of the appraiser is still to estimate a fair market value of similar adjacent land. However, the vocabulary of appraisal includes such terms as *unit value, depth factor, corner and alley benefits,* and the like, all of which are useful in the appraisal process described in this section.

The *unit of measurement of the value* of many industrial lands is frequently dollars per acre, although some business areas may be so valuable that they are priced in dollars per square foot. Many years ago the need of a common unit to which land values could be reduced led to the adoption of the unit value, or the fair price per foot of width of a rectangular lot whose depth was equal to the standard for that city.

The *standard depth* of a residential lot is generally 120 ft, although various other depths up to 150 ft have been used. For lots in the business district, 100 ft is the standard most used. Since the depths of lots vary widely, a conversion unit, relating the depth of any lot to the standard depth, is used. Such a unit is called the *depth factor.*

The value of the portion of a plot of land adjacent to a street is greater than the value of the portion remote from the street. It is generally agreed that the value gradually diminishes from front to rear, but not uniformly. Many theories have been advanced as to the law of this diminishing value, but none is universally accepted. Formulas suggested for the calculation of depth factors are:

1. Divide the standard depth into four equal parts. Forty percent of the value lies in the front section, 30 percent in the second section, 20 percent in the third section, and 10 percent in the rear section. For lots of greater depth than the standard, add 5 percent for an additional depth equal to one-fourth the standard depth.

For example, if the standard depth of a city lot is 100 ft, the depth factor for a lot 60 ft deep would be 0.78, for one 80 ft deep 0.92, and for one 120 ft deep 1.04.

2. Calculate the depth factor as the square root of the depth of the lot expressed in hundreds of feet.

For example, the depth factor for a lot 100 ft deep would be 1.00, for a lot 56 ft deep 0.75, for a lot 81 ft deep 0.90, and for a lot 121 ft deep 1.10.

Frequently, assessment boards of cities prepare depth factor tables which seem to fit their special problems more closely than the two formulas suggested above. An example is the set of depth factor tables prepared by the Tax Commission of Milwaukee, Wis., shown in Table 12.1 (page 261).

Consider now the unit value, that is, the fair market value, per front foot of an inside rectangular lot (one not subject to corner benefits) of a standard depth. Basically, the unit value is estimated for all similar lots in any area, using as data the fair average prices received in recent sales. Since so many lots are not of standard depths, a unit value for each may be determined by use of the formula

$$\text{Unit value} = \frac{\text{fair average price of a given lot}}{(\text{frontage of the lot})(\text{depth factor})}$$

The appraiser may find that there are not nearly enough sales to enable him to determine all of the required unit values. He must then use tests of similarity discussed in Sec. 12.3 as a means of estimating a quantitative differential between a known unit value and an unknown one. For example, business lots fronting on a street with curb and gutter and fully paved with best quality concrete should have a unit value 10 to 15 percent greater than one paved with tar-bound macadam or some 40 percent greater than one with no paving at all.[1] Further, other things being equal, a residential lot with sidewalks might have a unit value 10 percent greater than one without sidewalks. The cumulative effect of

[1] Boeckh, *op. cit.*, p. 353.

these several tests of similarity can be used without too much difficulty to translate a known unit value over to a lot with an unknown unit value.

Certain over-all guides can be mentioned. Unimproved lots may sell as low as $5 to $10 per front foot. Improvements which can make the lot a desirable one may cost an additional $10 to $30 per front foot. Another guide is the following table, which shows the relation of the sale price of a residential property, including house, to the normal unit value of the lot:[1]

Sale price of house and lot	Basic residential land value, fraction of sale price applicable to land value
$ 4,000	0.15–0.20
5,000	0.16–0.20
6,000	0.17–0.20
8,000	0.20
10,000	0.20
12,000	0.21
14,000	0.22
16,000	0.23
18,000	0.24
20,000	0.25
25,000	0.28
30,000	0.30
40,000	0.35
50,000	0.38

For example, if a certain type of house, situated on a 50- by 125-ft lot, sells for $10,000 on the average, the unit value of the lot should be about $39.20 (using a depth factor of 1.02).

Fortunately, the appraiser may obtain land-value maps to use as data for the determination of the unit value. These maps, generally prepared by a tax commission or by a land appraisal firm for use in determining the assessed value of the properties in a city, show the unit values for the lots in each block. These unit values are generally fixed on the basis of the prevailing market value of the properties at a certain date as evidenced by sales in the neighborhood, and after conferences with owners and many public hearings where real or imagined errors are ironed out. Often the most valuable plot of land in any district or zone is taken as a starting point, its unit value is determined, and then the other unit values are estimated by use of a quantitative differential between the known and the unknown. Although the unit values which are obtained from land-value maps are not to be considered authoritative,

[1] *Ibid.*, p. 347.

such figures afford the appraiser a good starting point for his quest to obtain a unit value for any specific lot.

The problem of relating lots of varying depths to the standard depth is not completely solved by the use of the depth factor tables for rectangular lots. Special depth factor tables as illustrated in Table 12.1 have been developed for triangular lots. One rule which may be used in lieu of depth factor tables is that the depth factor of such a lot is approximately two-thirds that of a rectangular lot of that depth. For the trapezoidal lot the depth factor could be the average of the depth factors corresponding to the depths on each side of the lot.

Irregular lots may be appraised by first calculating their area and then considering each lot to have a value equal to a rectangular lot of the equivalent area and approximate shape. In such cases much reliance must be placed on the judgment of the appraiser.

It will be apparent that, if proximity to a street influences the value of a parcel of land, a corner lot, which has access to two streets, will usually be more valuable than an inside lot, which has access to but one street. The determination of the magnitude of the *corner* and *side street benefits* depends on the size and shape of the lot and the relative unit values of the two streets. No generally accepted rule has been devised which can be used to compute these benefits, but the following suggested procedures have been made for rectangular corner business lots:

1. Ascertain the unit values on the two streets.
2. Calculate the value of the lot, considering it to be an inside lot facing the primary street.
3. Calculate the value of the lot, considering it to be an inside lot facing the secondary street.
4. To the calculation of step 2, add that portion of the amount determined in step 3 which appears to be appropriate.

Some appraisers compensate for corner benefits by adding a specified number of feet to the actual frontage of the lot. Others use a special additive correction factor to the depth factors for corner benefits. Still others add a variable amount, depending on the ratio of the main street unit value, to the secondary street unit value.

The appraisal of business or industrial land is then:

1. Determine the size of the plot.
2. Estimate the unit value.
3. Determine the depth factors.
4. Calculate the value of the plot, considering it to be an inside lot having access to but one street, using the formula which applies:

(a) V = (area, acres) (unit value, dollars per acre).

(b) V = (area, sq ft) (unit value, dollars per sq ft).

(c) V = (width, ft) (unit value, dollars per front foot) (depth factor).

5. Calculate any corner and side street benefits, and add to the amount determined in step 4 above.

6. Modify the above result as dictated by special circumstances.

12.8. Appraisal of "Made" Land, Abandoned Mines, and Rights of Way. In addition to the problems presented in the foregoing sections, the appraiser may need to appraise "made" land or land no longer useful to its present owner in its present state. Examples of the latter condition may be badly eroded farm lands, land formerly used as highway or railroad right of way, or worked-out gravel pits or strip mines.

Basically, the determination of the value of such land still is the estimation of the fair market value of similar adjacent land. Consider the land which is made over a period of years by use of dirt from excavations of various kinds. As these areas become suitable for building sites, the lands near them usually become more valuable and eventually the plots of made land are considered identical to the other areas.

However, until the land is made useful, its value is only a fraction of the fair market value of the adjacent land which is developed. Two possible solutions are presented:

1. Suppose it is possible to estimate that in the course of time, without cost to the owner, the land may be made useful, say in 20 years. Then the present value of the plot could be determined as the discounted worth of the estimated market value of similar land 20 years hence, less the present worth of the taxes paid and any other expenses incurred in the interval.

2. Suppose the appraiser can estimate the probable cost of making the fill, using the most reasonable means of acquiring and depositing the material. Then the value of the present nonuseful plot would be the fair market value of adjacent property developed to its best use, less the cost of making the nonuseful property similarly useful.

Of these two procedures, the latter is probably more efficacious since it is based on estimates which can be more easily determined.

With some modification, the method suggested above can be used in the other situations mentioned at the beginning of this section. Consider the land which forms the right of way of a branch railroad line recently abandoned. If the railroad company has permanent title to the land, the corporation will undoubtedly be glad to sell the land to adjacent landowners for a nominal sum just to get it off the railroad tax lists. In other cases the land may automatically revert to the owners of adjacent land. At any rate, an owner will need to "bulldoze" what ballast remains on the roadbed into the ditches, repair or augment the drainage, bring in some topsoil or equivalent, seed down, and fertilize. In a few years the old right of way takes on the character of adjacent property. At that time its value is that of similar adjacent land. At present, however, its value can be estimated quite adequately by the method suggested in the preceding paragraph.[1] Some rights of way may be valuable for industrial sites. If so, the basis of value is fair market price for similar property, because the land is almost always presently satisfactory for industrial use.

Finally, consider the worked-out gravel pits or strip mines. In the unusual case when the enterprise extracting the valuable material does considerable backfilling and smoothing in order to restore much of the general topography of the area, the present value of such land may not be materially less than the fair market price of similar adjacent land. The difference may be represented by the cost of restoring the fertility of the soil. However, when no efforts are made to improve the land and the land is badly impaired, two alternatives are presented:

1. If the pit or mine still contains valuable extractive material but it is not at present feasible to operate the pit or mine as an economic entity, then consider it to be an undeveloped limited life enterprise to be appraised by methods described in Chap. 18.

2. If the pit or mine is completely worked out, consider first what may be its probable highest and best use. Estimate what may be a fair market price of land devoted to that use; subtract the present worth of the estimated cost of developing the land to that degree of utility.

In the first alternative, the pit or mine is a marginal one, and the enterprise will have value as such only if the price of the material extracted advances sufficiently over present prices or if some new or less costly method of mining is utilized. The low-grade iron ore bodies of the Mesabi Range are cases in point. The value of such lands depends on so many imponderables that it is wisest to make conservative estimates.

In the second alternative, the worked-out pit or mine may be in such shape that only pasture or timber can be considered as the probable best use of the land. Then the present value of the land can be estimated as the difference between the market value of pasture or timberland in the general area and the cost of bringing the land up to that degree of usage. Since it will be some time before the land will be valuable for timber, this difference should be further discounted.

[1] The authors will not claim that such a procedure is applicable to the heavy cuts or fills or tunnels! Perhaps for such special properties another use can be discovered, a highway, farm road, or waterway, in which the value might be based on prospective returns.

The worked-out pit or mine may fill with water and may be of sufficient size to be useful as an artificial lake.   If so, it may be possible to appraise the land on the basis of reasonably anticipated earnings from its use for recreational purposes.

APPRAISAL PROCEDURE

In the two sections which follow, examples of the computations required to "calculate" the value of land are presented.   It is admitted again that the appraiser will in many cases determine the fair value directly, because of special considerations, without resort to formal calculations.   However, an estimate, computed by empirical formulas, is a good starting point; for many appraisals it is a fair final estimate.

The procedures illustrated are those recommended for the valuation of land in the city of Milwaukee by the Tax Commissioners Office of the city.   Although the formulas and the procedures are empirical and land appraisals undoubtedly could be made satisfactorily without these formulas, it is believed that estimates determined by these formulas and procedures can serve as bases for industrial land appraisals.

12.9. Urban Land Classifications.   In Milwaukee, Wis., urban business land is placed into five categories, designated by classes.   Class 1 land is represented by the principal retail business district.   Class 2 business land is found in the secondary retail business districts or areas adjoining the downtown Class 1 lands.   Class 3 lands comprise the remaining retail business areas in which much of the traffic is neighborhood shopping.   Classes 4 and 5 are industrial lands.

Residential lands comprise all areas zoned as residential areas, regardless of their current use.   The magnitude of the corner and alley benefits will vary with the zoning.

12.10. Corner, Side Street, and Alley Benefits.   The allowance for corner benefits of urban land in Milwaukee, Wis., is made by adding an arbitrary frontage to that of each lot; for business lands it is 10 ft, and for residential land the addition is 5 ft.   The allowance for side alley benefit is 5 ft for business land and 2 ft for residential property; no allowance is made when the alley is not improved.

Side street benefits are computed as a percentage of the calculated value of a standard lot of the given frontage.   The percentage decreases as the ratio of the main street unit value to the side street unit value increases.   Residential lands have no side street benefits unless an apartment house or business is located on the lot.

Rear alley benefits are included by increasing the actual depth of the lot by one-half the width of the rear alley and using a proportionately larger depth factor.   Rear alley benefits are not a factor in the appraisal of residential lands.

TABLE 12.1.   DEPTH FACTORS FOR ASSESSMENT OF CITY LOTS

From "Instructions for the Valuation of Land in the City of Milwaukee," Tax Commissioners Office, Milwaukee, January, 1950

Depth of lot, ft	Business land				Residential land	
	Class 1		Class 2		Rectangular lot	Triangular lot, base on street
	Rectangular lot	Triangular lot, base on street	Rectangular lot	Triangular lot, base on street		
5	0.14	....	0.12	....	0.06	
10	0.25	....	0.21	....	0.12	
15	0.34	....	0.30	....	0.17	
20	0.43	....	0.38	....	0.23	
25	0.50	....	0.45	....	0.28	
30	0.56	0.50	0.51	0.40	0.33	0.18
40	0.67	0.54	0.62	0.47	0.42	0.23
50	0.73	0.57	0.68	0.51	0.51	0.28
60	0.78	0.60	0.75	0.54	0.59	0.32
70	0.84	0.62	0.81	0.58	0.67	0.37
75	0.87	0.64	0.84	0.60	0.71	0.39
80	0.90	0.66	0.87	0.62	0.75	0.41
90	0.95	0.68	0.94	0.65	0.82	0.45
100	1.00	0.70	1.00	0.68	0.88	0.49
110	1.04	0.72	1.03	0.70	0.95	0.53
120	1.08	0.75	1.06	0.72	1.00	0.57
125	1.10	0.76	1.07	0.73	1.02	0.59
130	1.12	0.77	1.09	0.74	1.04	0.61
140	1.16	0.79	1.12	0.76	1.07	0.64
150	1.20	0.82	1.15	0.79	1.10	0.67
160	1.22	0.84	1.17	0.81	1.12	0.70
170	1.24	0.86	1.19	0.83	1.14	0.72
175	1.25	0.87	1.20	0.84	1.15	0.73
180	1.26	0.88	1.20	0.85	1.16	0.74
190	1.28	0.90	1.21	0.87	1.18	0.76
200	1.30	0.92	1.22	0.89	1.20	0.79
220	1.34	0.96	1.24	0.91	1.24	0.83
240	1.38	0.99	1.26	0.93	1.28	0.88

12.11. Adjustments for Size and Shape of Lots. The Milwaukee regulations provide depth factors for each type of land which indicate the variation in land values as the depth of a lot increases. Special depth factor tables for triangular lots with the base on the street are provided. If the plot is so shaped that the apex is on the street, the depth factor for such an area is obtained by subtracting the depth factor

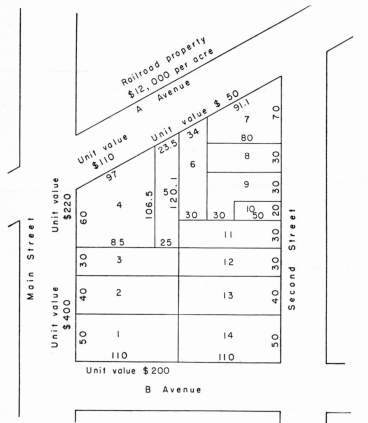

FIG. 12.1. Plat of business block to illustrate method of determining the calculated value of business property.

for a triangular lot with base on the street from the depth factor for a rectangular lot of the same depth.

When the sides of a lot are not perpendicular to a street, the calculated value may be obtained by considering the lot to be two triangles and a rectangle. Side street benefits may be similarly calculated.

A lot which has a slant street frontage but which is otherwise regular in shape may be appraised by considering that its frontage is equal to its perpendicular width, to which is added a percentage of the additional frontage caused by the slant. The additive amount depends on the class of land involved; the Milwaukee instructions suggest 40 percent for Class 1 land, 30 percent for Class 2 land, and so on to 0 percent for Class 5.

Corners which make an acute angle may not be always valuable. When appropriate, a line 10 ft in depth is drawn perpendicular to the front street, and the land in the resulting triangle is eliminated from the calculations.

A business lot either abnormally narrow or abnormally shallow should have an appropriate deduction. If a corner lot is less than 40 ft wide, it is assumed that the corner benefits extend to the next lot (40 percent in the first 10 ft, then 30 percent, 20 percent, and 10 percent, respectively).

The allowance for the added value of through lots is made on the basis of a percentage of the calculated value of a lot of standard depth of the given frontage facing the rear street. The percentage becomes smaller as the ratio of the main street unit value to the rear street unit value increases.

Residential lots of irregular shape may be considered as combinations of rectangles and triangles of equivalent area. When corner lots have excessive frontage because of rounded corners, the lot may be treated as a rectangular lot with no corner benefits added.

12.12. Examples of Procedure—Business Property. Consider the block of Class 2 business property shown in Fig. 12.1. If this property were in Milwaukee, Wis., the procedure might be as follows: Assume that lot 1 is the most valuable plot, and that Main Street is the primary street with A and B Avenues as secondary streets. Further assume that it has been decided that the unit value for lot 1 is $400 on Main Street, $200 for lots which front on B Avenue, and $50 for A Avenue (except lot 4, which is $110). The Milwaukee factors for business property, Class 2 business land, are used:

Main Street
Frontage, ft   50
Corner benefit, ft   10
    Total frontage equivalent, ft   60
Unit value $400
    Calculated value, standard lot $24,000
Depth, ft   110
Depth factor (Table 12.1) 1.03
    Calculated value, Main Street $24,720
Side street benefit
Unit value, Main Street $400
Unit value, side street $200
Ratio, Main Street value to side street value 2.0
Benefit, percent (Table 12.2) 17.5
Number of feet depth   110
    Calculated side street value at 100 percent (200)(110) $22,000
    Net side street benefit (22,000)(17.5)   3,850
      Total calculated value of lot 1 . . . . $28,570

Consider lot 4. Let it be assumed that the lot serves as the location of a hotel. The service usefulness of the lot is much different from lot 1, and so the unit value on Main Street should be examined critically. Suppose that the average earnings of lot 4 are about two-thirds those of lot 1. Then the unit value of lot 4 should be somewhat less than $400. Note also that unit values should gradually diminish from the higher to the lower values, and if lot 5 is definitely worth but $50 per front foot, the unit value of lot 4 should be intermediate. Allowing for the difference in frontage of the lots, the unit value of lot 4 might be approximately 55 percent of lot 1, or $220. At all events the appraiser will attempt to obtain as many data as possible in order to set a quantitative differential between the two unit values.

TABLE 12.2.   BENEFIT PERCENTAGES FOR BUSINESS LAND

From "Instructions for the Valuation of Land in the City of Milwaukee," Tax Commissioners Office, Milwaukee, January, 1950

Ratio*	Side street benefit percentages		Through lot benefit percentages
	Class 1	Class 2	
1.00	40	30	50
1.10	37	26	47.5
1.20	34.5	25	45
1.30	32.5	24	43
1.40	31.5	23	42
1.50	29	22	40
1.75	26	19	36
2.00	23	17.5	33
2.50	20	15	28
3.00	18	13	25
3.50	16	12	22
4.00	15	11	20
5.00	13.4	10	17
6.00	12.3	9	15
8.00	11	8	12
10.00	10	....	10

$$* \text{ Ratio} = \frac{\text{unit value of main street}}{\text{unit value of secondary street}}$$

Assuming that the Main Street unit value of lot 4 is $220, what unit value should be used for A Avenue? Suppose that it can be shown that the cumulative differential due to access and utility is in the ratio of 2:1; then the unit value of lot 4 on A Avenue should be about $110.

The calculations for lot 4 are:

Main Street
  Frontage, ft...   60
  Corner benefit, ft..................................   10
    Total frontage equivalent, ft.........................   70
  Unit value.. $220
    Calculated value, standard lot............................. $15,400
  Depth, ft...   85
  Depth factor (Table 12.1)...........................   0.91
    Calculated value (15,400)(0.91)............................ $14,014
For the triangle on A Avenue
  Width parallel to Main Street, ft.....................   46.5
  Unit value.. $220
    Calculated value, standard lot............................. $10,230
  Depth, ft...   85
  Depth factor, triangle apex on street $(0.91 - 0.64)$ (see
    Sec. 12.11).....................................   0.27
    Calculated value...   2,762
Side street
  Main Street unit value.............................. $220
  Side street unit value............................... $110
  Number of feet frontage.............................   85
    Calculated value at 100 percent (110)(85)................. $ 9,350
  Ratio, Main Street value to side street value.............   2.0
  Side street benefit, percent (Table 12.2).................   17.5
    Net side street benefit (9,350)(17.5).....................   1,636
Slant street
  Frontage equivalent, ft $(97 - 85)$.....................   12
  Unit value.. $110
    Calculated value at 100 percent.......................... $ 1,320
  Percentage (see Sec. 12.11).........................   30
    Net slant street value...................................   396
    Total calculated value of lot 4........................... $18,808

The calculation of the increment of value of lot 4 arising from the side street could have been accomplished by considering the perpendicular depths to A Avenue rather than the lot line depth. The scaled perpendicular depths corresponding to 60 ft and 106.5 ft are 68.3 and 93.4 ft, respectively.

Consider lot 10 on Second Street (Fig. 12.1). Because it is an extremely small lot, some deduction for its size is appropriate.

Frontage
  Number of front feet................................   20
  Unit value.. $200
    Calculated value, standard lot............................. $4,000
  Depth, ft...   50
  Depth factor (Class 2 land, Table 12.1)...............   0.68
    Calculated value, unadjusted for size...................... $2,720
Adjustment for size
  Reduction for size (Table 12.3) 12 percent.....................   326
    Final calculated value of lot 10........................... $2,394

TABLE 12.3. PERCENTAGE DEDUCTIONS FROM BASIC VALUE OF LOT
FOR SMALL LOTS, CLASS 2 BUSINESS PROPERTY

From "Instructions for the Valuation of Land in the City of Milwaukee," Tax Commissioners Office, Milwaukee, January, 1950

Depth of lot, ft	Width of lot, ft						
	20	25	30	35	40	45	50
20	18	15	12	9	7	6	5
25	16	13	11	8	6	5	4
30	15	12	10	7	5	4	4
40	13	11	8	6	4	3	3
50	12	9	7	5	3		
60	11	9	6	4			
70	11	8	6	4			
75	11	8	6	4			
80	11	8	5	3			
90	8	6	4				
100	4						

The reader is reminded that each of the examples has been treated as if it had been a separate appraisal problem. Undoubtedly, it would not be practical to investigate the unit value for every lot in every block if the appraisal involved the determination of city-wide tax assessments, although one might consider such an action when dealing with the more valuable lots. However, there will be many areas where unit values do not change materially from block to block.

Finally, the appraiser must always keep in mind that his final objective is an estimate of the fair market value of the land. Thus, he will modify calculated values whenever his judgment dictates such an action.

12.13. Examples of Procedure—Residential Property. The procedure for the determination of the calculated value of residential lots is the same for business lots, save that different depth factors and side street and corner benefits are applied. Deductions for small lots are more important although side street and corner benefits are less significant.

Consider that the residential lots shown in Fig. 12.2 were in Milwaukee, Wis. The rectangular pattern of streets has been avoided in this subdivision. Unit values are assumed identical for each lot with the exception of lots 4 and 24. Topographic features, improvements, and zoning classification are assumed to be the same for each lot.

Before establishing unit values, the appraiser will ascertain what percentage of the lots have houses on them. If the subdivision is less than 75 percent developed, he will reduce the normal unit values in these areas, perhaps as much as 25 percent if half of the lots have no houses. It is assumed that the lots of Fig. 12.2 are fully developed.

Consider lot 1, a corner lot. It is more valuable than lot 2 from the viewpoint of more flexibility in the possible arrangement of the house and garage, which outweighs somewhat the disadvantages of more traffic,

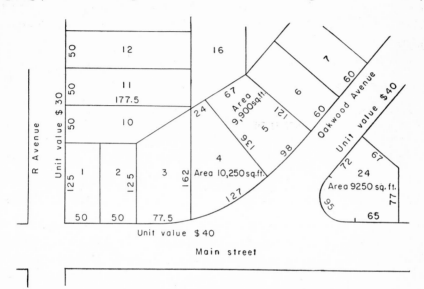

FIG. 12.2. Plat of residential lots to illustrate method of determining the calculated value of residential property.

more sidewalk, and a certain amount of decreased privacy. Thus corner benefits will be included in the calculations.

Main Street
Frontage, ft...	50	
Corner benefit, ft..........	5	
Total frontage equivalent, ft...	55	
Unit value (Fig. 12.2)................................	$40	
Calculated value, standard lot............................		$2,200
Depth, ft...	125	
Depth factor (Table 12.1).............................	1.02	
Calculated value of lot 1 (2,200)(1.02).....................		$2,244
Side street benefits....................................	None	

The reader is reminded that corner benefits do not extend beyond the corner lot unless the corner is abnormally small. Hence, lot 2 is considered as an inside lot.

In calculating the value of lot 3, the long dimension, 162 ft, should be reduced to a dimension perpendicular to the curved street, or 152 ft. The depth factor of this lot is then the average of 1.02 and 1.10, or 1.06.

Lot 4 has much frontage, an advantage, but the narrow rear of the lot reduces the usefulness of the lot. Hence the appraiser will reduce the calculated value materially, perhaps as much as 40 percent. The depth factor is 1.08, determined as the average between 1.10 (152 ft) and 1.06 (136 ft). Thus, its calculated value is determined to be:

Main Street
```
Frontage, ft.....................................          127
Unit value......................................          $40
   Calculated value, standard lot...........................   $5,080
Depth, ft....................................... 152 and 136
Average depth factor (Table 12.1) (1.10 and 1.06)...   1.08
   Calculated value (5,080)(1.08)............................        $5,486
Reduction for poor shape, 40 percent........................         2,194
   Calculated value, lot 4....................................        $3,292
```

TABLE 12.4. PERCENTAGE DEDUCTIONS FOR SMALL LOTS, RESIDENTIAL PROPERTY ZONED B AND C AREAS

From "Instructions for the Valuation of Land in the City of Milwaukee," Tax Commissioners Office, Milwaukee, January, 1950

Depth of lot, ft	Width of lot, ft											
	18	20	23	25	30	35	40	45	50	60	80	100
25	37	34	32	30	26	24	22	20	19	17	14	11
30	33	30	27	26	23	21	19	18	17	15	12	10
35	32	26	24	23	20	18	17	16	15	13	11	9
40	31	25	21	20	17	16	15	14	13	12	10	9
45	31	24	19	18	15	14	13	12	12	11	9	8
50	30	24	17	16	13	12	12	11	11	10	8	7
55	29	23	15	14	11	11	10	10	9	8	7	7
60	29	23	15	12	10	9	9	9	8	8	6	6
65	29	22	14	11	9	8	8	8	7	7	6	5
70	28	22	14	10	7	7	7	7	6	6	5	4
75	28	22	14	10	6	6	6	6	5	5	4	4
80	28	21	14	9	6	5	5	5	4	4	4	3
85	28	21	13	9	4	4	4	4	4	4	3	3
90	27	21	13	9	4	4	3	3	3	3	3	
100	27	20	13	9								
110	27	20	12	8								
120	26	20	12	8								
130	26	20	12	8								
140	26	19	12	8								
150 and over	26	19	12	7								

Although lot 5 is not trapezoidal, it is nearly so. The appraiser might reduce the standard unit value by say 10 percent to take care of the difference in the width of the lot in front and in back. The depth factor for lot 5 is 1.03.

Lot 24 is all front! However, the appraiser can imagine a rectangular lot of the same area and attempt to calculate a value. A glance at the figure indicates a reasonable frontage on Main Street to be, say 110 ft. A depth which will produce the given area, 9,250 sq ft, is 84 ft (depth factor 0.78). Corner benefits would be considered in this case; however, the appraiser may reduce the calculated value of lot 24 somewhat because the shape of the lot is odd and there is so much frontage.

THE TAXATION PROBLEM

Although it is true that the *tax value*, the value placed on land for taxation purposes, need not be even close to the fair appraised value of the land, the tax value should bear some definite relationship to it. Basically, property taxes are ad valorem taxes, and there is the definite implication that the assessments are somehow tied up to the value of the land and departures from that value should be only for good and sufficient reasons. But far greater in importance are the requirements that each tax value be in the proper relation to that of the neighboring plots and that the system of fixing tax values be one which can be operated impartially without the injection of any personal bias by any assessor.

Thus, it may be that the determination of tax values is not a valuation problem in the strict sense of the word. However, the data which are needed and the procedures which are used are so similar that a brief discussion of the land tax problem, from the viewpoint of an appraiser charged with the job, is warranted.

12.14. Assessing Taxable Land. The preparation of property tax assessments, and thus the proportion of the tax value of land, is generally on a city- or county-wide basis. As a result, there is often the temptation to avoid giving much attention to the preparation of the tax value of any single parcel of land. The assessor should resist such a temptation as strongly as consistent with the practicalness of the situation, because the individual owner invariably considers that the determination of assessment of his property is the number one problem of the city!

However, if the assessor can show that the unit values have been estimated fairly and impartially throughout the neighborhood of each protesting owner, the assessor will have more than won a battle; indeed, the protesting owner may even become a bearer of good tidings. However, protests generally come from owners in every area and who possess every kind of urban land. It follows, therefore, that unit values must be proper and fair throughout the whole political unit being assessed. These unit values need not represent the present fair market value of land; in fact, owners derive a curious satisfaction from seeing figures which may be some fraction, say 60 percent, of the real present values or which relate to some price period of the past when land values were lower than at present. The above situation is agreeable, even though the owner knows how the millage rule works. However, the paramount point is that unit values must be fairly and impartially determined for all areas.

Frequently it has been the custom to disallow any corner benefits on residential property except in unusual cases. Corner benefits on business property are often set as an arbitrary percentage, for example, 20 percent, of the calculated value of the lot, assuming it to be an inside lot facing the main street.

The determination of the taxable value of income-producing lands, particularly business properties, often requires that the earning value of the property be considered (Sec. 12.4). It is not unusual to find a property in an area where recent sales are few; consequently fair market values are not easy to establish. However, it may be possible to obtain data from which the earning value can be fairly estimated. Though the appraiser may not be able to separate the value of the land from the combined value of the land plus the value of the structures upon it, yet the total estimate may prove more appropriate as a measure of value than one made from other sources. Moreover, a value based on an average past and probable near future return may indicate a much higher tax value than would be warranted on the basis of average market values.

Finally, the assessor is cautioned that, in spite of everything, it often happens that tax lists do not include every parcel of land in the area. Extreme care should be exercised to avoid omissions and to reduce errors in lot measurements to an absolute minimum.

CHAPTER 13

Appraisal of the Liquid Assets

Managers of many enterprises have been accused of neglecting the records of the annual costs pertaining to the fixed assets of the enterprise in favor of a close scrutiny of the records showing the variations of the liquid assets. On the other hand, an appraiser can easily find that he is spending a disproportionate amount of time and energy on the valuation of the fixed assets of the enterprise. Not infrequently the liquid assets of an enterprise may be the larger of the two groups of assets. At all events, the appraiser must give the same quality of care and attention to the determination of the value of the liquid assets as he does to the fixed assets.

13.1. Constituents of the Liquid Assets. The liquid assets possessed by an enterprise can be classified into three main groups, (1) working capital, (2) segregated funds and special deposits, and (3) investments, depending on their nature and the particular circumstances. Items normally included in liquid assets may be:

1. Working capital
   Current assets
     Cash on hand
     Securities possessed for short terms
     Accounts receivable
     Prepayments
     Inventories
       Raw materials
       Goods in process
       Finished goods
       Miscellaneous materials and supplies
   Less current liabilities
     Accounts payable
     Accrued wages, taxes, dividends, interest, etc., recognized but not paid
     Customer advances
2. Segregated funds and special deposits
   Depreciation fund
   Fund to be used to retire a fixed liability
   Fund to be used for employee benefits

Fund earmarked for a near future construction
Customer deposits
Fund to apply against upward revision of federal income tax payments
3. Investments
Securities held for long terms
Securities of subsidiary companies
Other investments

Many enterprises may possess all items listed above; others just a few.

The book statement of the *working capital* can be estimated by determining the *net current assets* (current assets minus current liabilities) as of a certain date, although the appraiser may decide to include some of the segregated funds in the list of current assets in some specific case. The important thing, however, is that the appraiser include all items of value regardless of their listing. The reader may refer to Table 13.1 to see a typical statement of the financial position of an enterprise in which the working capital is shown as a separate section of the report.

Another way of estimating working capital, this approach being of more interest to the appraiser, is to consider working capital to be composed of two groups of property, (1) the operating materials and supplies and (2) the operating cash resources. The outline of the previous paragraph needs only slight modification to reflect this change of concept.

The segregated funds, almost always in the form of securities, are set aside for safekeeping for a variety of purposes. One such fund of particular interest to the appraiser is a *depreciation fund*. Here, the managers of an enterprise have purchased securities with a portion of the depreciation return pending the day when a construction project will be initiated which requires a considerable outlay. Another fund is the one created to provide cash for the future discharge of a fixed liability. A third fund is a temporary one, often composed of United States Treasury notes, which has been created to be used in case past federal income tax payments are determined to be insufficient.

Investments, if in the form of securities which are held widely and which are daily bought and sold in recognized markets, can certainly be liquid assets even though the intent of the managers of the enterprise is that the investment be a long-term one. If the latter is the case, the appraiser should show them for what they are rather than including the value of such securities either as a part of working capital or buried with other funds.

The appraiser may find securities reported as investments which cannot be considered as liquid assets. When a subsidiary is completely owned through the acquisition of its securities by a parent company and these securities cannot be obtained by the general public, the appraiser must consider the subsidiary to be an operating branch of the parent

TABLE 13.1. CONSOLIDATED STATEMENT OF FINANCIAL POSITION
OF THE UNITED STATES STEEL CORPORATION
Illustration of a Book Statement of Working Capital

	Dec. 31, 1951	Dec. 31, 1950
Current Assets:		
Cash...................................	$ 233,386,977	$ 259,291,292
United States government securities, at cost....	326,717,100	213,561,506
Receivables, less estimated bad debts..........	252,784,015	215,376,369
Inventories..............................	399,832,115	391,109,579
TOTAL.................................	$1,212,720,207	$1,079,338,746
Less:		
Current Liabilities:		
Accounts payable.........................	339,703,119	282,157,715
Accrued taxes............................	509,773,477	325,445,653
Dividends payable........................	25,887,237	25,887,237
Long-term debt due within one year..........	2,438,790	4,029,688
TOTAL.................................	$ 877,802,623	$ 637,520,293
Working Capital..........................	334,917,584	441,818,453
Miscellaneous investments, less estimated losses	19,779,076	24,903,605
United States government securities set aside, at cost		
For property additions and replacements.......	250,000,000	250,000,000
For expenditures arising out of war...........	12,000,000	14,000,000
Plant and equipment, less depreciation..........	1,571,334,234	1,386,610,601
Operating parts and supplies..................	48,317,344	40,370,893
Costs applicable to future periods..............	26,528,130	33,962,322
Intangibles...............................	1	1
TOTAL ASSETS LESS CURRENT LIABILITIES.....	$2,262,876,369	$2,191,665,875
Deduct:		
Long-term debt............................	54,879,636	61,782,446
Reserves		
For estimated additional costs arising out of war.	11,576,348	13,327,273
For insurance, contingencies, and miscellaneous expenses..........................	100,441,541	101,388,154
EXCESS OF ASSETS OVER LIABILITIES AND RESERVES............................	$2,095,978,844	$2,015,168,002
Ownership evidenced by:		
Preferred stock, 7% cumulative, par value $100 (3,602,811 shares)......................	360,281,100	360,281,100
Common stock (26,109,756 shares)..............	1,735,697,744	1,654,886,902
Stated capital, $33⅓ per share.. $870,325,200		
Income reinvested in business... 865,372,544		
TOTAL.................................	$2,095,978,844	$2,015,168,002

company.   The value of the securities can be determined correctly only
on the basis of the value of the subsidiary as a whole, by processes
described in this book.   In such a situation, the appraiser will find that
he lacks data from which to make an estimate of the value of the securities
by the customary methods.

13.2. The Appraisal Problem. The appraisal of the liquid assets of an enterprise requires no new concepts or bases of value beyond those already discussed. What the appraiser must attempt to do is to determine a fair current value for each of these assets considering the purpose for which the valuation is made.

There are numerous problems, however, which may make the appraiser's task difficult. Consider the constantly changing character of the working capital, particularly of a seasonal industry when large amounts of raw materials are collected periodically. The appraiser must appreciate that in this case the operating cash resources will at times be low. Again, when an appraisal is to be used as a basis for the determination of fair rates (a public utility valuation), it is usually necessary to determine an *average fair allowance* for the working capital rather than its value as of a certain date.

The appraiser must decide just how he will utilize the book records of the enterprise. Generally, each enterprise uses one or more systems designed to show the quantities of all inventories. How these quantities are to be verified constitutes a good problem for the appraiser. Then, too, these systems indicate some unit cost for the items comprising the inventories; whether or not these costs can be used by the appraiser as evidences of value without adjustment must also be decided.

In addition, the appraiser must ascertain for each valuation just what liquid assets are to be considered. Where a property is to change owners through inheritance or the settlement of an estate, all liquid assets must be reported and appraised as of a certain date. In a valuation which is to serve as a basis for an ordinary sale of an enterprise, only those items which are to be transferred need to be appraised. Usually the cash, accounts receivable, and certain funds would be excluded. In the case of valuation for property taxes, the policy of the interested taxing authority would necessarily serve as a guide.

Finally, the appraiser may be required to use price data which do not refer to the present time. For example, valuations of utilities are often based on a valuation date some months past. Appraisals for property taxes may use price levels which do not show the current situation; state laws may require that values be fixed at some arbitrarily determined fraction of current prices or values. In these cases, the policies of the respective authorities must serve as a guide for the appraiser.

APPRAISAL OF INVENTORIES

The appraisal of inventories includes two operations, (1) the determination of the quantities of these items or the verification of the reported quantities and (2) the estimation of the fair values to be applied to these quantities.

13.3. Quantity Determination as of a Specific Date. The several inventories include the raw materials, goods in process, and finished goods, and, in addition, the supplies and sundry items indirectly used in the manufacturing process. The latter include fuel, oils and greases, stocks of parts required in the maintenance of plant and equipment, office supplies, and the like, now at hand. The stocks of construction material which will eventually become a part of the fixed capital physical property may be included as a part of operating materials as long as they are kept in stock. However, it is desirable to segregate them from the operating materials as far as practicable. Then, as soon as these construction materials leave the warehouse and are at the site of the construction project, the inventory record should show their change in status.

Most enterprises use a continuous inventory system as a means of determining the amount of operating materials on hand. Some systems have ways of indicating when the supply of any item is running low and additional purchases are desirable. Regardless of the merits of the continuous inventory systems, the appraiser must satisfy himself regarding the correctness of the reported quantities as of a certain date. One way is to spot-check several items. Determine the quantities of a certain material, say a finished part purchased from another enterprise to be used in the assembly process, at the various places where it may be stocked prior to its use in manufacturing. If these several spot counts substantially agree with the tallies of the continuous inventory system, the latter can be said to function adequately for this and other materials. Another way is to take the reported quantities shown by the system for all items and examine each bin where the materials are found, accept each reported quantity which without counting appears to agree with the actual quantity, and make a count only if there appears to be a significant discrepancy.

Sometimes an appraiser must make an inventory of operating materials and supplies without the aid of a continuous inventory system. He should use enough assistants so that the job may be completed in as short a time as practicable. By so doing, he avoids setting up procedures which are required in order to convert counts made several weeks later back to an agreed common date. In any event, the appraiser must be satisfied that the quantity of each kind and type of operation material reported to him is actually in existence before he can conclude that he is ready to go ahead with the next step. Empty warehouses full of theoretically finished goods cannot have any place in an appraisal.

13.4. Estimating Average Quantities. If the purpose of the appraisal is such that an average quantity of operation materials and supplies is desired, rather than a quantity as of a certain date, other procedures are required. It is not so much a question of *what is determined to be the quantity as of a certain date*, but rather *what is thought to be allowable or proper for a certain period.* Graphs which show the variation from month to month of the quantities of certain critical operating materials on hand are most desirable. Furthermore, the policies of the enterprise regarding the stocking of materials in times when prices are "right" or when winter approaches must not be ignored. For example, if an electric utility depends on water transportation for the delivery of fuel and the river or lake is generally icebound for 60 to 100 days, an allowable peak supply of fuel, enough to last 100 days, should be considered. Further, the fact that emergencies may come which will require significantly more materials than normally must not be overlooked. Consider the stocks of wire and poles which must be maintained by telephone companies operating in areas where winters often are damaging to the property.

In utility appraisals involving the estimation of the allowable *average working capital,* the average quantity of operating materials must be tied in with the average allowable amount of the operating cash resources. The appraiser must be certain that the total of the two is sufficient for proper functioning of the enterprise. Examination of graphs which show the monthly amounts of each item for a year or more may disclose that the sum is relatively constant even though the quantity of cash may vary widely from month to month.

When a determination of the average working capital is required and excessive amounts of operating materials are found, the appraiser must recognize that the managers of the enterprise at some time decided to invest in what is at the date of valuation excess property. Such excess property must be excluded from the rate base in utility valuations.

13.5. Appraising Raw Materials and Supplies. The estimation of the value of the operation materials and supplies requires that the appraiser estimate a current market value for each. Price and cost data available from the recent records of the enterprise are the normal sources of information, although the appraiser must use them with discretion in order that his cost data can be useful as an evidence of value.

Consider first the miscellaneous indirect operation materials—oils, office supplies, and the like. The cost of a ream of paper in the stock of office supplies is the sum of the current delivered cost of the paper plus its fair share of purchase and stores expense and administrative expense. If an operating enterprise were to be sold lock, stock, and barrel, the paper would be as valuable to the new owners as to the old owners. A similar line of reasoning would indicate the same basis of value for all other raw materials. Further, this same basis of value would serve for the appraisal of raw materials in valuations used for rate-making purposes or as a basis for loans. However, the current delivered cost of the raw materials (excluding from consideration the various overhead expenses mentioned) would be a better basis of value of the raw materials in appraisals where the value of the enterprise as an operating entity is not necessary. Examples would be appraisals for property taxes, settlement of an estate, a condemnation case, or the appraisal of property lost or damaged by fire, or the like, which is covered by insurance. Generally, raw materials are appraised at their average current delivered cost and in certain cases, depending on the purpose of the valuation, their fair share of purchase, stores, and administrative expenses.

13.6. Appraising Goods in Process. Goods in process are those products now undergoing the manufacturing procedure. If it were possible to watch the cost tag of a single item in the manufacturing process, the observer would see, added to the delivered cost of the raw materials and the various overheads mentioned previously, the manufacturing expense for each department involved in the manufacture. It would seem, at this stage, that the value of this product normally should be equivalent to its cost to date, provided all the items mentioned above are priced at average current costs. It is reasonable to assume that if the owners of enterprise A were to purchase a competitive enterprise B, the goods in process should be equally valuable to the new owners and to the old owners. Whether the appraisal is made for sale or other purpose the basis of value for the goods in process would be the same.

There remains, however, the problem of analyzing the costs of the goods in process as shown by the accounting department. Different procedures are used by different enterprises. The appraiser must know what procedure is being followed by the particular enterprise in order to determine what costs, if any, need modification so that appropriate costs are used in all cases. The various procedures followed in costing the inventories are:

1. First-in, first-out (FIFO)
2. Last-in, first-out (LIFO)
3. Cost or market, whichever is lower
4. Moving average

Since the labor and the manufacturing overhead expense going into the cost of the goods in process are always current costs, the costs of raw materials are those affected by the above inventory pricing methods. The basis of determining the book cost of the raw materials used in the *goods in process* by each of the above inventory methods is as follows:

Inventory cost method	*Cost of the raw materials in the goods in process*
First-in, first-out	Cost, including overhead expenses, of the *oldest* purchases still remaining on the cost summary card
Last-in, first-out	Cost, including overhead expenses, of the most *recent* purchases still remaining
Cost or market, whichever is lower	As title indicates
Moving average	Weighted average of unit costs of all the accumulated purchases from the most recent backward whose quantity equals the requisitions of the goods in process and finished goods on hand

It is possible that none of these inventory methods will produce the costs of the raw materials in the goods in process which the appraiser can use without modification in estimating the value of the goods in process. Probably the last-in first-out method offers the best possibility, particularly if all raw materials are purchased almost continuously, because this method would more nearly approach the value of the material in terms of current costs. However, the appraiser must ascertain that the book costs shown by the records of the enterprise are based on current costs if he proposes to use these figures in his estimate of the value of the goods in process.

13.7. Appraising Finished Goods. The finished goods on hand present a different problem. Not only does the appraiser have at hand the total cost of the products which have been manufactured, but their tentative selling price is also known. If these products are moving readily into the open market, then the established selling price is the appropriate figure to use as the value of the finished goods at hand.

However, the appraiser may be called upon to value some finished goods now on hand which are not selling well or which have deteriorated from physical causes. Basically, the problem is not changed. What these finished goods can bring on the open market is the fundamental estimate of value; the book record of the total cost to the manufacturer is of academic interest only. The experience in selling similar finished goods under similar circumstances supplies the data of greatest use to the appraiser.

In the determination of a rate base, the finished goods on hand might consist of such items as water or gas and in some cases such by-product material as coke, tars, and oils. If appropriate, there might be merchandise purchased for resale. Although market value of these goods is a basis of value, it is possible that in a rate base determination only the cost of such property to the utility may be allowed.

13.8. Estimating Fair Average Values. In the special case when average rather than specific quantities are used, the appraiser will find that he needs to determine only a *fair average current value*, or *cost* if appropriate, for each item of operation materials and supplies under consideration.   In fact, there may be situations, as in rate making, where the cost of the operating materials and supplies to the owner may be the only admissible basis of appraisal.

13.9. Summary of Appraisal Procedure for Inventories. In summary, operation materials and supplies, goods in process, finished goods, and other inventories are appraised as follows:

Miscellaneous materials and supplies	Current delivered cost plus a fair share of the stores, purchasing and administrative expense (in some cases, overhead expenses may be excluded)
Raw materials	Same procedure as above
Goods in process	Current delivered unit cost plus overheads plus the direct and indirect manufacturing costs representing added investment in each unit in each stage of the manufacturing process
Finished goods	Current selling price new, f.o.b. factory, modified if necessary for lessened value from physical or functional causes (in some cases, the total cost to manufacture each unit might be the only admissible basis)

OPERATING CASH RESOURCES

The appraisal of the operating cash resources, although simpler in procedure than needed in the appraisal of the operating materials and supplies, requires (1) a determination of the items which are to be considered, (2) the quantities involved, and (3) the estimation of their present fair value.

13.10. Items Considered. The items which normally constitute the operating cash resources include cash on hand, short-term investments in securities, temporary investments in prepaid operating expense, and the accounts receivable.   Since the cash resources are always currently obligated to the extent of the current liabilities, these items are likewise considered.   The reader is referred to Table 13.1, which shows a typical report of the operating cash resources possessed by an enterprise.

The question may well be asked, "If the managers of an enterprise have decided to use several millions of dollars for plant additions, these moneys coming entirely from the cash now on hand, should not these sums be segregated from the operating cash resources?"   An affirmative answer would be correct; yet there is nothing gained in such a division. Management always has had the responsibility to employ the liquid assets of an enterprise wisely; one of the normal ways of using the cash on hand is to procure fixed assets. Even though the sums earmarked for construction are segregated, it would seem that they must be considered a part of the operating cash resources.

Following the same reasoning, a depreciation fund should likewise be considered a part of the operating cash resources. The purpose of the fund is the same as those sums mentioned in the previous paragraph, and basically the source of the moneys is the same.

Going one step further, sums now on hand and earmarked for construction, but which have been obtained from outside sources, either as equity capital or from the issue of new bonds, can also be considered as a part of operating cash resources. In summary then, all cash on hand (with a few possible exceptions) and readily liquidated securities, less the current liabilities, can be considered an operating cash resource.

One exception might be the funds used to retire a fixed liability, say a bond issue or a mortgage. It is recognized that as a fixed liability becomes current, as in the case of a bond issue in serial form, the operating cash resources will show this obligation. It would seem, therefore, that as soon as the management of an enterprise sees fit to segregate funds for the express purpose of retiring a fixed liability not now current, such funds should no longer be considered a part of the operating cash resources. The appraiser, therefore, should report such a segregated fund as a part of the total valuation, noting its specific purpose. Other segregated funds not considered a part of operating cash resources can be handled similarly.

By their very nature, prepaid operating expenses are a part of operating cash resources. In fact, some items, as prepaid insurance, can be readily converted into cash. However, some prepayments may not be considered as current assets, but rather as deferred, owing to the time of maturity. It behooves the appraiser, therefore, to examine the deferred assets to be sure he has included those items which may be a part of the operating cash resources. The reader should be cautioned, however, that many deferred charges, such as the financing expense on a bond issue, cannot be an operating cash resource.

13.11. Appraisal of Operating Cash Resources as of a Certain Date. The quantities of the operating cash resources can be obtained from the books of the enterprise, subject to verification by the appraiser. Bank statements can be examined, securities inventoried, the size of the accounts receivable and the current liabilities can be determined by reconciliation of the accounts and their controls, a procedure familiar to the auditor and the appraiser.

The amount of the cash and the value of the prepayments and the current liabilities can be determined generally by verification of the book record statements pertaining to these items. However, the amount shown as the accounts receivable must be modified by the appraiser. The various accounts may be separated into broad groups in which are placed all accounts having approximately the same percentage of uncollectability. The value of the accounts receivable is then

$$\text{Value} = \begin{pmatrix} \text{the amount of the} \\ \text{accounts receivable} \\ \text{in each group} \end{pmatrix} \begin{pmatrix} \text{the average fraction} \\ \text{collectible for the} \\ \text{group} \end{pmatrix}$$

The experience of the enterprise should serve as a guide in the assignment of the fractions representing the portion of accounts collected. Frequently the losses on accounts receivable are minute. However, the appraiser should not use the account, Reserve for Losses on Bad Debts, as basic data in determining the allowance to be made for the fraction uncollectible. This reserve is always conservatively estimated, with good reason, and represents a cushion against the unexpected rather than an attempt to make the book records show the value of the accounts receivable.

Securities which are to be considered a part of the operating cash resources may be appraised at their present average market price. Long-time trends should be examined, and valuations based on the high speculative prices of boom periods or the excessively low prices existing during depressions should be avoided.

Securities which provide a fixed income and a promise to pay the principal at maturity can be appraised at their present worths, if it is possible to estimate a "yield" rate which is satisfactory for the type of security considered. The value is determined by the formula

$$\text{Value} = \begin{pmatrix} \text{present worth of} \\ \text{interest payments} \end{pmatrix} + \begin{pmatrix} \text{present worth of principal} \\ \text{which is to be paid at} \\ \text{maturity} \end{pmatrix}$$

13.12. Appraisal of an Average Allowable Estimate of Operating Cash Resources. When an appraisal is to serve as a basis for the determination of fair charges for services or products produced, the estimation of the operating cash resources requires average quantities rather than specific quantities as of a certain date. The basis of appraisal of the items considered remains unchanged, however.

The appraisal of an average allowance of operating cash resources applies particularly to the rate-making process in utility regulation. Although the discussion which follows is pointed to this usage, there is need in certain types of appraisals of nonregulated enterprises for an estimate of the average amount of operating cash resources. For example, in considering the purchase of an operating enterprise, the purchaser would be interested in ascertaining the average amount of working capital which he might have to supply.

The allowable total of the operating cash resources depends on the day-to-day requirements of the enterprise under consideration, but it should, in addition, provide a working balance sufficient to meet such emergencies as can be forecast with some assurance. The needs of telephone companies for ready cash to finance immediate repairs to property damaged by storms and winters are typical of such emergency uses of working capital.

Further, the allowable cash should provide for the lag between income and outgo. This quantity is frequently estimated in terms of a certain number of weeks operating expenses. For example, a utility whose payrolls come twice a month and who bills all customers on the first of the month with the penalty date as the tenth of the month might be allowed 45 to 50 days operating expense. On the other hand, a passenger transportation company collecting all its fares in advance of the production of the service might not be allowed any cash balance for the lag between income and outgo.

No additional allowance for the operating cash tied up in accounts receivable is needed, provided the cash allowance for the lag between income and outgo takes into consideration the normal period for the conversion of accounts receivable into cash.

Only those securities which are required in the month-to-month operation of an enterprise should be included as a part of the average allowable operating cash resources. For example, in an area where the seasons cause major fluctuations in the size of the operating materials and supplies, some part of the operating cash resources may at times be in securities pending their investment in materials and supplies. A low average cash balance may indicate a large balance for operating materials, or vice versa. The appraiser should check, therefore, to see that his total of the value of the average allowable operating cash resources adds up to a reasonable average total working capital allowance for the enterprise.

It may be that a utility possesses an excessive amount of operating cash resources, far beyond any reasonable allowance for normal operations. Such an excess, although a part of the total value of the enterprise, cannot be considered a part of the rate base.

13.13. Summary of Appraisal Procedure for Cash Resources. In summary, operating cash resources include cash, short-term securities representing a temporary investment of moneys normally tied up in the inventories, prepaid operating expenses, accounts receivable, and any segregated funds which the appraiser deems should be a part of the operating cash resources. Other segregated funds are reported separately. Current liabilities representing a present obligation on the cash on hand should be included. All items are appraised at the current estimate shown on the company's books with the exception of the securities and the accounts receivable. Securities are valued at their fair average current market value. Accounts receivable are appraised by modifying their book balances by the fraction uncollectible.

An estimate of the average allowable amount of the operating cash resources must provide a reasonable cash balance sufficient to meet day-to-day requirements plus an adequate allowance for foreseeable emergencies. In addition, an allowance sufficient to cover the lag between income and outgo must be included. The appraiser must check his total allowance for working capital (allowance for operating materials and supplies plus allowance for operating cash resources) to verify its adequacy.

CHAPTER 14

Appraisal of Intangible Property

In every valuation of an entire operating enterprise, the appraiser will find a third group of valuable assets in addition to the fixed capital physical property and the liquid assets. This third group includes the intangible properties which have been acquired either through investment or by the process of attachment to the enterprise.

Intangible property is real property; it does not, however, have a physical existence. Such items as organization, financing, good will, going value, contracts and the like, patents, and rights of various kinds are included in the group of intangible properties. The purpose of this chapter is to define the more important intangibles, discuss their characteristics, and indicate reasonable processes by which each can be appraised.

14.1. Intangible Properties. *Organization* includes costs incurred in promoting the idea and in organizing the enterprise, including legal costs.

Financing includes those necessary costs of issuing and selling the securities of the enterprise.

Good will is all that good disposition which customers entertain toward the house of business identified by the particular name or firm and which may induce them to continue giving their custom to it. This definition is that given by Vice-Chancellor Wood in *Churton v. Douglas.*[1]

Going value is that "element of value of an assembled and established plant, doing business and earning money, over one not thus advanced."[2]

A *contract* is an agreement, usually written, which provides for the rendering of a service or the granting of a privilege under stipulated conditions at a stipulated price. Included are contracts for purchases or sale of products or services and leases of properties. Another type of contract is the *option*, the acquisition of the right to purchase or lease a property or to enter into any contract under special circumstances within a specified period of time. A third type of contract is the *easement*, the right to make some specific use of property owned by others, such as

---

[1] *Andrew Caird Churton, George Bankart, and Michael Stocks Hirst, Plaintiffs, and John Douglas, Defendant,* Johns England, Chap. 174, 189 (Mar. 16–17, 1859).

[2] *Los Angeles Gas & Electric Corp. v. Railroad Commission of California et al.* (No. 412), 289 U.S. 287, 313, P.U.R. 1933C, 229 (U.S. Sup. Ct. May 8, 1933).

the easement possessed by a telephone company to travel on private property in order to maintain its lines.   A fourth type is the *franchise*, the right to an exclusive activity in a specified area, such as the franchise held by a power company giving it the sole right to supply electric energy to a certain city.   Another type of franchise is the dealership for the sale of certain products (automobiles or electrical appliances) in a specified area.

Another intangible allied to those mentioned in the previous paragraph is the *water right*.   This agreement allows a party to take a specified amount of water from some source at a certain rate for a certain purpose. When the contract provides for the exclusive possession of or the access to the bank of a stream or lake, it is a *riparian right*.   A *mineral right* is a kind of contract which enables a party to extract the minerals found in the land (including nonmetallic items such as gas, oil, coal, construction materials, and the like).   A similar right is the *timber right*.

An intangible which is often most valuable is the *patent*, a government grant which gives to the inventor the exclusive right to make, use, and vend his invention in any proper way for a certain specified period.   If an invention is not patented but, on the contrary, the details are closely guarded by the enterprise possessing the invention, the intangible is known as a *trade secret*.   Usually, each enterprise possesses a *trade-mark*, properly registered, and thus a protected word or symbol or design which helps to identify the maker of the products.   For their protection, authors and artists and enterprises acquire *copyrights*, a government grant providing for the exclusive right to publish their literary or artistic endeavors for a specified time.

14.2. Basis of Appraisal.   An examination of the list of the intangible properties should make it evident to the reader that no single evidence of the value of such property can serve as a basis for the appraisal of all the items.   Some can be appraised on the basis of either their original cost or their replacement cost with a proper allowance for a decrease in value because of the passage of time.   The allowance for organization or financing is usually determined on this basis.

A second evidence of value is appropriate when intangibles similar to the one being appraised are frequently bought and sold.   When these sales occur in a way that stabilizes prices, a fair market value for the intangible item in question can be determined.   The option to acquire the right to drill for oil or gas in an unproved area is an example.

The third and final evidence of value which can be used in the appraisal of intangible properties is the value based on an estimate of the probable future dollar earnings to be derived from the intangible.   In such an instance it is necessary that the appraiser be able to obtain these appropriate data: (1) the probable future life of the intangible, (2) the average annual returns anticipated, and (3) the fair rate of return. Contracts, good will, trade secrets, and the like, are generally appraised by this method. Special procedures have been developed by which the probable average annual returns can be estimated for each of the items. These procedures are discussed in Secs. 14.5 to 14.12.

Table 14.1 shows in summary form the basis or evidence of value which can be used for each of the intangible properties.

TABLE 14.1.   BASIS OR EVIDENCE OF VALUE OF INTANGIBLE PROPERTIES

| Item | Basis or evidence of value | | |
	Cost (original, or replacement, or fair)	Market price of similar properties	Present worth of earnings derived solely from use of the intangible
Organization	x		
Financing	x		
Good will			x
Going value			x
Contracts:			x
Lease			x
Option		x (if well established)	
Easement	x	x	
Franchise	x (public utility)		x (other)
Water right	x (if recent)	x (if well established)	x (if not speculative)
Mineral right	x	x	x
Patent:			x
Active			x
Inactive	x		
Trade secret			x
Trade-mark			x
Copyright			x

14.3. Organization. The determination of a proper allowance for the costs of organization requires a careful search into the financial records of the enterprise. Necessary legal costs, fees, and permits should be included as well as a reasonable allowance for the time spent by the organizers in setting up the business. The costs of professional advice, such as the expense of market surveys indicating the feasibility of launching the new enterprise or engineering reports showing possible locations of the plants or sales offices, are proper items. The costs of engineering plans and specifications are not included here, but rather as a part of the total cost of the fixed capital physical property.

When an enterprise has passed through a reorganization, the items includable as the cost of the organization of the existing corporation would be those incurred in the reorganization plus only such portions of prior organization costs as are found applicable to the reorganized corporation.

If the present enterprise is many times as large as the original venture, an estimate of what it might cost to organize the present business is in order. The cost of additional market or plant location surveys, previously charged to expense, can be found in the records and included. Generally, reasonable recorded costs should prove to be the best basis for determining the value of the intangible property known as organization.

14.4. Financing. The determination of the amount expended by an enterprise for its financing requires a careful search of the book records. This expenditure may not represent the *value* of this intangible, even though the recorded costs were necessary at the time made, for the reason that the existing enterprise might be financed at the date of appraisal by more effective methods than those historically used. The determination of the historical cost of financing thus is reduced to one of including all proper items and excluding improper ones.

The necessary cost of issuing the securities, the advertising required to interest investors in the business, the fair customary costs of selling the securities through normal channels, and a reasonable allowance for office expense during the months required to obtain the necessary capital for construction are all proper items to include. During periods of expansion, costs of new issues of securities are encountered, and these costs, too, should be included. Financing should include the costs of obtaining the capital in use at the date of appraisal. However, when companies have been refinanced one or more times, the costs of prior financings should be excluded to the extent that refinancing has replaced the original capital.

The discounts or premiums on securities should not be considered in the determination of financing costs. In effect each is a change in the nominal interest or dividend rate reflecting the investor's concept of the relative risk of a venture with the enterprise. Suppose, for example, a bond issue of par value of $1,000,000 is purchased by a brokerage for $950,000, who in turn sells the issue to the public for $980,000.

As far as the enterprise is concerned the cost of selling the securities includes only legal, printing, and often sales cost in connection with the issuance of the bonds. The $50,000 difference between the par value of the bonds and the cash received for the bonds from the broker is considered as a bond discount which will be amortized by periodic charges against income.

Other items to be excluded are such things as promoters' remunerations, brokerage on preferred stocks of predecessor companies, and excess of predecessor companies' securities over book value of property acquired therefor. Such items, although each may represent a past expense to the enterprise, are doubtful evidences of a proper present allowance for the cost of financing.

The proper allowance for financing may be estimated by synthetic methods. The procedure followed would include a schedule of the theoretical acquisition of the capital needed to finance the construction of the enterprise as it exists at the date of appraisal. The estimated expenses required to carry out the program would then constitute the allowance for financing. It would be proper to assume that the sources of capital available to the enterprise at the date of appraisal would be used, although these sources may not have been used in the past. However, care must be exercised so that speculative assumptions are avoided.

14.5. Nature of Good Will. The definition of good will (Sec. 14.1) referred to " . . . all that good disposition which customers entertain toward the house of business. . . . " Discussed in this section are the characteristics of good will, those conditions under which good will may be transferred to a new owner, and the good will of public utilities.

Good will is evidenced primarily by the fact that the enterprise possesses many customers who continue to patronize the firm in good times and bad. Such patronage may result from personal relationships, as in professional businesses or retail establishments or to a lesser degree in great enterprises where in spite of size a certain amount of personal contacts are maintained. Such patronage may result from continued effective institutional advertising. Although it is true that some of the same activities promote both good will and going value, these two intangibles are different. Going value stems from the fact that a business has been established and that during the establishment of the business certain costs were incurred and certain expected returns on the investment were not realized. On the other hand, good will stems from the fact that an enterprise enjoys a certain amount of business obtained without effort because the old customers continue to return. Going value relates to the cost of establishing a business. Good will refers to the value which accrues to an already established and maintained business because of its continued favorable relations with its customers and because of its business policies.

Generally, appraisals of good will are made when an establishment is to be sold or an estate is to be settled. Both situations require that the good will of the enterprise be transferred. Good will can be transferable only when many conditions are met. The good will of a professional business is likely to be of value to the new owner only if the firm name is left unchanged, the bulk of the key personnel retained, and the places of doing business left unaltered, and if the old owners agree not to initiate a new establishment in the same area. The transfer of the good will of enterprises in which the personal element is not so important can be accomplished with much less difficulty.

In a competitive, nonregulated enterprise, there may be several evidences of existing good will, but the primary evidence that the good will is valuable is an excess profit over and above a fair return on the investment in the enterprise. Therefore, a public utility, whose earnings are generally limited to a fair return, would not be permitted to include the value of good will in its rate base. The utility, however, may possess good will highly valuable to it. If a public utility were to be sold, the new owner would not be willing to pay much for the good will of the enterprise, since he could not expect to realize therefrom any significantly excess returns in the future.

Established enterprises whose average returns are less than a fair return on the investment in the business may have good will, and it may be of some value. This is so because the average returns might be still less were it not for the good will which the enterprise possesses. However, there must be a reason for the fact that the average returns are less than a fair return; perhaps the risks of doing business are higher than normal for enterprises similar to the one in question, or perhaps the management has not been as alert as it should be. At all events, the earning value of this enterprise will be small. The replacement cost of the property adjusted for depreciation generally will be greater than the earning value.

As a result, even if a certain portion of the returns were attributed to good will and the value of the good will estimated, the value of the physical property must be just that much less.[1] Deficient earnings are criteria for estimating the fair value of the enterprise on the basis of earnings; earning value must be the maximum estimate of the value of the enterprise as a whole.

14.6. Appraisal of Good Will.   In its decision in *Von Au v. Magenheimer et al.*, the appellate division of the New York Supreme Court held that the courts of the United States have not adopted the English rule that the measure of the good will value is one year's purchase of the three years' average net profits or three years' purchase, but that the courts,[2] . . . .

---

[1] The reverse is also true. When the average annual returns are greater than a fair return on the investment in the enterprise, the enterprise may possess valuable good will. The earning value of the enterprise will be greater than the replacement cost of the property adjusted for depreciation. If the value of the enterprise is based primarily on its earning value, an appraisal of the value of good will as well as other property has been automatically included.

[2] *Tillie von Au, as Executrix, etc., of Otto E. von Au, Deceased, Respondent, v. Louis Magenheimer and Charles F. Haug, Appellants, Impleaded with John Noval, Defendant,*

. . . on the contrary, incline to the more equitable rule that the value of good will may be fairly arrived at by multiplying the average net profits (above fair interest) by a number of years, such number being suitable and proper, having reference to the nature and character of the particular business under consideration, and the determination of such proper number of years should be submitted to and determined by the jury as a question of fact. . . .

Such a procedure could be translated into the following formula:

$$\begin{pmatrix} \text{Value of} \\ \text{good} \\ \text{will} \end{pmatrix} = \left[\begin{pmatrix} \text{average} \\ \text{annual} \\ \text{profits} \end{pmatrix} - \begin{pmatrix} \text{fair rate} \\ \text{of re-} \\ \text{turn} \end{pmatrix} \begin{pmatrix} \text{investment} \\ \text{in prop-} \\ \text{erty} \end{pmatrix} \right] \begin{pmatrix} \text{number} \\ \text{of} \\ \text{years} \end{pmatrix} \quad (14.1)$$

To the reader, the expression may be only a way by which a court could ensure that the value of an entire enterprise was greater than the sum of the values of the tangible properties possessed by the enterprise. However, though the expression is an empirical one, it represents an attempt to determine a separate appraisal of good will by setting up a way to calculate what portion of the average returns of an enterprise may be attributed to good will.

How is it possible to estimate that portion of the probable future returns which may be properly attributed to good will? Consider the reason why an enterprise is able to report any positive return at all. It is because all the elements of the enterprise, the physical facilities, the processes, the many items comprising the working capital, the skill of all the employees, and many other things have been assembled into one harmonious whole. The products which have resulted from the activities of all the human and machine effort have been sold to customers who have come back for more. The aggregate of customer demands has resulted in profits to the enterprise.

The owners of the enterprise, under the economic system of this country, expect to receive those profits. They expect each machine to pay its way; they expect to receive a fair wage on their working capital of the enterprise; and they expect a reasonable reimbursement for return forgone during the lean days of the development of the business. Therefore, did not the court in its definition imply that if one were to determine what would be a fair return on all the elements of the property in which the owner had made an investment, the appraiser would have at hand the data to use in determining an estimate of the value of intangible property, including good will? Could not the "net profits above fair interest" represent the returns which can be attributed to those intangible properties which are not a part of the investment in the enterprise?

---

first trial, 115 App. Div. 84, 87, 100 N.Y. Supp. 659, 661 (Oct. 12, 1906); second trial, 126 App. Div. 257, 110 N.Y. Supp. 629, 661 (May 1, 1908) (N.Y. Sup. Ct., App. Div., Second Dept.).

If the questions are answered affirmatively, then the annual return attributed to good will may be determined by the expression

$$\begin{pmatrix} \text{Annual} \\ \text{return} \\ \text{attributed} \\ \text{to good will} \end{pmatrix} = \begin{pmatrix} \text{average} \\ \text{annual} \\ \text{return} \end{pmatrix} - \begin{pmatrix} \text{fair rate} \\ \text{of} \\ \text{return} \end{pmatrix} \begin{pmatrix} \text{investment} \\ \text{in the} \\ \text{enterprise} \end{pmatrix} - \begin{pmatrix} \text{annual return} \\ \text{credited to} \\ \text{specific other} \\ \text{intangible} \\ \text{properties} \end{pmatrix}$$

(14.2)

where the investment in the enterprise equals the sum of the fair cost adjusted for depreciation of the fixed capital physical property, the working capital, organization, financing, going value, and any other intangible properties acquired by investment.

The specific other intangible items are those intangibles for which a specific annual return can be estimated. Examples of such items are: most contracts, active patents, and trade secrets.

The average annual return used in the above determination is customarily a 3- to 5-year average of normal present and past returns, consideration being given to the trends of the near future. The fair rate of return is that appropriate for the enterprise (see Chap. 15).

Referring to the court's definition as expressed by Formula (14.1), the reader will note that "number of years" is the final requirement. This factor is included in the formula because it is assumed that a would-be purchaser of the enterprise might be willing to pay much more than just *one* year's excess return in order to acquire the good will of the enterprise. The "history and circumstances" of the enterprise might indicate a much larger figure. For example, the following are instances where good will was measured by several years' purchase:

In re Ball's Estate, N.Y. Sup. Ct. (1914), 3 years
In re Hearn's Estate, N.Y. Sup. Ct. (1917), 5 years
Von Au v. Magenheimer et al., N.Y. Sup. Ct. (1906), 6 years
Matter of Moore, N.Y. Sup. Ct. (1916), 10 years

Factors which bear on the size of the estimate are sales, earnings record, dividends record, reputation and standing of the enterprise in the industry, its permanence, and the like.

The number of years' purchase may be more real to the reader if he relates it to the factor obtained by capitalizing an annual income. Thus, the capitalization rates corresponding to the above-mentioned years' purchase would be equivalent to buying a perpetual annuity at the rates of $33\frac{1}{3}$, 20, $16\frac{2}{3}$, and 10 percent, respectively. These rates approximate the relative hazards of such a return continuing indefinitely.

It is true that if the good will of an enterprise centers completely in one person, the good will may not continue for any time after the separation of this person from the enterprise. On the other hand, a corporation may possess good will (and excess returns as a result) for an indefinite future period provided the management continues to advertise, promote new products, have sensible operating policies, and the like. Still, *the risk attending the continuance* of these excess returns is much greater than the ordinary risks of doing business. Accordingly, it should be expected that the rate used to determine the value of the returns attributed to good will should be 1½ to 5 times the fair rate of return for the enterprise as a whole.

The reader should appreciate, then, that to use a capitalization rate of 10 percent (corresponding to a 10 years' purchase) in determining the value of good will is to imply that in such an instance the risk of earning an excess return is little more than the ordinary hazards of doing business day by day.

Should the appraiser conclude that the returns attributed to good will may continue for only a limited period, the value of good will is the present worth of these returns at an appropriate rate of return.

In summary, a procedure for calculating an estimate of the value of good will is:

1. Estimate the fair cost, adjusted for depreciation, for the tangible properties possessed by the enterprise. Add the fair cost of such intangibles as organization, financing, and going value.

2. Estimate the average return of the entire enterprise based on a 3- to 5-year average of normal past and present operations.

3. Determine the excess return which can be attributed to the possession of good will, using Formula (14.2).

4. Estimate an appropriate rate of capitalization to be used in the appraisal of the good will, considering the hazards attending the indefinite continuance of the excess returns.

5. Capitalize the returns attributed to good will at the appropriate rate.

or

4a. Estimate the number of years the excess returns may be expected to continue.

5a. Compute the present worth of these returns at an appropriate rate of return.

14.7. Illustration of the Appraisal of Good Will. Suppose that the following data apply to an enterprise engaged in the production of a variety of small metal parts used extensively in the automotive industry. The company has been in existence for about 50 years, has enjoyed a steady growth, has competent progressive management, and follows sound policies in both its public and industrial relations.

Present investment in plant and equipment.............	$15,150,000
Fair allowance for organization and financing...........	330,000
Average requirement of working capital................	2,850,000
Estimate of going value...............................	500,000
Probable average annual return......	1,650,000
Portion of return attributable to patents........	0.05
Fair rate of return of enterprise......................	0.08

Using Formula (14.2), the return attributed to good will is

Annual return attributed to good will

$$= \$1,650,000 - (0.08)(18,830,000) - (0.05)(1,650,000)$$
$$= \$1,650,000 - 1,506,400 - 82,500$$
$$= \$61,100$$

Two solutions are presented, using the $61,100 annual return attributable to good will. First, let it be concluded that the good will of this enterprise can be maintained indefinitely by the continuance of present policies but that the risk attending the continuance of the excess return above a fair rate is twice that of the average risk which the enterprise encounters. Therefore, the capitalization rate used to find the value of the probable returns attributed to good will is 16 percent.

The value of good will $= \dfrac{61,100}{0.16} = 381,900$, or about $380,000

Second, suppose that the appraiser concludes that the returns attributed to good will can be expected to continue but 3 years because of the importance to the success of the enterprise of one of the men in top management who is slated for retirement. The hazard of the continuance of the returns attributed to good will for this limited period is no more than the ordinary risks of the enterprise. Then the value of the good will is:

$$P = R \left[\frac{(1 + r)^n - 1}{r(1 + r)^n} \right]$$

$$P = 61,100 \left[\frac{1.08^3 - 1}{(0.08)(1.08)^3} \right]$$

$$P = (61,100)(2.577) = \$157,500$$

14.8. Going Value. In the *Des Moines Gas Co.* case the United States Supreme Court said:[1]

[1] *Des Moines Gas Company v. City of Des Moines* (No. 75), 238 U.S. 153, 165, P.U.R. 1915D, 577 (U.S. Sup. Ct. June 14, 1915).

See also Appendix A, Cases 10, 30, 42, and 62, in which the Court expressed a similar opinion or reaffirmed its position in the *Des Moines Gas Co.* case.

. . . That there is an element of value in an assembled and established plant, doing business and earning money, over one not thus advanced, is self-evident. This element of value is a property right, and should be considered in determining the value of the property, upon which the owner has a right to make a fair return when the same is privately owned although dedicated to public use.

Though the courts recognize the property right of going value, they have not indicated a preferred method of determining its dollar value. They rely on data relating to the history and circumstances of each enterprise as a basis of allowances for going value.

What, then, are the details of the history and circumstances which would indicate that an enterprise possesses going value? First, the enterprise must be doing business and earning money, and there should be some evidence that the enterprise will continue to do so. Distribution outlets should be more or less fixed; each year's list of customers should contain the names of many of the same people. Contracts for future business or services or the franchises possessed by the enterprise should give some indication that the company is here to stay for an indefinite future period. It should be evident that the employees have become sufficiently trained and experienced so that they are a team.

In addition, the history and circumstances which indicate that an enterprise possesses going value should show something relating to the ways by which an enterprise acquired its going value. An enterprise usually obtains customers by going out after them. It makes an extraordinary promotional campaign; it offers its products at attractive prices; it opens up as many new sales outlets as possible. All such activities cost a great deal, and there will probably be a history of low returns for a short period before satisfactory returns are reached.

A *first method* by which an estimate of going value may be made is based on the expenditures that the company may have made in carrying out a program of promotion. The analyst can assemble the data in such a way as to show how much it has cost in promotional work of all kinds to acquire the present clientele. (He may estimate what it costs on the average to acquire one customer and multiply it by the present number of customers.) This estimate is an approximation of the cost of acquiring the present business. To the extent that cost is a measure of value, this estimated cost of acquiring customers may be used as an evidence of the going value.

The investigation of the history and circumstances of the enterprise may indicate that a slower, and perhaps surer, way of acquiring an established business was taken. Instead of the extraordinary campaign, the normal process of growth was followed. Perhaps a planned program of expansion was prescribed. In such a case, it would be normal to have a more or less constant excess of physical plant awaiting the day when actual customer demand necessitates its use. As a result of this excess investment, it would be normal to expect such an enterprise to have a history of low rates of returns. Eventually, of course, with the business established, these rates of returns will approach and pass a fair rate.

A *second method* of estimating the going value of an established enterprise is suggested by these data. The analyst can determine the annual difference between the annual returns of the enterprise and the fair return on the investment in the enterprise. The aggregate of this "return forgone" for the period of the development of the business may be a pertinent evidence of the going value of an established enterprise. Table 14.2 illustrates such a calculation.

Whether a business is established by extraordinary sales promotional activity, by filling a need so great that success is almost immediate, or by a program of gradual development, there should result a record of increasing returns in its early development and fair returns or larger in the period just preceding valuation. A situation of fair returns or larger is necessary to indicate that the present business is established, for this is one of the requirements of the existence of going value.

A *third evidence* of value, perhaps more correct from the standpoint of valuation theory, but more difficult as far as the collection of pertinent data is concerned, is an estimate based on a comparison of the potential returns of an "assembled and established plant" with one "not thus advanced." This latter enterprise is a theoretically exact duplicate of the established plant, but at the date of valuation possesses no customers. The present worth of the differences of the probable returns of the two plants for the period required for the latter plant to acquire the customers is one measure of the value of the established business.

14.9. Illustrations of Methods of Estimating Going Value. Suppose that the following data apply to an enterprise engaged in the fabrication of steel structures used by farmers, small power companies, and rural retail establishments.

Original investment in the enterprise	$ 50,000
Present investment in the enterprise	$150,000
Average annual gross income	$186,000
Average annual return	$ 40,000
Number of full-time salesmen	6
Present number of customers obtained primarily by salesmen through personal contact	700
Number of years required to develop present business	5
Average annual salary and expense paid each salesman	$ 8,500

TABLE 14.2. ESTIMATION OF GOING VALUE BASED UPON RETURNS BELOW A FAIR RETURN ON INVESTMENT DURING DEVELOPMENT PERIOD

Year	Total average plant and equipment in service	Working capital	Total investment	Revenues	Expenses	Actual return for year	Fair return on investment at 6%	Deficit below fair return	Present worth of deficit at 6%
1	$ 3,910,578	$133,140	$ 4,043,718	$ 830,488	$ 784,364	$ 46,124	$ 242,623	$196,499	$ 185,376
2	7,318,641	208,415	7,527,056	1,297,892	1,226,536	71,356	451,623	380,267	338,436
3	8,399,428	227,874	8,627,302	1,438,520	1,342,240	96,280	517,638	421,358	353,780
4	9,124,523	245,285	9,369,808	1,676,500	1,447,788	228,712	562,188	333,476	264,144
5	12,271,253	325,169	12,596,422	2,325,796	1,912,368	413,428	755,785	342,357	255,829
6	13,141,655	370,744	13,512,399	2,834,336	2,182,048	652,288	810,744	158,456	111,705
7	18,371,020	483,913	18,854,933	3,845,312	2,846,428	998,884	1,131,296	132,412	88,062
8	18,729,568	512,077	19,241,645	4,287,968	3,015,468	1,272,500	1,154,499	None	
Total									$1,597,332

Past operating statistics for the development of business period are:

Year	1	2	3	4	5
Average investment....	$50,000	$100,000	$130,000	$140,000	$150,000
Gross income..........	37,200	74,400	111,600	148,800	186,000
Expenses.............	49,000	69,000	116,400	135,200	146,000
Annual return.......	−$11,800	$ 5,400	−$ 4,800	$ 13,600	$ 40,000

Probable average return for each of the next 5 years......... $ 40,000 to $ 50,000
Probable average investment for the next 5-year period...... $150,000 to $175,000
Probable deficit of the theoretical duplicate enterprise for its
first year... $ 44,000

An estimate of the going value will now be made by each of the three methods presented in Sec. 14.8. For the first method, let it be assumed that each salesman has one-sixth of the present customers, or 117 customers, and that he spends about one-fourth of his time and effort each year in obtaining new customers. Then the average cost of acquiring each present customer would be

$$\left(\frac{1}{4}\right) \frac{(5)(\$8,500)}{117}, \text{ or } \$91$$

The cost of acquiring the present 700 customers would be about $63,700.

Method 2 would require an analysis of the past growth of the enterprise as given in Table 14.3. It would appear that the record shows a history

TABLE 14.3. COMPARISON OF PAST ACTUAL RETURNS WITH FAIR
RETURNS

Year	Average investment for year	Fair annual return at 12%	Record of return for year	Amount actual return is less than a fair return	Present worth of difference
1	$ 50,000	$ 6,000	−$11,800	$17,800	$15,900
2	100,000	12,000	5,400	6,600	5,300
3	130,000	15,600	−4,800	20,400	14,500
4	140,000	16,800	13,600	3,200	2,100
5	150,000	18,000	40,000	None	
Total.	....	....	....	$48,000	$37,800

of low rates of returns but that the present return is sufficient to consider the present business established. Consequently, another evidence of going value is $37,800.

The third method, the comparative method, requires as data a comparison of the probable returns of an assembled and established plant and its exact duplicate "not thus advanced." Figure 14.1 shows the comparisons graphically, and Table 14.4 indicates the detail of the calculations. Thus a third evidence of the going value of the established business is $79,000.

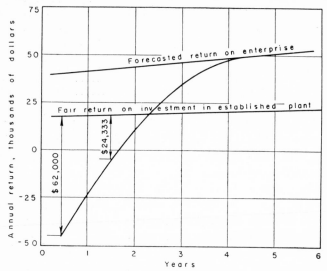

FIG. 14.1. Comparison of probable annual return of established plant with one not thus advanced.

The estimate of the return of the hypothetical plant for the first year was based on an assumption of what six salesmen could do in acquiring new business. Since it was assumed that 5 years would be required to develop the business, the smooth curve of Fig. 14.1 was drawn, starting

TABLE 14.4. COMPARATIVE METHOD OF ESTIMATING GOING VALUE

| Year | Forecasted annual return | | Difference | Present worth* at 12% |
	Established plant	Plant not thus advanced		
1	$18,000	−$44,000	$62,000	$58,500
2	19,333	− 5,000	24,333	20,530
Total....	$37,333	−$49,000	$86,333	$79,030

* Midyear assumed, giving $1.12^{0.5}$ and $1.12^{1.5}$ as present worth factors.

at $44,000 deficit and ending tangent to the return curve of the established plant. The forecasted annual returns of each plant and their differences for each year were taken directly from Fig. 14.1.

The differences are measured by reference not to the forecasted return of the established plant but rather to the fair return on the investment. The difference which is apparently unaccounted for consists of the return which can be attributed to such intangibles as good will, patents, trade secrets, and contracts. The purpose of an estimate of going value in an appraisal is to give monetary recognition to the fact that the business of the enterprise is established and that in acquiring going value an enterprise normally experiences a period where returns are below a *fair return*. Care must be taken to ensure that the allowance for this excess return above a fair return is not included twice, once incorrectly, as an increment of going value, and again as a part of good will value.

In summary, it is suggested that the appraiser attempt to secure data so that he may estimate going value by all three methods. It is not especially necessary that the results check closely. Instead, it should be considered that these results will indicate a satisfactory range for the final estimate of going value.

14.10. Contracts. The cost of a contract is sometimes the best evidence of its value. In fact, the amount paid by an enterprise for a contract such as an easement may often be the only data available. An example is the amount paid to a farm owner by a power company for the right to install the poles or towers of a transmission line across a section of the farm. Likewise, the reasonable cost of acquiring a franchise is the maximum generally allowed a utility in its rate base. Since a franchise does not prevent the issuing authority from initiating proceedings designed to alter the rate structure, there is no real basis for attempting to appraise a franchise from the standpoint of prospective earnings.

Other kinds of contracts may be appraised on the basis of the average market values of similar contracts. The option to buy or lease the mineral rights of a tract of land and the lease of the land are examples of this kind of contract. Care should be exercised, as is always the case in dealing with market values, that prices are representative and are stable.

When contracts have firm price provisions which are significantly different from average prevailing prices, then these agreements can be appraised on the basis of the present worth of the extra return attributed solely to the possession of the specific contract. Consider the agreement where A contracts to deliver, for a period of a year, 2,000 tons of coal monthly to B at an average delivered price of $5 per ton. After a few months, the average price for coal rises, say to $6 per ton. B has a firm contract; he ascertains that there is no other source where he may obtain coal at the old price. This contract has become valuable to B. Its worth is the present worth of $2,000 monthly for the remaining term of the contract. On the other hand, if this were to be appraised as the property of A, the contract has a negative value equal to its positive value to B. In fact, A would be no worse off if he were to pay B cheerfully the value of the contract, tear it up, and then write a new contract with B at the specified new price of $6 per ton.

14.11. Patents and Trade Secrets. Generally, the value of an active patent or a trade secret is determined by estimating the present worth of that part of the annual return which can be attributed to the patent or trade secret. Determining just what portion of the entire return can be considered to result from the operation of the patents constitutes the core of the appraiser's problem. These returns can be estimated easily in case the enterprise leases a certain patent to a competitor and receives royalties as a result. Suppose company Z owns a patent and produces 100,000 units annually of the product covered by the patent. Company Z also leases the patent to company Y, which produces and sells 50,000 units annually, paying Z $1 for each unit manufactured. In this instance, the annual return of company Z which can be attributed to the possession of the patent is $150,000.

If, however, company Z did not lease the patent, one might try to estimate the returns attributable to the possession of the patent on the basis of what might be a fair unit royalty if the patent were leased. Such a procedure is acceptable as long as the estimates are not fanciful or conjectural.

Another way of finding such data is by estimating the savings in production cost which may be obtained when a patent primarily covers a process improvement. Suppose the cost of producing the product using the old process is $10 per unit and by the new process $7. The unit return attributable to the possession of this patent is $3, and if the production is 100,000 units annually, the value of the patent is equal to the present worth, at an appropriate rate of interest, of $300,000 annually for the life of the patent provided the present conditions continue. However, the progress in engineering design may cause the appraiser to estimate that the expected savings may not continue for the remaining legal life of the patent, and so he might reduce accordingly the expected dollar return from the patent. The reduction may take the form of decreasing annual returns or constant returns for fewer years. When the appraiser considers that the hazard of the continuance of the savings is much greater than the fair rate of return, he may choose to use a rate of return in the annuity which is correspondingly greater than the fair rate of return for the business.

Generally, the value of an inactive patent is nominal. Since the patent is inactive, it is doubtful that the patent really provides any additional returns. However, if it can be shown that the patent, by not being used, is able to protect the earnings of the enterprise or give better service, then the customary determination of patent value can be made.

More often, such a computation cannot be made. About the only evidence of value is the record of the development cost or purchase price adjusted for the approach of the date of expiration of the right. The fact that the development cost was charged to expense in the past has no bearing on the valuation save in the determination of a rate base. The appraiser might seek to determine a theoretical market value for the patent by ascertaining what a competitor might be willing to bid on it or a theoretical earning value on the basis of a possible royalty. Such estimates may be too conjectural to be of much use in the appraisal of an inactive patent.

Patents and trade secrets possessed by a utility may be included in a rate base, but only on the basis of the investment still remaining unamortized. A further requisite is proof that the patent is used and useful in the public service. Such proof would include an indication that the use of the patent provides a better service to the public or that production costs are decreased.

In summary, the value of the probable earnings attributed to the intangible will generally be the most substantial evidence of the value of a patent or trade secret. In special cases, the cost adjusted for reduced expectancy may be significant.

14.12. Mineral Rights and Water Rights. The appraisal of the right to extract a mineral resource from a given area is based generally on the value of the probable earnings which can be attributed to the possession of the right. Since many of the details of such an appraisal are those involved in the valuation of an enterprise established to develop the right, this subject is discussed in Chap. 18.

Water rights, such as the right to use water for irrigation or for industrial purposes, owned by individuals or by private enterprises, may be appraised by use of any of the several evidences of value for which the data are available. If the right is of such a character that similar ones are frequently exchanged, then a market value can be obtained.

It may be that the right can be appraised on the basis of the value of the savings which can be attributed to the possession of the specific right. Comparison of the average production costs of the existing enterprise with the theoretical production costs of a hypothetical alternate of the same capacity for service, but without the water right, may be used as a basis for the estimate of the value of the water right.

Finally, if the development cost or the actual purchase price of the water right appears to the appraiser to be reasonable, such evidence may have a bearing on the establishment of the value of the right.

In the determination of a rate base, however, regulatory agencies have generally used market value or cost less the amount amortized as the figure to be included in the rate base for the value of the water right.

Usually, claims of an allowance for the value of a water right based upon the present worth of the earnings expected from the use of the right have been ignored or specifically excluded.

Utilities may have water rights involving the control or use of a watershed area for the impounding of water or the utilization of underground water. A second similar right is the riparian right in connection with a combination of land use and water use such as is found in a hydroelectric development.

In the first case, the primary evidence of the value of the watershed is the market value of similar lands devoted to the best feasible use. One might ask if the added value of the area has been accounted for adequately now that several parcels of land are in the hands of one owner. The development of the watershed generally makes it probable that the entire area in the vicinity of the watershed has enjoyed a period of substantially increased returns. Such situations are recognized by those who buy and sell such or similar lands, and market values reflect the influence of such factors. It thus appears that the value of the water right is an inherent part of the value of the land, and efforts to separate the two are illogical and unnecessary in an appraisal.

Watersheds which are developed in order to gain access to underground waters or to percolating waters are in a similar category. A waterworks company possessing such a watershed might have the water right appraised on the basis of the capitalized savings enjoyed by them in comparison with the annual cost of an alternate method of obtaining surface water and a purification plant. Consider, however, the more realistic evidence of the market value of such land or similar land as potential farm land, industrial sites, or as sites for gravel and sand pits. The objective is to obtain the value of such lands when devoted to their highest and most appropriate use. Again, the value of the water right is a part of the value of the land.

The riparian right and the water right used in a hydroelectric development can be appraised in various ways, but the cost of the rights themselves or the value of the land as a potential or actual development generally becomes the basis for their inclusion in a rate base.

One method, now generally discredited, of calculating the intangible value of a power site involved the capitalization of the annual savings of the hydroelectric development over a hypothetical steam plant of identical capacity located in the same general vicinity. Such a method involves many conjectural estimates. In addition, to include such a value in a rate base means that the customers will be forced to pay as much for their electrical energy produced by water power as if the energy were produced by coal. Obviously, the public is not sharing in the benefits of the development of the power site; in fact, they may be paying rates on an intangible value which may have belonged at one time to the public.

In summary, water rights may be appraised by any one of several ways for which data are available. But conjectural estimates are to be avoided. In rate base determinations, a reasonable cost or a market value usually represents the most substantial evidence of value.

CHAPTER 15

Rate of Return

The valuation process includes the determination of the elements discussed in Chaps. 3 to 14 and one additional inherent element. This additional element is the fair rate of return, discussed in this chapter.

The fair rate of return is a factor required in the estimation of the several evidences of the value of many different items of property. Usually, however, a circuitous relation can be said to exist between the value of property and the rate of return; thus it is necessary to obtain independent data for the latter estimate.

The fair rate of return might be approximated by use of allowances for each of its attributes—pure interest plus compensation for the risks, uncertainties, and the otherwise unrewarded managerial efficiency. A more objective estimate might be based on the average annual cost of the capital employed in the enterprise, modified as necessary to allow the enterprise to maintain its standing in the capital market.

It is the purpose of this chapter to discuss the evidences relating to the fair rate of return and to indicate how to estimate the fair rate of return for a specific enterprise.

15.1. Use and Significance of Rate of Return. In the discussion relating to the estimation of interest during construction (Chap. 6), the rate of return on the investment of funds in idle plant is considered. The point is made that the managers of the enterprise had employed funds in the construction of plant knowing full well what risks were present. The determination of the return foregone during construction should be at a rate appropriate with the risks involved. That rate is the fair rate of return.

Again, in Chap. 11, the role of depreciation in appraisals is outlined. It is pointed out that when value of depreciable property is the objective, such value may be determined by use of an expectancy-life factor in which a rate of return appears. Such a rate of return is most appropriately the fair rate of return.

The procedures required in the estimation of the evidences of value of many of the intangible properties are discussed in Chap. 14. Several of these procedures require the present worth of sums receivable in the future; the fair rate of return should be used as the appropriate rate in the present worth calculation. In addition, the determination of going value and the value of good will require the use of the fair rate of return as a frame of reference.

The determination of the earning value and the service worth value of an enterprise is discussed in Chap. 16. The formulas which are used require the fair rate of return.

It thus appears that the fair rate of return is an important element in the valuation process since it is used in so many calculations.

The size of the fair rate of return affects materially any calculation in which it is a factor. In the estimation of interest during construction, the amount of return foregone is directly proportional to the magnitude of the fair rate of return. Should the expectancy-life factor be used to calculate an evidence of value of a property of a given age and probable life, the factor will be larger as the rate of return is increased. Thus, the expectancy-life factor[1] for a unit of property aged 20 years and with a probable life of 40 years is 0.500 if the rate is 0 percent, 0.726 if the rate is 5 percent, and 0.823 if the rate is 8 percent.

As calculated in Chap. 14, the value of the good will of an enterprise is inversely proportional to the size of the fair rate of return, though the relationship is not linear.

15.2. Rate of Return Defined. Expressed most simply, the rate of return of an enterprise is the quotient of its annual return divided by an appropriate base, the result usually being expressed in percent. The base[2] can be the value of the enterprise, the original cost adjusted for the consumption of the useful service of the property, or the amount shown by the financial records to be the existing investment in the enterprise.

When the base and the annual return of an enterprise are known, the rate of return is determined easily. However, such a determination does not of itself disclose whether or not the rate is fair. There must be some standard. That standard is called the *fair rate of return.* It is determined by judgment, based on a proper consideration of the factors inherent in the rate.

Theoretically, the fair rate of return " . . . embodies at least three important and identifiable elements: (a) An amount equivalent to the alternative pure interest obtainable on a sum equal to the fair value; (b) compensation for risks and uncertainties; and (c) compensation for

---

[1] See Appendix C for expectancy-life factors.

[2] The rate base of a public utility is frequently used as the base upon which the rate of return is calculated. In those states where the regulation of security issues has been so thorough that no "watered stock" exists, the base may be taken from the book accounts pertaining to the securities issued by the corporation.

management functions not otherwise rewarded."[1] These attributes of the fair rate of return are discussed in the following sections.

15.3. Attributes of the Fair Rate of Return—Pure Interest. Pure interest is the compensation, based solely on the time factor, for the use of money. Pure interest also expresses the relative premium one would be willing to pay at the present time for the privilege of having cash or equivalent value on hand as compared with the receipt of that sum at some future date.

Pure interest may be defined as the market value of time preference. The reasons for people's time preference are many. Sufficient for these purposes that the general preference is for the present as against the future, to such an extent that the present purchasing power which funds give, commands a premium. This market value of time preference, as noted above, is only one of the elements in loan interest or the price of loanable funds, but it is a primary and important element.

Pure interest is difficult to measure because it never manifests itself in pure form. In "loan interest" it is always combined with elements of risk and management compensation.[2]

Unfortunately, pure interest is not easily determined because the use of the bulk of invested capital involves some risks and uncertainties. The annual cost of some short-term capital undoubtedly is as free of uncertainties and sometimes of risks as any, but such rates do not necessarily reflect the required rates for long-term capital.

The average yield of United States government bonds might be used as an indication of pure interest, but the sale of bonds by the government to banks is one method of influencing the yield on bonds. Hence, the yield on government bonds does not necessarily reflect risk-free rates. State governments and municipalities also issue bonds at rates of interest comparable with rates obtained by the United States government. The rates on the local bonds may be used as satisfactory evidence of pure interest rates. In comparing the interest rates of high-grade securities consideration should be given to whether or not the interest is taxable under state or federal income tax laws.

Another difficulty appears when the analyst investigates the status of the capital market. The employment of funds depends on the business cycle. During years of depression, the accumulating capital is employed chiefly in investments having a maximum of liquidity and a minimum of risk. Consequently, a surplus of capital then exists for minimum risk

---

[1] Testimony May 7, 1937, by Dr. Herbert B. Dorau in *The Peoples Gas Light and Coke Co., Appellee, v. James M. Slattery et al., Appellants* (No. 24,836), 373 Ill. 31, 31 P.U.R. (N.S.) 193 (Ill. Sup. Ct. Dec. 12, 1939). See Abstract of Testimony, Vol. 4, pp. 2558–2559; or Record, pp. 8268–8269.

[2] *Ibid.*, Abstract of Testimony, Vol. 4, p. 2560; or Record, pp. 8271–8272.

ventures, and the rate of interest declines. The reverse is true in times of prosperity. Thus, cycles in the magnitude of the risk-free interest rate appear. However, the financial policies of the government tend to eliminate the larger variations, with a trend toward the lower rates.

An evidence of the size of the pure interest component of the fair rate of return is shown in Table 15.1. The variations shown by these yields

TABLE 15.1. YIELDS OF UNITED STATES GOVERNMENT BONDS
Source: *Engineering News-Record*, Annual Survey of Costs and Trends, Vol. 146, Mar. 29, 1951
1933–1941: Average yield of long-term United States Treasury bonds, partially tax-exempt, not due or callable for 15 years—*Federal Reserve Bulletin*
1942 to date: Average long-term government bonds, taxable—*Standard Statistics and Poor's*

Year	Yield, percent	Year	Yield, percent
1933	3.31	1943	2.29
1934	3.12	1944	2.38
1935	2.79	1945	2.34
1936	2.69	1946	2.19
1937	2.74	1947	2.24
1938	2.61	1948	2.43
1939	2.41	1949	2.28
1940	2.26	1950	2.32
1941	2.05	1951	2.60
1942	2.27		

on United States government bonds are, of course, subject to changes in the financial policies of the government.

15.4. Attributes of the Rate of Return—Additive Compensations. The additive factor compensating for the risks and uncertainties accompanying an investment in an enterprise varies greatly. Such variation is inevitable because the hazards attending individual investments differ widely. The causes of these variations are likewise numerous. A list of such items might include:

Type of business
Competition
Competency of the management
Reputation of the business and the industry
Location of the plants and the markets of the enterprise
Relative age and the present stability of the enterprise
Stability of the past and the probable future earnings
Size, financial strength, and financial history of the enterprise
Past and current demands for capital
Relative price trends of the products of the enterprise

Space does not permit any extended discussion[1] of each of these items, nor is it possible to estimate what might be the effect of each item on the rate of return. However, an approximation of the aggregate effect of these items on the estimate of the fair rate of return is indicated in Table 15.2.

TABLE 15.2.   FAIR RATE OF RETURN FOR TYPES OF ENTERPRISES

Type of business	Allowance, percent, for			
	Pure interest	Risks and uncertainties	Managerial efficiency	Total
Permanent business, assured stable earnings.................	2¼–2¾	2–4	0–1	4¼–7¾
Permanent business with small risk......................	2¼–2¾	3–5	0–1	5¼–8¾
Public utilities under indefinite franchises, little risk..........	2¼–2¾	3–4	0–1	5¼–7¾
Business with average risk......	2¼–2¾	4–7	0–1	6 –11
Business likely not to be permanent, with average risk.......	2¼–2¾	5–9	0–1	7 –13
Business significantly affected by climatic conditions...........	2¼–2¾	8–12	0–1	10 –16
Business with high risk..........	2¼–2¾	10 up	0–1	12 up
Enterprises yet to be initiated...	2¼–2¾	5 up	0–1	7 up

The additive factor compensating for managerial efficiency otherwise unrewarded generally will be small. However, such a factor is desirable in utility regulation, for commissions[2] can set up a schedule so that the fair rate of return can increase slightly as the cost of service and the charges to customers decrease, provided the service to the customers is maintained at a high level of efficiency.

The size of such an additive factor is generally not determinable by quantitative means, but in one case it was testified that it might be 1 percent.[3]

15.5. Fair Rate of Return—Pure Interest Plus Additive Compensations.   The fair rate of return has been defined as a rate which includes a proper allowance for pure interest plus a proper provision for risks, uncertainties, and high managerial efficiency not otherwise

[1] A good discussion of many of the court cases in which the attributes of the rate of return have been mentioned is found in Henry C. Spurr, "Guiding Principles of Public Service Regulation," Vol. III, pp. 36–187, Public Utilities Reports, Inc., Washington, D.C., 1924.

[2] See *Connecticut Public Utilities Commission Re Eastern Motor Freight Bureau, Incorporated*, Docket No. 6438, 20 P.U.R. (N.S.) 50 (June 4, 1937).

[3] Dorau, *op. cit.*, Abstract of Testimony, Vol. 4, p. 2802, Record, p. 9274.

rewarded. It should be possible, then, to take the determinations of the two previous sections and estimate a fair rate of return for an enterprise. Table 15.2 shows such a summary.

However, the appraiser must be able to judge correctly the relative risks attending an investment in a specific enterprise; he must be aware of the hazards attending an investment in any certain industry; and he must have some knowledge of the relative standing of the enterprise being appraised. All these considerations are necessary factors in the estimation of a fair rate of return, and, in fact, some *close knowledge* must be obtained in order to narrow down the range of the possible fair rates of return.

The appraiser has no recourse, however, but to try to solve the problem. He cannot use, for example, a fair rate of return for a business with stable assured earnings as "something between 6 percent and $8\frac{1}{2}$ percent." This range is just too great. He can, however, obtain data relating to the past rates of return, the historical cost of the capital employed by the enterprise, or the theoretical cost of the capital under various assumed situations. Such estimates tend to eliminate to a large degree the vagueness of a fair rate of return set by methods suggested in the preceding two sections.

15.6. Fair Rate of Return—Public Utilities. The guiding legal principles relating to the rate of return which a public utility should be permitted to earn are found in the decisions of the courts. The following quotations from the United States Supreme Court summarize its judgment on the matter:[1]

What annual rate [of return] will constitute just compensation depends upon many circumstances and must be determined by the exercise of a fair and enlightened judgment, having regard to all relevant facts. A public utility is entitled to such rates as will permit it to earn a return on the value of the property which it employs for the convenience of the public equal to that generally being made at the same time and in the same general part of the country on investments in other business undertakings which are attended by corresponding risks and uncertainties; but it has no constitutional right to profits such as are realized or anticipated in highly profitable enterprises or speculative ventures. The return should be reasonably sufficient to assure confidence in the financial soundness of the utility and should be adequate, under efficient and economical management, to maintain and support its credit and enable it to raise the money necessary for the proper discharge of its public duties. A rate of return may be reasonable at one time and become too high or too low by changes affecting opportunities for investment, the money market and business conditions generally.

---

[1] *Bluefield Waterworks and Improvement Co. v. Public Service Commission of the State of West Virginia et al.* (No. 256), 262 U.S. 679, P.U.R. 1923D, 11 (U.S. Sup. Ct. June 11, 1923).

More recently, the Supreme Court restated these principles in the *Hope* case (1944):[1]

The rate-making process under the Act, i.e., the fixing of "just and reasonable" rates, involves a balancing of the investor and the customer interests. . . . the investor interest has a legitimate concern with the financial integrity of the company whose rates are being regulated. From the investor or company point of view it is important that there be enough revenue not only for operating expenses but also for the capital costs of the business. These include service on the debt and dividends on the stock. . . . By that standard the return to the equity owner should be commensurate with returns on investments in other enterprises having corresponding risks. That return, moreover, should be sufficient to assure confidence in the financial integrity of the enterprise, so as to maintain its credit and to attract capital.

The process by which a fair rate of return may be obtained has been a matter of discussion by other courts of the land. The Supreme Court of New Hampshire said, in part:[2]

The question of fixing a rate of return to be applied to the rate base is peculiarly within the discretion of the Commission. Whether it should rely upon the expert testimony presented by the State in preference to that offered by the Company cannot be decided as a matter of law. The proper rate of return is a matter for the judgment of the Commission, based upon the evidence before it. In fixing the rate the cost of capital may not be ignored; but what that cost may be is also a matter for determination by the Commission upon the evidence.

Another summary of the pertinent factors which should be investigated before setting a fair rate of return was made by the North Carolina Utilities Commission in 1949:[3]

In arriving at a rate of return . . . the Commission has given consideration to the financial history of the company; to its earning in the past as compared with the present; to the cost of rendering service under existing high prices; to the ratio of its debt capital to its equity capital; to the general market trends in the cost of labor, materials, and capital; to the opportunity of investors to invest in other business undertakings of comparable stability and soundness; to the opportunity for growth and expansion and to the public demand therefor; to the protection afforded against destructive competition; to the value of the service to telephone users and to the probability of diminishing returns from rates and charges that approach burdensome proportions.

[1] *Federal Power Commission et al. v. Hope Natural Gas Co.* (No. 34), 320 U.S. 591, 603, 51 P.U.R. (N.S.) 193 (U.S. Sup. Ct. Jan. 3, 1944).

[2] *New England Telephone & Telegraph Co. v. The State of New Hampshire et al.* (No. 3798), 78 P.U.R. (N.S.) 67 (N.H. Sup. Ct. Feb. 1, 1949).

[3] *North Carolina Utilities Commission Re Southern Bell Telephone & Telegraph Co.*, Docket No. 4574, 79 P.U.R. (N.S.) 109, 116 (Apr. 22, 1949).

Testimony introduced in a commission case involving a request of another operating telephone company for an increase in rates included:[1]

In determination of a fair rate of return, the cost of capital is the most important component and class of evidence; but other factors, many of which cannot be reduced to reliable mathematical calculations, must also be considered, in my opinion. Under almost any conceivable circumstance, the cost of capital would be a minimum and the fair rate of return would be somewhat more than the cost of capital.

Summarizing, the fair rate of return of utilities should be commensurate with the rate of return of other business undertakings with similar risks; it should be large enough to assure would-be investors of the credit standing of the utility and to enable the company to attract new capital at reasonable rates; it should be large enough to enable the utility to service its debt and to pay dividends on its stock; it should be at least equal to the average cost of capital.[2]

Such a summary, however, gives the reader only a clue regarding the method which is used to set a fair rate of return for a specific utility. It appears that regulating agencies frequently have set a fair rate of return by examining other litigations, finding out what rates of return were approved, and then setting a rate somewhere within the approved range. Such a procedure may not be scientific, but the pattern which has been set has reflected current trends. In addition, the results of the past several years have shown that, with the exception of local transit companies, utilities have been able to acquire new capital easily at reasonable rates.

Table 15.3 shows the fair rates of return approved by regulatory commissions, 1945–1950, for several utilities.

In the period following the Second World War many regulatory commissions adopted original cost as the rate base. Simultaneously, the commissions gave material weight to the cost of capital to the utility in determining the fair rate of return. However, the equating of the fair

[1] *Public Service Commission of Maryland Re The Chesapeake and Potomac Telephone Co.* (No. 4968), 84 P.U.R. (N.S.) 175 (Mar. 16, 1950).

[2] The cost of capital is an average. It is defined as the weighted average of the cost of the debt capital and the cost of the equity capital.

The cost of debt capital is defined as the quotient of the annual interest paid, divided by the average market price of the securities, usually bonds. Since many such securities sell at par, the cost of debt capital is frequently the same as the interest rate on the bonds.

The cost of equity capital is defined as the quotient of the annual dividends paid, divided by the average market price of the stocks. When an enterprise fails to declare a large portion of its earnings as dividends over a long period of time, such a ratio must be modified to reflect the additional earning capacity of the stocks. The earnings-price ratio as well as the dividends-price ratio may be considered in estimating what the fair rate of return might be.

TABLE 15.3. NUMBER OF UTILITY COMPANIES AND THE FAIR RATES OF RETURN APPROVED BY REGULATORY COMMISSIONS, 1945–1950
Information from Public Utility Reports, Inc., Washington, D.C.

Fair rate of return, %	1945	1946	1947	1948	1949	1950	1945	1946	1947	1948	1949	1950
	Combined Electric and Gas						Electric					
3.75–4.24	..	..	..	..	..	..	..	..	..	..	1	..
4.25–4.74	..	..	..	..	..	..	1	..	1	..	..	..
4.75–5.24	..	..	..	..	..	..	..	1	1	2	2	2
5.25–5.74	..	..	1	..	1	1	1	..	..	1	4	4
5.75–6.24	..	..	1	..	..	1	2	1	1	4	6	..
6.25–6.74	..	..	..	1	..	..	..	..	..	..	4	6
6.75–7.24	..	..	..	..	..	..	..	..	..	..	1	1
	Gas						Natural Gas					
2.25–2.74	..	1	1	..	..	..	..	..	..	..	..	..
2.75–3.24	..	..	..	..	..	..	..	..	..	..	..	..
3.25–3.74	..	..	..	..	..	..	..	..	..	..	..	..
3.75–4.24	..	..	1	1	..	..	..	..	..	..	..	..
4.25–4.74	..	..	2	..	1	1	..	..	..	..	..	1
4.75–5.24	..	..	1	..	3	1	..	..	..	..	..	..
5.25–5.74	..	..	3	2	2	1	..	..	..	..	..	..
5.75–6.24	2	1	..	4	2	3	1	4	..	1	2	2
6.25–6.74	1	1	..	..	1	1	4	..	..	..	1	2
6.75–7.24	..	..	3	..	..	1	1	..	..	..	..	..
	Telephone						Water					
2.25–2.74	..	..	..	..	..	..	1	..	..	..	..	..
2.75–3.24	..	..	..	1	..	..	..	..	..	..	..	..
3.25–3.74	..	..	..	..	..	..	..	..	..	..	1	..
3.75–4.24	..	..	1	..	..	2	..	..	..	..	3	1
4.25–4.74	..	1	..	1	..	2	..	..	..	1	5	3
4.75–5.24	2	..	..	2	5	3	1	1	..	3	5	3
5.25–5.74	..	2	4	8	15	5	2	..	1	3	9	6
5.75–6.24	10	7	8	7	20	9	2	..	..	1	8	5
6.25–6.74	1	2	1	3	8	3	..	..	..	..	..	..
6.75–7.24	..	1	..	1	..	..	..	..	..	1	..	1
7.25–7.74	..	1	..	1	..	..	..	..	..	..	..	..
7.75–8.24	..	..	..	..	2	..	..	..	..	..	..	..
	Street Railway						Motor Carrier					
3.75–4.24	..	..	..	..	1	..	..	..	..	..	..	..
4.25–4.74	..	..	..	..	1	..	..	..	..	..	..	1
4.75–5.24	..	..	..	..	1	..	..	..	..	..	..	..
5.25–5.74	1	1	..	..	..	..	..	..	..	..	..	1
5.75–6.24	..	..	..	..	2	2	..	1	..	..	1	..
6.25–6.74	..	..	..	..	..	2	..	1	..	..	..	..
6.75–7.24	..	..	..	1	1	..	..	..	1	..	2	..
7.25–7.74	1	..	1	..	..	..	..	..	..	..	1	..
7.75–8.24	..	..	..	..	2	..	..	..	..	..	1	..
Over 8.25	..	..	1	..	..	..	1	1	..	..	..	1

rate of return to the cost of capital is subject to the limitation that one is using past costs as a basis for future returns. This objection may be mitigated somewhat by using what should be the average cost of debt capital and what should be the proper cost of equity capital.

15.7. Fair Rate of Return for Enterprises in General. Examination of the quotations from the Supreme Court decisions discloses that one of the influences affecting the fair rate of return is " . . . a return . . . equal to that generally being made at the same time and in the same general part of the country on investments in other business undertakings which are attended by corresponding risks and uncertainties; . . . "[1] It appears, therefore, that on this basis discussions pertaining to the establishment of fair rates of return for public utilities may likewise be relevant for enterprises in general.

In Secs. 15.3, 15.4, and 15.5, it was stated that the fair rate of return depends upon the sum of a risk-free interest rate plus the additive rate commensurate with the risks and uncertainties and the rewards for managerial efficiency. The cost of capital is affected by those factors which in themselves are indicators of the magnitude of risk. Consequently, those procedures which are applicable in the field of public utilities in the estimation of a fair rate of return are also applicable for other types of business.

ESTIMATING THE FAIR RATE OF RETURN

In the sections which follow, quantitative determinations are made which are useful in setting the fair rate of return. These are:

1. Average past yield of the securities of the enterprise
2. Theoretical average yield of the securities based on security ratings
3. Theoretical cost of capital based on the average earnings-price ratio of the common stock
4. Theoretical cost of capital based on the price-earnings ratio and the average dividend payout
5. Theoretical cost of capital based on an assumed capital structure

These determinations are used as basic data in the estimation of the fair rate of return.

15.8. Calculation of the Average Past Yield of the Securities of an Enterprise. The calculation of the average past yield of the securities can be shown and described most simply by an example. Let it be assumed that the ABC Company is a small metal-fabricating enterprise and that the financial data in Table 15.4 apply. Earnings, divi-

---

[1] *Bluefield Waterworks and Improvement Co. v. Public Service Commission of the State of West Virginia, loc. cit.*

TABLE 15.4.   CONDENSED STATEMENT OF CONDITION OF THE ABC COMPANY

Assets		Sources of Capital		
			Amount	Percent
Current assets less current liabilities	$ 8,670,000	Debenture bonds, 2%, due 1956	$ 1,810,000	11.6
Land, buildings, and equipment, less depreciation	6,920,000	Preferred stock, $100 par, annual dividend $4.20	2,500,000	16.0
Investments	30,000	Common stock, $10 par	3,760,000	24.0
Deferred charges	20,000	Earned surplus	7,570,000	48.4
Total	$15,640,000	Total	$15,640,000	100.0

dends, and price of the common stock from 1943 to the year of inquiry are given in Table 15.5.

A summary of the 8-year period indicates that the average earnings of the common stock have been $3.28 and that the average annual dividend has been $1.56; thus, on the average, about 48 percent of the company's earnings have been paid out as dividends. If the analyst assumes that the average annual selling price is obtained by determining the mean of the high and the low price for the year, the approximate average price of the common stock of the ABC Company for the 8-year period is $30. With this figure as a base, the average yield of the stock to the investor is 5.2 percent. The average earnings-price ratio of the stock, indicating what the average yield would be if all the earnings were declared as dividends, is 10.9 percent.

Similar studies, made for the other securities of the company, show that the average yield of the debenture bonds over the 8-year period was 2.01 percent and the average yield of the preferred stock was 4.16 percent.

With these data, the analyst may now compute the historical cost of the capital of the ABC Company:

Item	Percent of total capital	Average annual yield, percent	Product
Common stock	72.4	5.20	376.5
Preferred stock	16.0	4.16	66.6
Debenture bonds	11.6	2.01	23.3
	100.0		466.4

The average yield of the securities of the ABC Company is 4.66 percent.

The number of years' records which are included in the study is subject to study by the analyst. The period should be long enough to include the bulk of the ups and downs of a business cycle and yet not so long that historical data of no significance are included.

However, the study just concluded is of little use to the analyst when large portions of the earnings of the common stock are retained in the business. In such cases, he must make estimates of the theoretical cost

TABLE 15.5. EARNINGS, DIVIDENDS, AND PRICE IN DOLLARS OF THE COMMON STOCK OF THE ABC COMPANY SINCE 1943

Year	1943	1944	1945	1946	1947	1948	1949	1950
Earnings per share......	2.17	2.04	1.73	1.62	2.65	3.61	4.89	7.49
Dividends per share.....	1.00	1.00	1.25	1.50	1.50	1.50	2.50	2.25
Selling price, high.......	27.25	27.00	35.50	40.50	32.00	34.25	37.50	55.00
Selling price, low........	20.00	22.12	23.88	27.13	24.62	25.00	26.88	32.12

of capital based on any of the assumptions described in the sections which follow.

15.9. Theoretical Average Yield of the Securities Based on Security Ratings. In the previous section, the average yield to the investors in ABC securities (or the average past cost of capital to the ABC Company) was calculated from specific historical data. Such an estimate is pertinent and important in the problem of estimating a fair rate of return, but it lacks a point of reference. That point can be supplied by use of ratings of the securities of an enterprise.

For many years, various investment houses[1] and financial service institutions have prepared many data relating to the analyses of securities. These data show the rating of each issue of securities. In some instances, summaries of the average yield of all the securities of a given type and equivalent rating are made. One such rating system[2] indicates the highest by A+, then A, B+, B, and so on to D. A stock which is rated as A+ will be that of an unquestioned leader in the industry, having considerable financial strength, a long, unblemished record of dividend payments, and a prospect of continued earnings with no indication that the present situation will change. Such a stock is sought by long-term investors, and the yield to these investors of such a stock is low, frequently as little as 3 to 3½ percent (before the investor pays his income tax). Corporate bonds are rated as Aaa, Aa, A, Baa, Ba, through C.

Table 15.6 shows the average yield of securities of various types and ratings per each of the years 1927 to 1951.

[1] See *Moody's Manual of Investments*, American and Foreign, Industrial Securities, Annual Publication, New York, Moody's Investors Service.

Financial World, Independent Appraisals of Listed Stocks (published weekly), New York, Guenther Publishing Corp.

[2] *Moody's Manual of Investments*.

TABLE 15.6.   AVERAGE YIELDS OF SECURITIES IN PERCENT BY TYPES
OF ENTERPRISES

Data from *Moody's Manual of Investments*, Industrial Securities, pp. a18 to a21,
New York, Moody's Investors Service, 1951

| Year | Industrial bonds | | | | | Common stocks | | | | 10 preferred industrial stocks | |
	Composite	Aaa	Aa	A	Baa	Composite of 200 stocks	125 industrial stocks	15 railroad stocks	24 utility stocks	High grade	Medium grade
1927	5.10	4.76	4.86	5.17	5.61	....	....	....	....	5.20	5.90
1928	5.10	4.73	4.82	5.12	5.71	....	....	....	....	4.90	5.72
1929	5.31	4.86	4.96	5.38	6.02	3.41	3.84	4.36	2.10	5.01	5.88
1930	5.25	4.69	4.86	5.35	6.09	4.54	4.93	5.55	3.45	4.85	6.05
1931	6.08	4.71	5.07	6.51	8.03	6.17	6.37	7.83	5.20	4.98	6.95
1932	6.71	5.09	6.06	6.94	8.76	7.36	7.28	6.15	7.53	5.89	10.06
1933	5.34	4.53	4.89	5.56	6.36	4.33	3.71	2.68	5.81	5.51	8.71
1934	4.52	4.02	4.20	4.72	5.15	4.11	3.42	3.01	5.86	4.98	7.70
1935	4.02	3.53	3.78	4.23	4.51	4.06	3.52	3.97	5.11	4.45	6.22
1936	3.50	3.03	3.18	3.71	4.07	3.50	3.36	2.74	3.66	4.24	5.02
1937	3.55	3.06	3.20	3.68	4.25	4.77	4.79	4.29	5.40	4.37	5.38
1938	3.50	2.85	3.05	3.61	4.49	4.38	3.86	5.29	7.27	4.19	5.83
1939	3.30	2.67	2.86	3.41	4.25	4.15	3.85	3.75	5.31	4.04	5.72
1940	3.10	2.44	2.67	3.19	4.08	5.31	5.30	5.41	5.99	4.00	5.74
1941	2.95	2.50	2.67	2.96	3.65	6.25	6.33	6.47	8.02	4.00	5.53
1942	2.96	2.57	2.73	2.98	3.55	6.60	6.44	7.73	9.75	4.16	5.74
1943	2.85	2.49	2.68	2.83	3.38	4.89	4.54	6.93	6.84	3.95	5.16
1944	2.80	2.57	2.66	2.81	3.15	4.81	4.56	6.75	6.28	3.90	4.89
1945	2.68	2.49	2.56	2.69	2.96	4.19	3.99	5.51	4.99	3.66	4.48
1946	2.60	2.44	2.52	2.60	2.84	3.97	3.75	5.38	4.22	3.50	4.31
1947	2.67	2.53	2.58	2.66	2.92	5.13	5.06	6.16	5.30	3.75	4.59
1948	2.87	2.71	2.78	2.86	3.13	5.78	5.87	6.04	5.85	4.02	4.97
1949	2.74	2.58	2.64	2.71	3.02	6.63	6.82	8.47	5.86	3.84	4.94
1950	2.67	2.55	2.59	2.66	2.86	6.27	6.51	6.50	5.66	3.79	4.79
1951	....	2.78	2.82	2.90	3.04	6.12	6.29	6.31	5.77	3.97	4.82

Using the data published by these financial service institutions, the
analyst can obtain an average cost of capital for securities of the same
type and equivalent rating.   Again, such a calculation can be for a single
year or for a period of years.

To illustrate, suppose that the securities of the ABC Company mentioned in the previous section are rated as follows:

Common stock   B+
Preferred stock   A
Debenture bonds Aa

The analyst determines that the average yield of industrial common stocks which are rated as B+ is 5.5 percent and that the figure is 4.0 percent for the preferred stock and 2.0 for the debenture bonds.

Then the weighted average cost of capital for the ABC Company is 4.85 percent.

Item	Percent of total capital	Average yield of equivalent securities, percent	Product
Common stock.............	72.4	5.5	398
Preferred stock.............	16.0	4.0	64
Debenture bonds...........	11.6	2.0	23
	100.0		485

The analyst may now conclude that the average yield of the securities of the ABC Company (4.66 percent, Sec. 15.8) was a fair estimate.

15.10. Use of Earnings-Price Ratios. It has been pointed out that the historical cost of capital may not be an appropriate indicator of the fair rate of return, because of the fact that past costs may not reliably indicate future trends. Besides, an average yield may not be a good indicator of the fair rate of return in those situations when a major portion of the earnings of an enterprise are not distributed as dividends.

Consider two enterprises, A and B, with like properties, capital structures, business outlooks, and present earnings. Corporation A has for some years paid out about 90 percent of its earnings as dividends, while B has paid out only 50 percent. A's stock will sell higher than B's, and it is probable that the yield of A's stock will be higher than B's. B's stock will probably have a lower market price, but the prospect of extra dividends, or stock dividends, will make B's stock sell sufficiently higher to effect lower yields.

Thus, the use of the dividend-price ratio on the stock of the two corporations does not give equal determinations of the yield; but neither does the earnings-price ratio give equal determinations of the theoretical cost of capital. Probably both are pertinent factors in the estimation of the fair rate of return.

Consider the ABC Company referred to in Sec. 15.8. The average earnings of the common stock over the 8-year period were $3.28, and since the average price of the stock over the same period was $30, the average earnings-price ratio is 10.9 percent.

The theoretical cost of capital, using the average earnings-price ratio on the common stock, and using the same yields on the preferred stock and bonds as before, is 8.79 percent.

Item	Percent of total capital	Theoretical cost of capital, percent	Product
Common stock..............	72.4	10.9	789.2
Preferred stock	16.0	4.16	66.6
Debenture bonds...........	11.6	2.01	23.3
	100.0		879.1

The estimate just computed is not the fair rate of return, nor is it the average yield of the securities were all the earnings paid out as dividends. If the ABC Company were to be so generous as to pay out all the earnings, the average price of the common stocks would be significantly higher and a lower average yield would have been obtained in this computation.

Another approach to the problem is provided by the data shown in Fig. 15.1. A study[1] made jointly by the American Gas Association and the Edison Electric Institute shows a definite linear relationship between the portion of annual earnings which are paid as dividends, called the *dividend payout*, and the corresponding price-earnings ratio (the reciprocal of the earnings-price ratio used in the preceding paragraph).

The data of Sec. 15.8 show that the ABC Company paid out approximately 48 percent of its earnings over the 8-year period as dividends. Reference to Fig. 15.1 indicates that a price-earnings ratio of about 8.16 could be expected for such a record of dividend payout. This figure corresponds to an earnings-price ratio of 12.25 percent.

Using this approach, the theoretical cost of capital is 9.77 percent.

Item	Percent of total capital	Theoretical cost of capital, percent	Product
Common stock..............	72.4	12.25	886.9
Preferred stock.............	16.0	4.16	66.6
Debenture bonds...........	11.6	2.01	23.3
	100.0		976.8

[1] American Gas Association and Edison Electric Institute, "Financing Utility Capital Requirements," p. 39, New York, 1949.

A third application of the earnings-price ratio in the estimation of the theoretical cost of capital is made by use of the average yield on the bonds and preferred stock and an *agreed* dividend-price or earnings-price ratio in percent.

For example, the analyst might conclude that a fair yield of the ABC Company common stock is 6 percent and that on the average it might be

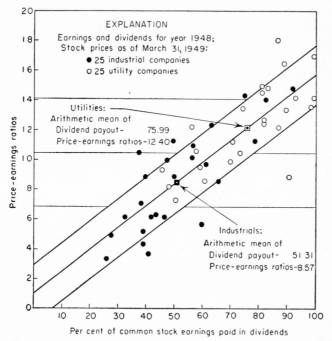

FIG. 15.1. Price-earnings ratios of industrial and utility companies as affected by common stock dividend payout ratios. (*From "Financing Utility Capital Requirements," page 39, American Gas Association and Edison Electric Institute, New York, 1949.*)

expected that the ABC Company will pay out 50 percent of its earnings as dividends. Thus, the earnings-price ratio is 12 percent, and the theoretical cost of capital is 9.59 percent. This approach may be most

Item	Percent of total capital	Theoretical cost of capital, percent	Product
Common stock.............	72.4	12.00	868.8
Preferred stock.............	16.0	4.16	66.6
Debenture bonds..........	11.6	2.01	23.3
	100.0		958.7

appropriate in considering the fair rate of return of utilities.

15.11. Use of Theoretical Capital Structures. As a part of his studies relative to the cost of capital, the analyst may wish to investigate the capital structure of the enterprise in order to ascertain whether or not management has utilized the existing sources of capital in the manner which will produce a minimum average cost of capital.

Up to a certain point, debt capital can be obtained more cheaply than equity capital. This statement is true because of the preferential treatment given to the creditors of an enterprise in the distribution of the income available for fixed charges. However, when incomes vary widely, there is a limit to the relative amount of debt capital which can be employed safely and economically in any specific enterprise or industry. Consequently, there must be a capital structure which is best suited for a given enterprise subject to a certain degree of risk and which should result in a minimum cost of capital. What ratio of debt capital to equity capital would be prescribed in all cases is probably not capable of scientific analysis. However, the collective experience of the larger corporations indicates that the changing requirements of industry are reflected in their capital structures. Table 15.7 shows this variation in the relative amount of debt capital employed in the several industries.

TABLE 15.7. ANALYSIS OF CONDENSED BALANCE SHEETS OF 300 LARGE CORPORATIONS IN SELECTED INDUSTRY GROUPS, 1948*

Industry	Number of corporations	Net total assets,† 000,000 omitted	Long-term debt, 000,000 omitted	Capital structure	
				Debt capital, percent	Equity capital, percent
Nonferrous metals...............	14	$ 2,841	$ 200	7	93
Retail trade....................	42	3,002	222	7	93
Other transportation equipment	19	1,237	108	9	91
Automobiles....................	12	3,336	381	11	89
Iron and steel.................	18	5,785	782	14	86
Chemicals......................	33	3,912	561	14	86
Petroleum......................	24	10,908	1,723	16	84
Food..........................	28	2,702	504	19	81
Machinery, including electrical..	46	4,174	778	19	81
Rubber........................	4	1,146	320	28	72
Tobacco.......................	4	1,378	539	39	61
Railroads.....................	20	16,165	6,257	39	61
Electric and gas..............	35	9,047	4,459	49	51
Communication................	1	6,785	3,443	51	49

* Charles H. Schmidt, Industrial Differences in Large Corporation Financing in 1948, *Federal Reserve Bulletin*, Vol. 35, part 1, p. 632, 1949.

† Equals total assets less reserve for depreciation (or depletion) of plant and equipment and less current liabilities.

The use of the data shown in Table 15.7 may be illustrated by considering the ABC Company of Sec. 15.8. It is noted that only 11.6 percent of the capital was obtained by borrowing. Since the ABC Company is in the metal-fabricating business, it will be assumed that it is included in the "machinery" industry group. Table 15.7 indicates that on the average about 20 percent of the capital in that industry is debt capital. If the ABC Company were to have such a capital structure, the cost of capital might be 9.8 percent.

Item	Percent of total capital	Theoretical cost of capital, percent	Product
Equity capital..............	80	11.7*	936
Debt capital..............	20	2.2†	44
	100		980

* Corresponding to the mean price-earnings ratio of 8.57 taken from Fig. 15.1.

† Increased from 2.0 percent because a much larger portion of the capital has been assumed to be debt capital.

Whether or not this study based on a theoretical capital structure should be made depends on the judgment of the analyst. In an occasional case this study may indicate that the existing capital structure is uneconomical and that the enterprise is paying more than necessary for the capital it requires. When this situation is encountered, the analyst should base his estimate of the fair rate of return on the most desirable theoretical capital structure rather than on the existing structure. Proper consideration, however, is to be accorded the views of management as to what is the most desirable capital structure.

Another situation requiring a study of a theoretical capital structure occurs when the securities representing the equity capital are so closely held that no records of their sales are obtainable. Since there will be no dividends-price ratios or earnings-price ratios available upon which the analyst may base an estimate of the cost of capital, he may assume a capital structure. Then he may calculate a theoretical cost of capital based on the average earnings-price ratios of similar enterprises possessing a capital structure similar to that assumed. Should the securities be completely owned by a parent organization, it would be reasonable to assume a theoretical capital structure similar to that of the parent organization, provided such a capital structure is considered to be reasonable and economical.[1]

[1] This situation is illustrated by the rate case in Maryland involving the Chesapeake and Potomac Telephone Company of Baltimore City, a corporation wholly owned by

15.12. Fair Rate of Return—ABC Company. The calculations made in the previous sections for the ABC Company may be summarized as follows:

Percent

Average past yield of the securities to the investors........................ 4.66
Theoretical average yield based on security ratings........................ 4.85
Theoretical cost of capital based on the average earnings-price ratio of the
common stock... 8.79
Theoretical cost of capital based on the price-earnings ratio and the average
dividend payout... 9.77
Theoretical cost of capital based on an assumed average capital structure.... 9.80

In addition, the analyst has considered the trends in markets, prices, the cost of new capital, the business outlook, the type of business, and the relative hazards attending similar business undertakings. He remembers that the fair rate of return ought to be at least equal to the historical cost of capital provided the capital structure is not inefficient.

In this illustration the analyst might conclude that the fair rate of return for the ABC Company is $8\frac{1}{2}$ to $9\frac{1}{2}$ percent, possibly $9\frac{1}{4}$ percent.

15.13. Fair Rate of Return for Enterprises in the Development Stage. There remains the problem of estimating the fair rate of return for enterprises which are still in the development stage. This problem is closely tied to the problem of financing the capital requirements of an enterprise or an industry; its solution requires considerable background in the field of investments. Consequently, the reader is referred to the many excellent treatises on the subject.[1]

Data required for the problem include (1) the amount of capital required, (2) the probable future earnings available after consideration of the probable selling prices and production costs of products to be manufactured, (3) the status of the capital market and a desirable capital structure based on the capital market, and (4) the probable earning requirements for each type of security which may be issued.

The amount of capital required for a specific enterprise will depend on (1) the necessary construction costs, (2) the amount of working capital, including an allowance for the extra expenses of the development period, and (3) the costs incident to the acquisition of the capital. These

the American Telephone and Telegraph Company. The Public Service Commission of Maryland gave great weight to a theoretical capital structure of 50 percent debt capital and 50 percent equity capital, which approximated that of the American Telephone and Telegraph Company, in its determination of the cost of capital and fair rate of return. *Public Service Commission of Maryland Re The Chesapeake and Potomac Telephone Co., loc. cit.*

[1] Charles Emery Troxel, "Economics of Public Utilities," New York, Rinehart & Company, Inc., 1947.

American Gas Association and Edison Electric Institute, "Financing Utility Capital Requirements," *op. cit.*

analyses form the basis of economy studies[1] when taken in conjunction with the second problem, that of investigating the capabilities of the venture in the production of sufficient returns.

Studies are necessary to show what may be the probable selling price of the products or services sold for several assumed production figures. These studies are desirable in that it may be possible to maximize the revenue of the venture by a judicious choice of an annual production estimate. Each production estimate, of course, will affect the size of the plant, the cost of construction, and the manufacturing costs.

The third series of studies relates to the estimates of manufacturing costs and revenues. From these estimates the net income before taxes is obtained. A fixed income tax rate can be assumed and the return estimated. This assumption will be modified later by the assumed bond interest paid. Bond interest is an allowable deduction in computing income tax, but it is considered as a part of the return of the enterprise.

The fourth study relates to the capital market and the probable sources of capital. Mention is made in Sec. 15.11 of the fact that a capital structure may be so made as to minimize the annual cost of capital. Nevertheless, it is necessary to be realistic about the sources of new capital. Significant changes in financing practice have occurred:

> . . . for every dollar of new debt financing for all domestic corporations in 1929, $2.59 of common and preferred stock was issued. By 1948 for every dollar of debt only 18 cents of stock was issued. Utility companies experienced a similar reversal. In 1929 for every dollar of debt the utility industry issued $1.88 of common and preferred stocks while by 1948 a dollar of debt was accompanied by only 15 cents of equity financing.
>
> The foregoing data illustrate the shift in investments from stock to debt, first because of the pressure of taxation on the upper income groups and secondly because of the rising importance of institutional investors, many of whom are limited by law to the senior securities of corporations.[2]

However, the trend which is becoming more important, that of financing extensions of existing enterprises by employing undistributed earnings, decreases the competition for equity capital to a degree.[3] The Joint

[1] Clarence E. Bullinger, "Engineering Economic Analysis," 2d ed., New York, McGraw-Hill Book Company, Inc., 1950.

Holger G. Thuesen, "Engineering Economy," New York, Prentice-Hall, Inc., 1950.

George Terborgh, "Dynamic Equipment Policy," 1st ed., New York, McGraw-Hill Book Company, Inc., 1949.

Eugene L. Grant, "Principles of Engineering Economy," 3d ed., New York, The Ronald Press Company, 1950.

Baldwin M. Woods and E. Paul DeGarmo, "Introduction to Engineering Economy," New York, The Macmillan Company, 1942.

[2] American Gas Association and Edison Electric Institute, "Financing Utility Capital Requirements," *op. cit.,* p. 15.

[3] *Ibid.,* p. 17.

Committee of the American Gas Association and Edison Electric Institute remarked in 1949:[1]

(a) If electric and gas utilities are successful in maintaining the sound capital structures now attained on the average by raising sufficient amounts of equity capital, the borrowing of debt capital in appropriate amounts from present sources should not be too difficult,

(b) Equity financing, through preferred and especially common stocks, is the crux of the present financing problem for most companies,

(c) The so-called shortage of equity capital is by and large a relative matter of pricing. . . . It should be recognized, however, by those who take this view and apply it that as a result more shares than really necessary may thus be issued and dividend requirements increased, and that these increased "wages" of capital may have to be transmuted into higher rates.

Such studies should indicate, however, what portion of the capital requirements can be obtained through debt financing and what through equity financing.

There remains the problem of determining the probable annual cost of capital of each kind of security based on the earning requirements enabling that security to be sold.

Suppose, for illustrative purposes, that the theoretical capital structure of the ABC Company, discussed in Sec. 15.11, has been determined as reasonable for a new venture. If the theoretical annual costs of capital assumed in that illustration were considered adequate for the new venture, the average cost of capital would be at least 10 percent. Such a figure would constitute an evidence of the fair rate of return applicable to the venture.

In summary, the reader is again reminded that the determination of the fair rate of return for a new venture is closely related to the field of investments. Such determinations should be made in the light of current practice in this highly technical field of finance.

[1] *Ibid.*, p. 17.

CHAPTER 16

Earning Value, Service Worth Value, and Stock and Bond Value

The foregoing chapters 4 to 15 are concerned with the examination of the tangible and intangible property as evidences of the over-all value of an enterprise. Other evidences of the value of an enterprise are its earnings, the worth of its services, and its market, or stock and bond, value. These evidences of value are examined in this chapter.

METHODS OF CALCULATING PRESENT WORTH

The more remote the receipt may be of money, property, a satisfaction, or a service, the less it is worth as of the present. Thus, the worths of future returns, services, or satisfactions are discounted to obtain their present (today's) worth. This discounting is accomplished by applying a discount factor which depends upon the rate of discount (interest rate) and the future periods until receipt of the return. Present worth formulas are standard mathematical derivations available in many books on finance, investment, economics, and mathematics. The following three sections present these well-known formulas without derivations but with a discussion of their application to the process of finding earning value.

16.1. Present Worth Formulas. The well-known compound interest formulas needed for calculating earning value are presented next, using the following notation:

i = interest rate per interest period (1 year in the calculations in this chapter)

r = rate of return per annum (also interest rate)

n = number of interest periods; in this chapter n is always used in integral years

d = a period of deferment in the receipt of R before the beginning of n

P = a present sum of money; a single payment; the present worth of an annuity (an amount payable yearly) or of a single sum

325

S = a sum at a future date n interest periods from the present, which sum is equivalent to P with compound interest at i (or r) rate

R = end-of-period annuity; annual operation return (return on investment plus the depreciation return)

V_s = salvage value; the amount of capital recoverable in a lump sum at a specific time, usually at the end of n years

Compound amount of a single payment P:

$$S = P(1 + r)^n \qquad (16.1)$$

Present worth of a single future payment S:

$$P = S\left[\frac{1}{(1 + r)^n}\right] \qquad (16.2)$$

Year-end sinking fund payment R to accumulate to S in n periods:

$$R = S\left[\frac{r}{(1 + r)^n - 1}\right] \qquad (16.3)$$

Uniform annual capital recovery with return for a sum P:

$$R = P\left[\frac{r(1 + r)^n}{(1 + r)^n - 1}\right] = P\left[\frac{r}{(1 + r)^n - 1} + r\right] \qquad (16.4)$$

Compound accumulation of a uniform year-end payment R:

$$S = R\left[\frac{(1 + r)^n - 1}{r}\right] \qquad (16.5)$$

Present worth of a uniform year-end payment R:

$$P = R\left[\frac{(1 + r)^n - 1}{r(1 + r)^n}\right] \qquad (16.6)$$

Present worth of a uniform year-end payment R at two rates, a rate of return and a sinking fund interest rate:

$$P = R\left\{\frac{1}{r + \left[\dfrac{i}{(1 + i)^n - 1}\right]}\right\} = R\left\{\frac{(1 + i)^n - 1}{i + r[(1 + i)^n - 1]}\right\}$$

$$= R\left\{\frac{\dfrac{(1 + i)^n - 1}{i}}{1 + r\left[\dfrac{(1 + i)^n - 1}{i}\right]}\right\} \qquad (16.7)$$

Present worth of a uniform year-end payment R at two rates, a rate of return and a sinking fund interest rate, and a deferment period:

$$P = R \left\{ \frac{\dfrac{(1 + i)^n - 1}{i}}{1 + r \left[\dfrac{(1 + i)^{n+d} - 1}{i} \right]} \right\} \qquad (16.8)$$

The uses of these formulas are next explained and illustrated. The factors involved in Formulas (16.1) to (16.6) may be selected from the tables of Appendix D.

16.2. Explanation of Present Worth Formulas. The present worth of a perpetual income of $1,200 receivable at the end of each year is obtained by capitalizing the annuity at the appropriate fair rate of return. Thus,

$$R \left[\frac{(1 + r)^n - 1}{r(1 + r)^n} \right] = \frac{R}{r} \left[\frac{(1 + r)^\infty - 1}{(1 + r)^\infty} \right] = \frac{R}{r} \left[1 - \frac{1}{(1 + r)^\infty} \right] = \frac{R}{r}$$

$$P = \frac{R}{r} = \frac{1,200}{0.08} = \$15,000 \qquad (16.9)$$

An annuity for a specific number of years would be equivalent to the annual return from an enterprise for a period equal to the period of the annuity. Assume a return of $1,200 a year for 15 years and a rate of return of 8 percent. The present worth, or earning value, would be

$$P = R \left[\frac{(1 + r)^n - 1}{r(1 + r)^n} \right] = (1,200)(8.559) = \$10,271 \qquad (16.10)$$

The foregoing calculated present worth of $10,271 is on the basis that there is no return of invested capital involved, that is, no investment to be recovered through depreciation or depletion charges, or if there is, such capital recovery is included in the $1,200 annual return. When there is a capital recovery to be earned, its present worth must also be evaluated as part of the earning value.

Assume the same factors as before, except that, in addition to the $1,200 a year return, there will be a capital recovery of $15,000 at the end of the 15 years.

$$P = R \left[\frac{(1 + r)^n - 1}{r(1 + r)^n} \right] + \frac{V_s}{(1 + r)^n} = (1,200)(8.559) + \frac{15,000}{3.172} \qquad (16.11)$$

$$P = 10,271 + 4,729 = \$15,000 \qquad (16.12)$$

This $15,000 earning value agrees with Solution (16.9). When the return of capital and an annual return of an amount equal to the rate of return times the remaining invested capital are considered for a limited life enterprise, the earning value of the enterprise is the same as the present worth of the annual return in perpetuity. Should the capital be recovered in annual year-end increments and the annual return be 8 percent on the unrecovered capital (a reducing investment), the earning value would still be $15,000.

Assume a recovery of capital at the uniform rate of $1,000 a year for the 15 years and a return at 8 percent, or $1,200, the first year, decreasing $80 a year to $80 the fifteenth year.

$$P = \frac{1,200}{(1+r)^1} + \frac{1,120}{(1+r)^2} + \frac{1,040}{(1+r)^3} + \cdots + \frac{80}{(1+r)^{15}}$$
$$+ 1,000 \left[\frac{(1+r)^n - 1}{r(1+r)^n} \right] \quad (16.13)$$

$$P = 1,111 + 960 + 826 + \cdots + 25 + (1,000)(8.559)$$
$$P = 6,441 + 8,559 = \$15,000 \quad (16.14)$$

Thus, when the annual return is computed on the unrecovered capital and the capital recovery is provided for, the earning value is the same amount regardless of how the annual allocations by which the capital is recovered are distributed over the period of n years.

Formula (16.4) for an end-of-period annuity is identical with the capital recovery with return formula for R developed in Sec. 9.14, Eq. (9.21), in the derivation of the present worth depreciation formula. A solution of Formula (16.4) for the present example at an 8 percent rate and n of 15 years is

$$R = 15,000 \left[\frac{r(1+r)^n}{(1+r)^n - 1} \right] = (15,000)(0.11683) = \$1,752 \quad (16.15)$$

The present worth of an annual operation return of $1,752 which includes both capital recovery and annual return is

$$P = 1,752 \left[\frac{(1+r)^n - 1}{r(1+r)^n} \right] = (1,752)(8.559) = \$15,000 \quad (16.16)$$

The foregoing examples show that when earning value is computed for limited life enterprises it is unnecessary to separate the *return on capital* from the *return of capital* and that the capital may be assumed to be recovered on any reasonable schedule. There is a difference, however, in the computed earning value should the annual return not be computed on the unrecovered capital at the beginning of each year.

Consider the example when the capital recovery is computed on the basis of a sinking fund deposit to accumulate to the capital investment by the end of the life of the enterprise, but with a uniform annual return. The sinking fund deposit to accumulate to $15,000 in 15 years at 8 percent is

$$R = 15,000 \left[\frac{r}{(1+r)^n - 1} \right] = (15,000)(0.03683) = \$552 \quad (16.17)$$

The $552 recovery for the annual sinking fund deposit plus the $1,200 return would give a total yearly operation return of $1,752, which will produce a present worth of $15,000 [see Solution (16.16)]. The annual sinking fund deposit concept is the same as considering that the capital investment is returned in one sum at the end of the 15 years. The sinking fund deposit of $552 would accumulate to $15,000 at the end of 15 years.

16.3. Formulas Involving Two Interest Rates. About 1877 Hoskold[1] developed a two-interest rate annuity formula which provided for a *return on* the investment at the fair rate of return (the speculative, or risk, rate) and the *recovery of* the investment at the end of the period of operation by a sinking fund which accumulates at a safe interest rate to the original investment during the period of operation. The two-rate formula may be developed as follows:

The return on the investment at the end of the first year would be rP; the sinking fund deposit would be $P\left[\dfrac{i}{(1+i)^n - 1}\right]$. The operation return R would be the sum of the two, or

$$R = rP + P\left[\frac{i}{(1+i)^n - 1}\right] = P\left[r + \frac{i}{(1+i)^n - 1}\right] \quad (16.18)$$

Assuming that the return on the investment would remain rP for the full term of n years (which it would not), the earning value would be the present worth of R, or

$$P = \frac{R}{r + \left[\dfrac{i}{(1+i)^n - 1}\right]} \quad (16.19)$$

The return on the investment at the end of the first year would be rP; the remaining amount available for the sinking fund would be $R - rP$. The accumulation of the sinking fund deposit in n years must be equal to P; therefore,

$$P = (R - rP)\left[\frac{(1+i)^n - 1}{i}\right]$$

$$P = \frac{R[(1+i)^n - 1] - rP[(1+i)^n - 1]}{i}$$

$$iP + rP[(1+i)^n - 1] = R[(1+i)^n - 1]$$

$$P = \frac{R[(1+i)^n - 1]}{i + r[(1+i)^n - 1]} = \frac{R}{r + \left[\dfrac{i}{(1+i)^n - 1}\right]}$$

[1] Henry D. Hoskold, "Engineer's Valuing Assistant," 2d ed. (1st ed. in 1877), New York, Longmans, Green & Co., Inc., 1905.

TABLE 16.1. CALCULATIONS ILLUSTRATING WORKING OF THE
HOSKOLD TWO-RATE ANNUITY FORMULA

$$R = 26.38,\ r = 10\%,\ i = 2\%,\ n = 5$$

$$P = 26.38 \left[\frac{1.10^5 - 1}{(0.10)(1.10)^5} \right] = 100.00, \qquad P_{r,i} = \frac{26.38}{0.10 + \dfrac{0.02}{1.02^5 - 1}} = 90.29$$

Year	Sinking fund deposit at end of year	Interest on sinking fund at i rate received at end of year	Depreciation return received at end of year, (2) + (3)	Sinking fund balance at end of year	Unallocated base at end of year
(1)	(2)	(3)	(4)	(5)	(6)
0	.....	....	.....	.....	90.29
1	17.35	0.00	17.35	17.35	72.94
2	17.35	0.35	17.70	35.05	55.24
3	17.35	0.70	18.05	53.10	37.19
4	17.35	1.06	18.41	71.51	18.78
5	17.35	1.43	18.78	90.29	0.00
Total.......	86.75	3.54	90.29	.....	.....

Year	Return on unallocated base at end of year, (6) × r	Operation return receivable at end of year, (4) + (7)	Present worth of operation return at r rate	Excess return, R minus operation return, 26.38 − (8)	Present worth of excess return
(1)	(7)	(8)	(9)	(10)	(11)
0	.....	.....	.....	.....	....
1	9.03	26.38	23.98	0.00	0.00
2	7.29	24.99	20.65	1.39	1.15
3	5.52	23.57	17.71	2.81	2.11
4	3.72	22.13	15.12	4.25	2.90
5	1.88	20.66	12.83	5.72	3.55
Total.......	27.44	117.73	90.29	14.17	9.71

This two-rate annuity formula is a capitalization of the operation return at the combined rate of fair return and the sinking fund factor.

In reality the Hoskold formula (16.7) [and (16.19)] provides for a decreasing annual operation return because the unrecovered investment times r rate of return decreases faster than the annual increment to the sinking fund increases. Table 16.1 illustrates the working of the Hoskold two-rate annuity formula for $R = \$26.38$, $r = 10$ percent, $i = 2$ percent, and $n = 5$. The one-rate annuity has a present value of $100, compared with $90.29 for the Hoskold formula. The difference of $9.71 is equal to the present worths [column (11)] of the differences [column (10)] between the \$26.38 annuity used in the calculation and the decreasing operation returns [column (8)] which are necessary to produce the present worth of \$90.29.

The theory upon which the Hoskold formula is based is that the original capital investment is nonrecoverable until the end of the period of operation. At this time the sinking fund at i rate is equal to the original investment. In the meantime the owner earns a return at r rate on the original investment less the sinking fund accumulation. The i rate instead of the r rate is used because the recovery of capital through the sinking fund necessitates investing in high grade safe securities which earn the low returns comparable with pure interest rates.

Essentially the Hoskold formula (16.7) is a means of producing a lower present worth of an anticipated annuity than is obtained by the single rate formula (16.6). The suitability of the Hoskold formula can be questioned, however, for the reason that the risk rate r should be fixed at the correct rate, considering all risks. If the risks are truly greater than the r rate used in the Hoskold formula, the use of the true r rate in the standard annuity formula (16.6) will produce the same result. Further, because the annuity R (operation return) is actually not constant for the n years and because n is also an estimated quantity, the so-called "refinement" introduced by the two-interest rates is of doubtful significance.

Based on the same concept as used in developing the annuity formula (16.19), the present worth of a single sum receivable in n years at two rates of interest is

$$P = S \left\{ \frac{1}{1 + r \left[\dfrac{(1 + i)^n - 1}{i} \right]} \right\} = S \left\{ \frac{i}{i + r[(1 + i)^n - 1]} \right\} \quad (16.20)$$

As defined in Sec. 1.8, the present worth of a given sum is that amount which if invested at compound interest for n years will accumulate to the given sum. If the definition is modified to include the provisions that the annual return is determined at an r rate and that the compounding is accomplished at an i rate, Formula (16.20) is derived as follows:

At the end of n years, when P = amount invested and rP = annual return,

$$S = P + rP(1 + i)^{n-1} + rP(1 + i)^{n-2} + \cdots + rP(1 + i) + rP$$

$$S = P + rP \left[\frac{(1 + i)^n - 1}{(1 + i) - 1} \right]$$

$$S = P \left\{ 1 + r \left[\frac{(1 + i)^n - 1}{i} \right] \right\}$$

whence

$$P = S \left\{ \frac{1}{1 + r \left[\dfrac{(1 + i)^n - 1}{i} \right]} \right\} = S \left\{ \frac{i}{i + r[(1 + i)^n - 1]} \right\}$$

A comparison of Formula (16.20) with Formula (16.2) (the present worth of a single future payment using only one rate of interest) shows that the former will always be larger for a given S, r, and n. For example, the present worth of $1,000 receivable in 10 years at $i = 3$ percent and $r = 7$ percent is $554.45; at $r = 7$ percent the result is $508.35. This difference is explained by the assumption that the return rP is compounded at a rate i which is smaller than the rate of return r.

It is doubtful that the situation normally will call for the use of Formula (16.20) in preference to Formula (16.2).   Possibly the best reason for its use is the desirability of being consistent when it has been decided to use Hoskold's two-interest rate annuity formula for other portions of a valuation problem.

16.4. Present Worth Formulas for Deferred Annuities.   There are some types of enterprises or proposals for which the start of the operation return may be deferred a number of years from the present. Mining developments, the development of a patent, or any business which may require a lapse of time before the operation return begins is valued by use of some deferment factor.

When there is no investment necessary prior to the starting of the return, the present worth of the capitalized value may be found by dividing the capitalized value by $(1 + r)^d$, where $d =$ the years of delay until the start of the return.

When there must be an investment over a period of development prior to the start of profitable operations, the earning value computation should involve consideration for the return foregone during the development period.   This return foregone is similar to the interest during construction considered in Secs. 6.5 to 6.9 as an overhead construction cost.

O'Donahue[1] modified the Hoskold annuity formula (16.7) by a deferment factor.   Formula (16.8) may be derived as follows:

An annuity of R at i rate of interest for n years will amount to

$$R \left[\frac{(1 + i)^n - 1}{i} \right]$$

After $n + d$ years the investor is to have his original investment at hand through the cumulations in the sinking fund for n years at i interest rate.   In addition, he should have the returns at r rate plus their cumu-

---

[1] T. A. O'Donahue, The Valuation of Mineral Properties, *Transactions of the Institution of Mining Engineers*, Vol. 32, pp. 399–419, London, 1906–1907; Notes on the Valuation of Mineral Properties, *ibid.*, Vol. 43, pp. 19–40, 1911–1912.

lations at i interest rate.   These amount to

$$P + rP \left[\frac{(1 + i)^{n+d} - 1}{i} \right] \tag{16.21}$$

Since the annual operation return R is composed of the return rP and the sinking fund factor, the present worth of the R's may be equated to the amount the investor should have at the end of $n + d$ years.

$$P + rP \left[\frac{(1 + i)^{n+d} - 1}{i} \right] = R \left[\frac{(1 + i)^{n} - 1}{i} \right]$$

$$P = \frac{R \left[\dfrac{(1 + i)^{n} - 1}{i} \right]}{1 + r \left[\dfrac{(1 + i)^{n+d} - 1}{i} \right]} \tag{16.22}$$

O'Donahue's formula (16.22) [or (16.8)] is the same as the Hoskold formula, except for the deferment factor d.   It would be used under the same conditions but, in addition, when the operation return would be delayed d years in starting.

When the standard annuity formula is to be used with a deferment factor, the solution would be to solve for P, using R, n, and r in the normal manner, then adjusting the normal solution for P by its present worth for d years; thus

$$P = R \left[\frac{(1 + r)^{n} - 1}{r(1 + r)^{n}} \right] \left[\frac{1}{(1 + r)^{d}} \right] \tag{16.23}$$

The foregoing formulas are those used in present worth and similar calculations.   These formulas and the principles on which they are based are used in the following sections in which earning values are estimated and also in Chap. 18, valuation of mines and natural resources.

Although the foregoing present worth formulas are each mathematically correct and their applications are correct in principle, the user of them should always bear in mind that the final calculated present worth should be viewed as an answer obtained by the use of judgment factors. Each of the factors, annual return R, the number of periods n, and the rate of return r, is dependent upon the judgment of the analyst.

ESTIMATING EARNING VALUE

Earning value is one evidence of the value of property.   Earning value is particularly important to consider in valuing a business selling a service or product which can be produced with a small investment in physical property compared with the earnings.

Estimating the earning value of an enterprise, an operating unit, or other property is essentially a process of estimating the present worth of the probable future returns from that property. Three factors are required in this process, (1) the amount of probable future returns, (2) the specific years such returns will be likely to be received, and (3) the fair rate of return applicable to the property. As indicated in the following sections, the procedure of estimating the present worth (earning value) differs slightly according to whether unlimited or limited life is assumed for the enterprise. Estimating the fair rate of return is discussed in Chap. 15.

16.5. Earning Value of Unlimited Life Enterprises. Although the annual returns of an enterprise are likely to fluctuate in the future, a forecast of returns on a uniform level for a limited period is an estimate within reason. The basis of such estimate, of necessity, is the past and present earnings, the future plans and policies of the enterprise, and the general business outlook within the particular industry. The earning value of an enterprise fluctuates from year to year, but in an appraisal the value of the enterprise at a specific date is wanted. The earning value, therefore, is estimated as of that date on the basis of what the future returns are expected to be.

The specific steps in estimating earning value of an unlimited life enterprise are as follows:

1. Ascertain from the book records the annual returns for the past 3 to 15 years, and average the annual returns for periods of years of somewhat similar business conditions. Note any special activity of the enterprise or general conditions which might have affected materially the net earnings. The returns for the purpose of estimating earning value are the net profits after payment of income taxes but before payment of interest on bonded indebtedness. Income taxes are regarded as an expense; bond interest, of course, is an earning on the investment.

2. For the specific enterprise, ascertain the future policies and production plans, its competitive position in the industry, and the probable effect on earnings of the probable future business outlook, including income tax, property tax, and labor situations.

3. By analysis of the information obtained in steps 1 and 2, decide what the probable average returns are most likely to be for the immediate future, say 3 to 5 years.

4. By the process given in Chap. 15, decide upon the fair rate of return for the enterprise under study.

5. Capitalize the estimated probable returns found in step 3 by the fair rate of return found in step 4. The capitalization process is the same as that used in finding the present worth of the average annual return as a perpetual annuity. Formula (16.6) becomes $P = R/r$ when n is infinitely great.

In accomplishing steps 3 and 4, the valuator may be helped by arriving at minimum and maximum earnings and rates in his process of determining the probable future averages.

The following numerical example illustrates the process of estimating the earning value as applied to a steel products manufacturing company. The past annual returns of this company are shown in Table 16.2.

TABLE 16.2.   NET PROFITS AFTER TAXES BUT INCLUDING PAYMENTS
OF INTEREST ON BONDED DEBT

1935	$ 80,618	1941	$463,878	1947	$309,436
1936	129,412	1942	453,442	1948	457,701
1937	134,437	1943	765,235	1949	549,373
1938	259,879	1944	718,925	1950	666,918
1939	302,318	1945	300,470	1951	706,606
1940	339,796	1946	56,389	1952	690,000 est.

The profits during the Second World War increased materially because of government contracts.   The low profits of 1946 resulted from the necessity of conversion to civilian needs in the postwar period.   The steady rise of returns beginning in 1947 reflects the general prosperity of the nation.   The steadiness of the earnings, except for influences of the war and general economic conditions, indicates a well-managed company and one with reasonable assurance of continued satisfactory profits. The 1948–1951 returns averaged $595,150.   Immediate future profits should be not less than $620,000, probably not more than $700,000, and perhaps about an average of $655,000.

This steel products company is justified in expecting a fair rate of return of 7½ percent.   This conclusion is reached by analysis of the industry in general, the earnings of similar enterprises, and other factors as outlined in Chap. 15.

The earning value is therefore

$$\text{Minimum:} \quad \frac{620,000}{0.075} = \$8,267,000$$

$$\text{Probable average:} \quad \frac{655,000}{0.075} = \$8,733,000$$

$$\text{Maximum:} \quad \frac{700,000}{0.075} = \$9,333,000$$

$$\text{Current:} \quad \frac{690,000}{0.075} = \$9,200,000$$

What earning value would be selected as the final choice is dependent upon many factors and conclusions which the analyst will be conscious of at the time.   He may not need to make a specific determination, however, because he can compare these earning values as they stand with his other evidences of value in the process of arriving at a fair value as discussed in Chap. 17.

When examining the property, the appraiser may discover repairs and modernizations which are necessary to maintain the earnings at maximum levels. He may estimate the costs of effecting such changes in the physical plant as are desirable to uphold the returns. These costs would be deducted from the calculated earning value to arrive at the proper estimate of the value of the enterprise based on prospective returns.

16.6. Earning Value of Limited Life Enterprises. In Sec. 16.2 it is shown that the earning value of an unlimited life enterprise is identical to that of an enterprise of limited life having the same annual return provided there is a complete recovery of capital during the limited life. When the recovery of capital is not separately provided, the procedure of estimating the earning value of a limited life enterprise is to determine the value of the future earnings for a specific future term of years rather than in perpetuity.

Other than enterprises which utilize natural resources such as ores, petroleum, coals, and timber, limited life industries are not common. There are some types of enterprises for which the future is so uncertain that a valuation based on earnings is on a much more realistic basis when based on a limited future period. An estimate of the earning value of limited life enterprises requires the following determinations:

1. Average returns during the future period of operation
2. Number of years that the average returns can be expected
3. Rate of fair return
4. Depreciation and depletion costs of the enterprise, or the operation return, including such income as may be earned to cover these costs combined with the return
5. Value of the residual property at the end of the period of operation

The future average earnings are estimated by studying the records of the past in the same manner as discussed in Sec. 16.5, when the life is unlimited. Consideration needs to be given to the possibility that the business may suffer a gradual decline in earnings from its peak reached some years prior to dissolution of the enterprise.

The number of years of profitable operation is determined by analysis of those factors which control the operations. In a mineral extraction activity, the size of the deposit and rate of extraction per year would control. A manufacturing concern organized to utilize certain accumulated waste products is similar to a mining enterprise. An industry supplying a manufactured product to a community or to specific industries might have a saturation limit which, when reached, would necessitate abandoning the company or seeking a new type of objective. An industry built for war purposes only may be profitable only during the war.

The fair rate of return would be established in accordance with the methods discussed in Chap. 15.   The specific risks would be of great importance in this instance.

Upon the dissolution of an enterprise, there may be properties remaining that have some value, either as scrap or for reuse elsewhere.   Such properties would bring in an income which should be considered in establishing an earning value.

When the enterprise has limited life, the average return must be estimated with proper consideration given to the return of invested capital.   There is apt to be a large decrease in the value of the physical property between the date of valuation and the date, years later, when operations cease.   An estimate of earning value is dependent upon this decrease.   The factor of depreciation (and depletion) is not directly considered in the unlimited life enterprise because the average returns are usually estimated on the basis that the depreciation is earned and that the physical plant is in perpetual existence.

16.7. Examples of Earning Value of Limited Life Enterprises. The earning value of a concern whose average returns are estimated at $40,000 a year for the next 12 years and whose fair rate of return is 10 percent would be calculated from Formula (16.6) as follows:

$$\text{Earning value} = R\left[\frac{(1 + r)^n - 1}{r(1 + r)^n}\right] = (40,000)(6.814) = \$272,560$$

A second example follows in which there is a residual value at the end of the profitable operations.

Assume that the estimates for company A are as follows:

Forecasted average annual operation return—$20,000
Years of probable profitable operations—12
Fair rate of return—10 percent
The depreciation returns are included in the $20,000
Residual value of property at end of operations—$25,000

The earning value would be calculated as follows:

$$\text{Earning value} = R\left[\frac{(1 + r)^n - 1}{r(1 + r)^n}\right] + \frac{V_s}{(1 + r)^n}$$

$$= (20,000)(6.814) + \frac{25,000}{3.138}$$

$$\text{Earning value} = 136,280 + 7,970 = \$144,250$$

16.8. Earning Value—Summary.   The earning value estimated as the present worth of the probable future earnings considers that the depreciation return will be earned and that such return will be reinvested in the property to the extent needed to maintain the earnings.   Further, the process is one of finding the value of the existing enterprise comprised of its tangible and intangible property; therefore, how the property may be expanded by additions is not a factor affecting present value.

The earning value of an enterprise, determined in the manner illustrated, depends wholly upon the judgment of the valuator, who determines the essential factors. Opinions on such factors are bound to vary as between competent appraisers. These variations might be sufficient to produce materially different earning values. For instance, the annual return may be estimated 10 percent more by valuator A than by B; A might choose a $7\frac{1}{2}$ percent fair rate of return and B an $8\frac{1}{2}$ percent rate. The final earning value by A under such estimates would be 24.7 percent more than that found by B.

But the wide variation in earning value which is possible between appraisers does not preclude the method from being a valuable evidence in the engineering valuation process. The weight to give earning value in determining the final fair value is discussed in Chap. 17. The earning value of a regulated enterprise would have little significance in establishing a rate base. Presumably, both the earnings and the rate of return were regulated in the past on the basis of a fair rate base. For non-regulated industry, particularly for specialized enterprises and those having relatively small investments in physical property, the earning value is of considerable assistance in establishing fair value. The method is frequently applied in condemnation appraisals. It is also recognized as being that used in the appraisal of contracts, leases, and other intangible property as discussed in Chap. 14.

SERVICE WORTH VALUE OF AN ENTERPRISE

In addition to the considerations discussed in Secs. 16.5 to 16.7 as affecting earning values, there is the added question of whether the recent earnings of industrial enterprises are or are not based on fair prices. When they are not, a change in earnings can be expected.

In the case of public utility properties, the United States Supreme Court has said:[1]

What the company is entitled to ask is a fair return upon the value of that which it employs for the public convenience. On the other hand, what the public is entitled to demand is that no more be exacted from it for the use of a public highway than the services rendered by it are reasonably worth.

The development of new methods, processes, and products is a force that tends to pull prices to lower levels. An enterprise within a given

---

[1] *Smyth v. Ames* (No. 49), *Smyth v. Smith* (No. 50), *Smyth v. Higginson* (No. 51), 169 U.S. 466, 547 (U.S. Sup. Ct. Mar. 7, 1898).

industry that does not yield to this force cannot long endure. Consequently, returns which have been earned at prices above that minimum which will sustain a competitive enterprise cannot be expected to continue. Such high prices are above the reasonable worth of the product or service to the customers. Earnings, therefore, will decline, and a service worth value of the enterprise may be a better indicator of fair value than is earning value.

16.9. Explanation of Service Worth Value. Service worth value is defined (Sec. 1.11) as what the earning value would be if the earnings were based on fair prices for the services or commodities.

The purpose of determining the service worth value of an enterprise is to enable "such weight as may be just and right" to be given to the principle that the customers should not, and in the long run will not, pay more than the reasonable worth of the commodities produced by industrial enterprises.

In many cases, it is not necessary to make an elaborate, formal estimate of service worth value; a simple general study of the facts often will show at once that the prices charged are not greater than the reasonable worths of the services rendered or products sold. The service worth value should be determined in each case in which it seems reasonably possible that past prices may have been materially higher than the principle of reasonable worth would justify.

16.10. Determination of Service Worth Value. The process of determining service worth value is as follows:

1. Determine the reasonable worths to customers of the services rendered or the commodities sold.

2. Determine what the recent past annual returns would have been if the rates or prices charged had been just equal to the reasonable worth to customers of the services or commodities purchased.

3. By proceeding as described in Sec. 16.5 or 16.6, determine what the earning value would be on the basis of these modified returns.

16.11. Determining the Reasonable Worth of the Service or Commodities Produced. There are three criteria for determining the reasonable worths to customers of the services rendered or commodities produced by industrial enterprises:

1. *Competitive prices.* Competitive prices can be relied upon to show the reasonable worths of services or commodities only when

  a. *Adequate free competition,* with unfair trade combinations and agreements barred, safeguards consumers against excessive prices
  b. *Absence of cutthroat competition* safeguards producers against inadequate prices

2. *Fair production expense plus fair return.* As industrial civilization becomes more and more complex, the principle of fair prices based on the lowest reasonable production costs and fair returns is becoming more operative. This is an extension of the principle which has been operative for many years in the regulation of public utilities. Substitute plants or modernized plants may be studied to arrive at reasonable fair prices.

3. *Relative cost at fair prices of substitute services.* Research and development have made available alternate services and alternate products, the prices for which may be used as a basis of determining fair prices for the older used services or commodities. For instance, natural gas is now widely used instead of manufactured gas; oil is used in the place of coal; airplane and motor vehicle transportation are supplanting railway transportation; and plastics and synthetics are widely used in preference to metals and natural chemical products.

16.12. Fair Prices Determined by Competition and Efficient Operation. In a strictly competitive industry, one enterprise could not long exist under a price schedule much higher or much lower than the general average of the industry. Therefore, when it is thought that the past prices of a specific enterprise resulted in costs to the customers not equal to the reasonable worth of the product, an investigation may be made of both prices and production costs within the industry. Within the general locality the costs and prices may be averaged, if possible, or only representative plants may be studied. Considerable judgment is required in comparing enterprises situated in geographical areas not having comparable situations governing transportation, labor supply, raw material sources, and markets. Nevertheless, the facts of competitive enterprises are helpful in reaching a conclusion of what prices are fair to customers of a particular enterprise.

The production costs of the existing enterprise are to be investigated to make certain that the management has been reasonably efficient in holding production costs to the lowest reasonable level. The production operations and plant in general should be studied to ascertain what improvements could be made to effect lower costs. Perhaps a modernization program is required in order to bring production costs to a level comparable with the average or below that of the industry in general. If so, the cost of this modernization should be subtracted from the service worth value based upon the revised prices. Engineering economy studies may be in order as a means of determining what machines or processes need replacement.

Included in the price analysis should be an investigation of whether prices are at that level which maximizes the return. An enterprise which is wisely managed or a utility which is wisely regulated will have a price schedule such that purchase of the commodity or service in quantity is encouraged. A lowering of the unit price may so increase sales that returns are increased. The rate structures for utilities are especially adapted to the principle of maximizing income through price schedules.

16.13. Use of Substitute Plants in Estimating Service Worth Value. The use of estimates of the costs of production by substitute plants of modern design (designed but not built) may be a desirable method to determine the reasonable worths of the services rendered by public utilities or other enterprises.

The use of a substitute plant must be only for the purpose of estimating the reasonable worths to its customers of the services rendered by the existing plant; the object is to determine what the earnings of the existing plant would be if only the reasonable worths of its services were exacted from the customers. The customers of an enterprise should not be required to pay prices high enough to support an antiquated, inefficient plant when less costly production may be had. The production cost, then, by the most efficient plant of latest design is important evidence supporting the service worth of an enterprise.

Although the substitute plant is not one to be built and its cost of production is entirely theoretical, such cost is based upon the latest experience within the industry. Most likely, plants similar to the proposed substitute plant are in operation elsewhere. There are many existing old steam generation electric power plants whose unit production costs are high in comparison with the costs of recently constructed plants. Automatic operation and control of many industrial plant processes has resulted in a lowering of production costs. Consequently, the values of old plants not similarly equipped are lowered.

The design of the substitute plant should be made on the basis of the same production capacity of the existing plant to produce a service or product of at least the same quality and serviceability. The objective is to determine whether the prices of the existing plant have been too high or too low, based upon what the customers should in all fairness be expected to pay.

16.14. Service Worth Prices Measured by Substitute Services. In addition to a study of a substitute plant, the valuator may also find that a study of substitute services will produce worth-while evidence of the service worth value. In the utility industries, natural gas is replacing manufactured gas. The availability of natural gas has a direct bearing on the value of an existing plant for the manufacture of gas. Motor buses within urban areas are being substituted for streetcars, and electrical power is being substituted for local steam plants.

The worth of substitute services is not in itself always a direct index of the value of an enterprise producing a similar, but different, product.

Nevertheless, the investigation of the worth of substitute services to the customers is one means of checking to see that the price schedule and value of an existing enterprise are not out of line with the cost of alternatives available to the customers.

STOCK AND BOND VALUE OF THE ENTERPRISE

Land, residential real estate, small business properties, and commodities frequently are sold. The sales establish values for these properties on the basis of the market. Market value is one of the evidences of fair value. Corporate enterprises which are financed through ownership of stocks and bonds are sold only as the sale of these securities from one owner to another constitutes a sale of the enterprise. Thus, the market value may be simulated by determining the stock and bond value. The established price on the market of the securities of an enterprise, together with the amount of such securities outstanding, furnishes the information for calculating the stock and bond value of an enterprise.

16.15. Stocks and Bonds and Their Owners. The capital required for constructing an industrial property, including improvements and enlargements, is represented by its stocks and bonds and earned surplus. These securities are sold outright to investors, awarded in payment for the services of individuals, or are issued to stockholders from time to time to cover property paid for by reservations from the earnings of the enterprise.

The *bondholders* are preferred creditors; they have loaned money for the enterprise upon a security for each bond issue which constitutes a lien upon the property prior to the rights of the stockholders. The bond interest rate is therefore usually materially lower than the fair rate of return on the property. Bondholders have no voice in the management of the corporation. Capital raised by sale of bonds is debt capital; that received by sale of stock is equity capital.

The *stockholders* own the property, manage it through their board of directors, and assume the risks of its possible failure. They are entitled to a return on the fair value of the entire property (including that constructed with borrowed money and with money reserved from income) at a rate sufficiently higher than prevailing interest rates on good bonds to remunerate them for the risks of the undertaking. There are two general classes of stocks, common and preferred.

The *common stockholders* have no special safeguards against the risks of the enterprise. On the other hand, they are entitled to receive, wholly or in common with preferred stockholders, all excess of the total returns over the sum of bond interest plus guaranteed dividends on preferred stock.

The *preferred stockholders* are given special guarantees (subject to the bondholders' liens) such as the right, after bond interest is paid, to receive dividends up to a guaranteed rate and, in the case of "cumulative" preferred stock only, with the further guarantee that deficiencies in lean business years below the guaranteed rate shall be made up in later good years. The guaranteed rate of dividends on preferred stock will usually be higher than prevailing bond interest rates but lower than the fair rate of return on the entire property.

Dividends are the earnings of the enterprise which are paid to the stockholders, usually at a rate per share of stock as voted by the board of directors. The directors usually hold back part of the earnings, which become *earned surplus*. In lean profit years, dividends on stock are sometimes paid from surplus, that is, from earnings of prior years. Bond interest is paid from the general income of the enterprise and is considered an expense to the stockholders prior to the determination of the return. For valuation purposes, however, bond interest paid must be considered as a part of the annual return of the enterprise.

16.16. Determining Stock and Bond Value.   As indicated by the definition in Sec. 1.11, the stock and bond value of an enterprise can be determined by proceeding as follows:

1. Make a complete list of all outstanding issues of bonds, stocks, and trust certificates, including the par value of each issue of bonds and the total par value or the total number of shares of each issue of stock.

2. From stock exchange reports, determine the current and recent past market prices of the several issues; the average over a period at least long enough to eliminate irregular temporary market fluctuations will be helpful, but the prices of the immediate future are wanted. The past records are a guide to making an estimate of future prices.

For properties whose securities are not listed on a stock exchange, it may be possible to establish reasonably correct prices by investigation of private sales and by the opinions of disinterested brokers. For certain enterprises, especially small properties, stock and bond values must be eliminated from consideration as an evidence of value because the prices of their stocks and bonds are not ascertainable.

3. Calculate the total stock and bond value, using the total par values or numbers of shares listed for the several issues and their respective market prices judged to be proper for this purpose. When there is a significantly large fixed liability in the form of a loan, the amount should be included in the calculation.

16.17. Example of Estimation of the Stock and Bond Value. Table 16.3 gives the high and low market price for the securities of a gas and fuel manufacturer and distributor enterprise for 1929–1951. These prices show the effects of periods of prosperity, depression, and war and perhaps also some speculative buying and selling on the stock exchange. Scrutiny of these prices and of the dividend policies of the company leads to the selection of the probable average prices of these securities as

TABLE 16.3.   MARKET PRICE OF SECURITIES FOR USE IN ESTIMATING STOCK AND BOND VALUE OF THE ENTERPRISE

A = common stock, no par value, 1,988,400 shares
B = 6 percent cumulative preferred stock, $100 par value, 374,138 shares
C = 4½ percent cumulative prior preference stock, $100 par value, 246,373 shares
D = first mortgage and collateral trust bonds, 3½ percent, 1965, $38,090,000
E = first mortgage and collateral trust bonds, 3¾ percent, 1974, $12,000,000

Year	Stock A		Stock B		Stock C		Bond D		Bond E	
	High	Low	High	Low	High	Low	High	Low	High	Low
1929	55¼	23	94¾	89	93	74				
1930	42	14⅝	98	90	85¼	76				
1931	27¼	7	95	60	89½	63½				
1932	8¾	2⅞	68	30½	65	48				
1933	12½	3¾	69	35	70	53				
1934	10½	4¾	70	45	80½	55				
1935	5	2½	53½	36	68½	54				
1936	11⅜	3¾	83	41½	85	59½				
1937	10¼	2¾	69	25⅛	81	49				
1938	3¼	1¼	31	9⅛	52	17⅜				
1939	.5⅜	1	25¾	6	48¾	16				
1940	4	1¾	40½	12⅛	60½	26				
1941	3¼	¾	42	23¾	58¾	40				
1942	1½	¾	33	17¾	52½	41				
1943	2⅞	⅞	38¼	19½	59¾	42				
1944	2⅞	1⅝	52½	32⅛	85	56¼				
1945	8⅝	2⅛	82¼	46½	100½	78½	107¼	105⅛		
1946	7⅜	2⅞	100	53	104½	93	107¾	102½		
1947	4⅝	2½	82¼	49	97¾	81	106	96		
1948	7	3⅛	83	65½	88½	73¾	103¾	97½		
1949	6	2⅞	77½	61½	77	62	103¼	96¾	103	101⅛
1950	....	....	.....	....	73½	62½				
1951	....	....	.....	....	81	67¼				

indicated in Table 16.4. The selection of minimum, probable average, maximum, and current prices of these stocks and bonds furnishes a comparatively accurate picture of the range of prices which the future might bring.

In the lower half of Table 16.4 the selected prices of the stocks and bonds are converted into stock and bond values. The four values shown range from $94,489,779 to $116,139,653. In the determination of the final fair value, as discussed in Chap. 17, the appraiser has before him

TABLE 16.4.   CALCULATION OF STOCK AND BOND VALUE

Stock or bond issue	Probable near future price			Current
	Minimum	Probable average	Maximum	
A. Common stock..........	4	5	7	5½
B. 6 percent preferred stock	60	75	80	78
C. 4½ percent prior preferred stock..........	63	77	81	80⅜
D. 3½ percent first mortgage bonds, 1965......	96	102	104	103¼
E. 3¾ percent first mortgage bonds, 1974......	100	104	106 ·	104⅛

Stock or bond issue	Total market value of security			Current
	Minimum	Probable average	Maximum	
A. 1,988,400 shares common	$ 7,953,600	$ 9,942,000	$ 13,918,800	$ 10,936,200
B. 374,138 shares preferred, 6%.................	22,448,280	28,060,350	29,931,040	29,182,764
C. 246,373 shares prior preferred, 4½%.........	15,521,499	18,970,721	19,956,213	19,802,230
D. $38,090,000 bonds, 3½%	36,566,400	38,851,800	39,613,600	39,327,925
E. $12,000,000 bonds, 3¾%	12,000,000	12,480,000	12,720,000	12,495,000
Total stock and bond value	$94,489,779	$108,304,871	$116,139,653	$111,744,119

considerably more evidence from these four calculations than he would have had he chosen only one. He thus is in a better position to find the total fair value of the enterprise when giving weight to the several separate evidences of value.

CHAPTER 17

Fair Value of the Enterprise

The foregoing chapters present detailed processes by which evidences of value may be gathered. The fair value of the property or enterprise, however, must be arrived at by the exercise of judgment in analyzing all factors which affect value and by according each factor just and right weight in establishing the fair value.

Fair value, as explained in Chap. 2, can be determined only by qualified persons and for a particular purpose and at a particular time.

Each valuation is a particular one to be decided upon its own merits by judgment applied to the evidences and conditions. Nevertheless, certain considerations and principles are offered as guides to the formation of judgment. This chapter is concerned with the determination of this final judgment by which fair value is established. Value, it is to be noted, is a quality always determined by judgment, not by formula, and so specific weight and factors cannot be given.

17.1. Art of Estimating Fair Value. The term fair value suggests that there are two or more persons who are interested in the determination of the value. Whether the property is being appraised for sale, insurance or estate settlement, or the establishment of fair prices, two or more persons are involved. The valuator, although engaged by only one of the parties to an appraisal, has to some extent a mutual responsibility. If his fair value is high, his client, the owner, may not make the sale. The appraiser, although professionally bound to do as well as he can for his client, must not fail to judge also the position and circumstances of the other side. The appraiser desires that all parties to the valuation be satisfied with the final settlement. When the final settlement of value is such that both parties are of the opinion that they "got the best of the deal," fair value must certainly have been found.

The appraiser has himself to consider also. His work, if he is to succeed in the field, must be such that he establishes the reputation of being fair and well informed and of finding values upon which final agreements can be reached.

Careful consideration is due every evidence of value, every factor upon which value may depend. The valuator must be fully aware of all conditions governing the purpose for which the value of the property or enterprise is being established and exactly what property is being valued. By skillful exercise of judgment in his considerations of original cost, replacement cost, market value, earning value, service worth value, stock and bond value, and all other pertinent factors he arrives at the fair value. This fair value is the measure of the desirability of ownership of the property under the conditions set forth.

Not all valuators will arrive at their answers by exactly the same process; further, their estimates of fair value probably will differ. The art of valuation, however, is such that any difference in value of a given property or enterprise as found by more than one valuator should be comparatively small. The practice is comparable with the submission of bids on a proposed construction project in which usually there are two or more contractors whose bids are quite close to that of the successful bidder. Likewise, among a group of competent appraisers, their fair values should clearly indicate a close grouping around a central value.

JUST AND RIGHT WEIGHTS DUE THE FACTORS AFFECTING THE VALUE OF THE ENTERPRISE

The principle that *all factors* affecting value are to be given just and right weights in valuation is completely in accord with the methods by which values for all commodities and services are ordinarily fixed. The value of property, however, will always be subject to differences in opinion, because value is the end point of judgment of at least two parties with opposite interests. The general principles by which sound judgment should be guided in deciding what weights are just and right in particular cases are presented in the following sections.

17.2. Weights Due Original Cost and Replacement Cost. The general principles governing the selection of the just and right relative weights due original cost and replacement cost under different circumstances are as follows:

Case 1. *New Physical Property.* When the physical property is new, its fair value is strongly evidenced by its original cost new, provided that there has been no change in potential usefulness and that the costs of original construction were prudent and normal in all respects. This value adjusted for decreased usefulness will continue to be the fair value until there is a change in the price level at which this type of property can be constructed or purchased new.

This principle was stated in 1926 by the United States Supreme Court in *McCardle et al. v. Indianapolis Water Company* (Appendix A, Case 42) in the following words:

. . . Undoubtedly, the reasonable cost of a system of waterworks, well-planned and efficient for the public service, is good evidence of value at the time of construction. And such actual cost will continue fairly well to measure the amount to be attributed to the physical elements of the property so long as there is no change in the level of applicable prices.

Case 2. *Rising or Falling Cost Levels.* During periods of rising or falling construction cost levels the original cost of physical property adjusted for decreased usefulness is no longer dominant evidence of its fair value. The changes in fair values lag behind the changes in replacement costs but gradually shift closer to replacement cost levels; the relative weights given original cost and replacement cost should shift accordingly.

Case 3. *Uniform Cost Levels.* During periods of uniform construction cost levels distinction must be made between property installed *before* and that installed *after* the beginning of the period of uniform cost.

The shift of the value of previously installed property toward replacement cost continues for some years, and eventually evidences of values should be based on prevailing prices. For such older property, the relative weights given original cost and replacement cost should shift accordingly. This principle was also stated by the United States Supreme Court in the *McCardle et al. v. Indianapolis Water Company Case* (Appendix A, Case 42) in the following words:

And, as indicated by the report of the commission, it is true that, if the tendency or trend of prices is not definitely upward or downward and it does not appear probable that there will be a substantial change of prices, then the present value of lands plus the present cost of constructing the plant, less depreciation, if any, is a fair measure of the value of the physical elements of the property.

In the majority of valuations other than for rate regulation purposes, replacement cost will be an evidence of value receiving dominant weight as compared with that given original cost. In giving attention to original cost and replacement cost (or reproduction cost) the appraiser probably will choose to merge original cost and replacement cost into one weighted value—a tentative value of the property based on cost without considering other evidences. Such a figure, although not to be assumed to be fair value, serves as a useful quantity to compare with other evidences of value, such as the earning value or the stock and bond value. In the following sections the phrase "value based on cost" is used frequently. This phrase is to be interpreted as meaning the particular estimate arrived at by giving appropriate consideration to original cost and replacement or reproduction cost, each adjusted for consumed usefulness of the property.

17.3. Weights Due Earning Value. In discussing the just and right weights due earning value, three cases are considered; in each of these cases distinction is made between nonregulated industrial enterprises and public utilities.

Case 1. *Earnings Equal to Fair Return on Value Based on Cost.*   When the past, present, and the estimated comparatively near future earnings are *approximately equal* to a fair return on the value of the property based on original and replacement costs as explained in Sec. 17.2:

1. For *nonregulated enterprises* the earning value simply confirms the value based on cost.

2. For *public utilities* the earning value should be given no weight in determining fair value, but its equality with value based on cost indicates that present rates are fair rates.

Case 2. *Earnings Less than Fair Return on Value Based on Cost.*   When the past, present, and estimated comparatively near future earnings are *materially less* than a fair return on the value based on costs:

1. For *nonregulated enterprises*, when this deficiency of earnings is practically certain to continue a long time, the value based on earnings should be given dominant weight over the evidences of the value of the property based on cost.   When there is a reasonable prospect that the probable earnings may be materially increased in the near future, say enough to approximate the conditions of Case 1, then it may be proper to give considerable weight to the evidences of the value of the property based on cost.

2. For *public utilities*, when the valuation is for rate making, deficient earnings should be given no weight except when the rates necessary to earn a fair return are higher than the reasonable worths of the services rendered (see Sec. 17.14).   For *immediate sale* purposes, deficient earnings may be given some weight.

Case 3. *Earnings Greater than a Fair Return on Value Based on Cost.* When the past, present, and the estimated comparatively near future earnings are *materially greater* than a fair return on the value based on cost:

1. For *nonregulated enterprises*, when this excess of earnings is practically certain to continue a long time, say 5 years or more, the value of the property based on earnings should be given dominant weight over the evidences of value based on cost.   If there is some doubt as to the ability of the enterprise to maintain this high level of earnings over a long period of time, the relative weights due earning value and the value based on cost may be approximately equal.   If the annual variation in the earnings is high, although the general level of earnings is in excess of a fair return on the value of the property based on cost, major weight

should be given to evidences of value based on costs, because in the long run the effects of competition and fair prices should make cost a good indicator of what the probable earnings of an enterprise may be.

2. For *public utilities* the excess earnings should be given no weight in valuations for rate making; the rates which give earnings in excess of fair return are subject to compulsory revision downward. For *immediate sale* purposes, excess earnings may be given some minor weight when action for their reduction by regulatory authority is not likely to be started soon.

17.4. Relative Weights Due Values Based on Cost and on Earnings. Although the general weights to accord earning value are given in Sec. 17.3, the following statements are in support of that discussion. In comparing the value based on costs with earning value it must be remembered that, although probable future earnings are the true fundamental basis of all values, the returns on which earning value is based are not necessarily the most probable future returns. They are merely those which have been forecasted on the basis of past, present, and estimated comparatively near future income and expenses.

In the long run, owing to the effects of competition and the principle of fair prices, the cost (reproduction or replacement cost) of a nonregulated enterprise may be a better indicator of future earnings than are averages of the past earnings and expenses. But when future earnings have a high probability of being realized, earning value is deserving of the major weight.

The service rates charged by public utilities are subject to regulation, up or down, to make them just sufficient to yield a fair return. Hence, to give earning value any weight in establishing the rate base of a public utility would be to enter upon a vicious circle of reasoning.

17.5. Weight Due Service Worth Value. In considering the just and right weights due service worth value, distinction must be made between nonregulated industrial enterprises and public utility enterprises.

Nonregulated Enterprises. The service worth value of a nonregulated enterprise, estimated on a fair price basis, would seem entitled to material weight in determining fair value. Moreover, determination of the estimated earnings of an industrial property on the basis of fair prices for its products will often afford some aid in determining whether abnormally high or low returns are likely to continue in the future.

Public Utilities. When the service worth value of a public utility determined upon an adequate, just basis, supported by convincing evidence, is *materially less* than its value based on cost, the service worth value is entitled to relatively high, in extreme cases predominant, weight in the estimation of fair value.

In the case of the majority of utilities, a comparatively brief general investigation readily shows that the reasonable worths of the services rendered are at least equal to charges which will yield a fair return on fair value; in such cases, it is unnecessary to estimate the service worth value.

17.6. Weight Due Stock and Bond Value.   Stock and bond value must be given such weight as is just and right in each case.   However, a study of court decisions in many valuation litigations shows that:

1. In general, stock and bond value is entitled to little weight, relative to value based on cost and earning value, in determining the values of an industrial property.

   a. The fair values sought in valuations are comparatively stable values, which do not fluctuate in close accord with stock tickers.

   b. The market prices of stocks and bonds generally reflect the earnings of the enterprise and the dividend payout (Sec. 15.10).   Frequently, subsidiary operations of the enterprise are particularly remunerative.   When these earnings are included as a part of those of the enterprise, the stock and bond value may be materially higher than it would be if the subsidiary investment were not so remunerative. The reverse is also true.   In either case, the stock and bond value may not reflect adequately the earning capacity of the property under valuation.

   c. Public utilities frequently issue bonds or stocks for the purpose of acquiring new capital to be used for construction of additional property which will be under the jurisdiction of more than one regulatory agency, or which will be used for different types of services (as natural gas and electric properties).   When there is no way of dividing the value of the securities proportionately among the several uses of the property, the stock and bond value cannot be considered appropriate, nor can it serve as a basis for the determination of fair rates.

   d. It is often impossible to ascertain a reliable stock and bond value of the enterprise because its securities are not listed on the stock exchanges.

2. In some abnormal cases, stock and bond value may be entitled to material or even predominant weight.

For example, in the final decision, 1934, in the *Lindheimer et al. v. Illinois Bell Telephone Co. Case* (Appendix A, Case 63), the United States Supreme Court used the high and greatly increasing values of the stocks and bonds of the company during 1923 to 1934 to help sweep away the mass of technical rulings on annual depreciations, returns, and fair values by which the lower court decided that the company, in spite of its prosperity, had not been earning fair returns on the fair value of its property devoted to public service.

17.7. Weights Due Other Pertinent Factors. All other pertinent factors found to affect values in particular cases must be thoroughly investigated; they must be given such weights, of a general character, as are found to be just and right. No definite general instructions as to the magnitudes of such weights can be given. Other pertinent factors affecting value include materials and labor supply; transportation facilities and costs; size, character, and prospects of growth of the local and of neighboring communities; present and probable future local and general markets; present and probable future competition; present and probable future local and general business conditions; and present and probable future price trends.

FAIR VALUES FOR SPECIFIC PURPOSES

The relative weights an appraiser gives to the various evidences of value and factors affecting value depend on the particular purposes for which the value is sought and the conditions governing at the time. Particularly are the weights different as between nonregulated enterprises and regulated public utilities. Valuation for purposes other than rate base establishment are next considered.

17.8. Valuation for Ordinary Sales. An enterprise under consideration for sale (or purchase) would be valued primarily on the basis of its earning value or replacement cost. When the earnings result from services and intangibles rather than from physical properties, the earning value is a better criterion of fair value than is replacement cost. Earning value is also a better evidence of value when replacement cost is considerably higher than earning value.

When a property or enterprise is under negotiations for sale, it is the probable future returns which give that property value. When the conditions of purchase are such that the purchaser has the alternative of buying the property or constructing anew, replacement cost is deserving of dominant weight for the reason that the physical property is of greater importance than are earnings.

Original cost is not to be accorded much weight in estimating fair value of properties for sale, except when they are relatively new or when there has been no material change in the price levels since construction of the property.

Service worth value is an important evidence of value of property for sale when prices on which the past earnings were made seem to be out of line with the reasonable worth of the products or services in the immediate future.

17.9. Fair Value in Condemnations.   The condemnation of property by public authority constitutes a form of forced sale.   In almost every condemnation, however, the property condemned is put to entirely different use than when under private ownership.   In fact, buildings as condemned properties are often destroyed or moved to other locations.

Fair value in condemnations is usually earning value; market value is likewise a good base when it can be established reliably.   The owner of condemned property is giving up his future returns, and only infrequently is he able to replace his business or property under similar surroundings and conditions.

When an earning value cannot be established, market value is the preferred evidence; when neither earning value nor market value can be reliably established, replacement cost may be the best evidence of fair value.   Stock and bond value and service worth value seldom can be applied to condemnations, because enterprises as a whole are seldom condemned.   Further, the bases upon which these evidences of value are determined are often inappropriate.   Securities of enterprises in the process of condemnation frequently sell at depressed prices, and actual earnings rather than estimated fair earnings are better measures of the value of that which is being condemned.

17.10. Fair Value in Settlement of Estates.   The property of an estate is valued at the time of death of the owner for two primary purposes, namely, for inheritance taxes and for division among heirs or other beneficiaries.   The fair value found is most often market value for all property, including securities, for which sale prices are or can be established by recent past or current sales.   A small business which can be disposed of by sale would be valued on the basis of sale as discussed in Sec. 17.8.

An enterprise for which stock and bonds were issued, these securities having been closely held and not traded, should be valued primarily on its replacement cost and earning value.   The original cost, unless the property was mainly new, would not be given any weight.   Replacement cost would be a significant evidence of value of the enterprise should it be one whose earnings were dependent more on the physical property than on managerial success.   Fair value would be established by weighting replacement cost and earning value according to the particular circumstances, with perhaps dominant weight being given to earning value. Proper consideration of the statutes and regulations governing the valuation of inherited property for taxation is, of course, essential.   Such statutes may prescribe the basis of the value for taxation, which may not be the fair base for other purposes.

17.11. Fair Value for Insurance Purposes.   Property is valued for insurance purposes both as a basis of issue of policies and as a basis of settlement of claims for damage. Assuming that it is the physical property that is being insured rather than the business or enterprise as a whole, the basis of value is market value or replacement cost. All other evidences have little or no weight.

The owner of insurable property, if he is to have the protection he seeks, desires to insure his property for a principal sum close to its replacement cost, including in most instances the proper allowance for consumed useful service. The owner does not wish to carry insurance in excess of this value, because he would then be required to pay a premium higher than necessary.

In settlement for damage incurred, the insurance company is obligated only up to the principal sum named in the contract, and then only if the damage actually reached the insured value. Insurance companies settle claims for damage by rebuilding, replacing, or paying in cash the equivalent value of the damage. Consequently, the damage must be appraised. Professional claim adjusters usually act for the insurance company, and their fair values are determined on the replacement basis, either through reconstruction or direct replacement with equivalent property.

17.12. Fair Value as a Basis of Security Issues. The United States Securities Exchange Commission and state agencies of similar function examine or approve the issue of securities by industrial enterprises. The main objective of such agencies is to protect the investing public from the flotation of unsound stocks and bonds.

Securities, to be good investments, need to be backed by property of sufficient value to protect the equity of the investors and an enterprise of sufficient earning power to maintain the value of the securities. Consequently, the value of the physical property (and in certain cases of intangible property) based on cost and the prospective earnings of the enterprise become the chief evidences of value upon which to base the issuance of securities.

Original cost and replacement cost adjusted for consumed useful service of the property are each a good basis for establishment of value for the purpose of security issues. Whichever is the lower would be the safer, but neither would be safe if the outlook of price trends was such as to produce the possibility of a near future replacement cost less than the lower of original cost or replacement cost as of the present. When the immediate future replacement cost is considerably above the original cost and in a price level era established firmly above the price level era of the original cost, replacement cost should receive dominant weight in establishing the fair value of the property.

The value of the enterprise, on the other hand, is a factor of the earnings of the future. Since the issuance of securities should also be related to future earnings, earning value is an important factor. The fair value of an enterprise on which to base the approval of security issues should perhaps be chosen between the fair value of the property as property and the earning value, giving material weight to whichever is the smaller.

Another consideration, but not always an appraisal question, is whether the enterprise can earn a sufficient return to maintain the value of all its outstanding securities.

17.13. Valuation for Property Taxation. Ad valorem taxes are levied by various governments and their agencies on the basis of tax rates applied to assessed values. Assessed values are determined on the basis of the statutes, though the tax commission's assessor or administrative unit usually must issue regulations which interpret the statutes.

Assessed valuations are generally poor indicators of fair values of properties. The aim of the law is to achieve equitable assessed values among the property owners within a given assessment district. Whether the assessed value is in close agreement to fair value is not an important matter as long as the equitableness is achieved. Because of the magnitude of the task and because of the variety of types of properties that one assessing agency must handle, assessed values frequently are not equitable.

Assessing bodies sometimes apply arbitrary formulas for assessing utility holdings that extend throughout several taxing districts. Railway, electric power, and pipe-line companies are examples of properties so assessed. Original cost, replacement cost, earnings, and stock and bond value each may be given a certain weight as set by the policy of the taxing agency.

Finding fair value for tax assessment purposes is mainly a procedure of following out the law and its accepted interpretations.

RATE BASE DETERMINATION FOR PUBLIC UTILITIES

Governmental commissions and agencies charged with the responsibility of regulating public utilities may attempt to establish the value of a utility, but more probably their objective is to establish a rate base. A rate base may or may not be a fair value. Particularly since 1944 many commissions have not found fair value as stated in the *Smyth v. Ames* case but have merely established a rate base and a fair rate of return. The result in a given rate case must conform to the statutes which are governing and the policy and precedents of the commission (unless specific evidence and conditions warrant departures). Three procedures will be presented for establishing a rate base for a public utility: the original cost (prudent investment), fair value, and adequate income.

17.14. Original Cost Rate Base. An original cost rate base is now used by the majority of state public utility commissions. An original cost rate base is supported on the theory that the owners are entitled to a fair return on their investment. Investment, or prudent investment as it is usually meant, is the dollars invested in the used and useful property adjusted for decreased usefulness. When the rate base is to be original cost, six principal determinations need to be made:

1. Original cost of the presently used and useful property
2. Amount to allow for decreased usefulness on the original cost
3. Fair allowance for working capital
4. Present net cost of intangibles
5. Fair rate of return
6. Service worth value

The determination of these six items for use in establishing an original cost rate base should proceed as outlined in the several foregoing chapters. Once the six factors are known, the rate base is set accordingly. Judgment must be carefully exercised to ascertain that the net earnings provided by the rate base and rate of return are sufficient to ensure adequate financing and adequate service to the customers.

The service worth value is not an important factor in a rate base determination of a prosperous and growing utility. The service of some declining utilities, such as some street railways and interurban railways, may not be in sufficient demand to support a fair rate of return on original cost adjusted for decreased usefulness, using age-life adjustments or book accrued depreciation. The rate base, in such circumstances, may be determined by giving dominant weight to service worth value or by making substantial allowance for decreased usefulness of the physical property.

17.15. Fair Value Rate Base. When the rate base of a public utility is to be fair value, the following factors should be determined:

1. Original cost of used and useful property adjusted for decreased usefulness
2. Reproduction cost or replacement cost of used and useful property adjusted for decreased usefulness
3. Fair allowance for working capital
4. Present value of intangibles
5. Fair rate of return
6. Earning value
7. Service worth value
8. Stock and bond value

The problem is to determine the fair value base from these eight items and other pertinent factors. As stated in Secs. 17.4 and 17.5, the earning value and service worth value are of no great weight in considering a utility enterprise which is prosperous and which has a good outlook of continuing to render a satisfactory and essential service to the community. For much the same reasons, the stock and bond value is to be given little or no weight, because the prices of these securities on the market have been influenced by the regulated earnings of the past. For those regulated utilities in currently sound operating and financial condition, establishing a fair value rate base is largely a process of determining the fair value of the enterprise from items 1 to 5 as listed.

If a utility is not prosperous or is in fact declining, the rate base may be determined by giving dominant weight to service worth value. There is so little demand for the service of such an enterprise that it is probably impossible to set a schedule of rates which will enable the utility to earn a fair rate of return on its original cost adjusted for decreased usefulness. Nor will it be reasonable to assume that the existing property of such an enterprise would be reproduced or even substantially duplicated. Hence, since neither evidence of value, that based on original cost or that based on replacement cost, is particularly appropriate, the fair value may be determined by giving material weight to service worth value.

17.16. Adequate Income Rate Schedule. The chief objective of rate regulation of public utilities is to protect the utility from prices that are too low considering returns to the owners thereof while at the same time preventing the prices from being so high that the returns are more than the owners are reasonably entitled to. One approach to this objective is to consider the income necessary to the utility to enable it to meet all necessary operating expenses including amortization of the cost of depreciable property, bond interest, dividends to stockholders, and a reasonable addition to earned surplus. The tests of the result reached by this approach are two: (1) Will such income enable the utility to attract and hold sufficient capital to continue efficient and satisfactory operation? (2) Are the prices necessary to maintain this income reasonable to the customers?

With the exception of the investigation of the proper allowance for amortization of the cost of depreciable property, the adequate income process is not one involving engineering valuation. Principally, the problem is one of finance and plant operation.

17.17. Example of Determination of the Rate Base for the XYZ Utility. Consider the XYZ Utility, a small enterprise providing telephone service. The steady increase in prices has brought on a situation where the fairness of the existing rates for telephone service is questionable. The company has petitioned the state public service commission for authority to increase rates. Commission hearings have been held, and the following findings have been made by the commission:

1. Property and Working Capital:

	Book record	Original cost	Reproduction cost (10-year average prices)
Total plant in service....................	$301,589	$301,589	$382,670
Depreciation adjustment..................	122,673	117,514	149,241
Depreciated plant in service...............	$178,916	$184,075	$233,429
Allowance for materials and supplies...............		9,000	9,000
Allowance for cash working capital..................		5,000	5,000
Totals..		$198,075	$247,429

2. The fair value for rate-making purposes:
By commission decision the fair value rate base is $230,000.

3. The capital structure of the enterprise as shown on the book records:

Debt capital, 3½ percent bonds (43.7 percent of total)................. $ 78,100
Equity capital (56.3 percent of total)
    Common stock.. $50,890
    Surplus.. 49,768   100,658
        Total capital... $178,758

4. The annual operating expenses, exclusive of depreciation and income taxes:

	Claimed by company	Allowed by commission
Maintenance expense...............................	$ 26,048	$ 22,434
Traffic expense.......................................	46,180	46,180
Commercial expense...................................	16,305	16,305
General office salaries and expense....................	7,245	7,245
Other operating expenses.............................	5,662	5,662
Taxes, other than income taxes.......................	3,870	3,723
Total..	$105,310	$101,549

The major difference between the amount claimed and the amount allowed was in maintenance expense. The commission explained that the allowance was based on experience rather than proposed expenditures.

The annual depreciation provision claimed by the company was allowed by the commission, since the annual depreciation rate for each account was previously approved by the commission. The total annual allowance was $13,366.

State and federal income taxes were averaged at 25 percent of net income before income taxes with an allowed deduction from income of $4,965 for bond interest paid and other nontaxable items.

The fair rate of return was set at 0.06. Hence, the fair return was (230,000)(0.06), or $13,800.

The following expressions indicate the approximate allowable gross revenue of the enterprise under the aforementioned conditions:

Let G = the allowable annual gross revenue

M = annual operating expense exclusive of depreciation and income taxes

D = the annual depreciation charge

T = allowable deductions for bond interest and other nontaxable items

R = the allowable fair return = (rate base) (fair rate of return)

The annual income tax = $(G - M - D - T)(0.25)$

The annual return = $G - M - D -$ income tax

$$= G - M - D - (0.25)(G - M - D - T)$$
$$= 0.75G - 0.75M - 0.75D + 0.25T$$

If the expression for the annual return is set equal to the fair return, the allowable annual gross revenue may be expressed in terms of the fair return.

$$0.75G - 0.75M - 0.75D + 0.25T = R$$
$$G - M - D + \tfrac{1}{3}T = \tfrac{4}{3}R$$
$$G = \tfrac{4}{3}R + M + D - \tfrac{1}{3}T$$
$$G = \tfrac{4}{3} \text{ (rate base)(fair rate of return)} + M + D - \tfrac{1}{3}T.$$

Using the findings of the commission, the allowable annual gross revenue is

$$G = (\tfrac{4}{3})(230{,}000)(0.06) + 101{,}549 + 13{,}366 - (\tfrac{1}{3})(4{,}965)$$
$$G = 18{,}400 + 101{,}549 + 13{,}366 - 1{,}655 = 131{,}660$$

An increase in the fair rate of return from 0.06 to 0.07 will provide for an increase in the allowable gross revenue of $(\tfrac{4}{3})(2{,}300)$, or \$3,070.

An increase of 10 percent in the rate base will provide for an increase in the allowable annual gross revenue of $(\tfrac{4}{3})(23{,}000)(0.06)$, or \$1,840.

Using the depreciated reproduction cost determined by the commission will provide for an increase in the allowable annual gross revenue of $(\tfrac{4}{3})(17{,}429)(0.06)$, or \$1,394.

If to the net book cost of the plant in service, \$178,916, the allowance for working capital is added, the resulting total is \$192,916. If this figure were used as a rate base, the annual allowable gross revenue would be decreased by $(\tfrac{4}{3})(230{,}000 - 192{,}916)(0.06)$, or \$2,967.

The company claimed that an 11 percent return on the common stock equity was necessary to maintain the attractiveness of that type of investment. Hence, the weighted average return on capital desired is 7.72 percent:

$$\text{Debt capital:} \quad (0.437)(3.5) = 1.53$$
$$\text{Equity capital:} \quad (0.563)(11) = \underline{6.19}$$
$$7.72$$

The use of this rate of return and the company capitalization as shown on the books produces a fair allowable return of (178,758)(0.0772), or $13,800, equal to the fair return allowed by the commission. It is only when the claimed rate of return on capital is applied to the commission's rate base that the resulting increase in the allowable annual gross revenue exceeds the amount of the disagreement of the company and the commission over the operating expenses.

The foregoing discussion has served to point out the relatively minor role which the rate base may play in the rate-making problem compared with that of the operating expenses. As mentioned in Sec. 17.16, the chief objective of rate regulation is to protect the utility from an income which is inadequate to meet the expenses of operation necessary to provide the proper service and at the same time to protect the customers from rates which are excessive. Therefore, an adequate rate schedule will enable the utility to meet operating expenses, pay bond interest, pay dividends on its stock, and add a reasonable amount to surplus.

The proposed rates in this illustration will be tested on this basis. The commission has set up $131,660 as a fair annual gross income. Using the amount claimed by the company for operating expenses, the net income for the company is:

Allowed annual gross revenue		$131,660
Operating expenses, exclusive of depreciation and income taxes	$105,310	
Annual depreciation expense	13,366	
Income deductions (including bond interest)	4,965	123,641
Net income before income taxes		$ 8,019
Income taxes, averaging 25 percent		2,005
Net income (not annual return)		$ 6,014

Figure 15.1 indicates that on the average approximately 76 percent of the net income of utilities is paid as dividends and that the corresponding price-earnings ratio is 12.40. Applying these figures to the net earnings of the XYZ Utility, the dividends might be $4,570, and the stock should be selling for $74,570. The yield on the stock is 4,570/74,570, or about 6.1 percent, which is satisfactory though not especially remunerative. The addition to surplus, $1,444, is small, although if the company were able to keep its operating expenses down to that allowed by the commission, the addition to surplus would be materially larger.

In summary, it might be concluded that the proposed rates meet the test of adequacy in that the company can meet its operating expenses and bond interest and in addition pay a reasonable dividend, although not a particularly attractive one.

This discussion serves to illustrate that the art of engineering valuation is fundamental to the establishment of the information from which a rate

base is set.   However, the establishment of a rate base from the facts
presented is not necessarily an engineering valuation process.   The
regulating agency begins where the valuation engineer leaves off.   His
responsibility is to gather the information and to find value if value is
sought, but from then on the problem is one of regulatory policy, finance,
management, and a judicious balancing of consumer and investor
interests.   Under present utility commission policies, in many states,
the rate base no longer can be assumed to be the value of the useful
properties of the utility; it is simply a rate base.

CHAPTER 18

Valuation of Mines and Other Limited Life Properties

The water, power, gas, transportation, and other public utility enterprises and the larger manufacturing establishments are generally valued on the assumption that they will continue to do business for an indefinite period in the future. For certain enterprises and businesses, however, such assumption is not warranted. An enterprise may be of such a character that its future is completely tied to the productive capacities of one person. The future of another enterprise may depend on the kind of tenants which can be attracted to it or on the shift of the business district of a city. A third enterprise may depend completely upon the supply of an irreplaceable asset. These latter enterprises are limited life enterprises, of which private professional practices, office buildings, motels, mines, and other natural resource enterprises are examples.

18.1. Comparison of Limited and Unlimited Life Enterprises. Profitable enterprises of unlimited life normally will conserve the investment in the plant and equipment by reinvesting in the business the prior invested capital recovered through depreciation charges (Sec. 10.14). To be profitable, enterprises of limited life must return currently to the owner a proper portion *of* his investment in addition to a fair return *on* his investment, but the owner is not in a position to reinvest in the enterprise his recovered capital because of the forthcoming exhaustion of his natural resources or patronage. The hazard attending the return of the investment in limited life enterprises occasionally differs so significantly from the normal risk of doing business that the ordinary present worth formulas used in computing present value are sometimes modified to permit the use of two interest rates (Sec. 16.3). A third difference between limited life and unlimited life enterprises exists in the degree of preciseness with which they may be appraised. Consider a gas well. As Justice Jackson said in the *Hope* case:[1]

The amount and quality of service rendered by the usual utility will, at least roughly, be measured by the amount of capital it puts into the enterprise. But it has no rational application where there is no such relationship between invest-

[1] *Federal Power Commission et al. v. Hope Natural Gas Co.* (No. 34), 320 U.S. 591, 649, 51 P.U.R. (N.S.) 193 (U.S. Sup. Ct. Jan. 3, 1944).

ment and capacity to serve.   There is no such relationship between investment and amount of gas produced. . . .

Consequently, the several evidences of value which may be applicable in any situation may not check to the entire satisfaction of the appraiser; he, perforce, is required to decide what evidences of value are applicable. In addition, limitations attending an estimate of the quantity and of the quality of a deposit of a natural resource make computations containing more than four or five significant digits quite unrealistic.

18.2. Evidences of Value of a Limited Life Enterprise. The appraisal of a limited life enterprise can proceed along the lines discussed in the preceding chapters and summarized in Chap. 17, provided modifications are incorporated in the procedure whenever the factor of limited life warrants a deviation in procedure.   Another deviation occurs when the appraisal applies to undeveloped resources or an inactive enterprise. The determination of the present investment requires no modification unless there happens to be a deposit of a natural resource involved.   In such a case the original cost of the deposit is modified by an amount representing that part of the natural resource which has been removed, commonly called *depletion* of the asset.   The expectancy of the separate classes of property, tangible and intangible, must be tied in with the useful probable life of those assets which will determine the working life of the enterprise.   In some cases, the estimate of the salvage of the property of the enterprise may be large enough to be significant to the appraiser.

Similar modifications are necessary in the estimation of the cost of the enterprise based on current prices.   A trended original cost may be more realistic than either a reproduction or a replacement cost study.

The appraiser may elect to establish a market value for the enterprise. Hotels, motels, and office buildings are examples.   Deposits of a natural resource may be similarly appraised on the basis of so many dollars per ton of ore in the ground.

Generally, the appraiser will find that his most substantial evidence of value is the estimated earning value of the enterprise (considering the enterprise as a single operating entity).   The process of estimating earning value is described in Chap. 16, but because of its importance to the valuation of limited life enterprises, the following details are repeated:

1. The probable average annual operation return, not the net return, is used in computing the earning value of a limited life enterprise:

$$\begin{Bmatrix} \text{Operation} \\ \text{return} \end{Bmatrix} = \begin{bmatrix} \text{gross} \\ \text{income} \end{bmatrix} - \begin{bmatrix} \text{operating expenses (exclusive of} \\ \text{depreciation or depletion expense)} \end{bmatrix}$$

Operating expenses include wages, salaries, selling and administrative expenses, materials, supplies, maintenance, cost of replacements of property other than the natural resource, property taxes, income taxes, and interest on short-term notes. Exclude any depreciation or depletion allowance, interest on funded debt, or any entries in the earned surplus account. If the unit prices used in estimating gross income are based on a delivered price, operating expenses must include transportation expense.

2. The average unit prices used in predicting the gross income must take the expectancy of the enterprise into consideration. The longer the expectancy the more conservative the estimate of gross income should be. Estimates should be based on minimums rather than maximums.

3. The formula used in this instance is (16.6) [or (16.7) when two rates are used]. As applied to the sample problems in this chapter, R is the annual operation return, and n is the expectancy of the enterprise. When there is considered a period of deferment of d years before the beginning of the annual operation returns, the calculation requires the use of Formula (16.23) [or (16.8) when two rates are used].

In the appraisal of a natural gas well, the valuator might need to determine its service worth value if the appropriateness of existing rates charged for gas is in question. Average prices for gas at the wellhead in similar areas may be used to estimate a fair gross income. The reasonable worth of gas service determined by comparison with competing facilities, electricity, oil, or coal, may serve as a basis.

The stock and bond value of a limited life enterprise frequently does not exist because the securities of the enterprise are often closely held. Even when the stock and bond value is available, care must be exercised in its use. For example, when the business enters its latter stages, its securities often sell at depressed prices. The use of such figures can result in a stock and bond value far below the value of the enterprise.

VALUATION OF MINES

The discussion which follows is limited to a brief description of the considerations surrounding the appraisal of minerals and mines. Further discussion may be found in the extensive writings on the examination of mineral properties, their valuation, and methods of mining.

In this discussion, the term *mineral* includes all materials belonging to the mineral kingdom that may be won and marketed by commercial enterprises. The term *mine* designates the enterprise, consisting of the plant, workings, liquid assets, and intangibe prolperty which is utilized in winning and preparing the mineral for market. Although quarries, clay pits, and sand and gravel plants are not mines according to the above definition, their characteristics are such that the procedures of mining valuation will apply to them without modification.

Some mineral deposits are so extensive that no error will be incurred if the enterprise working them is considered to have an unlimited life. However, it is generally necessary to consider the fact that the main asset of the enterprise, the ore deposit, is depleting and cannot be replaced as such.

18.3. Valuation of Mining Properties in Various Stages of Development. Occasionally, an appraiser is called upon to indicate what might be the value of the mineral rights of a property in one of its several stages of development. What importance he attaches to the prospective earnings which may be derived from these lands depends much on the stage of development of the property as a mine.

The first stage is illustrated by the situation when a landowner merely supposes that valuable deposits are present. The land may be in the vicinity of valuable deposits, or the owner may be just optimistic. In such cases, the mineral rights are without value until the existence of a profitable deposit is proved.

The next stage of development can be described by the situation when some prospecting has been done. Then there is some geological or other reason to suspect that there might be valuable deposits present. Probably these deposits are valuable, but to the appraiser this value will be a minimum because there are so many uncertainties to be estimated—transportation, probable investment required to obtain the mineral, mining costs, and the unknown quantity and quality of the deposit.

The third stage is illustrated by the situation when some mineral has been found, but the amount, position, quantity, and quality of the deposit are still unknown. The same factors mentioned in the preceding paragraph are undetermined; hence the value of the deposit is nominal. However, there may be justification for a decision by the owner to go ahead and obtain many of the answers to the above uncertainties.

The fourth stage of development is reached when a fair amount of exploratory work has been done. Test holes have been drilled and samples taken. Maps have been prepared, and it is now possible to make some kind of estimate of the quality and quantity of the mineral deposit. Since an enterprise has not yet been organized, the evidences of value mentioned in Sec. 18.2 pertaining to the present investment, the stock and bond value, and the market value are not applicable. The primary evidence of value necessarily is based on the estimated earnings of the prospective enterprise. The appraiser should then proceed to estimate the cost of developing the deposit, the probable income, and the accompanying production costs which could be expected over a specific number of years. From these estimates he may obtain the earning value of the venture which he may use as the warranted investment. This process of determining the earning value of an undeveloped mining reserve is illustrated in detail in Sec. 18.6.

The fully developed and operating mine represents the next stage in the life history of the mine. In this situation, quantities are fairly well assured, and the production costs are known. The marketing factors, the business cycle, the political situation, and other prospects are unknown, but these are not unlike the usual hazards underwritten by any venture. The value of the mine in this state of development is estimated after consideration of all the applicable evidences of value which are described in Sec. 18.2. The procedure is illustrated in detail in Sec. 18.5 for an operating mine.

The final stage of the development of the mine is reached when the mine is either inoperative or about ready to close down. If the mineral deposit is exhausted and the mine is scheduled for closing, the value of the mine equals the present worth of the salvage which can be received from the equipment. Suppose, however, that a satisfactory quantity of the deposit remains but the average quality of it is questionable, the selling price has decreased, or the production costs have risen and the mine has ceased to be profitable. An analysis may show that a modernization program can be instituted which will again make the mine show favorable returns. If so, the value of the mine is the present worth of the probable returns minus the cost of the modernization program. The details of establishing the value would follow the appropriate items given in Sec. 18.5 for an operating mine.

18.4. Mine Examination. The examination of mines, both undeveloped ore reserves and going mines, is sufficiently technical and demanding of such extensive knowledge and training that the services of mining engineers and geologists are imperative. Since this chapter deals with the appraisal of mines, it will be assumed that the general data required in a mine valuation will be obtained by personnel competent to cope with the many problems encountered in every mine examination.[1]

In brief, the mine examination is divided into two sections, (1) the

[1] See Roland D. Parks, "Examination and Valuation of Mineral Property," 3d ed., Cambridge, Mass., Addison-Wesley Press, Inc., 1949.

Robert Peele and John P. Church (eds.), "Mining Engineers' Handbook," New York, John Wiley & Sons, Inc., 1941.

Herbert C. Hoover, "Principles of Mining," New York, McGraw-Hill Book Company, Inc., 1909.

Frederick H. Lahee, "Field Geology," 4th ed. rev. and enlarged, New York, McGraw-Hill Book Company, Inc., 1941.

Alan M. Batemen, "Economic Mineral Deposits," 2d ed., New York, John Wiley & Sons, Inc., 1950.

C. A. Heiland, "Geophysical Exploration," New York, Prentice-Hall, Inc., 1940.

acquisition of data from the field and (2) the combination of the field data with the necessary cost data.

The field work includes such items as:

1. Geography and geology of the ore reserve
2. Legal history of the operations
3. Production history of the operation, if any, including a study of mining methods
4. Estimation of the quantity of the ore deposit, including the amount which is assured comparable with the probable ore reserve
5. Estimation of the probable quality of the deposit so that mining costs can be estimated
6. Plant and equipment used or required in the operations

Each of the tasks enumerated is important, but it must be stressed that the estimation of the quantity and quality of the ore reserve must be well done. The sampling methods employed must be thorough, based on sound theory, and to the highest degree possible statistically in control, so that the possible variance of the samples from that of the entire ore reserve can be estimated.

The second part of the mine examination is one of interpretation. The data acquired from the field are not exact; also, the ore reserve may at different times possess different values depending on economic conditions.

One of the necessary early determinations is the estimation of the tonnage of the ore which will be profitable to mine. The ore may be separated into different grades according to location, mining methods, and mining costs. Whether a particular grade of ore is profitable to mine depends upon the cost-price relationship forecasted over the period during which the operation will be active. Once a cost-price relationship is forecast, the appraiser may determine the dividing line between profitable grades and unprofitable grades of ore.

From the field surveys and drillings, the extent of the deposits is estimated. The assay reports from the laboratory furnish the essential information from which the quality of the ore is determined. Thus, the final determinations are based upon a planned scheme of mining the ore deposit by which the highest tonnage of the most profitable ores can be produced.

The cost-price relationship is the crux of the mine examination problem; it is inherent in the mine appraisal problem as well. The estimation of the mining cost depends on investigation of the mining methods which are applicable, the capacity of the actual or proposed mine plant, and, as a consequence, the life of the venture. The estimate of the price of the ore depends on the life of the venture as well as the immediate economic conditions. Hence, it is possible to make studies which can indicate a maximum profit for the venture. The longer period of years the analyst forecasts for the future life of the venture, the more conservatively he must estimate his predictions of the cost-price relationship.

18.5. Illustration of the Appraisal of an Operating Mine. The appraisal of an operating mine should proceed along the lines of estimating the evidence of value as given in Sec. 18.2. The past operating conditions of the mine and the probable future operating conditions need thorough investigation. The consideration given to the investment, the stock and bond value, and the earning value will be governed in each case by the particular prevailing conditions. Perhaps the earning value is the more important evidence of value, and in the example which follows the procedure of estimating earning value is stressed.

Let it be supposed that an operating iron mine is to be appraised. Examinations indicate that the titles to the property are clear, that the market and price of the ore are steady, that no hazards such as excess drainage or quick decline in the quality of the deposit are apparent; however, the mining methods practiced by the enterprise are not modern. It is estimated that by expending $150,000 for new equipment the present mining costs can be lowered from $0.626 to $0.506 per ton of iron ore produced.

The following additional data apply:

1. Probable tons of iron ore in the deposit............................ 2,100,000
2. Annual production, tons... 260,000
3. Average selling price at Lake Erie ports, per ton................... $6.954
4. Costs of production, per ton
    a. Mining, including labor, power, and supplies............ $ 0.506
    b. Crushing and screening.............................. 0.050
    c. Administration and miscellaneous..................... 0.160
    d. Stripping and drainage ($25,000 annually)............. 0.096
    e. Maintenance of plant and equipment ($37,700 annually) 0.145
    f. Selling cost....................................... 0.050
    g. Rail and water transportation....................... 2.781
    h. Social security taxes............................... 0.020
    i. Taxes on ore remaining in deposit.................... 0.334
    j. Occupation tax $(0.11)(6.954 - \text{sum of items } a \text{ to } i)$..... 0.309
    k. Allowance for depreciation, amortization and depletion— not used in appraisal calculations, but needed for calculation of federal income tax........................... 0.800
    l. Federal income tax at 40 percent of income per ton less production cost per ton including depletion and depreciation expense per ton.............................. 0.681
    m. Total production cost per ton delivered............... $5.932
    n. Production cost per ton less depreciation and depletion.. 5.132
5. Estimated average operation return per ton ($6.954 - 5.132) $1.822

6. Working capital at date of appraisal.................... $ 407,787
7. Estimate of average required working capital.............   300,000
8. The recorded organization and financing costs, approximately
   9.9 percent of the original investment...................   426,500
9. The recorded cost of the mineral rights..................   2,000,000
10. Estimated current market cost of the mineral rights.......   3,500,000
11. The present plant and equipment (including development
   costs)
   a. Original cost..   1,581,826
   b. Original cost adjusted for consumed useful service based
      upon age and expectancy............................   910,195
   c. Replacement cost new   2,450,000
12. Through periodic depletion allowances, 68 percent of the cost
   of the mineral rights has been written off................   1,360,000
13. Probable salvage value of equipment when the mine is finally
   closed down...   50,000
14. Reasonable remaining investment of the $426,500 financing
   and organization costs; estimated at 30 percent by an age and
   expectancy study of the enterprise......................   127,950

The appraiser considers that the mine has no apparent hazards which should be compensated for except those customarily encountered in the industry. Consequently, he decides to use a single-interest annuity formula with a fair rate of return of 8 percent.

The calculations necessary to the determination of the value of the mine follow:

$$\text{Expectancy of mine} = \frac{2,100,000}{260,000} = 8.08 \text{ years; use 8 years.}$$

Present worth factor: $1 receivable in 8 years, $r = 8$ percent, is 0.5403.

Present worth of capital to be recovered when the mine will be closed down is the present worth of the salvaged equipment plus the present worth of the working capital recovered:

$$(50,000 + 300,000)(0.5403) = \$189,105$$

The earning value of the mine is calculated as follows:

Annual operation return $= (260,000)(1.822) = \$473,720$

$$\left.\begin{array}{c}\text{Earning value}\\\text{of the mine}\end{array}\right\} = R\left[\frac{(1+r)^n - 1}{r(1+r)^n}\right]$$

$$\left.\begin{array}{c}\text{Earning value}\\\text{of the mine}\end{array}\right\} = (473,720)\left[\frac{1.08^8 - 1}{(0.08)(1.08)^8}\right]$$

$$\left.\begin{array}{c}\text{Earning value}\\\text{of the mine}\end{array}\right\} = (473,720)(5.74664) = \$2,722,300[1]$$

[1] If Hoskold's formula were used, with a redemptive rate on the capital of 3 percent and a remunerative rate of 6 percent, the present worth factor would be 5.799; the earning value of the enterprise would be $2,747,000.

Thus, the present worth of the anticipated returns from the mine ore are:

Present worth of operation returns	$2,722,300
Present worth of salvaged property	189,100
Total	$2,911,400
Less immediate outlay for new equipment	150,000
Value of mine	$2,761,400

Other evidences of value which the appraiser may use are (1) the original cost of the facilities adjusted for the consumption of service utility and (2) an estimate of those costs based on prices applicable at the date of appraisal. It is recognized that these estimates may not be particularly significant, but perhaps one may serve as a check on the estimate of the earning value of the mine.

Consider the present investment in this mine:

Organization and financing: estimated amount of original costs which are presently of value to enterprise		$ 127,950
Plant and equipment	$1,581,826	
Less adjustment for consumed (42.4592 %) useful service based upon age and expectancy	671,631	
		$ 910,195
Ore deposit	$2,000,000	
Less depletion (68 %)	1,360,000	
		$ 640,000
Present working capital (determined as current assets less current liabilities)		$ 407,787
Total present investment		$2,085,932

The appraiser may subtract $107,787 from the working capital in order to compare the investment with the earning value, because the data indicate that the present working capital is excessive. The resulting figure, $1,978,145, does not supply the appraiser with much evidence, except that he may conclude that the mine is now a profitable venture, investmentwise, and that the owners can probably expect to have their remaining capital returned to them.

Consider the probable investment in the mine were it to be theoretically replaced under price conditions applicable at the date of appraisal. Suppose, then, that the appraiser uses the same percentage factors for amortization, depreciation, and depletion previously determined.

Plant and equipment: $(1 - 0.424592)(\$2,450,000)$	$1,409,700
Ore deposit: $(0.32)(\$3,500,000)$	1,120,000
Working capital	300,000
Organization and financing:	
$(0.30)(0.099)(\$2,450,000 + \$3,500,000 + \$300,000)$	185,600
Total value based on replacement cost	$3,015,300

The appraiser should search for the basis of the discrepancy between the earning value of the mine and the theoretical required investment based on current prices. He should check to see whether or not the expenditures for modernizing the equipment were economically justified.[1] He might re-examine his forecasts of the selling price and his costs of production to ascertain whether or not any change in the estimate of the earning value was possible. If not, the appraiser would give considerable weight to the estimate of the earning value of the property; he might tell his client that it is a good thing that the venture was not developed using current prices. Perhaps $2,800,000 is a fair estimate of the current value of the mine works and ore deposit.

EXAMPLE OF THE VALUATION OF AN ORE RESERVE

The value of an undeveloped ore reserve is determined primarily by the process of finding the earning value of the enterprise required to win and market the ore deposit. Such an estimate of earning value is the total warranted investment in the mining venture, including the cost of the mineral deposit, the plant and equipment, the required working capital, and the necessary costs of acquiring the capital. Thus, the total warranted investment in the venture less the required investment in plant, equipment, working capital, and financing costs gives the warranted investment in the mineral deposit. This warranted investment is the value of the ore body in its undeveloped state.

18.6. Appraisal of an Undeveloped Iron Ore Reserve. An appraisal of a certain iron ore reserve is to be made. The development has progressed to the stage where the amount of ore of a given average quality is fairly well known. The normal production period of this mine is estimated to be 10 years. The active operation of the mine will be delayed 2 years while the development work is being done and the plant installed. An estimate has been made of the probable cost of the plant required to produce the expected tonnage. The fair rate of return is assumed to be 8 percent.

Part of the development cost is considered to be an annual cost, just as is any item of production cost. However, the bulk of the development cost, the cost of the plant, the required working capital, and the taxes on the ore reserve during the development period are necessary capital investments.

---

[1] Since the new equipment is expected to produce a net savings in mining cost of $0.12 per ton mined, the annual savings are $31,200. The present worth of a $31,200 annuity for 8 years at 8 percent is $(31,200)(5.747) = $179,300$. The estimated cost of the equipment is $150,000; thus, the appraiser would conclude that the proposed expenditure for new equipment is justified and probably would include the details of his investigation in his report on the appraisal.

The data and computations follow:

1. *Reserve Tonnage.* The tonnage in the ore reserve was determined by core drilling, and the quantities were computed according to the usual practice. Part of the area is favorable to open-pit mining and part to underground methods. The reserves suitable to each method of mining were ascertained because of the difference in mining cost. The estimated reserves are as follows:

> Available for open-pit mining, tons.............. 5,102,100
> Available for underground mining, tons.......... 1,025,000
> Total, tons in the reserve.................... 6,127,100

Annual production of ore on the basis of 10 years for exhaustion:

> Open pit, tons.............. 510,210
> Underground, tons.......... 102,500
> Total, tons.............. 612,710

2. *Selling Price.* The selling price is chosen as the average Lake Erie selling price for ore of basic grade for the 5-year period immediately preceding the valuation. The annual gross receipts based on the Lake Erie selling price are computed upon the basis of the analyses of core-drill samples, as follows:

	Natural iron, percent	Tons	Lake Erie selling price per ton	Total selling price
Bessemer ore.....................	52.50	3,490,500	$7.545	$26,335,823
Non-Bessemer ore	48.00	2,217,000	6.591	14,612,247
Paint rock ore...................	44.00	419,600	5.457	2,289,757
Total.............................		6,127,100	$7.057	$43,237,827
Less 1 percent adjustment to bill of lading weights			0.071	432,378
Total receipts..................................			$6.986249	$42,805,449

Annual gross receipts: $42,805,449/10 = $4,280,545

3. *Annual Cost of Operating the Mine.* The annual cost of operating the mine is determined from the records of operating units in the area, supplemented by an analysis of the operating conditions expected to prevail when this particular ore reserve is developed. The unit costs upon which these estimates are made do not include future development costs or plant investment, these being estimated separately.

	Tons handled	Cost per ton	Total cost
Power shovel mining.......................	3,165,200	$0.45	$1,424,340
Power shovel mining, lean ore.................	119,200	0.50	59,600
Milling and scram..........................	1,767,900	0.55	972,345
Milling and scram, lean ore..................	49,800	0.60	29,880
Total...................................	5,102,100		$2,486,165

$$\text{Annual cost of open-pit mining} = \frac{2,486,165}{10} = \$248,616$$

$$\text{Average cost per ton, open-pit mining} = \frac{2,486,165}{5,102,100} = \$0.4873$$

Average cost per ton, underground mining = $2.75
Total cost of underground mining = (1,025,000)(2.75) = $2,818,750

$$\text{Annual cost of underground mining} = \frac{2,818,750}{10} = \$281,875$$

4. *Transportation.* The cost of transportation by rail and lake, including 3 percent transportation tax and insurance, as calculated from published tariffs and standard insurance rates is $2.781 per ton.

Total cost of transportation and insurance = (6,127,100)(2.781) = $17,039,465

$$\text{Annual cost of transportation and insurance} = \frac{17,039,465}{10} = \$1,703,947$$

5. *Miscellaneous.* Miscellaneous costs include administration, legal, fire insurance, medical and hospital, workmen's compensation, contingencies, crushing and screening, cost adjustments, stockpile loading, and taxes on stockpile and equipment. These costs determined from average experience are:

For open-pit mining: (5,102,100)(0.180).............	$ 918,378
For underground mining: (1,025,000)(0.300)........	307,500
Total..	$1,225,878

Miscellaneous cost per year: $1,225,878/10 = $122,588

6. *Selling Commission.* The selling commission is fixed for this class of ore at 5 cents per ton.

Total selling cost = (6,127,100)(0.05) = $306,355

$$\text{Annual cost of selling} = \frac{306,355}{10} = \$30,635$$

7. *Development.* The development consists in stripping the reserves to be operated by the open-pit method and in sinking a shaft and constructing the accompanying underground development in the reserves to be operated by underground mining methods.

Cost of open-pit stripping:

3,500,000 cu yd of soil at $0.45..............	$1,575,000
1,500,000 cu yd of rock at $0.90..............	1,350,000
Total cost of open-pit development........	$2,925,000

Underground development, direct estimate: $75,000 during the deferment period and $450,000 during the production period.   It is considered that 75 percent of the cost of stripping will be incurred during the period of deferment.

$$\text{Annual cost of development} = \frac{(0.25)(2,925,000)}{10} + \frac{450,000}{10}$$
$$= 73,125 + 45,000 = \$118,125$$

8. *Plant.*   The cost of plant is estimated at $850,000 from experience of the properties in the area and the records in the files of the valuator. The cost of plant will be incurred during the 2-year period of deferment. The plant consists of those facilities required to handle and prepare the ore for shipping.

9. *Taxes.*   Taxes are estimated on the basis of rates of taxation, including federal income taxes, prevailing at the date of valuation.   The taxes being paid on active properties are of three kinds as follows:

	Per ton
Taxes on ore remaining in deposit, per ton of production[1]	$0.376
An occupation tax averaging 4.75 percent of remainder when unit costs of production, except income taxes, are subtracted from unit selling price	0.120
Federal income tax	0.350
Taxes per ton during the production period	$0.846

Total cost of taxes = (6,127,100)(0.846) = $5,183,527

$$\text{Annual cost of taxes} = \frac{5,183,527}{10} = \$518,353$$

During the deferment period an "inactive" annual tax on the ore reserve of $0.0346 per ton will be paid.

$$\text{Inactive tax} = (0.0346)(6,127,100) = \$211,998 \text{ annually}$$

This tax will be paid at the rate of $106,000 at the end of each 6 months during the deferment period.

10. *Annual Operation Return.*   The annual operation return is calculated as follows:

[1] The tax on the ore remaining in the deposit is paid yearly during the operation period at the rate of $0.06837 per ton of ore estimated to remain in the reserve.   Since this item is a quantity variable each year as ore is produced, it is simpler for this problem to convert the rate into one applicable to the projected annual production. This equivalent tax rate t_p per ton of annual production is given by the expression

$$t_p = t \left\{ n - \left[\frac{n(n-1)A}{2T} \right] \right\}$$

where t is the tax rate per ton of ore remaining in the reserve, n is the estimated years of production at the annual rate of A tons, and T is the tonnage in the reserve at the beginning of operation.   Solution of this formula for the present case will give $0.376 per ton.

Annual gross receipts (step 2)		$4,280,545
Annual costs of production		
Mining, open pit (step 3)	$ 248,616	
Mining, underground (step 3)	281,875	
Transportation, including insurance (step 4)	1,703,947	
Miscellaneous (step 5)	122,588	
Selling commission (step 6)	30,635	
Annual development costs (step 7)	118,125	
Taxes during production period (step 9)	518,353	
		3,024,139
Annual operation return		$1,256,406

11. *Warranted Investment in the Venture.* The warranted investment in the venture is determined by calculating the present worth of an annuity equal in amount to the annual operation return, using a rate of return of 8 percent. The period of deferment of the annuity is 2 years, and the term is 10 years.

$$P = R\left[\frac{(1+r)^n - 1}{r(1+r)^n}\right]\left[\frac{1}{(1+r)^d}\right] = (1,256,406)\left[\frac{1.08^{10} - 1}{(0.08)(1.08)^{10}}\right]\left[\frac{1}{(1.08)^2}\right]$$
$$P = (1,256,406)(6.71008)(0.85734)$$
$$P = (1,256,406)(5.75282) = \$7,227,878$$

12. *Present Worth at Date of Appraisal of Expenses Incurred during the Deferment Period.* In order to calculate the warranted investment in the ore reserve, it is necessary to determine the present worth of the expenses, including the taxes paid, which were made during the development period. It may be assumed that the expenditures for the plant are spread more or less uniformly over the 2-year period, and therefore the expenditures for each year will be concentrated at its mid-point.

Stripping (step 7) (0.75)(2,925,000)	$2,193,750
Underground development (step 7)	75,000
Plant (step 8)	850,000
Total	$3,118,750

Assume that one-half, $1,559,375, is paid at the middle of each of the 2 years of the construction period.

$$P = \frac{S}{(1+r)^n} = \frac{\$1,559,375}{1.08^{1/2}} + \frac{\$1,559,375}{1.08^{3/2}}$$
$$P = (1,559,375)(0.962250 + 0.890973)$$
$$P = (1,559,375)(1.853223) = \$2,889,870$$

The present worth of the "inactive taxes," $106,000, assumed to be paid at the end of each 6-month period (step 9) is

$$P = \frac{\$106,000}{1.08^{1/2}} + \frac{\$106,000}{1.08^1} + \frac{\$106,000}{1.08^{3/2}} + \frac{\$106,000}{1.08^2}$$
$$P = (106,000)(0.96225 + 0.92593 + 0.89097 + 0.85734)$$
$$P = (106,000)(3.63649) = \$385,468$$

13. *Working Capital.* The working capital required is determined by estimating the average monthly production during the life of the property by each mining method. Since the open-pit property may work but 6 months per year, the average monthly production is 510,210/6, or 85,035 tons per month. The underground operation can use a 12-month season, and hence the average monthly production is 102,500/12, or 8,542 tons per month.

The capital required for the open-pit operation is the mining, miscellaneous, and transportation costs for 1½ months plus active taxes for 4½ months.

	Cost per ton	Cost per month
Mining costs (step 3)	$0.4873	$ 41,437
Miscellaneous costs (step 5)	0.180	15,306
Transportation costs (step 4)	2.781	236,482
Total	$3.448	$293,225
Active taxes	0.376	31,973

Required production capital = (1.5)(293,225) + (4.5)(31,973)
Required production capital = 439,837 + 143,879 = $583,716

If to this estimate there is added the average cost of 1 month's operation supplies, $30,000, the total required working capital for the open-pit operation is $613,716.

The working capital for the underground operation is taken as the cost of 6 months' mining, miscellaneous, and active taxes, plus 2 months' transportation cost.

	Cost per ton	Cost per month
Mining	$2.750	$23,490
Miscellaneous	0.300	2,563
Taxes	0.376	3,212
Total	$3.426	$29,265
Transportation	2.781	23,755

Required production capital = (6)(29,265) + (2)(23,755)
Required production capital = $175,590 + $47,510 = $223,100

If to this estimate there is added the average cost of 1 month's operation supplies, $25,000, the total required working capital for the underground operation is $248,100.

The total required working capital for the venture is obtained by adding the two estimates, that for the open-pit operation—$613,716—and for the underground operation—$248,100. This sum is $861,816.

However, in this illustration, the mine is assumed not to go into operation for 2 years, the period of deferment. Thus, it is necessary to determine the present worth of a sum receivable 2 years hence. The present worth of the working capital is ($861,816)(0.85734), or $738,869.

14. *Warranted Investment in the Ore Reserve.* The warranted investment in the ore reserve (the prospective value of the reserve) may be obtained by subtracting the present worth of the capital investments required in order that the venture may be put into operation from the warranted investment in the venture. Since it is assumed that the working capital can be recovered in its entirety at the end of the production period, the present worth of the working capital is added to the net result obtained.

Warranted investment in the venture (item 11)		$7,227,878
Present worth of capital requirements to be incurred in deferment period		
Plant and facilities (item 12)	$2,889,870	
Inactive taxes (item 12)	385,468	
Working capital required at beginning of production period (item 13)	738,869	
		4,014,207
Total		$3,213,671

Present worth of working capital recoverable at end of production period $= \dfrac{861,816}{1.08^{12}} = (861,816)(0.397114)$ 342,239

Warranted investment in ore reserve at a fair rate of return of 8 percent $3,555,910

18.7. Appraisal of an Undeveloped Iron Ore Reserve Using Two Rates.

In Sec. 18.6 the determination of the probable value of an undeveloped ore reserve is illustrated by use of present worth formulas which contain but one rate, the rate of return. However, some authorities prefer to make the necessary calculations by use of two-rate formulas. As discussed in Sec. 16.3, the theory underlying such a practice involves a *remunerative* rate, the rate of return on the investment, and the *redemptive* rate, the rate of accumulation of the return of the investment. The calculations of Sec. 18.6 will be repeated here where necessary with the appropriate two-rate formulas.

Let it be assumed that the remunerative rate is 7 percent and the redemptive rate is 3 percent.

15. *Warranted Investment in the Venture at Two Rates* (*Compare with Step* 11). The warranted investment is calculated by use of Formula (16.8) with $i = 3$ percent, $r = 7$ percent, $n = 10$ years, $d = 2$ years, and an annual operation return of $1,256,406.

$$P = R \left\{ \frac{\dfrac{(1 + i)^n - 1}{i}}{1 + r \left[\dfrac{(1 + i)^{n+d} - 1}{i} \right]} \right\}$$

$$P = 1,256,406 \left[\frac{\dfrac{1.03^{10} - 1}{0.03}}{1 + 0.07 \left(\dfrac{1.03^{12} - 1}{0.03} \right)} \right]$$

$$P = 1{,}256{,}406 \left[\frac{11.46388}{1 + (0.07)(14.19203)} \right]$$

$$P = 1{,}256{,}406 \left(\frac{11.46388}{1.993442} \right)$$

$$P = (1{,}256{,}406)(5.750796) = \$7{,}225{,}335$$

16. *Present Worth at Date of Appraisal of Expenses Incurred during the Deferment Period (Compare with Step 12).* The present worth of a single sum receivable in n years at two rates of interest is given by Formula (16.20),

$$P = S \left\{ \frac{1}{1 + r\left[\frac{(1 + i)^n - 1}{i} \right]} \right\} = S \left\{ \frac{i}{i + r[(1 + i)^n - 1]} \right\}$$

Since it is assumed that the cost of 75 percent of the stripping and the cost of the plant and underground facilities would be incurred over the entire 2-year period, the expenses of each year of construction are concentrated at its mid-point.

$$P = (1{,}559{,}375) \left\{ \frac{0.03}{0.03 + (0.07)[(1.03)^{\frac{1}{2}} - 1]} \right\}$$
$$+ (1{,}559{,}375) \left\{ \frac{0.03}{0.03 + (0.07)[(1.03)^{1\frac{1}{2}} - 1]} \right\}$$

$$P = (1{,}559{,}375) \left[\frac{0.03}{0.03 + (0.07)(0.014889)} + \frac{0.03}{0.03 + (0.07)(0.045336)} \right]$$
$$P = (1{,}559{,}375)(0.966425 + 0.904336)$$
$$P = (1{,}559{,}375)(1.870761) = \$2{,}917{,}218$$

The present worth of the inactive taxes to be paid at the end of each 6 months during the deferment period is

$$P = (\$106{,}000) \left\{ \frac{0.03}{0.03 + (0.07)[(1.03)^{\frac{1}{2}} - 1]} \right.$$
$$+ \frac{0.03}{0.03 + (0.07)[(1.03)^1 - 1]} + \frac{0.03}{0.03 + (0.07)[(1.03)^{1\frac{1}{2}} - 1]}$$
$$\left. + \frac{0.03}{0.03 + (0.07)[(1.03)^2 - 1]} \right\}$$
$$P = (106{,}000)(0.966425 + 0.934579 + 0.904336 + 0.875580)$$
$$P = (106{,}000)(3.680920) = \$390{,}178$$

17. *Present Worth of the Required Working Capital (Compare with Step 13).* It has been assumed that the working capital will not be required until the beginning of mine operation, 2 years from the date of appraisal. The present worth of the working capital, \$861,816, is

$$P = (861{,}816) \left\{ \frac{0.03}{0.03 + (0.07)[(1.03)^2 - 1]} \right\}$$
$$P = (861{,}816)(0.875580) = \$754{,}589$$

18. *Warranted Investment in the Ore Reserve (Compare with Step 14).* The warranted investment in the ore reserve is again obtained by sub-

tracting the present worth of the capital investments required to enable the venture to get into production from the warranted investment in the entire venture. Again, it is assumed that the entire working capital can be recovered at the end of the life of the mine.

Warranted investment in the venture		$7,225,335
Present worth of capital requirements		
Plant and facilities	$2,917,218	
Inactive taxes	390,178	
Working capital	754,589	
		4,061,985
Total		$3,163,350

Present worth of the working capital which is salvaged:

$$P = (861,816) \left\{ \frac{0.03}{0.03 + (0.07)[(1.03)^{12} - 1]} \right\}$$

$$P = (861,816)(0.501645) = \qquad 432,326$$

Warranted investment in the ore reserve at a remunerative
rate of 7 percent and a redemptive rate of 3 percent $3,595,676

The estimate just obtained with rates of 3 and 7 percent may be compared with $3,555,910 obtained in Sec. 18.6 for a rate of return of 8 percent. The fact that the two estimates agree so closely is not due to the similarity of method; rather it is because the effect of the two rates, 3 percent and 7 percent on present worth, is about the same as the effect of 8 percent. Had the calculations of Sec. 18.6 been made with 7 percent as a fair rate of return, the warranted investment in the ore reserve would have been about $4,030,000.

18.8. Consideration Given to Working Capital. One other variation in procedure in the practice of the valuation of mining properties is found in the method of handling the working capital. Working capital as a general practice is not consumed in the mining operation; at least the major portion of it would be recovered before the mining operation came to an end.

One method of handling working capital is to consider it in the same manner as any other capital investment and then provide for its recovery, or such portion of it as is recoverable, at the close of mining operations as a salvage value. This is the method followed in the preceding examples.

A second method of handling working capital is to assume that it is fully recoverable and to make no provision for its amortization. However, a fair rate of return on the working capital is charged to production cost.

In item 14 of Sec. 18.6 and item 18 of Sec. 18.7, the working capital, along with other capital costs, has been deducted from the warranted investment in the venture in order to obtain the net warranted investment in the ore reserve. The portion of the working capital (100 percent in the examples) and any other investments which can be salvaged at the end of the operation are added in at their present worth as the last step in obtaining the warranted investment in the ore reserve.

These two methods produce identical results when but one interest rate is used in the calculations; the assumption of a period of deferment does not produce any differences. But when a two-rate formula is used and when a period of deferment is involved, the two methods produce slightly different results. The warranted investment in the ore reserve obtained by the method which treats the working capital the same as any other investment is always larger than the warranted investment in the ore reserve calculated by assuming that no amortization of the working capital is required and that interest on the working capital is charged as a production cost.

This difference in the warranted investment is shown by the expression

$$\begin{Bmatrix} \text{Difference} \\ \text{in the} \\ \text{warranted} \\ \text{investment} \\ \text{as calcu-} \\ \text{lated by} \\ \text{the two} \\ \text{methods} \end{Bmatrix} = \begin{Bmatrix} \text{estimate} \\ \text{of the} \\ \text{required} \\ \text{working} \\ \text{capital} \end{Bmatrix} \left\{ \frac{r(r-i)[(1+i)^d - 1][(1+i)^n - 1]}{[i + r(1+i)^{n+d} - 1][i + r(1+i)^d - 1]} \right\}$$

This difference is small; for the preceding example the value of this fractional expression is but 0.028621. Since in the example the estimated required working capital is $861,816, the calculated difference in the warranted investment using the two methods should be $24,666. This may be verified by completely solving the problem by using both methods. When the working capital is treated as a capital investment and recovered at the end of the operation of the mine, the warranted investment in the ore reserve is calculated to be $3,595,676. When interest on the working capital is used as a production cost and no amortization of the working capital is required, the warranted investment in the ore reserve is $3,571,-010. The difference between these two calculations is $24,666.

A variation as small as $25,000 in a calculation of the magnitude of $3,600,000 is not significant for all practical purposes because the variation in the estimates of the quantity of mineral as well as other factors is usually much greater. Hence, to assume that return on the working capital shall be included as a cost of production and that no provision for its amortization shall be included is correct for all practical purposes. However, the authors prefer the other treatment because of its appropriateness and the ease of taking care of an assumption that part of the working capital will not be recovered.

VALUATION OF LEASES ON MINERAL LANDS

Although mineral rights are often purchased outright, it is also a custom to secure a lease on the property and to pay royalties. Under terms of the lease, the landowner is compensated on the basis of a cash bonus plus either a royalty on each ton (or other unit) of product marketed during the life of the enterprise or an agreed share of the gross receipts of the venture. Often the owner is paid a certain sum for an option to lease on or before some fixed date in the future, thus giving time to prospect the property and establish a value. If the property proves to have value, the owner will be paid the bonus for the lease. The purchaser may then develop the property himself, organize a new company, or sell the lease to an operating company. Even if he develops the property himself, he is likely to need to borrow capital or to sell stock. Hence, in nearly all instances, it is necessary to establish the value of the lease as a basis for borrowing capital, selling securities, or selling the lease.

18.9. Valuation of Mining Leases. The maximum value of a lease to mineral rights is the difference between the value of the mineral deposit and the cost of development, with proper account being taken of the dates when payments must be made. Since the development is fraught with all the hazards of mining, the investor should receive a risk rate of return upon his investment during the period of deferment as well as during the period of production.

Suppose, in the illustration of Sec. 18.6, the ore reserve is leased rather than purchased. The value of the lease to those who might direct the operation is equivalent to the calculated warranted investment in the ore reserve, \$3,555,910. Theoretically, the owner of the mineral could be paid this lump sum in royalties, but since the venturer would then underwrite all the risks and the owner none, such a course is not practical. What is wanted, then, is the amount of the cash bonus and the royalty per ton of ore mined which might be offered the owner of the mineral land.

The formula is

$$\begin{Bmatrix} \text{Warranted investment} \\ \text{in the ore reserve} \end{Bmatrix} = \begin{bmatrix} \text{desirable} \\ \text{cash bonus} \end{bmatrix} + \begin{bmatrix} \text{present worth} \\ \text{of royalties} \end{bmatrix}$$

$$\$3,555,910 = C + R \left[\frac{(1 + r)^n - 1}{r(1 + r)^{n+d}} \right]$$

where R equals the amount of the annual royalty. The annual royalty may be expressed in cents per ton mined by dividing by the annual production. As before, $r = 8$ percent, $n = 10$ years, and $d = 2$ years.

Suppose a desirable cash bonus is \$100,000. Then the royalty per ton mined can be about 98 cents.

$$3,555,910 = 100,000 + R(5.75282)$$

$$R = \frac{3,455,910}{5.75282} = \$600,732$$

$$\frac{600,732}{612,710} = \$0.980$$

Or suppose that a royalty of $0.90 per ton mined is an acceptable rate in the area. With an average annual production of 612,710 tons, this means an annual royalty of $551,439. Then the cash bonus can be $383,581.

$$\$3,555,910 = C + (551,439)(5.75282)$$
$$C = 3,555,910 - 3,172,329 = \$383,581$$

If the provisions of the lease call for a cash bonus plus a fraction of the gross receipts, the procedure is unaltered. Suppose that in the above illustration the annual royalty is one-eighth of the gross receipts, $4,280,545/8, or $535,068. The warranted cash bonus can be $477,760, as shown by the equation

$$\$3,555,910 = C + (535,068)(5.75282)$$
$$C = 3,555,910 - 3,078,150 = \$477,760$$

This section should not be completed without reminding the reader that the illustrations deal with the cash bonus and royalties which might be paid the owner of an iron ore reserve in a proved field. When mining ventures have not reached this stage of development, such careful calculations have but little meaning. However, mining ventures in these early stages have "booms," and there is brisk trading in the sale of leases of mineral lands. The figures obtained are usually highly speculative and may be far from what eventually comes to be the value of leases in the area when that area is fully proved.

18.10. Leases Held by Public Utilities. Public utilities often hold leases on lands in gas-, oil-, or coal-producing areas. Litigations over the valuation of leases of this type have been frequent in the courts, and in general they have been bitterly contested and long drawn out.

A review of the legal decisions germane to the subject indicates that the courts generally take the position that the value of a lease of this type often depends primarily upon the original cost, since that is the one substantial fact that generally can be determined. Where market value can be established, as has been possible in a few instances involving leases on gas-producing lands, that is strong evidence of value. Ordinarily the stock and bond value of an enterprise is assumed to be an indication of its market value, but in the case of enterprises organized to develop oil or gas there are so many other facilities necessary that the portion of the indebtedness that rests upon the lease itself is hard to segregate.

Oil-land leases and gas-land leases are sometimes the object of barter, and thus a market value may be established. Generally this is not the case, as the companies which are in a position to bid for such leases are not in competition with each other, and although the willing seller element is present, the willing buyer is not.

The value of mineral leases owned by a utility would not be included in the rate base unless the mineral resources were necessary in the production of the services covered by the rates in question.

VALUATION OF TIMBERLANDS

When possible to obtain, the market value of standing timber is one of the most significant evidences of the value of the property. However, it is often desirable to estimate the present worth of the anticipated returns of the forest property based on the probable margin of the selling price of the lumber in the stand over the costs of logging, transportation, and milling. If the estimate of the value of a stand of timber is based on the anticipated returns from a single cut, the procedure of appraisal is identical to that followed in mining valuation. However, there is a growing tendency to consider the maximum value obtainable by following a plan of partial cutting. For example, suppose that studies of a timber tract indicate that 50 years is a proper interval of time to allow for the growth of a tree from a seedling to a mature tree. If the stand contains trees of all degrees of maturity, a cycle of cutting, say 1 year out of every 10, may provide the opportunity for maximum returns from the tract. The stand is considered to be divided into 10 parts, and each year's logging will consist of the harvesting of the mature trees in that area. Hence, during one rotation of the stand, 50 years, five cutting cycles will have been completed. Using such a plan, the forest property becomes for all practical purposes a going concern of unlimited life, and its appraisal may be made by methods appropriate to such enterprises. Thus, timberlands are appraised by the same procedures applied to mineral properties, except when a plan of partial cutting is followed and the venture is an operation of unlimited life.

18.11. Estimation of the Amount of Marketable Timber. An important trend in the industry is the increasing tendency to consider a forest as a collection of individual trees of variable worth rather than an area of trees of average quality. Chapman and Meyer in their text on forest valuation have commented on this trend:[1]

In assessing the financial results of any kind of selective cutting it is necessary to have considerably more detailed knowledge of the values produced by logs,

---

[1] Herman H. Chapman and Walter H. Meyer, "Forest Valuation," p. 427, New York, McGraw-Hill Book Company, Inc., 1947.

trees, and stands than is the case with clear cutting. With the latter it is feasible to make a satisfactory analysis with knowledge of the lumber grade return and the operating costs of the stand as a whole. . . . Clear cutting commonly takes sizes and qualities of trees that are of zero or negative value and in this way leads to a less profitable operation. If the zero-margin limits are known, there is little excuse for an operator to cut unprofitable trees. A definite incentive exists to leave uncut a certain portion of the stand.

Thus the appraiser is confronted with the task of determining, by a sampling process, the approximate number of valuable trees in the tract under consideration. He may determine what is a valuable tree based upon the conditions which are applicable at the date of appraisal by use of the following procedure:

1. Determine the average selling price of lumber (f.o.b. mill) of various grades and sizes. Generally the appraiser will be aware of the probable market where the lumber under consideration will be sold.

2. Summarize the output of marketable lumber from each grade and size of log. For example, logs might come in three grades and range in diameter from 10 to 20 in. by 2-in. increments. Studies of the practices of the mill where the lumber will be sawed or of the records of the enterprise contemplating the erection of a mill will show what portion of a log of given grade and size can be graded as B select, or C select, or No. 2 common, and so on. These estimates may be combined with the price data of step 1 to obtain the value of the marketable lumber in a log of a given size and grade.

3. Determine the unit milling costs for logs of various sizes. Cost studies relating to the sawing and overhead mill costs are needed. Include maintenance, normal depreciation expense, and interest on the average investment in the fixed assets and working capital of the mill. These items may be expressed in units of production, as dollars per thousand board-feet of lumber, and in annual costs.

4. Determine the unit value of logs of various sizes and quality as they arrive at the mill[1] (step 2 minus step 3).

5. Estimate the unit logging, including felling, and transportation costs for logs of various sizes. Although recorded costs may not always be available, these costs are generally fairly uniform within a logging region. Include the average maintenance and depreciation of logging equipment and return on the average investment in logging equipment and working capital required in these operations.

6. Summarize the preceding estimate to obtain the margin above cost of each size tree. Some of the logs in a tree will not have a positive value

---

[1] This estimate could serve as the basis for the determination of the warranted price a mill might pay for a log. However, the total investment in the mill, including working capital, and the overhead milling costs must be known factors.

at the date of valuation; hence, it is often agreed that no tree is considered valuable unless the margin above cost of all of its logs is greater than a certain minimum.

The appraiser is now ready to determine the amount of valuable timber in the tract. This highly specialized operation is a distinctive feature of timberland valuation called *cruising* and is a sampling method which can be accomplished acceptably only by trained personnel.

Two methods of sampling are employed, the choice being based on the nature of the stand of timber. These are the *plot method*, in which systematically selected areas of $\frac{1}{5}$ acre to 5 acres each is sampled, and the *strip method*, by which strips extending entirely across the stand are sampled. The proportion of the total area to be sampled varies from 1 to 10 percent, but occasionally a higher percentage is sampled, particularly when the timber tract is small. The size of the plots or the width and distribution of the strips selected for sampling depend upon the kind and character of the growth and the topography.

18.12 Estimating the Present Worth of the Anticipated Returns of the Timber Tract. After the appraiser has obtained an estimate of the amount of marketable timber in the tract, he may estimate the operation return to be expected from the cut. If it is impracticable to make the cutting in one year, the average annual operation return may be estimated by proper modification for the growth of the timber. In fact, such a study forms the basis for the computation of the theoretical cycle of cutting of a timber tract so that a maximum present worth of the returns from the property may be realized.

The estimation of the present worth of the returns is accomplished by use of the usual present worth formulas. If any significant amount can be realized from the sale of the land after the logging operations are complete, its present worth should be added at this point in the sequence of calculations. Although there may be some justification for the use of Hoskold's two-rate annuity formula because investors in timber ventures have demanded high rates of return, it appears that the formula has not been used extensively.

The estimation of the fair rate of return for timberlands is based on those principles enumerated in Chap. 16. Rates of 6 to 10 percent may be appropriate for the easy logging chances—especially good stands and particularly favorable or accessible terrain—and 8 to 15 percent may be applicable for those ventures having average to high risk. Higher rates of return may be used in particular instances.

The results of the calculations just described indicate the present worth of the returns and thus the warranted investment in the timber tract itself. The problem can be treated, however, as an integrated enterprise combining the operations of logging, transportation, and milling.   Depreciation expense on the fixed assets and the return on the average investment in the fixed assets and in the working capital are excluded.   The present worth of the operation returns using the revised estimates, then, represents the warranted investment in the entire venture; the warranted investment in the timber tract may be obtained by subtracting the required investment in the mill, the logging and transportation equipment, and the working capital from the warranted investment in the entire venture.   If the estimates of the life of the equipment and the timber tract are comparable and the rate of return used is the same in each case, the two methods should produce comparable results.

VALUATION OF OIL PROPERTY

The appraisal of oil wells and gas wells or oil and gas lands is fundamentally similar in procedure to that discussed in Secs. 18.3 to 18.7. The details of the acquisition of the data and their interpretation are so technical that specially trained personnel are required in this kind of appraisal.   Only the general process is outlined in the following sections.[1]

18.13. Customs Relating to the Handling of Costs of Oil Production. The several items of costs incurred in the development and operation of an oil or gas well are handled differently by the various companies in the petroleum industry.   The following represent policies and practices followed by a typical petroleum enterprise:

The exploration and operating costs of oil wells are collected and classified according to a specified accounting procedure in the normal process of the operation of the enterprise.   The direct and indirect overheads are likewise classified and allocated to the various operating units, usually on the basis of a net barrel (gross production less royalty) of production.   The unit costs of development and operation as determined during these normal operations are those used in the economic analysis leading to the appraisal of a proposed well.   The example valuation given in Table 18.1, in combination with the following explanations, illustrates how these unit costs are used in the process of the valuation of an oil well.   Through the general accounting classification the annual expenses are collected under the following major groups:

1. Annual production costs
2. Overhead costs and taxes (exclusive of income taxes)

[1] See the following for additional information:

T. A. Hall, Appraisal of Oil Properties, *Oil Weekly*, Vol. 93, No. 2, pp. 38–46, Mar. 20, 1939.

Paul M. Paine, "Oil Property Valuation," New York, John Wiley & Sons, Inc., 1942.

Parks, *op. cit.*, pp. 299–342.

3. Indirect overhead costs
4. Land, geological, and geophysical costs
5. Development costs which are capitalized

Annual production costs include direct lifting costs, such as labor, power, repairs, well reconditioning, and the like. Production costs also include the direct costs of field supervision, engineering, clerical, camps, communications, and similar items. These costs are those included in Table 18.1, column (4).

Included in the group of *overhead costs and taxes* are the main office, regional, and divisional costs of the production department. Salaries, rents, accounting, and depreciation cost on general equipment are examples of these overhead costs. The taxes include ad valorem, school, production, and severance taxes. In the example to be given, income taxes are excluded. These overhead and tax costs are illustrated in Table 18.1, column (5).

Indirect overhead costs include executive salaries, costs of the service departments—legal, economics, comptroller, public relations—and costs of borrowed money [see column (6) of Table 18.1].

Land, geological, and *geophysical costs* include those costs incident to the procurement of leases, such as brokers' fees and registration, and the salaries, rents, and operating expense of the field exploration crews and of the office staff engaged on exploration work. The rent on a lease prior to the development of the well is also included. These costs are included in column (6) of Table 18.1.

Although the foregoing four groups of costs could be considered as development costs and thus capitalized, the custom of the industry is to consider them as items of annual expense to be allocated to specific operations on a net barrel basis.

The remaining *development costs are capitalized* and allocated to expense through annual depreciation charges. The cost of equipment which may be used in more than one well, such as casing, control valves, steel work, tubing, lead line to storage tanks, power equipment, storage tanks, and the like, is charged as depreciation expense over the useful life of the equipment. Those development costs incurred in bringing in a specific well are depreciated over the life of the particular well for which the costs were incurred. Such items are labor, supervision, drilling mud, fuel, trucking, power, and similar drilling costs. In the example to be given these costs total $120,000.

For the purposes of analysis, only the land, geological, and geophysical costs are prorated to production as an operation cost. The problem before the analyst, therefore, is to determine whether or not the present worth of the prospective returns from the venture at a specified rate of

TABLE 18.1. ANALYSIS OF THE FORECASTED RATE OF RETURN OF A
PROPOSED OIL WELL

Development costs are estimated at $120,000 to drill and equip the well plus $20,000 at the end of the fourth year for pumping equipment. The lease is on 40 acres.

Year (n)	Annual oil production, gross bbl	Annual oil production less ⅛ royalty, net bbl	Annual production cost	Overhead cost and taxes at 20 cents per net bbl	Land, geo-logical, geo-physical, and indirect over-head costs at 40 cents per net bbl	Total annual expenses (4) + (5) + (6)
(1)	(2)	(3)	(4)	(5)	(6)	(7)
1	31,500	27,560	$ 3,000	$ 5,510	$11,020	$ 19,530
2	25,100	21,960	3,000	4,390	8,780	16,170
3	19,100	16,710	3,000	3,340	6,680	13,020
4	14,400	12,600	3,000	2,520	5,040	10,560
5	11,200	9,800	5,000	1,960	3,920	10,880
6	9,000	7,880	5,000	1,580	3,160	9,740
7	7,300	6,390	5,000	1,280	2,560	8,840
8	6,100	5,340	5,000	1,070	2,140	8,210
9	5,400	4,720	5,000	940	1,880	7,820
10	4,500	3,940	5,000	790	1,580	7,370
11	3,900	3,410	5,000	680	1,360	7,040
12	3,500	3,060	5,000	610	1,220	6,830
13	3,000	2,630	5,000	530	1,060	6,590
Total	144,000	126,000	$57,000	$25,200	$50,400	$132,600

Year (n)	Value of annual net production at $2.65 per bbl	Annual operation return, (8) − (7)	Additional invest-ment in plant	Annual oper-ation return less addi-tional investments	Present worth factor for n = 15%*	Present worth of net oper-ation return, (11) × (12)
(1)	(8)	(9)	(10)	(11)	(12)	(13)
1	$ 73,030	$ 53,500	....	$ 53,500	0.8696	$ 46,520
2	58,190	42,020	....	42,020	0.7561	31,770
3	44,280	31,260	....	31,260	0.6575	20,550
4	33,390	22,830	$20,000	2,830	0.5718	1,620
5	25,970	15,090	....	15,090	0.4972	7,500
6	20,880	11,140	....	11,140	0.4323	4,820
7	16,940	8,100	....	8,100	0.3759	3,040
8	14,150	5,940	....	5,940	0.3269	1,940
9	12,510	4,690	....	4,690	0.2843	1,330
10	10,440	3,070	....	3,070	0.2472	760
11	9,040	2,000	....	2,000	0.2149	430
12	8,110	1,280	....	1,280	0.1869	240
13	6,970	380	....	380	0.1625	60
Total	$333,900	$201,300	$20,000	$181,300	......	$120,580

* The factor, $1/(1 + r)^n$, using various values of r, is applied to column (11) until the r is found that produces the summation of column (13) equal to the initial invest-ment. In this example a rate of return of 15 percent (before income taxes) produces a present worth of the annual operation returns approximately equal to the initial investment of $120,000.

return is equivalent to the required investment in the venture. This required investment is the total cost of development less the items which are charged as annual expense.

Royalty costs at one-eighth of the production are neither capitalized nor expensed. The royalty is deducted from gross production to get the net production which is the basis of the company's records and calculations. Settlement is made on the basis of the current market price of oil and is free to the royalty owner of all costs of production except his taxes.

18.14. Example of an Oil-well Valuation. The following example indicates the analysis required in determining the attractiveness of an investment in a proposed oil well. The acreage is already held by the company on a nominal rent basis until the well is brought in or decision to give up the lease is made.

From experience and the company records, the required expenditure to drill and equip the well and to install pipe lines and other development expense is estimated at $120,000. At the end of the fourth year of production it will be necessary to install pumping equipment at an estimated cost of $20,000.

Royalty is one-eighth of the production. The current price of the oil, $2.65 per barrel, is used in the analysis, because of the uncertainty of any forecasted price of oil during the life of the well. The productive life of the well is estimated at 13 years. The annual production is distributed as shown in Table 18.1, column (2), and totals 144,000 bbl over the 13 years. Salvage value of the lease, well, and equipment is assumed to be zero.

Production costs are estimated as follows on the basis of current costs in the area:

1. Direct lifting costs are expected to average $3,000 a year for the first 4 years and then $5,000 annually for the remaining 9 years.

2. Overhead production costs and taxes are included at $0.20 a net barrel, in line with current costs.

3 and 4. Land, geological, geophysical, and indirect overhead costs are set at $0.40 a net barrel, likewise on the basis of current experience in the area.

5. The capitalized development cost is estimated at $120,000.

The analysis leading to the valuation is presented in Table 18.1. The objective is to determine the average rate of return, before income taxes, that can be expected on the investment in the well.

The footnote and column (13) of Table 18.1 indicate an average over-all rate of return of slightly more than 15 percent. With income taxes assumed at 40 percent of the return, the forecasted rate of return on the original investment of $120,000 is approximately 9 percent.

Should the company have a policy indicating that a minimum return of 10 percent after taxes is necessary to justify an investment of this character, the conclusion would follow that the proposed well is not attractive at the current price of oil, the forecasted production, and the estimated production costs.   Final decision, however, of whether or not to drill the proposed well probably would depend upon the results of a reanalysis of the proposal, the competitive situation in the area, and current factors to be judged by management.

Important Valuation Decisions of the Courts

Presented herewith is a list of the more important valuation decisions which have been made during the past century, together with a limited number of decisions from the English courts which have been precedent for decisions in the United States.

These decisions are arranged in chronological order by periods each of which is marked by significant policies, events, or valuation practice. Each decision is referenced, and one or two of its more important rulings are named. A more extended review of these cases up to 1935 is contained in "Engineering Valuation," by Marston and Agg.[1]

A.1. The Period Prior to 1830. Engineering valuation can hardly be said to have existed. The general legal principles of ordinary property rights, established in statute law and common law by centuries of legislation and court decisions, were applicable in valuations of industrial property.

There were no large utility companies. The public had acquired the right, by common and statute law, to prescribe maximum rates of charges for grist mills, toll bridges, toll roads, ferries, and some other enterprises. Such regulation was in the main accomplished by ordinances, franchises, and by licensing.

A.2. The Period from 1831 to 1865. An extensive railway net was constructed in the United States to the Mississippi River, and a few lines extended farther west. City waterworks, sewer systems, gas lighting systems, and horse-drawn streetcar lines were built.

At first, the regulation of these enterprises was accomplished by general statutes and by franchises. Abuses in the railway industry led to the development of more extensive and systematic public regulation. By 1860 seven state railway commissions had been established.

1. *The Louisiana Bread Case. J. A. Guillotte v. City of New Orleans*, 12 La. 432 (La. Sup. Ct. June, 1857).

One of the first instances in the United States when an enterprise was held to be subject to public regulation.

2. *Mellersh v. Keen* (No. 2), 28 Beav. 453 (English courts July 6, 1860).

An English case, often referred to in the courts of the United States as furnishing an important precedent in good will valuation.

A.3. The Period from 1866 to 1900. During this period, the rapid development of the utility company of the type furnishing water, gas, electricity, and

---

[1] Anson Marston and Thomas R. Agg, "Engineering Valuation," 1st ed., Chap. 8. pp. 186–252, New York, McGraw-Hill Book Company, Inc., 1936.

transportation and the many resulting abuses and dissensions brought out a number of important court decisions relating to valuation and regulation. By these, many of the fundamental principles of the regulation and the appraisal of public utilities were gradually established.

The "Granger Laws" to control railways were passed. The Interstate Commerce Commission was established in 1887; by 1885, some 27 state railroad commissions had been set up.

3. *Munn v. Illinois*, 94 U.S. 113, 123 (U.S. Sup. Ct. October, 1876).

Decision upholding the right of the general assembly of the state of Illinois to

. . . fix by law the maximum of charges for the storage of grain in warehouses at Chicago and other places in the State having not less than one hundred thousand inhabitants, "in which grain is stored in bulk." . . .

4. *Stone & Others v. Farmers' Loan & Trust Co.*, 116 U.S. 307, 331 (U.S. Sup. Ct. Jan. 4, 1886).

One of the "railroad commission cases," in which the right of the several states to regulate their intrastate railways, by statute, through supervisory state railroad commissions, was upheld by the United States Supreme Court.

However, Mr. Chief Justice Waite remarked significantly that:

It is not to be inferred that this power of limitation or regulation is itself without limit. This power to regulate is not a power to destroy, and limitation is not the equivalent of confiscation.

5. *Chicago, Milwaukee and St. Paul Railway Co. v. Minnesota* (No. 762), 134 U.S. 418 (U.S. Sup. Ct. Mar. 24, 1890).

It was held in this case that the courts necessarily have the power to declare a rate fixed by a commission to be unreasonable and illegal provided the evidence before the court is conclusive.

6. *Budd v. New York* (error to the Superior Court of Buffalo, State of New York) (No. 719), *New York ex rel. Annan v. Walsh* (No. 644), *New York ex rel. Pinto v. Walsh* (error to the Supreme Court of the State of New York) (No. 645), 143 U.S. 517 (U.S. Sup. Ct. Feb. 29, 1892).

This case and *Brass v. North Dakota* (Case 8) are two of the pioneer decisions upholding the right of public regulation of those businesses which are "endued with public interest." These two cases involved railway rate regulation.

7. *Monongahela Navigation Co. v. United States* (No. 722), 148 U.S. 312, 337, 343 (U.S. Sup. Ct. Mar. 27, 1893).

An often quoted decision involving the condemnation of a lock and dam. In the decision, the Court ruled that all the various elements of its value must be duly considered in determining the value of a property, and

Whatever be the true value of that which it (Congress) takes from the individual owner must be paid to him. . . . and the question of just compensation is not determined by the value to the government which takes, but the value to the individual from whom the property is taken.

8. *Brass v. North Dakota, ex rel. Stoeser* (No. 768), 153 U.S. 391 (U.S. Sup. Ct. May 14, 1894).

See Case 6.

9. *Reagan v. Farmers' Loan and Trust Co.* (No. 928), 154 U.S. 362, 394, 399 (U.S. Sup. Ct. May 26, 1894).

A noted decision upholding the Texas Railroad Commission law. The right of the state to regulate railways through the commission was upheld; " . . . there can be no doubt of the general power of a State to regulate the fares and freights which may be charged and received by railroad or other carriers, and that this regulation can be carried on by means of a commission." Mr. Justice Brewer said further, however, that

. . . while it is not the province of the courts to enter upon the merely administrative duty of framing a tariff of rates for carriage, it is within the scope of judicial power and a part of judicial duty to restrain anything which, in the form of a regulation of rates, operates to deny to the owners of property invested in the business of transportation that equal protection which is the constitutional right of all owners of other property.

10. *National Waterworks Co. v. Kansas City* (No. 469), *Kansas City v. National Waterworks Co.* (No. 470), 62 Fed. 853, 865 (U.S. Circ., 8th Circ. July 2, 1894).

A pioneer valuation case in which the court discussed several evidences of the value of the property. " . . . It [the city] steps into possession of a property which not only has the ability to earn, but is in fact earning. It should pay therefor not merely the value of the system which might be made to earn, but that of a system which does earn." This decision has been used as precedent for the separate allowance of going value in the appraisal of a utility property.

11. *Page v. Ratliffe*, 75 L.T. 371 (English High Ct. of Justice, Chancery Div. Oct. 29, Nov. 18, 1896).

This litigation was over the valuation of a partnership business in England in which the appraisal of the good will was an important part of the decision.

12. *Smyth v. Ames* (No. 49), *Smyth v. Smith* (No. 50), *Smyth v. Higginson* (No. 51), 169 U.S. 466, 546 (U.S. Sup. Ct. Mar. 7, 1898).

A most famous and much cited valuation decision. In holding a Nebraska railway rate law unconstitutional because the rates would be confiscatory, the United States Supreme Court established the *Smyth v. Ames* rule that all factors affecting value must be given such weight as may be just and right in each case.

We hold, however, that the basis of all calculations as to the reasonableness of rates to be charged by a corporation maintaining a highway under legislative sanction must be the fair value of the property being used by it for the convenience of the public. And in order to ascertain that value, the original cost of construction, the amount expended in permanent improvements, the amount and market value of its bonds and stock, the present as compared with the original cost of construction, the probable earning capacity of the property under particular rates prescribed by statute, and the sum required to meet operating expenses, are all matters for consideration, and are to be given such weight as may be just and right in each case. We do not say that there may not be other matters to be regarded in estimating the value of the property. What the company is entitled to ask is a fair return upon the value of that which it employs for the public convenience. On the other hand, what the public is entitled to demand is that no more be exacted from it for the use of a public highway than the services rendered by it are reasonably worth.

13. *The People of the State of New York ex rel. The A. J. Johnson Company, Appellant, v. James A. Roberts, as Comptroller of the State of New York, Respondent,* 159 N.Y. 70, 79 (N.Y. Ct. App. Apr. 25, 1899).

This case is a privilege tax case involving the question of the taxation of the value of copyrights and good will in New York. The court held that copyrights " . . . stand on the same basis as patent rights, with reference to the subject of taxation by the state, and, as we have held that the former are exempt the latter should be held exempt also." The court, however, held that the value of the good will was taxable.

A.4. The Period from 1901 to 1915. During 1901 to 1915, construction costs remained fairly constant. Adequate and reliable book records of the original costs of existing property were generally lacking. In consequence, many appraisals were based primarily on cost of reproduction with some adjustment for depreciation.

14. *The Cedar Rapids Water Co., Appellee, v. The City of Cedar Rapids, Appellant,* 118 Iowa 234, 263 (Iowa Sup. Ct. Oct. 27, 1902).

This decision is cited because it shows the failure of the courts at that time to realize the existence or the true nature of depreciation. The court refused to allow the inclusion of a depreciation charge in the determination of the fair revenues, saying:

. To hold otherwise is to say that the public must not only pay the reasonable and fair value of the services rendered, but must, in addition, pay the company the full value of its works every forty years. . . .

15. *San Diego Land & Town Co. v. Jasper* (No. 193), 189 U.S. 439, 446 (U.S. Sup. Ct. Apr. 6, 1903).

In this decision, the United States Supreme Court overruled the "contention of the appellant, that there should have been allowance for depreciation, over and above the allowance for repairs," in the annual revenues required to yield a fair rate of return.

In *City of Knoxville v. Knoxville Water Co.,* Case 18, the same Court reversed itself on this question only six years later.

16. *Brunswick & Topsham Water District v. Maine Water Company,* 99 Me. 371, 386–388 (Me. Sup. Ct. Dec. 14, 1904).

This waterworks valuation case relates to the bases upon which the worth of a public service may be estimated.

In estimating what it is reasonable to charge for a water service, that is, not exceeding its worth to the consumers, water is to be regarded as a product, and the cost at which it can be produced or distributed is an important element of its worth. It is not the only element, however. . . . If there is more than one source of supply, other things being equal, the community is entitled to have the least expensive one used. . . . the company ought not to be permitted to charge a higher rate based upon the expense of bringing it from a farther and more expensive source.

17. *Tillie von Au, as Executrix, etc., of Otto E. von Au, Deceased, Respondent, v. Louis Magenheimer and Charles F. Haug, Appellants, Impleaded with John Noval, Defendant,* first trial, 115 App. Div. 84, 100 N.Y. Supp. 659 (Oct. 12, 1906);

second trial, 126 App. Div. 257, 110 N.Y. Supp. 629 (May 1, 1908) (N.Y. Sup. Ct., App. Div., 2d Dept.).

Frequently cited in the United States on questions relating to the valuation of the good will possessed by nonregulated enterprises.

18. *City of Knoxville v. Knoxville Water Co.* (No. 17), 212 U.S. 1 (U.S. Sup. Ct. Jan. 4, 1909).

Famous as the first in which the United States Supreme Court ruled that all accrued depreciation must be deducted from the value of the property new to determine its present fair value.   The Court ruled that it is the duty of the owner of the property to set aside each year, out of current earnings before return, sufficient annual depreciation costs to keep his investment unimpaired and that it is the right of the owners to make such a provision.

19. *Willcox et al., Constituting The Public Service Commission of New York v. Consolidated Gas Company* (No. 396), *City of New York v. Consolidated Gas Company of New York* (No. 397), *Jackson, Attorney General of the State of New York v. Consolidated Gas Company* (No. 398), 212 U.S. 19 (U.S. Sup. Ct. Jan. 4, 1909).

Ruling that the owners of the property were entitled to the benefit of the increase of values caused by appreciation, except where such an increase would be so enormous as to make the rates unreasonable.   The Court recognized as binding "the value of the company's franchises as fixed in 1884 under legislative authority and made the basis for stock issued at that time."   The Court excluded any allowance for the value of good will.

20. *City of Omaha v. Omaha Water Co.* (No. 159), 218 U.S. 180 (U.S. Sup. Ct. May 31, 1910).

Review of the appraisal of a water company which was to be purchased by the city.   The Court approved a separate allowance for going value.

21. *The Minnesota Rate Cases.   Simpson et al., Constituting the Railroad and Warehouse Commission of the State of Minnesota v. Shepard* (No. 291), *Same v. Kennedy* (No. 292), *Same v. Shillaber* (No. 293), 230 U.S. 352 (U.S. Sup. Ct. June 9, 1913).

These cases involved the constitutionality of intrastate railway schedules prescribed by the Minnesota railway acts.   The Court upheld the right of the state to regulate intrastate rates on interstate carriers, that "the rate making power is a legislative power," and that the courts are not boards of review, substituting their judgment for that of the commissions, but rather are to pass on the legality of the acts performed by the commissions.   The *Smyth v. Ames* rule was cited as the law of the land; the value of the stocks and the bonds of the enterprises was held to be an unreliable evidence of value in this case.

These cases are often cited because of the ruling that the basis of the value of utility lands is the market value of similar adjacent or nearby lands.   The requirement that accrued depreciation must be deducted in the determination of present value was upheld.

22. *Missouri Rate Cases.   Knott et al., Railroad and Warehouse Commissioners v. Chicago, Burlington & Quincy R.R. Co.* (No. 9), 230 U.S. 474 (U.S. Sup. Ct. June 16, 1913).

In these railway rate cases, the Court held that the proof of fair value must be full and convincing and that tax assessments are not necessarily good evidence of value.

23. *In the Matter of the Appraisal of the Estate of Thomas R. Ball, Deceased, under the Acts in Relation to the Taxable Transfers of Property. William Sohmer, Comptroller of the State of New York, Appellant; Theodore Wentz and Mary J. Ball, as Executors, etc., of Thomas R. Ball and Others, Respondents,* 161 App. Div. 79, 146 N.Y. Supp. 499 (N.Y. Sup. Ct., App. Div., 2d Dept. Mar. 6, 1914).

The court allowed 3 years' purchase of the excess returns as the basis of the value of the good will of a merchandising firm in New York.

24. *German Alliance Insurance Co. v. Lewis, Superintendent of Insurance of the State of Kansas* (No. 120), 233 U.S. 389 (U.S. Sup. Ct. Apr. 20, 1914).

The question at issue was the right, under the Constitution, of the state of Kansas to regulate fire insurance rates. The right was upheld.

25. *San Joaquin & Kings River Canal and Irrigation Co. v. County of Stanislaus, in the State of California* (No. 303), 233 U.S. 454 (U.S. Sup. Ct. Apr. 27, 1914).

Litigation involving rates charged by an irrigation company. The Court, in reversing the decree of the circuit court, held that the value of the water rights owned by the company should have been valued as a part of the property.

26. *In re Demarest's Estate,* 157 N.Y. Supp. 653 (Surr. Ct., N.Y. Co. May 6, 1914).

27. *Seaich v. Mason-Seaman Transp. Co.,* 156 N.Y. 579 (N.Y. Sup. Ct., App. Div., 1st Dept. Dec. 30, 1915).

28. *Matter of the Transfer Tax upon the Estate of Mary McMullen, Deceased,* 92 Misc. Rep. 637, 157 N.Y. Supp. 655 (Surr. Ct., Bronx Co. Dec. 1915).

Cases 26, 27, and 28 involved the appraisal of the good will of three New York enterprises. The courts reiterated that the basis of the value of good will was the average annual profit in excess of a return on other values of the property and that the "number of years purchase" must be based on the evidence in each case.

29. *Des Moines Gas Co. v. City of Des Moines* (No. 75), 238 U.S. 153, 165, P.U.R. 1915D, 577 (U.S. Sup. Ct. June 14, 1915).

A rate ordinance case. The decision is often cited for its ruling against including in the estimate of fair value the extra costs of reproduction due to paving built after mains were laid.

The Court said about going value,

That there is an element of value in an assembled and established plant, doing business and earning money, over one not thus advanced, is self-evident. This element of value is a property right, and should be considered in determining the value of the property, upon which the owner has a right to make a fair return.

Nevertheless, the Court upheld the master's exclusion of his $300,000 estimated going value on the ground that going value was already sufficiently allowed for in the items for overhead costs and organization expenses.

A.5. The Period from 1916 to 1925. The extraordinary rise in construction costs between 1915 and 1920, due to the First World War, forced the reproduction costs of items of industrial properties materially above their original costs and brought on violent differences of opinion as to their "just and right" relative weights. In important valuation decisions after the war, the United States Supreme Court continued to reject all valuation formulas, and to uphold the *Smyth v. Ames* rule, that all elements of value must be given such weight as sound judgment determines are "just and right" in each particular case.

30. *City and County of Denver et al. v. Denver Union Water Company* (No. 294), 246 U.S. 178, P.U.R. 1918C, 640 (U.S. Sup. Ct. Mar. 4, 1918).

An important valuation case in which the appraisal of the several items comprising the property is discussed thoroughly. The value of the water rights was determined to be equal to the market value of similar water rights in the same locality.

A separate allowance for going value was made.

31. *Newton, Attorney General of the State of New York, et al. v. Consolidated Gas Company of New York* (No. 257), 258 U.S. 165, P.U.R. 1922B, 752 (U.S. Sup. Ct. Mar. 6, 1922).

The decision in this case upheld the principle that rates once nonconfiscatory and lawful may later, by the increase of the costs of operation, become confiscatory and unlawful.

32. *Galveston Electric Co. v. City of Galveston et al.* (No. 455), 258 U.S. 388, P.U.R. 1922D, 159 (U.S. Sup. Ct. Apr. 10, 1922).

The decision is noteworthy as the first by the Supreme Court to allow a material increase in the values of physical property items installed before 1915, because of their greatly increased reproduction costs caused by the First World War. This property was valued 33⅓ percent higher than its original cost less depreciation, obtained by giving equal weight to original cost and to period reproduction costs, which were estimated to be 66⅔ percent higher than original costs.

A claim for "development cost" was disallowed. According to Mr. Justice Brandeis, the master who had approved the valuation had calculated it by capitalizing the net deficits, on an 8 percent basis, over the entire 15 years since the company purchased the property.

33. *State of Missouri ex rel. Southwestern Bell Telephone Co. v. Public Service Commission of Missouri et al.* (No. 158), 262 U.S. 276, P.U.R. 1923C, 193 (U.S. Sup. Ct. May 21, 1923).

In this case, the United States Supreme Court reversed the Missouri Supreme Court, which had upheld a rate order reducing telephone rates charged by the company in the state. The reversal was because the commission valued the property entirely on the basis of original cost new less depreciation, giving no weight at all to reproduction costs, which had been greatly increased by the First World War.

Mr. Justice Brandeis, though concurring in the reversal, wrote a long opinion dissenting from the reason assigned by the majority. He argued strongly in favor of the use of the prudent investment in the useful property of the enterprise as a rate base. Mr. Justice Holmes concurred.

34. *Bluefield Water Works & Improvement Co. v. Public Service Commission of the State of West Virginia et al.* (No. 256), 262 U.S. 679, P.U.R. 1923D, 11 (U.S. Sup. Ct. June 11, 1923).

A rate case in which the Court did not sustain the valuation made by the West Virginia Public Service Commission because a fair and just consideration of all of the facts was not obtained.

This case is often cited, however, because of the résumé of the principles underlying the estimation of the fair rate of return of a regulated enterprise.

35. *Georgia Railway & Power Co. et al. v. Railroad Commission of the State of Georgia et al.* (No. 298), 262 U.S. 625, P.U.R. 1923D, 1 (U.S. Sup. Ct. June 11, 1923).

This litigation was over a rate reduction order by the commission in which a rate base was used which was substantially equal to the depreciated original cost of the property. This rate base was not sustained by the Supreme Court, and a new rate base was determined, this time making replacement cost rather than investment the dominant element.

36. *Colorado Power Co. v. Halderman et al.* (No. 7473), 295 Fed. 178, P.U.R. 1924D, 789 (U.S. Dist. Ct., D. Colo. Jan. 4, 1924).

Litigation arising out of an application of the company for an increase of rates. The controversy finally centered in the constitutionality of the Colorado Power Act, which the court upheld in so far as it pertained to the case at hand, and the question of the inclusion of a large portion of the property which was to produce energy sold wholesale under special contracts.

37. *Pacific Gas & Electric Co. v. City and County of San Francisco* (No. 34), 265 U.S. 403, 406, P.U.R. 1924D, 817 (U.S. Sup. Ct. June 2, 1924).

Reversal of an order reducing gas rates.

The depreciation had been estimated using the sinking fund method with a 5 percent interest rate. The Court indicated that proper consideration had not been given to the testimony of experts who had examined the property, observed the conditions, saying: "Facts shown by reliable evidence were preferable to averages based upon assumed probabilities."

The failure of the master and the lower court to consider properly the value of newly acquired patent rights and "to make proper allowance for the successful use of such rights" was the main cause for the reversal.

38. *Southern Bell Telephone & Telegraph Co. v. Railroad Commission of South Carolina et al.* (No. 253), 5 F.2d 77, 95, P.U.R. 1926A, 6 (U.S. Dist. Ct., E.D. S.C. Apr. 30, 1925).

Rate reduction order suspended by court injunction. The court approved including in the valuation certain equipment installed in planning for the future growth of the business in certain towns and cities, saying:

Of course, proper business prudence also requires that additional equipment for future use, which must in a certain sense be unused for a period of time, should not be laid out, where such additional equipment can as readily be placed in the plant at the time it is needed. But the evidence in this case shows that the provision for future use was not of that character, but a proper provision such as would effect a large saving in the long run.

A.6. The Period from 1926 to 1930. A price "plateau" about double the level of pre-First World War prices was maintained. The United States Supreme Court continued to uphold the *Smyth v. Ames* rule, despite the arguments of those who would favor making the rate base equal to the prudent investment or the depreciated reproduction cost.

Depreciation questions were prominent in the litigation. Depreciation estimates based on inspections were preferred to those based on assumed average lives and probabilities. Attention was called to the anomaly existing when utilities were permitted to make large annual depreciation charges and yet use only small allowances for depreciation in the rate base.

39. *City of Fort Smith, Arkansas, et al., v. Southwestern Bell Telephone Co.* (No. 151), 270 U.S. 627 (U.S. Sup. Ct. Jan. 25, 1926).

The United States Supreme Court, in a memorandum decision, sustained the decision of the United States District Court in granting a permanent injunction restraining the city from enforcing a telephone rate ordinance. *Southwestern Bell Telephone Co. v. City of Fort Smith* (No. 407), 294 Fed. 102, 106, P.U.R. 1924E, 662 (U.S. Dist. Ct., W.D. Ark., Ft. Smith Div. Sept. 17, 1923. District Judge Youmans).

Judge Youmans' decision, sustained by the United States Supreme Court, is of special interest for its rulings on going value, because it followed so soon after the 1922 decision of the United States Supreme Court in *Galveston Electric Co. v. Galveston* (Case 32). In that case the question was raised of whether any going values should be allowed in rate cases (as distinguished from purchase cases), a claim for going value based on "capitalization of past deficits" was rejected and no going value separate from the overhead cost allowance was made.

In this case the court approved the company's claim of $115,005 going value, based on the "cost of establishing the business," as follows:

(1)	Cost of attaching subscribers	$ 12,540
(2)	Cost of training employees of organization	7,985
(3)	Cost of records	3,500
(4)	Administration 10 % of (1) + (2) + (3)	2,403
(5)	Maintenance and depreciation of idle plant	69,038
(6)	Interest on above costs before exchange opens	2,984
(7)	Interest and taxes on idle plant afterwards	16,555
	Total	$115,005

Judge Youmans held that:

The above method does not undertake to capitalize past losses. It assumes a reconstructed plant without business, and gives the cost of securing business of the character and magnitude the company now has in Fort Smith.

40. *Monroe Gaslight & Fuel Co. v. Michigan Public Utilities Commission et al.* (No. 540), 11 F.2d 319, P.U.R. 1926D, 13 (U.S. Dist. Ct., E.D. Mich., S.D. Feb. 27, 1926).

A rate case in which dominant weight was given to reproduction cost in fixing a rate base. The court ruled that the value of property paid for by funds made available through depreciation charges must be included in the rate base.

41. *Board of Public Utilities Commissioners et al. v. New York Telephone Co.* (No. 567), 271 U.S. 23, 31, P.U.R. 1926C, 740 (U.S. Sup. Ct. Apr. 12, 1926).

This case, often referred to as the *New Jersey Telephone* case, is a leading case with regard to the relationship between the depreciation reserve account and the annual depreciation expense account. The New Jersey Commission had found that the depreciation reserve account balance was $4,750,000 greater than the correct accrued depreciation and that the charge for depreciation for 1924 was $772,000 too large.

On the basis of these findings the commission ordered in effect, until such time as the excess would be absorbed, rates which admittedly would be insufficient to pay future fair annual depreciation charges in addition to a fair return. However, the Supreme Court overruled the commission, saying:

Past losses cannot be used to enhance the value of the property or to support a claim that rates for the future are confiscatory. . . . Profits of the past cannot be used to sustain confiscatory rates for the future.

42. *McCardle et al. v. Indianapolis Water Company* (No. 37), 272 U.S. 400, P.U.R. 1927A, 15 (U.S. Sup. Ct. Nov. 22, 1926).

Famous rate case decision in which the United States Supreme Court held that due weight must be given to both original cost and reproduction cost in fixing a rate base.

43. *Ottinger, Attorney General of New York, v. Consolidated Gas Co. of New York* (No. 357), 272 U.S. 576, P.U.R. 1927A, 37 (U.S. Sup. Ct. Nov. 29, 1926).

44 and 45. *Ottinger, Attorney General of New York, v. Brooklyn Union Gas Company* (No. 358), *Ottinger, Attorney General of New York, v. Kings County Lighting Company* (No. 365), 272 U.S. 579, P.U.R. 1927A, 39 (U.S. Sup. Ct. Nov. 29, 1926).

Cases 43, 44, and 45, often referred to as the *New York Gas* cases, affirmed the unconstitutionality of the New York state gas rate act of 1923. The decision was based upon the Fourteenth Amendment of the Constitution, " . . . nor shall any State deprive any person of life, liberty, or property without due process of law. . . . "

46. *United States et al. v. Los Angeles & Salt Lake Railroad Co.* (No. 414), 273 U.S. 299, P.U.R. 1927B, 357 (U.S. Sup. Ct. Feb. 21, 1927).

A rate case including a ruling on the value of water rights. The company owned the rights to the use of water from springs and streams, which, the Interstate Commerce Commission indicated, had a present value of $26,150. The Court quoted as follows from the previous case, *San Pedro, Los Angeles & Salt Lake Railroad Co.* (Valuation Docket No. 26), 75 I.C.C. 463, 504 (I.C.C. June 7, 1923):

. . . [water rights may be appraised] as nearly as possible by the methods which we approved in the *Texas Midlands* case for determining the present value of lands. Original cost to date will be reported whenever possible to determine it from reliable evidence. It is no more possible to ascertain the cost of reproduction of water rights than the cost of reproduction of land. These cannot be reproduced but only developed and put to beneficial use by human effort.

47. *Idaho Power Co. v. Thompson et al.* (No. 1143), 19 F.2d 547, 567, P.U.R. 1927D, 388 (U.S. Dist. Ct., D. Idaho, S.D. Apr. 28, 1927).

A rate case which included a discussion of the several aspects of the determination of depreciation. The court rejected the estimate of accrued depreciation determined by the commission by the straight line method. However, the company's estimate, based upon a determination of the aggregate outlay required to put the property into a condition as good as new, was also rejected. This use of deferred maintenance as a full measure of depreciation was refused because:

. . . When analyzed it is clear that plaintiff's estimates are of only a part of the elements that must be taken into account, and, even if accepted as correct in respect to the elements considered, it would furnish an inadequate measure of entire depreciation.

48. *United Fuel Gas Co. et al. v. Railroad Commission of Kentucky et al.* (No. 1), 278 U.S. 300, 311, 318, P.U.R. 1929A, 433 (U.S. Sup. Ct. Jan. 2, 1929).

A decision involving the amounts to be included in a rate base for gas lands, leases, and rights. The company claimed a valuation for these amounting to $36,449,176; the Supreme Court allowed only $6,732,920.

Appellants, as will more fully appear, reached their claimed value by an estimate by experts of the profits to be derived from the sale, in an unregulated market, of the quantity of gas estimated to underlie the proven and probable areas. The court below found that the value of appellant's gas field did not exceed its "book cost" which it took to be $6,732,920. . . .

Concerning the company experts' estimates, the Supreme Court said:

Such predictions can only be made on the basis of data which are not and cannot be known, and most of which are in the highest degree speculative. Such a process of estimating value is without any known sanction.

49. *Gilchrist et al., Constituting the Transit Commission et al., v. Interborough Rapid Transit Co. et al.* (No. 159), 279 U.S. 159, 211, P.U.R. 1929B, 434 (U.S. Sup. Ct. Apr. 8, 1929). See also Case 53.

Interlocutory United States District Court injunction against New York City subway contracts' 5-cent clauses stayed, pending litigation in the state courts. The Court said:

The transit Commission has long held the view that it lacks power to change the five cent rate established by contract; and it intended to test this point of law by an immediate orderly appeal to the courts of the State. This purpose should not be thwarted by an injunction.

50. *St. Louis & O'Fallon Railway Co. et al. v. United States et al.* (No. 131), *United States et al. v. St. Louis & O'Fallon Railway Co. et al.* (No. 132), 279 U.S. 461, 487, P.U.R. 1929C, 161 (U.S. Sup. Ct. May 20, 1929).

Rejection of a "recapture" order of the Interstate Commerce Commission.

The Court ruled that appraisals made by the Commission were invalid because the evidence showed that the Commission gave little or no consideration to present construction costs.

In the exercise of its proper function this court has declared the law of the land concerning valuations for rate-making purposes. The Commission disregarded the approved rule and has thereby failed to discharge the definite duty imposed by Congress. . . .

The question on which the Commission divided is this: When seeking to ascertain the value of railroad property for recapture purposes, must it give consideration to current, or reproduction, costs? The weight to be accorded thereto is not the matter before us. No doubt there are some, perhaps many, railroads the ultimate value of which should be placed far below the sum necessary for reproduction. But Congress has directed that values shall be fixed upon a consideration of present costs along with all other pertinent facts; and this mandate must be obeyed.

51. *New York Telephone Co. v. Prendergast et al.* (City of New York, intervener), 36 F.2d 54, 59, 66, P.U.R. 1930B, 33 (U.S. Dist. Ct., S.D. N.Y. Nov. 7, 1929).

Lengthy litigation finally ended in 1934, when the appeal to the United States Supreme Court was dismissed.

In the determination of the rate base the Court said:

Reproduction cost, less actual depreciation, is not the legal equivalent of fair value, as the master stated it to be, for it is, as a matter of law, but evidence of value. . . . the weight of which is to be determined with all the other evidence in the case, as tending to show both the value and the relative importance of all the evidence on the subject.

The claim for very large annual depreciation charges and very small deductions for accrued depreciation was stoutly defended by the company. However, the Court denied the claim, saying:

The record satisfactorily shows that there is more reason to believe that the actual existing depreciation in the plaintiff's property is reflected by the amount of its reserve for depreciation than that it is shown by the estimate of experts who stated observed depreciation. . . .

52. *United Railways & Electric Company of Baltimore v. West, Chairman, et al.* (No. 55), *West, Chairman, et al. v. United Railways & Electric Company of Baltimore* (No. 64), 280 U.S. 234, 253, P.U.R. 1930A, 225 (U.S. Sup. Ct. Jan. 6, 1930).

Important ruling, until its reversal in the *Hope* case in 1944, Case 73, that the legal depreciation base for public utilities was present value. The Court said:

The allowance for annual depreciation made by the commission was based upon cost. The court of appeals held that this was erroneous and that it should have been based upon present value. The court's view of the matter was plainly right. One of the items of expense to be ascertained and deducted is the amount necessary to restore property worn out or impaired, so as continuously to maintain it as nearly as practicable at the same level of efficiency for the public service. The amount set aside periodically for this purpose is the so-called depreciation allowance. Manifestly, this allowance cannot be limited by the original cost, because, if values have advanced, the allowance is not sufficient to maintain the level of efficiency. The utility "is entitled to see that from earnings the value of the property invested is kept unimpaired, so that at the end of any given term of years the original investment remains as it was at the beginning." *Knoxville v. Knoxville Water Co.*, 212 U.S. 1, 13–14. This naturally calls for expenditures equal to the cost of the worn out equipment at the

time of replacement; and this, for all practical purposes, means present value. It is
the settled rule of this Court that the rate base is present value, and it would be
wholly illogical to adopt a different value for depreciation. . . .

53. *City of New York v. Interborough Rapid Transit Co.*, 136 Misc. Rep. 569,
579, 240 N.Y. Supp. 316, 327, P.U.R. 1930C, 144 (N.Y. Sup. Ct. Feb. 28, 1930).

Decision upholding the validity of the New York City subway contracts'
5-cent fare clauses. The court said:

The fare clauses appearing in the contracts here were specifically authorized and the
obligation of both parties remains. The defendant cannot repudiate the portion
which may have become onerous. The city is entitled to a specific performance on
the part of the defendant of its contractual duty. . . .

54. *Cumberland Glass Mfg. Co. v. United States* (No. J-315), 44 F.2d 433, (No.
J-102) 44 F.2d 455, 460, 462 (U.S. Ct. Cl.) (both cases decided Nov. 3, 1930).

Suits to recover alleged overpayment of income and excess profit taxes. The
main issue involved controversial claims regarding depreciation. The Court
stated:

What is reasonable allowance for "wear and tear" to be charged off by a taxpayer as
depreciation is one of fact to be determined in each case by the peculiar facts of such
case. While the commissioner's determination is presumptively correct, it must give
way if the proof shows this computation is erroneous and not in consonance with the
actual facts. . . .
While the straight-line or fixed-percentage method used by the commissioner in
determining plaintiff's allowable depreciation . . . is the one most generally used in
determining depreciation for tax purposes, and is quite generally accepted as the
simplest and most accurate of the various methods used, computations made on that
basis can not stand where the facts in a particular case, as here, show that the result
reached by the use of such methods would not be a reasonable allowance within the
meaning of the statute.

55. *Smith et al., constituting the Illinois Commerce Commission et al., v. Illinois
Bell Telephone Co.* (No. 90), 282 U.S. 133, 158 P.U.R. 1931A, 1 (U.S. Sup. Ct.
Dec. 1, 1930).

An important case in which the decision of the lower court was set aside and
the case remanded for further findings of fact. However, the Court spoke out
strongly about the relation of the annual depreciation charge and the corresponding depreciation reserve requirement, saying:

While it has been held by this Court that property paid for out of moneys received
for past services belongs to the Company, and that the property represented by the
credit balance in the reserve for depreciation cannot be used to support the imposition
of a confiscatory rate (*Board of Commissioners v. New York Telephone Co., supra*), it
is evident that past experience is an indication of the Company's requirements for
the future. The recognition of the ownership of the property represented by the
reserve does not make it necessary to allow similar accumulations to go on if experience shows that these are excessive. . . .

A.7. The Period from 1931 to 1941. The depression, leading up to the
Second World War, had a profound impression on the litigation of this period.
Governmental efforts to bolster the economy included new legislation to strengthen

the regulative powers of commissions, and much of the litigation of this period dealt with tests of the constitutionality of this legislation.

In general, the courts upheld their former rulings on valuation questions. However, their decisions tended to give more weight to facts, as disclosed by reliable and comprehensive records, than to the speculative assumptions and opinions of expert witnesses.

56. *Excess Income of Richmond, Fredericksburg & Potomac Railroad Co.* (Finance Docket No. 3898), 170 I.C.C. 451 (I.C.C. Apr. 7, 1931).

First attempt by the Interstate Commerce Commission to recapture excess railway income after the United States Supreme Court had overruled the Commission in the *O'Fallon Railway* case (Case 50). The Commission specifically noted that it had given substantial consideration to both original cost and to reproduction cost.

57. *Georgia Public Service Commission et al. v. United States et al.* (No. 555), 283 U.S. 765, P.U.R. 1931C, 560 (U.S. Sup. Ct. June 1, 1931).

58. *Alabama et al. v. United States et al.* (No. 513), 283 U.S. 776, P.U.R. 1931C, 559 (U.S. Sup. Ct. June 1, 1931).

Cases 57 and 58 both were related to the right of the Interstate Commerce Commission to intervene in the regulation of intrastate rates.

The United States Supreme Court has repeatedly upheld the principle that the several states have the authority, subject to the United States Constitution, to control intrastate rates. The decisions in these two cases uphold the principle that state authority over intrastate rates must not be exercised in such a manner as to nullify interstate rates properly ordered by United States authorities.

59. *City of Logansport v. Public Service Commission of Indiana et al.* (No. 25389), 202 Ind. 523, P.U.R. 1931E, 179 (Ind. Sup. Ct. July 1, 1931).

Important ruling by the Supreme Court of Indiana that municipally owned public utilities are subject to regulation by the Indiana Public Service Commission and that the municipally owned public utility is entitled to earn a fair return on its investment, if it so desires, just the same as a privately owned utility.

60. *New State Ice Co. v. Liebmann* (No. 463), 285 U.S. 262, P.U.R. 1932B, 433 (U.S. Sup. Ct. Mar. 21, 1932).

Ruling by the United States Supreme Court that the business of manufacturing, selling, or distributing ice in the state of Oklahoma was not a public utility subject to licensing by the state.

61. *Wabash Valley Electric Co. v. Young et al.* (No. 128), 287 U.S. 488, P.U.R. 1933A, 433, 435 (U.S. Sup. Ct. Jan. 9, 1933).

Ruling that, in fixing rates, the rate base need not necessarily be the value of the entire interconnected operating property of the utility but may be the value of the property included in a single community of the system. In determining the rate base, the district court

. . . determined the value of the local property, to which it added that proportionate part of the value of the system property which it found to be fairly attributable to the Martinsville service.

This allocation was made on the basis of the portion of the total sales of electrical energy attributed to the city.

62. *Los Angeles Gas & Electric Corp. v. Railroad Commission of California et al.* (No. 412), 289 U.S. 287, P.U.R. 1933C, 229 (U.S. Sup. Ct. May 8, 1933).

Affirmation of a rate reduction order. The discussion of the principles of rate regulation was most thorough, and the former rulings of the Court were upheld. In this case, dominant weight was given to original cost, and by inference, though not by a specific estimate, an allowance for going value was included.

63. *Lindheimer et al. v. Illinois Bell Telephone Co.* (No. 440), *Illinois Bell Telephone Co. v. Lindheimer et al.* (No. 548), 292 U.S. 151, 167, 175, 3 P.U.R. (N.S.) 337 (U.S. Sup. Ct. Apr. 30, 1934).

A notable decision, written by Mr. Chief Justice Hughes, in which the Supreme Court set aside an injunction restraining the Illinois Commerce Commission from enforcing a rate reduction order. The lower court had found that the rates had been unreasonably low during the period 1923–1932, but the Supreme Court found otherwise, mainly because the rates of return were based upon annual depreciation allowances sufficient to maintain depreciation reserve balances far in excess of the highest estimates of the total accrued depreciation. On this point the Court said:

The questionable amounts annually charged to operating expenses for depreciation are large enough to destroy any basis for holding that it has been convincingly shown that the reduction in income through the rates in suit would produce confiscation. . . .

The discussion of depreciation and the depreciation accounting procedure found in this decision is often cited:

Broadly speaking, depreciation is the loss, not restored by current maintenance which is due to all the factors causing the ultimate retirement of the property. These factors embrace wear and tear, decay, inadequacy, and obsolescence. Annual depreciation is the loss which takes place in a year. In determining reasonable rates for supplying public service, it is proper to include in the operating expenses, that is, in the cost of producing the service, an allowance for consumption of capital in order to maintain the integrity of the investment in the service rendered. The amount necessary to be provided annually for this purpose is the subject of estimate and computation. . . . If the predictions of service life were entirely accurate and retirements were made when and as these predictions were precisely fulfilled, the depreciation reserve would represent the consumption of capital, on a cost basis, according to the method which spreads that loss over the respective service periods. But if the amounts charged to operating expenses and credited to the account for depreciation reserve are excessive, to that extent subscribers for the telephone service are required to provide, in effect, capital contributions, not to make good losses incurred by the utility in the service rendered and thus to keep its investment unimpaired, but to secure additional plant and equipment upon which the utility expects a return.
. . . The calculations are mathematical but the predictions underlying them are essentially matters of opinion. They proceed from studies of the "behavior of large groups" of items. These studies are beset with a host of perplexing problems. Their determination involves the examination of many variable elements, and opportunities for excessive allowances, even under a correct system of accounting, are always present. The necessity of checking the results is not questioned. The predictions must meet the controlling test of experience.

In this instance, the evidence of expert computations of the amounts required for annual allowances does not stand alone. In striking contrast is the proof of the actual condition of the plant as maintained. . . .

64. *West et al. v. Chesapeake & Potomac Telephone Company of Baltimore* (No. 648), 295 U.S. 662, 672, 8 P.U.R. (N.S.) 433 (U.S. Sup. Ct. June 3, 1935).

First authoritative ruling on the proper use of indexes in valuation proceedings. The Court set aside the commission's appraisal because it was based on the application of an empirically weighted average of some 16 construction cost indexes to the historical cost of the property. However, the Court stated: "This is not to suggest that price trends are to be disregarded; quite the contrary is true."

65. *Nebbia v. New York* (No. 531), 291 U.S. 502, 2 P.U.R. (N.S.) 337 (U.S. Sup. Ct. Mar. 5, 1934).

In this litigation relating to unfair price practices, the United States Supreme Court stated that the private character of a business does not necessarily remove it from the realm of public regulation.

66. *American Telephone & Telegraph Co. et al. v. United States et al.* (No. 74), 299 U.S. 232, 16 P.U.R. (N.S.) 225 (U.S. Sup. Ct. Dec. 7, 1936).

Affirmation by the United States Supreme Court that the Federal Power Act of 1935 had conferred on the Federal Power Commission the authority to require all licensees under their jurisdiction to keep accounting records according to prescribed standards and to furnish the Commission pertinent data upon request.

67. *Townsend et al. v. Yeomans, Attorney General of Georgia, et al.* (No. 781), 301 U.S. 441, 19 P.U.R. (N.S.) 535 (U.S. Sup. Ct. May 24, 1937).

A statute fixing maximum rates for the handling and selling of leaf tobacco was held to be valid.

68. *Electric Bond & Share Co. et al. v. Securities and Exchange Commission et al.* (No. 636), 303 U.S. 419, 22 P.U.R. (N.S.) 465 (U.S. Sup. Ct. Mar. 28, 1938).

First of a series of cases upholding the constitutionality of the Public Utility Holding Company Act of 1935.

69. *Solar Electric Company, Appellant, v. Pennsylvania Public Utility Commission et al. Stewart et al., Appellants, v. Same*, 137 Super. Ct. 325, 31 P.U.R. (N.S.) 275 (Pa. Super. Ct. Nov. 15, 1939).

Statement by the Pennsylvania Superior Court affirming the rate-making procedures followed by the Pennsylvania Public Utility Commission in conformity with statutes of the commonwealth of Pennsylvania.

70. *The Peoples Gas Light and Coke Company, Appellee, v. James M. Slattery et al., Appellants* (No. 24836), 373 Ill. 31, 69, 31 P.U.R. (N.S.) 193 (Ill. Sup. Ct. Dec. 12, 1939).

An appeal from a rate reduction order of the Illinois Commerce Commission which had been enjoined by an Illinois circuit court. Reversed and remanded.

The court swept aside the claims of the company regarding depreciation allowances and cited the fact that the retirement experience of the company had been such as to cloud the company's claim. The *Illinois Bell* case was used as a precedent for the court's inference that the commission's estimate was fair.

The court commented that fair rate of return must be tested primarily by present-day conditions and, after pointing out the annual cost of capital to the company, said:

. . . the company would have great difficulty in realizing five per cent upon the money it has invested in its utility enterprise, in securities which would be as sound and as certain to return a like percentage.

A.8. The Period from 1942 to 1945. Litigation during this period of wartime included the important *Hope* case, in which the Supreme Court discussed the status of fair value in the rate-making process and reversed itself on the matter of the depreciation base.

Further litigation resulted in reviews of the authority of the Federal Power Commission and the Securities and Exchange Commission conferred by the Federal Power Acts, the Natural Gas Act, and the Public Utility Holding Company Act.

71. *Federal Power Commission et al. v. Natural Gas Pipeline Co. et al.* (No. 265), 315 U.S. 575, 606, 42 P.U.R. (N.S.) 129 (U.S. Sup. Ct. Mar. 16, 1942).

Affirmation by the Court of the constitutionality of the Federal Natural Gas Act of 1938.

The Court stated that there is no constitutional requirement for a separate allowance for going value or that there is a confiscation of property when a company is denied the claim of capitalizing the maintenance cost of excess plant capacity. The Court emphasized that investment is the proper amortization base and that courts are required to accept the findings of the Commission relating to the rate base and fair rate of return provided they are supported by substantial evidence.

In a concurring opinion, Mr. Justice Black said:

As we read the opinion of the Court, the Commission is now freed from the compulsion of admitting evidence on reproduction cost or of giving any weight to that element of "fair value." The Commission may now adopt, if it chooses, prudent investment as a rate base. . . .

72. *Niagara Falls Power Co. v. Federal Power Commission* (No. 293), 137 F.2d 787, 51 P.U.R. (N.S.) 40 (U.S. Circ., 2d Circ. July 29, 1943).

In this decision, the court reviewed the authority of the Federal Power Commission in fixing the capitalization of the power company under the provisions of the Federal Power Act of 1935. The court stated that the "net investment" in a licensed power project must exclude any allowance for good will, going value, or prospective revenues. Statement that the actual legitimate cost of a federally licensed power project under the Federal Power Act cannot be the price paid by the buyer of a going plant because that price must inevitably include prospective revenues.

73. *Federal Power Commission et al. v. Hope Natural Gas Co.* (No. 34), together with *City of Cleveland v. Hope Natural Gas Co.* (No. 35), 320 U.S. 591, 51 P.U.R. (N.S.) 193 (U.S. Sup. Ct. Jan. 3, 1944).

In this important decision the United States Supreme Court set aside a ruling of the Circuit Court of Appeals which had protested that the Federal Power Commission had erred in its rate-making procedure.   The circuit court had held that the Commission should have determined a "fair value" as a rate base, that the "actual legitimate cost" was not a proper measure of "fair value" where price levels have changed, and that the accrued depletion and depreciation should have been based on "present fair value" rather than "actual legitimate cost."   All this was excluded by the Supreme Court when it said that

the heart of the matter is that rates cannot be made to depend upon "fair value" when the value of the going enterprise depends on earnings under whatever rates may be prescribed. . . . fair value is the end product of the process of rate-making and not the starting point as the Circuit Court of Appeals held.

The Court went on to say that the rate-making process of fixing just and reasonable rates involved a "balancing of the investor and the consumer interests," and concluded that the Federal Power Commission had acted properly within the framework of the Federal Power Act.

A second important ruling involved the depreciation base.   The Court reversed its decision in *United Railways v. West* and held that cost, not fair value, is the proper depreciation base.

74. *Colorado Interstate Gas Co. v. Federal Power Commission et al.* (No. 2550), *Canadian River Gas Co. v. Same* (No. 2551), *Colorado-Wyoming Gas Co. v. Same* (No. 2561), 142 F.2d 943, 54 P.U.R. (N.S.) 1 (U.S. Circ., 10th Circ. May 16, 1944).

Statement by the Circuit Court of Appeals that in fixing the "actual legitimate cost" of the property of a natural gas company such items as capital expenditures previously charged to expense and unproven costs of engineering to affiliates must be excluded.   Interest during construction cannot be continued after operation earnings are received, and no separate allowance for going value may be made.

75. *Colorado Interstate Gas Co. v. Federal Power Commission et al.* (No. 379), together with *Canadian River Gas Co. v. Federal Power Commission et al.* (No. 380), 324 U.S. 581, 58 P.U.R. (N.S.) 65 (U.S. Sup. Ct. Apr. 2, 1945).

Restriction of the authority of the Federal Power Commission from exercising jurisdiction over the regulation of the production and gathering of natural gas.

76. *Market Street Railway Co. v. Railroad Commission of California et al.* (Nos. 510, 511), 324 U.S. 548, 58 P.U.R. (N.S.) 18 (U.S. Sup. Ct. Mar. 26, 1945).

Statement that to disregard a theoretical reproduction cost of a street railway is not erroneous when it appears that no responsible person would think of reproducing the present plant.   Those principles applicable to the determination of the sufficiency of a return do not apply to a company whose financial integrity is hopelessly undermined and which could not attract capital at any possible rate.

77. *Panhandle Eastern Pipe Line Co. et al. v. Federal Power Commission et al.* (No. 296), 324 U.S. 626, 58 P.U.R. (N.S.) 100 (U.S. Sup. Ct. Apr. 2, 1945).

Restatement by the United States Supreme Court that the Federal Power Commission in fixing natural gas rates is not bound to any single formula and is not precluded from using actual legitimate cost as a rate base.

78. *Pittsburgh et al., Appellants, v. Pennsylvania Public Utility Commission*, 158 Pa. Super. Ct. 229, 61 P.U.R. (N.S.) 226 (Pa. Super. Ct. Nov. 20, 1945).

Affirmation by the Pennsylvania Superior Court that the Public Utility Law of Pennsylvania is the "law of the land" for the commonwealth.

A.9. The Period from 1946 to 1950. By the ruling of the *Hope* case the United States Supreme Court has eliminated much of the necessity for regulating agencies to go to court to obtain compliance with their rate orders. Procedures and findings based on sufficient evidence will be accepted subject to the restriction that the resulting orders are just and reasonable.

Litigation in this period includes decisions relating to the authority of regulating agencies.

79. *Public Service Commission of New York et al. v. Securities and Exchange Commission* (No. 179, Docket 20892), 166 F.2d 784, 788, 73 P.U.R. (N.S.) 38 (U.S. Circ., 2d Circ. Mar. 5, 1948).

Statement by the Circuit Court of Appeals that " . . . the value of investment securities may be measured by the prospective earning power of a company is now too well settled to admit of debate." Reference was made to the following cases 80, 81, and 82 in support of this view:

80. *Consolidated Rock Products Co. et al. v. Du Bois* (No. 400), together with *Badgley et al. v. Du Bois* (No. 444), 312 U.S. 510 (U.S. Sup. Ct. Mar. 3, 1941).

81. *Ecker et al., Constituting Institutional Bondholders Committee, v. Western Pacific Railroad Corp. et al.* (No. 7), together with *Crocker First National Bank et al., Trustees, v. Western Pacific Railroad Corp. et al.* (No. 8), *Western Pacific Railroad Co. v. Ecker et al.* (No. 20), *Reconstruction Finance Corp. v. Western Pacific Railroad Corp. et al.* (No. 33), *Irving Trust Co., Substituted Trustee, v. Crocker First National Bank et al.* (No. 61), 318 U.S. 448 (U.S. Sup. Ct. Mar. 15, 1943).

82. *Group of Institutional Investors et al. v. Chicago, Milwaukee, St. Paul & Pacific Railroad Co.* (No. 11), together with *Group of Institutional Investors et al. v. Union Trust Co. et al.* (No. 12), *Group of Institutional Investors et al. v. Abrams et al.* (No. 13), *Group of Institutional Investors et al. v. Orton et al.* (No. 14), *Group of Institutional Investors et al. v. Guaranty Trust Co. of New York et al.* (No. 15), *Group of Institutional Investors et al. v. Chicago, Terre Haute & Southeastern Ry. Co. et al.* (No. 16), *Group of Institutional Investors et al. v. United States Trust Co. of New York, Trustee* (No. 17), *Group of Institutional Investors et al. v. Trustees of Princeton University et al.* (No. 18), *Group of Institutional Investors et al. v. Glines et al.* (No. 19), *Reconstruction Finance Corporation v. Chicago, Milwaukee, St. Paul & Pacific Railroad Co. et al.* (No. 32), 318 U.S. 523 (U.S. Sup. Ct. Mar. 15, 1943).

83. *Securities and Exchange Commission v. Central-Illinois Securities Corp. et al.* (No. 226), together with *Streeter et al. v. Central-Illinois Securities Corp. et al.* (No. 227), *Home Insurance Co. et al. v. Central-Illinois Securities Corp. et al.* (No. 243), *Central-Illinois Securities Corp. et al. v. Securities and Exchange Commission et al.* (No. 266), 338 U.S. 96, 80 P.U.R. (N.S.) 282 (U.S. Sup. Ct. June 27, 1949).

Statement by the Supreme Court that the findings of a commission which are based upon judgment and prediction as well as "facts" are not subject to re-examination by the Court unless they are not supported by substantial evidence or were not arrived at "in accordance with legal standards."

Iowa 18 Type Survivor and Frequency Curves

Appendix B presents the equations and their solutions for the Iowa 18 type survivor and frequency curves which were discussed in Chap. 7. These type curves are smoothed composites of curves taken from industrial retirement experience, as explained in Bulletin 125, where they were first published.[1] The equations and solutions given here, slightly modified from their original form, are as published in Bulletins 155 and 156[2] in 1942.

B.1. General Equations of the Iowa 18 Type Frequency Curves.

Left Mode Nos. 0 and 1

$$y_x = y_0 \left[1 - \frac{(x \pm d_m)^2}{a^2} \right]^m \text{ for } x \text{ values to left of mode}$$

$$y_x = y_0 \left[1 - \frac{(x \pm D_m)^2}{A^2} \right]^M \text{ for } x \text{ values to right of mode}$$

Left Mode Nos. 2, 3, and 5 and
Right Mode Nos. 1, 2, 3, 4, and 5

$$y_x = Y_e \left(1 + \frac{x \pm D_m}{A_1} \right)^{M_1} \left(1 - \frac{x \pm D_m}{A_2} \right)^{M_2}$$

$$+ y_e \left(1 + \frac{x \pm d_m}{a_1} \right)^{m_1} \left(1 - \frac{x \pm d_m}{a_2} \right)^{m_2}$$

Left Mode No. 4

$$y_x = Y_0 \left[1 - \left(\frac{x + D}{A_1} \right)^2 \right]^{M_1} + y_0 \left[1 - \left(\frac{x + d}{a_1} \right)^2 \right]^{m_1} \quad -10 \leqq x \leqq -D$$

$$y_x = Y_0 \left[1 - \left(\frac{x + D}{A_2} \right)^2 \right]^{M_2} + y_0 \left[1 - \left(\frac{x + d}{a_1} \right)^2 \right]^{m_1} \quad -D \leqq x \leqq -d$$

$$y_x = Y_0 \left[1 - \left(\frac{x + D}{A_2} \right)^2 \right]^{M_2} + y_0 \left[1 - \left(\frac{x + d}{a_2} \right)^2 \right]^{m_2} \quad -d \leqq x \leqq (A_2 - D)$$

[1] Robley Winfrey, "Statistical Analysis of Industrial Property Retirements," Iowa State College, Engineering Experiment Station, Bulletin 125, 1936.

[2] Robley Winfrey, "Depreciation of Group Properties," Bulletin 155; and "Condition-Percent Tables for Depreciation of Unit and Group Properties," Bulletin 156, Iowa State College, Engineering Experiment Station, 1942.

Symmetrical Nos. 0, 1, 2, 3, 4, 5, and 6

$$y_x = y_0 \left(1 - \frac{x^2}{a^2}\right)^m$$

in which y_x = ordinate to the frequency curve at age x (origin at the mean age)

y_0 = ordinate to the frequency curve at its mode

Y_e = ordinate to the major constituent curve at its mean

y_e = ordinate to the minor constituent curve at its mean

x = age (in units equal to 10 percent of average life), measured from the average-life ordinate

D_m, d_m = x distance from the mean of the type curve to the mean of the constituent curve

$A, A_1, A_2, a, a_1, a_2, M, M_1, M_2, m, m_1, m_2$ are parameters.

B.2. Equations of the Iowa 18 Type Frequency Curves. In the following 18 equations, x is measured from the mean, or average life, negative values of x being to the left of 100 percent of average life and positive values to the right. An age interval of 10 percent of average life is equal to x. Therefore, if $x = -2.5$, the equivalent age is 75 percent of average life. When $x = +4.2$, the equivalent is 142 percent of average life.

Left Mode No. 0

$$y_x = 6.24256418 \left[1 - \frac{(x + 5.06)^2}{24.60758105}\right]^{0.4411811} \quad \text{for } x \text{ values to left of 49.4 percent of average life}$$

$$y_x = 6.24256418 \left[1 - \frac{(x + 5.06)^2}{1569.183739}\right]^{7.75906308} \quad \text{for } x \text{ values to right of 49.4 percent of average life}$$

Left Mode No. 1

$$y_x = 7.45095687 \left[1 - \frac{(x + 4)^2}{85.49500000}\right]^{4.77742941} \quad \text{for } x \text{ values to left of 60 percent of average life}$$

$$y_x = 7.45095687 \left[1 - \frac{(x + 4)^2}{697.8983268}\right]^{4.74147112} \quad \text{for } x \text{ values to right of 60 percent of average life}$$

Left Mode No. 2

$$y_x = 6.2 \left(1 + \frac{x - 0.56632298}{10.56632298}\right)^{2.00691507} \left(1 - \frac{x - 0.56632298}{18.11962398}\right)^{4.15639835}$$

$$+ 4.03141046 \left(1 + \frac{x + 1.98831766}{4.90258200}\right)^{2.73360830} \left(1 - \frac{x + 1.98831766}{12.07825433}\right)^{8.19831032}$$

Left Mode No. 3

$$y_x = 6.12 \left(1 + \frac{x - 0.69997304}{9.94997304}\right)^{2.51767682} \left(1 - \frac{x - 0.69997304}{13.35543784}\right)^{3.72163230}$$

$$+ 8.19722280 \left(1 + \frac{x + 1.22119072}{6.98766177}\right)^{10.15754029} \left(1 - \frac{x + 1.22119072}{16.85048078}\right)^{25.90598437}$$

Left Mode No. 4

$$y_x = 10.811999434 \left[1 - \frac{(x + 0.600)^2}{51.8400} \right]^{25.300}$$

$$+ 9.901828065 \left[1 - \frac{(x + 0.300)^2}{56.2500} \right]^{3.650} \qquad -10 \leqq x \leqq -0.6$$

$$y_x = 10.811999434 \left[1 - \frac{(x + 0.600)^2}{184.9600} \right]^{62.000}$$

$$+ 9.901828065 \left[1 - \frac{(x + 0.300)^2}{56.2500} \right]^{3.650} \qquad -0.6 \leqq x \leqq -0.3$$

$$y_x = 10.811999434 \left[1 - \frac{(x + 0.600)^2}{184.9600} \right]^{62.000}$$

$$+ 9.901828065 \left[1 - \frac{(x + 0.300)^2}{176.8900} \right]^{8.350} \qquad -0.3 \leqq x \leqq (13.6 - 0.6)$$

Left Mode No. 5

$$y_x = 12.76925713 \left(1 + \frac{x - 0.088051975}{5.9500} \right)^{4.7715} \left(1 - \frac{x - 0.088051975}{10.7500} \right)^{9.4275}$$

$$+ 16.28938438 \left(1 + \frac{x + 0.161460055}{4.0000} \right)^{11.8000} \left(1 - \frac{x + 0.161460055}{5.7000} \right)^{17.2400}$$

Symmetrical No. 0

$$y_x = 6.95219904 \left(1 - \frac{x^2}{100} \right)^{0.74857140}$$

Symmetrical No. 1

$$y_x = 9.08025966 \left(1 - \frac{x^2}{100} \right)^{1.82839970}$$

Symmetrical No. 2

$$y_x = 11.91103882 \left(1 - \frac{x^2}{100} \right)^{3.70009374}$$

Symmetrical No. 3

$$y_x = 15.61048797 \left(1 - \frac{x^2}{100} \right)^{6.9015918}$$

Symmetrical No. 4

$$y_x = 22.32936082 \left(1 - \frac{x^2}{81} \right)^{11.93537940}$$

Symmetrical No. 5

$$y_x = 33.22051575 \left(1 - \frac{x^2}{64} \right)^{21.43782170}$$

Symmetrical No. 6

$$y_x = 52.47259169 \left(1 - \frac{x^2}{49}\right)^{41.63414220}$$

Right Mode No. 1

$$y_x = 4.87234751 \left(1 + \frac{x + 2.1173}{19.08200310}\right)^{2.16036988} \left(1 - \frac{x + 2.1173}{12.2}\right)^{1.02056945}$$

$$+ 2.95921394 \left(1 + \frac{x - 2.03848}{9.25013197}\right)^{2.69374074} \left(1 - \frac{x - 2.03848}{6.76380495}\right)^{1.69831583}$$

Right Mode No. 2

$$y_x = 6.89465710 \left(1 + \frac{x + 0.470}{30.05448169}\right)^{9.16816044} \left(1 - \frac{x + 0.470}{9.05171312}\right)^{2.06241419}$$

$$+ 3.34428110 \left(1 + \frac{x - 0.470}{91.60465100}\right)^{100.000} \left(1 - \frac{x - 0.470}{7.80000000}\right)^{7.600}$$

Right Mode No. 3

$$y_x = 9.4035297069 \left(1 + \frac{x + 0.235}{17.61801370}\right)^{7.950} \left(1 - \frac{x + 0.235}{7.18500000}\right)^{2.650}$$

$$+ 5.5945716839 \left(1 + \frac{x - 0.698}{17.31323077}\right)^{27.800} \left(1 - \frac{x - 0.698}{6.25200000}\right)^{9.400}$$

Right Mode No. 4

$$y_x = 15.20129316 \left(1 + \frac{x + 0.11}{17.92683200}\right)^{14.05850860} \left(1 - \frac{x + 0.11}{5.41801100}\right)^{3.55112010}$$

$$+ 5.85667821 \left(1 + \frac{x - 0.70}{2.56783700}\right)^{3.66879450} \left(1 - \frac{x - 0.70}{3.45398750}\right)^{5.27997721}$$

Right Mode No. 5

$$y_x = 14.99330391 \left(1 + \frac{x + 0.12869}{7.0000000}\right)^{5.79473520} \left(1 - \frac{x + 0.12869}{3.8764409}\right)^{2.76276990}$$

$$+ 15.44614441 \left(1 + \frac{x - 0.2086}{4.2350000}\right)^{6.05833400} \left(1 - \frac{x - 0.2086}{2.4150000}\right)^{3.02500040}$$

TABLE B.1. PERCENT SURVIVING AND PROBABLE LIVES OF THE IOWA 18 TYPE CURVES

Source: Robley Winfrey, "Condition-Percent Tables for Depreciation of Unit and Group Properties," Iowa State College, Engineering Experiment Station, Bulletin 156, 1942

Age, percent of average life	Type curve L_0		Type curve L_1		Type curve L_2		Type curve L_3	
	Percent surviving	Probable life, per-cent of average life	Percent surviving	Probable life, per-cent of average life	Percent surviving	Probable life, per-cent of average life	Percent surviving	Probable life, per-cent of average life
0	100.00000	99.99089	100.00000	100.00591	100.00000	100.00021	100.00000	99.99845
5	98.88950	101.08161	99.63717	100.36022	99.98516	100.01451	100.00000	99.99845
10	97.09985	102.80445	99.05431	100.90562	99.88940	100.10272	99.99965	99.99876
15	94.91674	104.88011	98.19015	101.68240	99.64732	100.31485	99.98571	100.01084
20	92.45291	107.20770	96.98956	102.72297	99.20930	100.67961	99.92003	100.06478
25	89.77813	109.73060	95.40973	104.04967	98.53977	101.20981	99.75597	100.19186
30	86.94316	112.41127	93.42541	105.67380	97.61555	101.90662	99.44760	100.41659
35	83.98860	115.22191	91.03275	107.59530	96.41791	102.76752	98.95304	100.75520
40	80.94912	118.13988	88.25133	109.80281	94.85656	103.83997	98.23067	101.21934
45	77.85578	121.14498	85.12428	112.27369	92.77820	105.21155	97.22244	101.82694
50	74.73764	124.21747	81.71638	114.97383	90.07738	106.93905	95.82788	102.61565
55	71.61815	127.34132	78.11040	117.85716	86.72860	109.03813	93.88854	103.64810
60	68.50728	130.51283	74.40204	120.86522	82.78113	111.49302	91.20570	105.00185
65	65.41269	133.73056	70.67865	123.93996	78.33876	114.26913	87.59534	106.74906
70	62.34191	136.99306	66.96789	127.06747	73.53626	117.32197	82.95922	108.93749
75	59.30233	140.29892	63.28229	130.24572	68.51802	120.60387	77.33872	111.58081
80	56.30114	143.64678	59.63417	133.47273	63.42158	124.06752	70.92603	114.65849
85	53.34528	147.03529	56.03557	136.74659	58.36648	127.66832	64.02853	118.12085
90	50.44141	150.46313	52.49810	140.06547	53.44823	131.36588	57.00209	121.89571
95	47.59585	153.92902	49.03293	143.42757	48.73660	135.12517	50.17916	125.89546
100	44.81457	157.43172	45.65060	146.83119	44.27685	139.12062	43.81420	130.02557
105	42.10313	160.97001	42.36105	150.27465	40.09316	142.72029	38.05845	134.19523
110	39.46666	164.54272	39.17345	153.75638	36.19309	146.51867	32.96348	138.32936
115	36.90985	168.14870	36.09618	157.27483	32.57226	150.30366	28.50446	142.37842
120	34.43690	171.78684	33.13678	160.82853	29.21877	154.07214	24.61134	146.32230
125	32.05150	175.45606	30.30187	164.41606	26.11696	157.82557	21.19779	150.16671
130	29.75687	179.15533	27.59711	168.03608	23.25024	161.56858	18.18205	153.93424
135	27.55566	182.88363	25.02721	171.68727	20.60301	165.30765	15.49809	157.65409
140	25.45004	186.63999	22.59584	175.36838	18.16176	169.04987	13.09864	161.35412
145	23.44162	190.42346	20.30567	179.07823	15.91540	172.80201	10.95300	165.05640
150	21.53151	194.23313	18.15836	182.81566	13.85508	176.56980	9.04239	168.77609
155	19.72030	198.06812	16.15455	186.57958	11.97372	180.35762	7.35497	172.52213
160	18.00807	201.92758	14.29388	190.36894	10.26528	184.16841	5.88180	176.29886
165	16.39443	205.81068	12.57504	194.18272	8.72414	188.00373	4.61406	180.10757
170	14.87851	209.71662	10.99580	198.01998	7.34447	191.86401	3.54138	183.94776
175	13.45901	213.64466	9.55304	201.87979	6.11983	195.74884	2.65120	187.81802
180	12.13419	217.59403	8.24285	205.76127	5.04292	199.65727	1.92866	191.71659
185	10.90195	221.56404	7.06053	209.66358	4.10549	203.58804	1.35694	195.64161
190	9.75982	225.55399	6.00073	213.58501	3.29841	207.53975	0.91776	199.59130
195	8.70500	229.56322	5.05748	217.52750	2.61180	211.51131	0.59197	203.56400
200	7.73441	233.59110	4.22433	221.48760	2.03522	215.50128	0.36025	207.55823
205	6.84472	237.63700	3.49436	225.46551	1.55792	219.50860	0.20376	211.57267
210	6.03238	241.70032	2.86034	229.46057	1.16899	223.53224	0.10480	215.60622
215	5.29368	245.78052	2.31483	233.47212	0.85763	227.57124	4.7392*-2	219.65804
220	4.62473	249.87702	1.85022	237.49955	0.61326	231.62472	1.7822*-2	223.72779
225	4.02158	253.98930	1.45887	241.54228	0.42576	235.69186	5.0302*-3	227.81621
230	3.48020	258.11684	1.13320	245.59973	0.28560	239.77193	8.5317*-4	231.92737
235	2.99653	262.25915	0.86577	249.67137	0.18396	243.86424	4.5269*-5	236.08217
240	2.56649	266.41576	0.64937	253.75670	0.11287	247.96820	1.2840*-8	240.50000
245	2.18608	270.58622	0.47711	257.85521	6.5248*-2	252.08326	Absolute zero at age 256.29	
250	1.85133	274.76467	0.34247	261.96644	3.5011*-2	256.20897		
255	1.55287	278.96689	0.23940	266.08995	1.7066*-2	260.34501		
260	1.30345	283.17628	0.16234	270.22531	7.3138*-3	264.49126		
265	1.08297	287.39783	0.10626	274.37212	2.6141*-3	268.64793		
270	0.89347	291.63117	6.6733*-2	278.53000	7.0921*-4	272.81610		

*Condensed from the usual form 6.6733×10^{-2}.

TABLE B.1. PERCENT SURVIVING AND PROBABLE LIVES OF THE IOWA 18 TYPE CURVES (*Continued*)

Source: Robley Winfrey, "Condition-Percent Tables for Depreciation of Unit and Group Properties," Iowa State College, Engineering Experiment Station, Bulletin 156, 1942

Age, percent of average life	Type curve L_4		Type curve L_5		Type curve S_0		Type curve S_1	
	Percent surviving	Probable life, per-cent of average life	Percent surviving	Probable life, per-cent of average life	Percent surviving	Probable life, per-cent of average life	Percent surviving	Probable life, per-cent of average life
0	100.00000	100.00000	100.00000	100.00000	100.00000	100.00000	100.00000	100.00000
5	100.00000	100.00000	100.00000	100.00000	99.64988	100.34029	99.97697	100.02220
10	100.00000	100.00000	100.00000	100.00000	98.83704	101.10222	99.84198	100.14667
15	100.00000	100.00000	100.00000	100.00000	97.66579	102.16343	99.51978	100.42955
20	100.00000	100.00000	100.00000	100.00000	96.18813	103.46285	98.95479	100.90197
25	99.99994	100.00004	100.00000	100.00000	94.44074	104.95979	98.10590	101.57914
30	99.99491	100.00364	100.00000	100.00000	92.45276	106.62440	96.94397	102.46569
35	99.95590	100.02975	100.00000	100.00000	90.24878	108.43369	95.45014	103.55926
40	99.81999	100.11433	100.00000	100.00000	87.85047	110.36934	93.61458	104.85306
45	99.49620	100.30086	99.99994	100.00003	85.27737	112.41641	91.43547	106.33757
50	98.87810	100.62951	99.99221	100.00400	82.54749	114.56250	88.91814	108.00180
55	97.85817	101.12929	99.91441	100.04046	79.67768	116.79719	86.07422	109.83412
60	96.33923	101.81492	99.59667	100.17473	76.68385	119.11161	82.92102	111.82276
65	94.23074	102.69191	98.77418	100.48580	73.58124	121.49814	79.48078	113.95626
70	91.40395	103.77670	97.15592	101.03139	70.38447	123.95016	75.78013	116.22361
75	87.59685	105.13067	94.48180	101.83388	67.10774	126.46193	71.84942	118.61443
80	82.36077	106.87908	90.38589	102.92896	63.76487	129.02839	67.72221	121.11903
85	75.23825	109.17620	84.04805	104.45606	60.36941	131.64506	63.43466	123.72839
90	66.20766	112.12265	74.41381	106.63177	56.93468	134.30800	59.02506	126.43422
95	56.03106	115.68281	61.43633	109.59890	53.47385	137.01367	54.53322	129.22889
100	45.92922	119.68734	46.93011	113.33734	50.00000	139.75891	50.00000	132.10541
105	36.82670	123.94999	33.60849	117.66137	46.52615	142.54088	45.46678	135.05737
110	29.20175	128.26669	23.25529	122.24209	43.06532	145.35702	40.97494	138.07892
115	23.07537	132.47687	15.99530	126.73263	39.63059	148.20503	36.56533	141.16474
120	18.18649	136.52655	11.00040	130.99004	36.23513	151.08200	32.27779	144.30994
125	14.22200	140.45874	7.44648	135.10346	32.89226	153.98841	28.15058	147.51008
130	10.95212	144.35016	4.86568	139.20493	29.61552	156.92014	24.21987	150.76110
135	8.24831	148.26014	3.02930	143.35702	26.41876	159.87638	20.51922	154.05930
140	6.04296	152.21838	1.78262	147.56930	23.31614	162.85568	17.07898	157.40128
145	4.28876	156.23332	0.98432	151.83527	20.32232	165.85670	13.92578	160.78396
150	2.93706	160.30381	0.50557	156.14726	17.45251	168.87822	11.08186	164.20450
155	1.93260	164.42557	0.23884	160.49860	14.72263	171.91911	8.56453	167.66033
160	1.21574	168.59388	0.10227	164.88452	12.14953	174.97833	6.38542	171.14910
165	0.72670	172.80433	3.8912*-2	169.29999	9.75122	178.05493	4.54986	174.66867
170	0.40962	177.05300	1.2804*-2	173.74155	7.54724	181.14740	3.05603	178.21712
175	0.21565	181.33633	3.5047*-3	178.20627	5.55926	184.25699	1.89410	181.79275
180	0.10473	185.65127	7.5300*-4	182.69165	3.81187	187.38111	1.04521	185.39421
185	4.6162*-2	189.99496	1.1578*-4	187.19677	2.33421	190.52013	0.48022	189.02070
190	1.8062*-2	194.36507	1.0862*-5	191.71987	1.16296	193.67471	0.15802	192.67315
195	6.0815*-3	198.75944	4.5233*-7	196.26370	0.35012	196.85095	2.3033*-2	196.36205
200	1.6836*-3	203.17626	3.8160*-9	200.83860	0.00000	200.00000	0.00000	200.00000
205	3.5703*-4	207.61398	2.4958*-13	205.51817				
210	5.1468*-5	212.07250			Absolute zero at age 200.0		Absolute zero at age 200.0	
215	4.0358*-6	216.55238	Absolute zero at age 208.38					
220	1.0376*-7	221.05924						
225	1.6690*-10	225.62577						
230	0.00000	230.00000						

Absolute zero at age 230.0

*Condensed from the usual form 4.6162x10⁻².

TABLE B.1. PERCENT SURVIVING AND PROBABLE LIVES OF THE IOWA
18 TYPE CURVES (Continued)

Source: Robley Winfrey, "Condition-Percent Tables for Depreciation of Unit and Group Properties," Iowa State College, Engineering Experiment Station, Bulletin 156, 1942

Age, percent of average life	Type curve S_2		Type curve S_3		Type curve S_4		Type curve S_6	
	Percent surviving	Probable life, per cent of average life	Percent surviving	Probable life, per cent of average life	Percent surviving	Probable life, per cent of average life	Percent surviving	Probable life, per cent of average life
0	100.00000	100.00000	100.00000	100.00000	100.00000	100.00000	100.00000	100.00000
5	99.99977	100.00022	100.00000	100.00000	100.00000	100.00000	100.00000	100.00000
10	99.99438	100.00516	99.99998	100.00002	100.00000	100.00000	100.00000	100.00000
15	99.96508	100.03065	99.99955	100.00039	100.00000	100.00000	100.00000	100.00000
20	99.87562	100.10424	99.99626	100.00308	100.00000	100.00000	100.00000	100.00000
25	99.67336	100.26114	99.98158	100.01439	100.00000	100.00000	100.00000	100.00000
30	99.29313	100.53891	99.93451	100.04835	99.99994	100.00004	100.00000	100.00000
35	98.66236	100.97274	99.81435	100.12926	99.99925	100.00050	100.00000	100.00000
40	97.70666	101.59210	99.55468	100.29188	99.99445	100.00347	100.00000	100.00000
45	96.35547	102.41897	99.06070	100.57890	99.97162	100.01648	100.00000	100.00000
50	94.54722	103.46727	98.21171	101.03602	99.89006	100.05898	99.99986	100.00007
55	92.23368	104.74343	96.86915	101.70637	99.65644	100.16958	99.99803	100.00092
60	89.38348	106.24745	94.88992	102.62546	99.09588	100.40916	99.98250	100.00741
65	85.98454	107.97422	92.14318	103.81800	97.93460	100.85553	99.89372	100.04020
70	82.04539	109.91488	88.52850	105.29680	95.81171	101.58974	99.52630	100.15847
75	77.59546	112.05802	83.99263	107.06350	92.33195	102.67936	98.36721	100.47958
80	72.68428	114.39069	78.54224	109.11051	87.15666	104.16613	95.47669	101.16553
85	67.37969	116.89776	72.25073	111.42339	80.11173	106.06203	89.62837	102.36758
90	61.76531	119.56988	65.25765	113.98329	71.27816	108.35315	79.84902	104.16759
95	55.93719	122.38914	57.76056	116.76904	61.03029	111.00766	66.16179	106.56047
100	50.00000	125.34413	50.00000	119.75873	50.00000	113.98428	50.00000	109.47834
105	44.06281	128.42274	42.23944	122.93091	38.96971	117.23905	33.83821	112.82728
110	38.23469	131.61370	34.74235	126.26526	28.72184	120.72977	20.15098	116.51424
115	32.62031	134.90665	27.74927	129.74306	19.88827	124.41839	10.37163	120.45988
120	27.31572	138.29213	21.45776	133.34737	12.84334	128.27194	4.52331	124.60162
125	22.40454	141.76152	16.00737	137.06307	7.66805	132.26258	1.63279	128.89201
130	17.95461	145.30705	11.47150	140.87676	4.18829	136.36718	0.47370	133.29585
135	14.01546	148.92167	7.85682	144.77670	2.06540	140.56669	0.10628	137.78717
140	10.61652	152.59905	5.11008	148.75260	0.90412	144.84554	1.7505*-2	142.34693
145	7.76632	156.33349	3.13085	152.79550	0.34356	149.19105	1.9664*-3	146.96095
150	5.45278	160.11988	1.78829	156.89763	0.10994	153.59287	1.3506*-4	151.61900
155	3.64453	163.95363	0.93930	161.05224	2.8348*-2	158.04267	4.7901*-6	156.31432
160	2.29334	167.83069	0.44532	165.25372	5.5528*-3	162.53372	6.5855*-8	161.04285
165	1.33764	171.74735	0.18565	169.49639	7.4641*-4	167.06104	2.0400*-10	165.80504
170	0.70687	175.70044	6.5494*-2	173.77668	5.8485*-5	171.62133	4.1151*-14	170.61149
175	0.32664	179.68720	1.8423*-2	178.09091	1.9628*-6	176.21146	8.2575*-21	175.50523
180	0.12438	183.70544	3.7393*-3	182.43656	1.3859*-7	180.84334	0.00000	180.00000
185	3.4916*-2	187.75240	4.5414*-4	186.81280	2.0195*-12	185.55252	Absolute zero at age 180.0	
190	5.6228*-3	191.83362	2.1671*-5	191.22341	0.00000	190.00000		
195	2.3407*-4	195.96419	1.0622*-7	195.69685				
200	0.00000	200.00000	0.00000	200.00000	Absolute zero at age 190.0			
205								
	Absolute zero at age 200.0		Absolute zero at age 200.0					

*Condensed from the usual form 3.4916x10⁻².

TABLE B.1. PERCENT SURVIVING AND PROBABLE LIVES OF THE IOWA 18 TYPE CURVES (*Continued*)

Source: Robley Winfrey, "Condition-Percent Tables for Depreciation of Unit and Group Properties," Iowa State College, Engineering Experiment Station, Bulletin 156, 1942

Age, percent of average life	Type curve S_6 Percent surviving	Type curve S_6 Probable life, percent of average life	Type curve R_1 Percent surviving	Type curve R_1 Probable life, percent of average life	Type curve R_2 Percent surviving	Type curve R_2 Probable life, percent of average life	Type curve R_3 Percent surviving	Type curve R_3 Probable life, percent of average life
0	100.00000	100.00000	100.00000	100.00180	100.00000	100.00000	100.00000	100.00000
5	100.00000	100.00000	98.67319	101.31249	99.49224	100.49725	99.90802	100.08961
10	100.00000	100.00000	97.25548	102.67964	98.89359	101.05981	99.77155	100.21605
15	100.00000	100.00000	95.74739	104.09966	98.19184	101.69229	99.57488	100.38902
20	100.00000	100.00000	94.14988	105.56867	97.37369	102.39917	99.29891	100.61902
25	100.00000	100.00000	92.46439	107.08252	96.42474	103.18491	98.92096	100.91703
30	100.00000	100.00000	90.69276	108.63674	95.32938	104.05390	98.41475	101.29408
35	100.00000	100.00000	88.83506	110.22850	94.07074	105.01055	97.75059	101.76079
40	100.00000	100.00000	86.88515	111.86026	92.63063	106.05929	96.89555	102.32699
45	100.00000	100.00000	84.83266	113.53789	90.98955	107.20471	95.81369	103.00148
50	100.00000	100.00000	82.66538	115.26865	89.12668	108.45158	94.46607	103.79204
55	100.00000	100.00000	80.37080	117.06003	87.02008	109.80490	92.81029	104.70569
60	100.00000	100.00000	77.93721	118.91905	84.64706	111.26991	90.79948	105.74941
65	99.99996	100.00001	75.35462	120.85185	81.98479	112.85214	88.38061	106.93112
70	99.99835	100.00052	72.61549	122.86346	79.01133	114.55726	85.49283	108.26067
75	99.96681	100.00889	69.71522	124.95773	75.70717	116.39102	82.06693	109.75071
80	99.64167	100.07979	66.65272	127.13731	72.05731	118.35898	78.02814	111.41669
85	97.71260	100.41499	63.43064	129.40376	68.05401	120.46632	73.30461	113.27609
90	90.70910	101.37934	60.05571	131.75762	63.70000	122.71746	67.84370	115.34643
95	74.50386	103.25562	56.53884	134.19860	59.01217	125.11571	61.63582	117.64274
100	50.00000	106.03512	52.89519	136.72566	54.02510	127.66288	54.74208	120.17476
105	25.49614	109.51346	49.14416	139.33722	48.79396	130.35885	47.31746	122.94457
110	9.29090	113.46679	45.30930	142.03122	43.39604	133.20108	39.61801	125.94491
115	2.28740	117.72763	41.41805	144.80529	37.92987	136.18423	31.98179	129.15823
120	0.35833	122.18704	37.50154	147.65686	32.51131	139.29962	24.78027	132.55624
125	3.3192^{*-2}	126.77740	33.59414	150.58322	27.26603	142.53491	18.34962	136.10033
130	1.6488^{*-3}	131.45697	29.73303	153.58167	22.31913	145.87373	12.92397	139.74426
135	3.8261^{*-5}	136.19977	25.95763	156.76125	17.78236	149.29606	8.59763	143.44083
140	3.3790^{*-7}	140.98968	22.30885	159.78422	13.74239	152.77927	5.33296	147.15341
145	8.2277^{*-10}	145.81720	18.82834	162.98331	10.25227	156.30063	3.00720	150.86725
150	3.1928^{*-12}	150.67814	15.55747	166.24450	7.32937	159.84111	1.46794	154.59151
155	6.9354^{*-16}	155.57400	12.53623	169.56552	4.96076	163.38985	0.56322	158.34810
160	7.5148^{*-25}	160.51341	9.80182	172.94384	3.11416	166.94690	0.13638	162.15692
165	1.0945^{*-37}	165.50004	7.38707	176.37592	1.74922	170.52220	9.9847^{*-6}	166.03924
170	0.00000	170.00000	5.31832	179.85535	0.82235	174.13012	Absolute zero at age 169.50	
175	Absolute zero at age 170.0		3.61284	183.36828	0.28040	177.78323		
180			2.27508	186.88301	4.5610^{*-2}	181.49239		
185			1.29047	190.33183	6.5960^{*-5}	185.50000		
190			0.61061	193.65695				
195			0.17949	196.99140	Absolute zero at age 185.82			
200			4.5573^{*-3}	200.50000				
205			0.00000	205.00000				
210			Absolute zero at age 200.83					

*Condensed from the usual form 3.3192x10⁻².

TABLE B.1. PERCENT SURVIVING AND PROBABLE LIVES OF THE IOWA 18 TYPE CURVES (*Continued*)

Source: Robley Winfrey, "Condition-Percent Tables for Depreciation of Unit and Group Properties," Iowa State College, Engineering Experiment Station, Bulletin 156, 1942

Age, percent of average life	Type curve R_4		Type curve R_5		Type curve L_9, concluded		
	Percent surviving	Probable life, percent of average life	Percent surviving	Probable life, percent of average life	Age, percent of average life	Percent surviving	Probable life, percent of average life
0	100.00000	100.00049	100.00000	99.99926	275	0.73167	295.87593
5	99.99432	100.00601	100.00000	99.99926	280	0.59449	300.13177
10	99.98287	100.01658	100.00000	99.99926	285	0.47904	304.39833
15	99.96090	100.03575	100.00000	99.99926	290	0.38262	308.67529
20	99.92061	100.06894	100.00000	99.99926	295	0.30276	312.96234
25	99.84968	100.12389	100.00000	99.99926	300	0.23719	317.25916
30	99.72952	100.21114	100.00000	99.99926	305	0.18385	321.56548
35	99.53311	100.34439	99.99998	99.99928	310	0.14089	325.88100
40	99.22264	100.54048	99.99916	99.99978	315	0.10666	330.20545
45	98.74727	100.81910	99.99100	100.00441	320	$7.9690*^{-2}$	334.53858
50	98.04124	101.20197	99.95114	100.02514	325	$5.8700*^{-2}$	338.88014
55	97.02304	101.71159	99.82089	100.08662	330	$4.2579*^{-2}$	343.22988
60	95.59608	102.36961	99.49249	100.22610	335	$3.0373*^{-2}$	347.58758
65	93.65182	103.19487	98.80274	100.48760	340	$2.1275*^{-2}$	351.95302
70	91.07592	104.20140	97.53512	100.91344	345	$1.4608*^{-2}$	356.32609
75	87.75801	105.39634	95.39673	101.54592	350	$9.8117*^{-3}$	360.70651
80	83.60532	106.77778	91.94655	102.44128	355	$6.4322*^{-3}$	365.09417
85	78.55460	108.33401	86.55794	103.67210	360	$4.1041*^{-3}$	369.48663
90	72.42015	110.09162	78.54068	105.30800	365	$2.5406*^{-3}$	373.88746
95	64.75218	112.16416	67.46899	107.39151	370	$1.5200*^{-3}$	378.29492
100	55.38004	114.63438	53.61839	109.92926	375	$8.7481*^{-4}$	382.70842
105	44.79042	117.49630	38.27696	112.90149	380	$4.8165*^{-4}$	387.12827
110	33.97478	120.68251	23.63847	116.27958	385	$2.5188*^{-4}$	391.55417
115	24.00508	124.10272	12.08071	120.03018	390	$1.2402*^{-4}$	395.98600
120	15.65853	127.67001	4.95374	124.03417	395	$5.6842*^{-5}$	400.42364
125	9.26945	131.31951	1.61653	127.91040	400	$2.3894*^{-5}$	404.86698
130	4.80402	135.02206	0.29276	131.69264	405	$9.0286*^{-6}$	409.31583
135	2.02527	138.78538	$5.3622*^{-3}$	135.63094	410	$2.9812*^{-6}$	413.77071
140	0.59682	142.63490	0.00000	140.00000	415	$8.2579*^{-7}$	418.23126
145	$8.5247*^{-2}$	146.58440			420	$1.8014*^{-7}$	422.69784
150	$1.2803*^{-1}$	150.66575	Absolute zero at age 137.48		425	$2.7860*^{-8}$	427.17126
155	0.00000	155.00000			430	$2.5148*^{-9}$	431.65335
					435	$8.6258*^{-11}$	436.14968
	Absolute zero at age 153.08				440	$2.9897*^{-13}$	440.68596
					445	$1.1790*^{-30}$	445.50000

Absolute zero at age 445.53

Continuation of Left Mode Types

	Type curve L_1		Type curve L_2	
275	$3.9886*^{-2}$	282.69860	$1.2032*^{-4}$	276.99972
280	$2.2451*^{-2}$	286.87760	$7.6517*^{-6}$	281.21830
285	$1.1731*^{-2}$	291.06671	$2.6860*^{-8}$	285.92359
290	$5.5762*^{-3}$	295.26570		
295	$2.3399*^{-3}$	299.47442	Absolute zero at age 286.86	
300	$8.2700*^{-4}$	303.69289		
305	$2.2723*^{-4}$	307.92147		
310	$4.1607*^{-5}$	312.16147		
315	$3.5342*^{-6}$	316.41771		
320	$3.8022*^{-8}$	320.71968		

Absolute zero at age 324.18

*Condensed from the usual form 8.5247×10^{-2}.

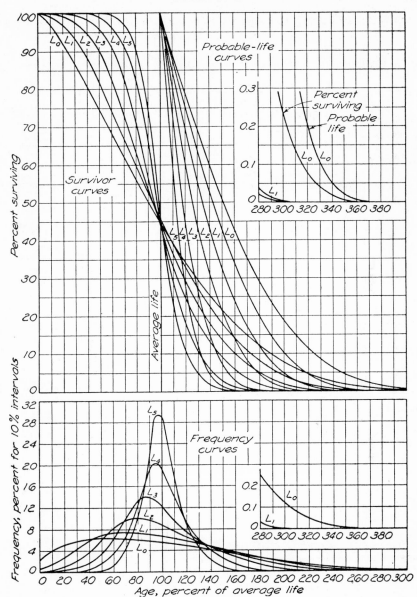

FIG. *B*.1. Left modal Iowa type survivor, probable-life, and frequency curves.

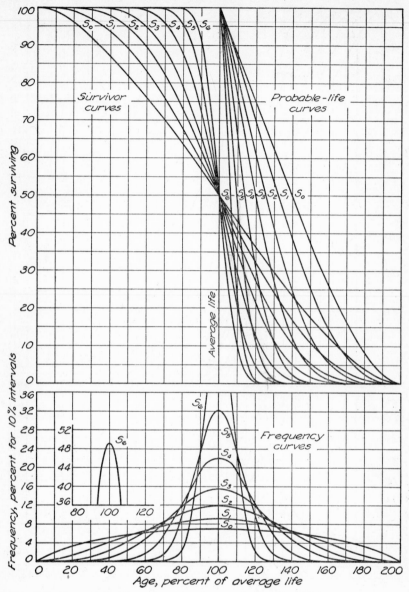

Fig. *B*.2. Symmetrical Iowa type survivor, probable-life, and frequency curves.

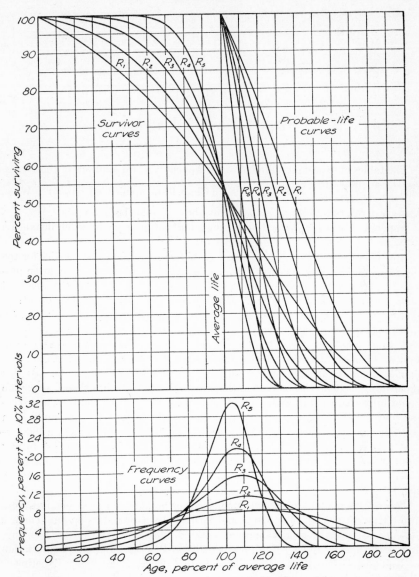

FIG. *B*.3. Right modal Iowa type survivor, probable-life, and frequency curves.

Expectancy-Life Factors

The tables of expectancy-life factors in Appendix C are solutions of the expression $\dfrac{(1 + r)^n - (1 + r)^x}{(1 + r)^n - 1}$ as developed in Chap. 9 and applied in Chap. 11. When the rate of return (or interest) is 0 percent, the expression becomes $(n - x)/n$.

Appendix C.1 is for application to single units of property in which instance n is the probable life of the unit and x is its age.

Appendix C.2 presents the expectancy-life factors for group properties for the L_2, S_2, and R_2 Iowa type curves. These factors are for the unit summation procedure of calculation (see Sec. 11.7 and Table 11.1), which produces a weighted factor on the basis of treating each year's retirement as though it were one unit.

Appendix C.3 presents the expectancy-life factors for group properties for the L_2, S_2, and R_2 Iowa type curves for the average life and unit summation calculation procedures (see Sec. 11.7 and Tables 11.1 and 11.2) at 0 percent rate of return. The average-life factors correspond to the results obtained in the usual application of the straight-line accounting procedure to group accounts. By this procedure, the depreciation base of the units retired at ages less than average life is not fully recovered at their date of retirement; the recovery on the units serving longer than average life is greater than their base. The unit-summation factors result when each unit in the group is assumed to build up its own 100 percent reserve by the date of its retirement. Table C.3 may be applied to any average service life because the expectancy-life factor is the same for all average service lives at identical ages when expressed as a percentage of average service life.

The single unit tables C.1 were published for all ages and probable lives from 1 to 100 for rates of 0, 2, 3, 4, 5, 6, 7, and 8 percent by Anson Marston and Thomas R. Agg in "Engineering Valuation," 1st ed., McGraw-Hill Book Company, Inc., 1936, and by Robley Winfrey, "Condition-Percent Tables for Depreciation of Unit and Group Properties," Iowa State College, Engineering Experiment Station, Bulletin 156, 1942.

The unit summation tables C.2 for each of the 18 Iowa type curves for 10, 20, 25, 30, 40, and 50 years average service lives and 0, 2, 4, 6, and 8 percent rates were published in Bulletin 156 referenced in the preceding paragraph.

The expectancy-life factors in Table C.3 are from unpublished work of Robley Winfrey for the Engineering Experiment Station, Iowa State College.

TABLE C.1. EXPECTANCY-LIFE FACTORS FOR UNIT PROPERTIES
0 Percent Interest Rate

1–10 years probable life

Age, years	1	2	3	4	5	6	7	8	9	10	Age, years
1	0.000000	0.500000	0.666667	0.750000	0.800000	0.833333	0.857143	0.875000	0.888889	0.900000	1
2		0.000000	0.333333	0.500000	0.600000	0.666667	0.714286	0.750000	0.777778	0.800000	2
3			0.000000	0.250000	0.400000	0.500000	0.571429	0.625000	0.666667	0.700000	3
4				0.000000	0.200000	0.333333	0.428571	0.500000	0.555556	0.600000	4
5					0.000000	0.166667	0.285714	0.375000	0.444444	0.500000	5
6						0.000000	0.142857	0.250000	0.333333	0.400000	6
7							0.000000	0.125000	0.222222	0.300000	7
8								0.000000	0.111111	0.200000	8
9									0.000000	0.100000	9
10										0.000000	10

11–20 years probable life

Age, years	11	12	13	14	15	16	17	18	19	20	Age, years
1	0.909091	0.916667	0.923077	0.928571	0.933333	0.937500	0.941176	0.944444	0.947368	0.950000	1
2	0.818182	0.833333	0.846154	0.857143	0.866667	0.875000	0.882353	0.888889	0.894737	0.900000	2
3	0.727273	0.750000	0.769231	0.785714	0.800000	0.812500	0.823529	0.833333	0.842105	0.850000	3
4	0.636364	0.666667	0.692308	0.714286	0.733333	0.750000	0.764706	0.777778	0.789474	0.800000	4
5	0.545455	0.583333	0.615385	0.642857	0.666667	0.687500	0.705882	0.722222	0.736842	0.750000	5
6	0.454545	0.500000	0.538462	0.571429	0.600000	0.625000	0.647059	0.666667	0.684211	0.700000	6
7	0.363636	0.416667	0.461538	0.500000	0.533333	0.562500	0.588235	0.611111	0.631579	0.650000	7
8	0.272727	0.333333	0.384615	0.428571	0.466667	0.500000	0.529412	0.555556	0.578947	0.600000	8
9	0.181818	0.250000	0.307692	0.357143	0.400000	0.437500	0.470588	0.500000	0.526316	0.550000	9
10	0.090909	0.166667	0.230769	0.285714	0.333333	0.375000	0.411765	0.444444	0.473684	0.500000	10
11	0.000000	0.083333	0.153846	0.214286	0.266667	0.312500	0.352941	0.388889	0.421053	0.450000	11
12		0.000000	0.076923	0.142857	0.200000	0.250000	0.294118	0.333333	0.368421	0.400000	12
13			0.000000	0.071429	0.133333	0.187500	0.235294	0.277778	0.315789	0.350000	13
14				0.000000	0.066667	0.125000	0.176471	0.222222	0.263158	0.300000	14
15					0.000000	0.062500	0.117647	0.166667	0.210526	0.250000	15
16						0.000000	0.058824	0.111111	0.157895	0.200000	16
17							0.000000	0.055556	0.105263	0.150000	17
18								0.000000	0.052632	0.100000	18
19									0.000000	0.050000	19
20										0.000000	20

21–30 years probable life

Age, years	21	22	23	24	25	26	27	28	29	30	Age, years
1	0.952381	0.954545	0.956522	0.958333	0.960000	0.961538	0.962963	0.964286	0.965517	0.966667	1
2	0.904762	0.909091	0.913043	0.916667	0.920000	0.923077	0.925926	0.928571	0.931034	0.933333	2
3	0.857143	0.863636	0.869565	0.875000	0.880000	0.884615	0.888889	0.892857	0.896552	0.900000	3
4	0.809524	0.818182	0.826087	0.833333	0.840000	0.846154	0.851852	0.857143	0.862069	0.866667	4
5	0.761905	0.772727	0.782609	0.791667	0.800000	0.807692	0.814815	0.821429	0.827586	0.833333	5
6	0.714286	0.727273	0.739130	0.750000	0.760000	0.769231	0.777778	0.785714	0.793103	0.800000	6
7	0.666667	0.681818	0.695652	0.708333	0.720000	0.730769	0.740741	0.750000	0.758621	0.766667	7
8	0.619048	0.636364	0.652174	0.666667	0.680000	0.692308	0.703704	0.714286	0.724138	0.733333	8
9	0.571429	0.590909	0.608696	0.625000	0.640000	0.653846	0.666667	0.678571	0.689655	0.700000	9
10	0.523810	0.545455	0.565217	0.583333	0.600000	0.615385	0.629630	0.642857	0.655172	0.666667	10
11	0.476190	0.500000	0.521739	0.541667	0.560000	0.576923	0.592593	0.607143	0.620690	0.633333	11
12	0.428571	0.454545	0.478261	0.500000	0.520000	0.538462	0.555556	0.571429	0.586207	0.600000	12
13	0.380952	0.409091	0.434783	0.458333	0.480000	0.500000	0.518519	0.535714	0.551724	0.566667	13
14	0.333333	0.363636	0.391304	0.416667	0.440000	0.461538	0.481481	0.500000	0.517241	0.533333	14
15	0.285714	0.318182	0.347826	0.375000	0.400000	0.423077	0.444444	0.464286	0.482759	0.500000	15

TABLE C.1.   EXPECTANCY-LIFE FACTORS FOR UNIT PROPERTIES
0 Percent Interest Rate (Continued)

21–30 years probable life

Age, years	21	22	23	24	25	26	27	28	29	30	Age, years
16	0.238095	0.272727	0.304348	0.333333	0.360000	0.384615	0.407407	0.428571	0.448276	0.466667	16
17	0.190476	0.227273	0.260870	0.291667	0.320000	0.346154	0.370370	0.392857	0.413793	0.433333	17
18	0.142857	0.181818	0.217391	0.250000	0.280000	0.307692	0.333333	0.357143	0.379310	0.400000	18
19	0.095238	0.136364	0.173913	0.208333	0.240000	0.269231	0.296296	0.321429	0.344828	0.366667	19
20	0.047619	0.090909	0.130435	0.166667	0.200000	0.230769	0.259259	0.285714	0.310345	0.333333	20
21	0.000000	0.045455	0.086957	0.125000	0.160000	0.192308	0.222222	0.250000	0.275862	0.300000	21
22		0.000000	0.043478	0.083333	0.120000	0.153846	0.185185	0.214286	0.241379	0.266667	22
23			0.000000	0.041667	0.080000	0.115385	0.148148	0.178571	0.206897	0.233333	23
24				0.000000	0.040000	0.076923	0.111111	0.142857	0.172414	0.200000	24
25					0.000000	0.038462	0.074074	0.107143	0.137931	0.166667	25
26						0.000000	0.037037	0.071429	0.103448	0.133333	26
27							0.000000	0.035714	0.068966	0.100000	27
28								0.000000	0.034483	0.066667	28
29									0.000000	0.033333	29
30										0.000000	30

31–40 years probable life

Age, years	31	32	33	34	35	36	37	38	39	40	Age, years
1	0.967742	0.968750	0.969697	0.970588	0.971429	0.972222	0.972973	0.973684	0.974359	0.975000	1
2	0.935484	0.937500	0.939394	0.941176	0.942857	0.944444	0.945946	0.947368	0.948718	0.950000	2
3	0.903226	0.906250	0.909091	0.911765	0.914286	0.916667	0.918919	0.921053	0.923077	0.925000	3
4	0.870968	0.875000	0.878788	0.882353	0.885714	0.888889	0.891892	0.894737	0.897436	0.900000	4
5	0.838710	0.843750	0.848485	0.852941	0.857143	0.861111	0.864865	0.868421	0.871795	0.875000	5
6	0.806452	0.812500	0.818182	0.823529	0.828571	0.833333	0.837838	0.842105	0.846154	0.850000	6
7	0.774194	0.781250	0.787879	0.794118	0.800000	0.805556	0.810811	0.815789	0.820513	0.825000	7
8	0.741935	0.750000	0.757576	0.764706	0.771429	0.777778	0.783784	0.789474	0.794872	0.800000	8
9	0.709677	0.718750	0.727273	0.735294	0.742857	0.750000	0.756757	0.763158	0.769231	0.775000	9
10	0.677419	0.687500	0.696970	0.705882	0.714286	0.722222	0.729730	0.736842	0.743590	0.750000	10
11	0.645161	0.656250	0.666667	0.676471	0.685714	0.694444	0.702703	0.710526	0.717949	0.725000	11
12	0.612903	0.625000	0.636364	0.647059	0.657143	0.666667	0.675676	0.684211	0.692308	0.700000	12
13	0.580645	0.593750	0.606061	0.617647	0.628571	0.638889	0.648649	0.657895	0.666667	0.675000	13
14	0.548387	0.562500	0.575758	0.588235	0.600000	0.611111	0.621622	0.631579	0.641026	0.650000	14
15	0.516129	0.531250	0.545455	0.558824	0.571429	0.583333	0.594595	0.605263	0.615385	0.625000	15
16	0.483871	0.500000	0.515152	0.529412	0.542857	0.555556	0.567568	0.578947	0.589744	0.600000	16
17	0.451613	0.468750	0.484848	0.500000	0.514286	0.527778	0.540541	0.552632	0.564103	0.575000	17
18	0.419355	0.437500	0.454545	0.470588	0.485714	0.500000	0.513514	0.526316	0.538462	0.550000	18
19	0.387097	0.406250	0.424242	0.441176	0.457143	0.472222	0.486486	0.500000	0.512821	0.525000	19
20	0.354839	0.375000	0.393939	0.411765	0.428571	0.444444	0.459459	0.473684	0.487179	0.500000	20
21	0.322581	0.343750	0.363636	0.382353	0.400000	0.416667	0.432432	0.447368	0.461538	0.475000	21
22	0.290323	0.312500	0.333333	0.352941	0.371429	0.388889	0.405405	0.421053	0.435897	0.450000	22
23	0.258065	0.281250	0.303030	0.323529	0.342857	0.361111	0.378378	0.394737	0.410256	0.425000	23
24	0.225806	0.250000	0.272727	0.294118	0.314286	0.333333	0.351351	0.368421	0.384615	0.400000	24
25	0.193548	0.218750	0.242424	0.264706	0.285714	0.305556	0.324324	0.342105	0.358974	0.375000	25
26	0.161290	0.187500	0.212121	0.235294	0.257143	0.277778	0.297297	0.315789	0.333333	0.350000	26
27	0.129032	0.156250	0.181818	0.205882	0.228571	0.250000	0.270270	0.289474	0.307692	0.325000	27
28	0.096774	0.125000	0.151515	0.176471	0.200000	0.222222	0.243243	0.263158	0.282051	0.300000	28
29	0.064516	0.093750	0.121212	0.147059	0.171429	0.194444	0.216216	0.236842	0.256410	0.275000	29
30	0.032258	0.062500	0.090909	0.117647	0.142857	0.166667	0.189189	0.210526	0.230769	0.250000	30
31	0.000000	0.031250	0.060606	0.088235	0.114286	0.138889	0.162162	0.184211	0.205128	0.225000	31
32		0.000000	0.030303	0.058824	0.085714	0.111111	0.135135	0.157895	0.179487	0.200000	32
33			0.000000	0.029412	0.057143	0.083333	0.108108	0.131579	0.153846	0.175000	33
34				0.000000	0.028571	0.055556	0.081081	0.105263	0.128205	0.150000	34
35					0.000000	0.027778	0.054054	0.078947	0.102564	0.125000	35
36						0.000000	0.027027	0.052632	0.076923	0.100000	36
37							0.000000	0.026316	0.051282	0.075000	37
38								0.000000	0.025641	0.050000	38
39									0.000000	0.025000	39
40										0.000000	40

TABLE C.1. EXPECTANCY-LIFE FACTORS FOR UNIT PROPERTIES
0 Percent Interest Rate (*Continued*)

41–50 years probable life

Age, years	41	42	43	44	45	46	47	48	49	50	Age, years
1	0.975610	0.976190	0.976744	0.977273	0.977778	0.978261	0.978723	0.979167	0.979592	0.980000	1
2	0.951220	0.952381	0.953488	0.954545	0.955556	0.956522	0.957447	0.958333	0.959184	0.960000	2
3	0.926829	0.928571	0.930233	0.931818	0.933333	0.934783	0.936170	0.937500	0.938776	0.940000	3
4	0.902439	0.904762	0.906977	0.909091	0.911111	0.913043	0.914894	0.916667	0.918367	0.920000	4
5	0.878049	0.880952	0.883721	0.886364	0.888889	0.891304	0.893617	0.895833	0.897959	0.900000	5
6	0.853659	0.857143	0.860465	0.863636	0.866667	0.869565	0.872340	0.875000	0.877551	0.880000	6
7	0.829268	0.833333	0.837209	0.840909	0.844444	0.847826	0.851064	0.854167	0.857143	0.860000	7
8	0.804878	0.809524	0.813953	0.818182	0.822222	0.826087	0.829787	0.833333	0.836735	0.840000	8
9	0.780488	0.785714	0.790698	0.795455	0.800000	0.804348	0.808511	0.812500	0.816327	0.820000	9
10	0.756098	0.761905	0.767442	0.772727	0.777778	0.782609	0.787234	0.791667	0.795918	0.800000	10
11	0.731707	0.738095	0.744186	0.750000	0.755556	0.760870	0.765957	0.770833	0.775510	0.780000	11
12	0.707317	0.714286	0.720930	0.727273	0.733333	0.739130	0.744681	0.750000	0.755102	0.760000	12
13	0.682927	0.690476	0.697674	0.704545	0.711111	0.717391	0.723404	0.729167	0.734694	0.740000	13
14	0.658537	0.666667	0.674419	0.681818	0.688889	0.695652	0.702128	0.708333	0.714286	0.720000	14
15	0.634146	0.642857	0.651163	0.659091	0.666667	0.673913	0.680851	0.687500	0.693878	0.700000	15
16	0.609756	0.619048	0.627907	0.636364	0.644444	0.652174	0.659574	0.666667	0.673469	0.680000	16
17	0.585366	0.595238	0.604651	0.613636	0.622222	0.630435	0.638298	0.645833	0.653061	0.660000	17
18	0.560976	0.571429	0.581395	0.590909	0.600000	0.608696	0.617021	0.625000	0.632653	0.640000	18
19	0.536585	0.547619	0.558140	0.568182	0.577778	0.586957	0.595745	0.604167	0.612245	0.620000	19
20	0.512195	0.523810	0.534884	0.545455	0.555556	0.565217	0.574468	0.583333	0.591837	0.600000	20
21	0.487805	0.500000	0.511628	0.522727	0.533333	0.543478	0.553191	0.562500	0.571429	0.580000	21
22	0.463415	0.476190	0.488372	0.500000	0.511111	0.521739	0.531915	0.541667	0.551020	0.560000	22
23	0.439024	0.452381	0.465116	0.477273	0.488889	0.500000	0.510638	0.520833	0.530612	0.540000	23
24	0.414634	0.428571	0.441860	0.454545	0.466667	0.478261	0.489362	0.500000	0.510204	0.520000	24
25	0.390244	0.404762	0.418605	0.431818	0.444444	0.456522	0.468085	0.479167	0.489796	0.500000	25
26	0.365854	0.380952	0.395349	0.409091	0.422222	0.434783	0.446809	0.458333	0.469388	0.480000	26
27	0.341463	0.357143	0.372093	0.386364	0.400000	0.413043	0.425532	0.437500	0.448980	0.460000	27
28	0.317073	0.333333	0.348837	0.363636	0.377778	0.391304	0.404255	0.416667	0.428571	0.440000	28
29	0.292683	0.309524	0.325581	0.340909	0.355556	0.369565	0.382979	0.395833	0.408163	0.420000	29
30	0.268293	0.285714	0.302326	0.318182	0.333333	0.347826	0.361702	0.375000	0.387755	0.400000	30
31	0.243902	0.261905	0.279070	0.295455	0.311111	0.326087	0.340426	0.354167	0.367347	0.380000	31
32	0.219512	0.238095	0.255814	0.272727	0.288889	0.304348	0.319149	0.333333	0.346939	0.360000	32
33	0.195122	0.214286	0.232558	0.250000	0.266667	0.282609	0.297872	0.312500	0.326531	0.340000	33
34	0.170732	0.190476	0.209302	0.227273	0.244444	0.260870	0.276596	0.291667	0.306122	0.320000	34
35	0.146341	0.166667	0.186047	0.204545	0.222222	0.239130	0.255319	0.270833	0.285714	0.300000	35
36	0.121951	0.142857	0.162791	0.181818	0.200000	0.217391	0.234043	0.250000	0.265306	0.280000	36
37	0.097561	0.119048	0.139535	0.159091	0.177778	0.195652	0.212766	0.229167	0.244898	0.260000	37
38	0.073171	0.095238	0.116279	0.136364	0.155556	0.173913	0.191489	0.208333	0.224490	0.240000	38
39	0.048780	0.071429	0.093023	0.113636	0.133333	0.152174	0.170213	0.187500	0.204082	0.220000	39
40	0.024390	0.047619	0.069767	0.090909	0.111111	0.130435	0.148936	0.166667	0.183673	0.200000	40
41	0.000000	0.023810	0.046512	0.068182	0.088889	0.108696	0.127660	0.145833	0.163265	0.180000	41
42		0.000000	0.023256	0.045455	0.066667	0.086957	0.106383	0.125000	0.142857	0.160000	42
43			0.000000	0.022727	0.044444	0.065217	0.085106	0.104167	0.122449	0.140000	43
44				0.000000	0.022222	0.043478	0.063830	0.083333	0.102041	0.120000	44
45					0.000000	0.021739	0.042553	0.062500	0.081633	0.100000	45
46						0.000000	0.021277	0.041667	0.061225	0.080000	46
47							0.000000	0.020833	0.040816	0.060000	47
48								0.000000	0.020408	0.040000	48
49									0.000000	0.020000	49
50										0.000000	50

TABLE C.1.　EXPECTANCY-LIFE FACTORS FOR UNIT PROPERTIES
0 Percent Interest Rate (Continued)

51–60 years probable life

Age, years	51	52	53	54	55	56	57	58	59	60	Age, years
1	0.980392	0.980769	0.981132	0.981481	0.981818	0.982143	0.982456	0.982759	0.983051	0.983333	1
2	0.960784	0.961538	0.962264	0.962963	0.963636	0.964286	0.964912	0.965517	0.966102	0.966667	2
3	0.941176	0.942308	0.943396	0.944444	0.945455	0.946429	0.947368	0.948276	0.949153	0.950000	3
4	0.921569	0.923077	0.924528	0.925926	0.927273	0.928571	0.929825	0.931034	0.932203	0.933333	4
5	0.901961	0.903846	0.905660	0.907407	0.909091	0.910714	0.912281	0.913793	0.915254	0.916667	5
6	0.882353	0.884615	0.886792	0.888889	0.890909	0.892857	0.894737	0.896552	0.898305	0.900000	6
7	0.862745	0.865385	0.867925	0.870370	0.872727	0.875000	0.877193	0.879310	0.881356	0.883333	7
8	0.843137	0.846154	0.849057	0.851852	0.854545	0.857143	0.859649	0.862069	0.864407	0.866667	8
9	0.823529	0.826923	0.830189	0.833333	0.836364	0.839286	0.842105	0.844828	0.847458	0.850000	9
10	0.803922	0.807692	0.811321	0.814815	0.818182	0.821429	0.824561	0.827586	0.830508	0.833333	10
11	0.784314	0.788462	0.792453	0.796296	0.800000	0.803571	0.807018	0.810345	0.813559	0.816667	11
12	0.764706	0.769231	0.773585	0.777778	0.781818	0.785714	0.789474	0.793103	0.796610	0.800000	12
13	0.745098	0.750000	0.754717	0.759259	0.763636	0.767857	0.771930	0.775862	0.779661	0.783333	13
14	0.725490	0.730769	0.735849	0.740741	0.745455	0.750000	0.754386	0.758621	0.762712	0.766667	14
15	0.705882	0.711538	0.716981	0.722222	0.727273	0.732143	0.736842	0.741379	0.745763	0.750000	15
16	0.686275	0.692308	0.698113	0.703704	0.709091	0.714286	0.719298	0.724138	0.728814	0.733333	16
17	0.666667	0.673077	0.679245	0.685185	0.690909	0.696429	0.701754	0.706897	0.711864	0.716667	17
18	0.647059	0.653846	0.660377	0.666667	0.672727	0.678571	0.684211	0.689655	0.694915	0.700000	18
19	0.627451	0.634615	0.641509	0.648148	0.654545	0.660714	0.666667	0.672414	0.677966	0.683333	19
20	0.607843	0.615385	0.622642	0.629630	0.636364	0.642857	0.649123	0.655172	0.661017	0.666667	20
21	0.588235	0.596154	0.603774	0.611111	0.618182	0.625000	0.631579	0.637931	0.644068	0.650000	21
22	0.568627	0.576923	0.584906	0.592593	0.600000	0.607143	0.614035	0.620690	0.627119	0.633333	22
23	0.549020	0.557692	0.566038	0.574074	0.581818	0.589286	0.596491	0.603448	0.610169	0.616667	23
24	0.529412	0.538462	0.547170	0.555556	0.563636	0.571429	0.578947	0.586207	0.593220	0.600000	24
25	0.509804	0.519231	0.528302	0.537037	0.545455	0.553571	0.561404	0.568966	0.576271	0.583333	25
26	0.490196	0.500000	0.509434	0.518519	0.527273	0.535714	0.543860	0.551724	0.559322	0.566667	26
27	0.470588	0.480769	0.490566	0.500000	0.509091	0.517857	0.526316	0.534483	0.542373	0.550000	27
28	0.450980	0.461538	0.471698	0.481481	0.490909	0.500000	0.508772	0.517241	0.525424	0.533333	28
29	0.431373	0.442308	0.452830	0.462963	0.472727	0.482143	0.491228	0.500000	0.508475	0.516667	29
30	0.411765	0.423077	0.433962	0.444444	0.454545	0.464286	0.473684	0.482759	0.491525	0.500000	30
31	0.392157	0.403846	0.415094	0.425926	0.436364	0.446429	0.456140	0.465517	0.474576	0.483333	31
32	0.372549	0.384615	0.396226	0.407407	0.418182	0.428571	0.438596	0.448276	0.457627	0.466667	32
33	0.352941	0.365385	0.377358	0.388889	0.400000	0.410714	0.421053	0.431034	0.440678	0.450000	33
34	0.333333	0.346154	0.358491	0.370370	0.381818	0.392857	0.403509	0.413793	0.423729	0.433333	34
35	0.313725	0.326923	0.339623	0.351852	0.363636	0.375000	0.385965	0.396552	0.406780	0.416667	35
36	0.294118	0.307692	0.320755	0.333333	0.345455	0.357143	0.368421	0.379310	0.389830	0.400000	36
37	0.274510	0.288462	0.301887	0.314815	0.327273	0.339286	0.350877	0.362069	0.372881	0.383333	37
38	0.254902	0.269231	0.283019	0.296296	0.309091	0.321429	0.333333	0.344828	0.355932	0.366667	38
39	0.235294	0.250000	0.264151	0.277778	0.290909	0.303571	0.315789	0.327586	0.338983	0.350000	39
40	0.215686	0.230769	0.245283	0.259259	0.272727	0.285714	0.298246	0.310345	0.322034	0.333333	40
41	0.196078	0.211538	0.226415	0.240741	0.254545	0.267857	0.280702	0.293103	0.305085	0.316667	41
42	0.176471	0.192308	0.207547	0.222222	0.236364	0.250000	0.263158	0.275862	0.288136	0.300000	42
43	0.156863	0.173077	0.188679	0.203704	0.218182	0.232143	0.245614	0.258621	0.271186	0.283333	43
44	0.137255	0.153846	0.169811	0.185185	0.200000	0.214286	0.228070	0.241379	0.254237	0.266667	44
45	0.117647	0.134615	0.150943	0.166667	0.181818	0.196429	0.210526	0.224138	0.237288	0.250000	45
46	0.098039	0.115385	0.132075	0.148148	0.163636	0.178571	0.192982	0.206897	0.220339	0.233333	46
47	0.078431	0.096154	0.113208	0.129630	0.145455	0.160714	0.175439	0.189655	0.203390	0.216667	47
48	0.058824	0.076923	0.094340	0.111111	0.127273	0.142857	0.157895	0.172414	0.186441	0.200000	48
49	0.039216	0.057692	0.075472	0.092593	0.109091	0.125000	0.140351	0.155172	0.169492	0.183333	49
50	0.019608	0.038462	0.056604	0.074074	0.090909	0.107143	0.122807	0.137931	0.152542	0.166667	50
51	0.000000	0.019231	0.037736	0.055556	0.072727	0.089286	0.105263	0.120690	0.135593	0.150000	51
52		0.000000	0.018868	0.037037	0.054545	0.071429	0.087719	0.103448	0.118644	0.133333	52
53			0.000000	0.018518	0.036364	0.053571	0.070175	0.086207	0.101695	0.116667	53
54				0.000000	0.018182	0.035714	0.052632	0.068966	0.084746	0.100000	54
55					0.000000	0.017857	0.035088	0.051724	0.067797	0.083333	55
56						0.000000	0.017544	0.034483	0.050847	0.066667	56
57							0.000000	0.017241	0.033898	0.050000	57
58								0.000000	0.016949	0.033333	58
59									0.000000	0.016667	59
60										0.000000	60

TABLE C.1. EXPECTANCY-LIFE FACTORS FOR UNIT PROPERTIES
0 Percent Interest Rate (Continued)

					61–70 years probable life						
Age, years	61	62	63	64	65	66	67	68	69	70	Age, years
1	0.983607	0.983871	0.984127	0.984375	0.984615	0.984848	0.985075	0.985294	0.985507	0.985714	1
2	0.967213	0.967742	0.968254	0.968750	0.969231	0.969697	0.970149	0.970588	0.971014	0.971429	2
3	0.950820	0.951613	0.952381	0.953125	0.953846	0.954545	0.955224	0.955882	0.956522	0.957143	3
4	0.934426	0.935484	0.936508	0.937500	0.938462	0.939394	0.940299	0.941176	0.942029	0.942857	4
5	0.918033	0.919355	0.920635	0.921875	0.923077	0.924242	0.925373	0.926471	0.927536	0.928571	5
6	0.901639	0.903226	0.904762	0.906250	0.907692	0.909091	0.910448	0.911765	0.913043	0.914286	6
7	0.885246	0.887097	0.888889	0.890625	0.892308	0.893939	0.895522	0.897059	0.898551	0.900000	7
8	0.868852	0.870968	0.873016	0.875000	0.876923	0.878788	0.880597	0.882353	0.884058	0.885714	8
9	0.852459	0.854839	0.857143	0.859375	0.861538	0.863636	0.865672	0.867647	0.869565	0.871429	9
10	0.836066	0.838710	0.841270	0.843750	0.846154	0.848485	0.850746	0.852941	0.855072	0.857143	10
11	0.819672	0.822581	0.825397	0.828125	0.830769	0.833333	0.835821	0.838235	0.840580	0.842857	11
12	0.803279	0.806452	0.809524	0.812500	0.815385	0.818182	0.820896	0.823529	0.826087	0.828571	12
13	0.786885	0.790323	0.793651	0.796875	0.800000	0.803030	0.805970	0.808824	0.811594	0.814286	13
14	0.770492	0.774194	0.777778	0.781250	0.784615	0.787879	0.791045	0.794118	0.797101	0.800000	14
15	0.754098	0.758065	0.761905	0.765625	0.769231	0.772727	0.776119	0.779412	0.782609	0.785714	15
16	0.737705	0.741935	0.746032	0.750000	0.753846	0.757576	0.761194	0.764706	0.768116	0.771429	16
17	0.721311	0.725806	0.730159	0.734375	0.738462	0.742424	0.746269	0.750000	0.753623	0.757143	17
18	0.704918	0.709677	0.714286	0.718750	0.723077	0.727273	0.731343	0.735294	0.739130	0.742857	18
19	0.688525	0.693548	0.698413	0.703125	0.707692	0.712121	0.716418	0.720588	0.724638	0.728571	19
20	0.672131	0.677419	0.682540	0.687500	0.692308	0.696970	0.701493	0.705882	0.710145	0.714286	20
21	0.655738	0.661290	0.666667	0.671875	0.676923	0.681818	0.686567	0.691176	0.695652	0.700000	21
22	0.639344	0.645161	0.650794	0.656250	0.661538	0.666667	0.671642	0.676471	0.681159	0.685714	22
23	0.622951	0.629032	0.634921	0.640625	0.646154	0.651515	0.656716	0.661765	0.666667	0.671429	23
24	0.606557	0.612903	0.619048	0.625000	0.630769	0.636364	0.641791	0.647059	0.652174	0.657143	24
25	0.590164	0.596774	0.603175	0.609375	0.615385	0.621212	0.626866	0.632353	0.637681	0.642857	25
26	0.573770	0.580645	0.587302	0.593750	0.600000	0.606061	0.611940	0.617647	0.623188	0.628571	26
27	0.557377	0.564516	0.571429	0.578125	0.584615	0.590909	0.597015	0.602941	0.608696	0.614286	27
28	0.540984	0.548387	0.555556	0.562500	0.569231	0.575758	0.582090	0.588235	0.594203	0.600000	28
29	0.524590	0.532258	0.539683	0.546875	0.553846	0.560606	0.567164	0.573529	0.579710	0.585714	29
30	0.508197	0.516129	0.523810	0.531250	0.538462	0.545455	0.552239	0.558824	0.565217	0.571429	30
31	0.491803	0.500000	0.507937	0.515625	0.523077	0.530303	0.537313	0.544118	0.550725	0.557143	31
32	0.475410	0.483871	0.492063	0.500000	0.507692	0.515152	0.522388	0.529412	0.536232	0.542857	32
33	0.459016	0.467742	0.476190	0.484375	0.492308	0.500000	0.507463	0.514706	0.521739	0.528571	33
34	0.442623	0.451613	0.460317	0.468750	0.476923	0.484848	0.492537	0.500000	0.507246	0.514286	34
35	0.426229	0.435484	0.444444	0.453125	0.461538	0.469697	0.477612	0.485294	0.492754	0.500000	35
36	0.409836	0.419355	0.428571	0.437500	0.446154	0.454545	0.462687	0.470588	0.478261	0.485714	36
37	0.393443	0.403226	0.412698	0.421875	0.430769	0.439394	0.447761	0.455882	0.463768	0.471429	37
38	0.377049	0.387097	0.396825	0.406250	0.415385	0.424242	0.432836	0.441176	0.449275	0.457143	38
39	0.360656	0.370968	0.380952	0.390625	0.400000	0.409091	0.417910	0.426471	0.434783	0.442857	39
40	0.344262	0.354839	0.365079	0.375000	0.384615	0.393939	0.402985	0.411765	0.420290	0.428571	40
41	0.327869	0.338710	0.349206	0.359375	0.369231	0.378788	0.388060	0.397059	0.405797	0.414286	41
42	0.311475	0.322581	0.333333	0.343750	0.353846	0.363636	0.373134	0.382353	0.391304	0.400000	42
43	0.295082	0.306452	0.317460	0.328125	0.338462	0.348485	0.358209	0.367647	0.376812	0.385714	43
44	0.278689	0.290323	0.301587	0.312500	0.323077	0.333333	0.343284	0.352941	0.362319	0.371429	44
45	0.262295	0.274194	0.285714	0.296875	0.307692	0.318182	0.328358	0.338235	0.347826	0.357143	45
46	0.245902	0.258065	0.269841	0.281250	0.292308	0.303030	0.313433	0.323529	0.333333	0.342857	46
47	0.229508	0.241935	0.253968	0.265625	0.276923	0.287879	0.298507	0.308824	0.318841	0.328571	47
48	0.213115	0.225806	0.238095	0.250000	0.261538	0.272727	0.283582	0.294118	0.304348	0.314286	48
49	0.196721	0.209677	0.222222	0.234375	0.246154	0.257576	0.268657	0.279412	0.289855	0.300000	49
50	0.180328	0.193548	0.206349	0.218750	0.230769	0.242424	0.253731	0.264706	0.275362	0.285714	50
51	0.163934	0.177419	0.190476	0.203125	0.215385	0.227273	0.238806	0.250000	0.260870	0.271429	51
52	0.147541	0.161290	0.174603	0.187500	0.200000	0.212121	0.223881	0.235294	0.246377	0.257143	52
53	0.131148	0.145161	0.158730	0.171875	0.184615	0.196970	0.208955	0.220588	0.231884	0.242857	53
54	0.114754	0.129032	0.142857	0.156250	0.169231	0.181818	0.194030	0.205882	0.217391	0.228571	54
55	0.098361	0.112903	0.126984	0.140625	0.153846	0.166667	0.179104	0.191176	0.202899	0.214286	55
56	0.081967	0.096774	0.111111	0.125000	0.138462	0.151515	0.164179	0.176471	0.188406	0.200000	56
57	0.065574	0.080645	0.095238	0.109375	0.123077	0.136364	0.149254	0.161765	0.173913	0.185714	57
58	0.049180	0.064516	0.079365	0.093750	0.107692	0.121212	0.134328	0.147059	0.159420	0.171429	58
59	0.032787	0.048387	0.063492	0.078125	0.092308	0.106061	0.119403	0.132353	0.144928	0.157143	59
60	0.016393	0.032258	0.047619	0.062500	0.076923	0.090909	0.104478	0.117647	0.130435	0.142857	60

TABLE C.1. EXPECTANCY-LIFE FACTORS FOR UNIT PROPERTIES
0 Percent Interest Rate (Continued)

Age, years	61	62	63	64	65	66	67	68	69	70	Age, years
						61–70 years probable life					
61	0.000000	0.016129	0.031746	0.046875	0.061538	0.075758	0.089552	0.102941	0.115942	0.128571	61
62		0.000000	0.015873	0.031250	0.046154	0.060606	0.074627	0.088235	0.101449	0.114286	62
63			0.000000	0.015625	0.030769	0.045455	0.059702	0.073529	0.086956	0.100000	63
64				0.000000	0.015385	0.030303	0.044776	0.058824	0.072464	0.085714	64
65					0.000000	0.015152	0.029851	0.044118	0.057971	0.071429	65
66						0.000000	0.014925	0.029412	0.043478	0.057143	66
67							0.000000	0.014706	0.028985	0.042857	67
68								0.000000	0.014493	0.028571	68
69									0.000000	0.014286	69
70										0.000000	70

Age, years	71	72	73	74	75	76	77	78	79	80	Age, years
						71–80 years probable life					
1	0.985915	0.986111	0.986301	0.986486	0.986667	0.986842	0.987013	0.987179	0.987342	0.987500	1
2	0.971831	0.972222	0.972603	0.972973	0.973333	0.973684	0.974026	0.974359	0.974684	0.975000	2
3	0.957746	0.958333	0.958904	0.959459	0.960000	0.960526	0.961039	0.961538	0.962025	0.962500	3
4	0.943662	0.944444	0.945205	0.945946	0.946667	0.947368	0.948052	0.948718	0.949367	0.950000	4
5	0.929577	0.930556	0.931507	0.932432	0.933333	0.934211	0.935065	0.935897	0.936709	0.937500	5
6	0.915493	0.916667	0.917808	0.918919	0.920000	0.921053	0.922078	0.923077	0.924051	0.925000	6
7	0.901408	0.902778	0.904110	0.905405	0.906667	0.907895	0.909091	0.910256	0.911392	0.912500	7
8	0.887324	0.888889	0.890411	0.891892	0.893333	0.894737	0.896104	0.897436	0.898734	0.900000	8
9	0.873239	0.875000	0.876712	0.878378	0.880000	0.881579	0.883117	0.884615	0.886076	0.887500	9
10	0.859155	0.861111	0.863014	0.864865	0.866667	0.868421	0.870130	0.871795	0.873418	0.875000	10
11	0.845070	0.847222	0.849315	0.851351	0.853333	0.855263	0.857143	0.858974	0.860759	0.862500	11
12	0.830986	0.833333	0.835616	0.837838	0.840000	0.842105	0.844156	0.846154	0.848101	0.850000	12
13	0.816901	0.819444	0.821918	0.824324	0.826667	0.828947	0.831169	0.833333	0.835443	0.837500	13
14	0.802817	0.805556	0.808219	0.810811	0.813333	0.815789	0.818182	0.820513	0.822785	0.825000	14
15	0.788732	0.791667	0.794521	0.797297	0.800000	0.802632	0.805195	0.807692	0.810127	0.812500	15
16	0.774648	0.777778	0.780822	0.783784	0.786667	0.789474	0.792208	0.794872	0.797468	0.800000	16
17	0.760563	0.763889	0.767123	0.770270	0.773333	0.776316	0.779221	0.782051	0.784810	0.787500	17
18	0.746479	0.750000	0.753425	0.756757	0.760000	0.763158	0.766234	0.769231	0.772152	0.775000	18
19	0.732394	0.736111	0.739726	0.743243	0.746667	0.750000	0.753247	0.756410	0.759494	0.762500	19
20	0.718310	0.722222	0.726027	0.729730	0.733333	0.736842	0.740260	0.743590	0.746835	0.750000	20
21	0.704225	0.708333	0.712329	0.716216	0.720000	0.723684	0.727273	0.730769	0.734177	0.737500	21
22	0.690141	0.694444	0.698630	0.702703	0.706667	0.710526	0.714286	0.717949	0.721519	0.725000	22
23	0.676056	0.680555	0.684932	0.689189	0.693333	0.697368	0.701299	0.705128	0.708861	0.712500	23
24	0.661972	0.666667	0.671233	0.675676	0.680000	0.684211	0.688312	0.692308	0.696203	0.700000	24
25	0.647887	0.652778	0.657534	0.662162	0.666667	0.671053	0.675325	0.679487	0.683544	0.687500	25
26	0.633803	0.638889	0.643836	0.648649	0.653333	0.657895	0.662338	0.666667	0.670886	0.675000	26
27	0.619718	0.625000	0.630137	0.635135	0.640000	0.644737	0.649351	0.653846	0.658228	0.662500	27
28	0.605634	0.611111	0.616438	0.621622	0.626667	0.631579	0.636364	0.641026	0.645570	0.650000	28
29	0.591549	0.597222	0.602740	0.608108	0.613333	0.618421	0.623377	0.628205	0.632911	0.637500	29
30	0.577465	0.583333	0.589041	0.594595	0.600000	0.605263	0.610390	0.615385	0.620253	0.625000	30
31	0.563380	0.569444	0.575342	0.581081	0.586667	0.592105	0.597403	0.602564	0.607595	0.612500	31
32	0.549296	0.555556	0.561644	0.567568	0.573333	0.578947	0.584416	0.589744	0.594937	0.600000	32
33	0.535211	0.541667	0.547945	0.554054	0.560000	0.565789	0.571429	0.576923	0.582278	0.587500	33
34	0.521127	0.527778	0.534247	0.540541	0.546667	0.552632	0.558442	0.564103	0.569620	0.575000	34
35	0.507042	0.513889	0.520548	0.527027	0.533333	0.539474	0.545455	0.551282	0.556962	0.562500	35
36	0.492958	0.500000	0.506849	0.513513	0.520000	0.526316	0.532468	0.538462	0.544304	0.550000	36
37	0.478873	0.486111	0.493151	0.500000	0.506667	0.513158	0.519481	0.525641	0.531646	0.537500	37
38	0.464789	0.472222	0.479452	0.486486	0.493333	0.500000	0.506494	0.512821	0.518987	0.525000	38
39	0.450704	0.458333	0.465753	0.472973	0.480000	0.486842	0.493506	0.500000	0.506329	0.512500	39
40	0.436620	0.444444	0.452055	0.459459	0.466667	0.473684	0.480519	0.487179	0.493671	0.500000	40
41	0.422535	0.430556	0.438356	0.445946	0.453333	0.460526	0.467532	0.474359	0.481013	0.487500	41
42	0.408451	0.416667	0.424658	0.432432	0.440000	0.447368	0.454545	0.461538	0.468354	0.475000	42
43	0.394366	0.402778	0.410959	0.418919	0.426667	0.434211	0.441558	0.448718	0.455696	0.462500	43
44	0.380282	0.388889	0.397260	0.405405	0.413333	0.421053	0.428571	0.435897	0.443038	0.450000	44
45	0.366197	0.375000	0.383562	0.391892	0.400000	0.407895	0.415584	0.423077	0.430380	0.437500	45

TABLE C.1. EXPECTANCY-LIFE FACTORS FOR UNIT PROPERTIES
0 Percent Interest Rate (*Continued*)

71–80 years probable life

Age, years	71	72	73	74	75	76	77	78	79	80	Age, years
46	0.352113	0.361111	0.369863	0.378378	0.386667	0.394737	0.402597	0.410256	0.417722	0.425000	46
47	0.338028	0.347222	0.356164	0.364865	0.373333	0.381579	0.389610	0.397436	0.405063	0.412500	47
48	0.323944	0.333333	0.342466	0.351351	0.360000	0.368421	0.376623	0.384615	0.392405	0.400000	48
49	0.309859	0.319444	0.328767	0.337838	0.346667	0.355263	0.363636	0.371795	0.379747	0.387500	49
50	0.295775	0.305556	0.315069	0.324324	0.333333	0.342105	0.350649	0.358974	0.367089	0.375000	50
51	0.281690	0.291667	0.301370	0.310811	0.320000	0.328947	0.337662	0.346154	0.354430	0.362500	51
52	0.267606	0.277778	0.287671	0.297297	0.306667	0.315789	0.324675	0.333333	0.341772	0.350000	52
53	0.253521	0.263889	0.273973	0.283784	0.293333	0.302632	0.311688	0.320513	0.329114	0.337500	53
54	0.239437	0.250000	0.260274	0.270270	0.280000	0.289474	0.298701	0.307692	0.316456	0.325000	54
55	0.225352	0.236111	0.246575	0.256757	0.266667	0.276316	0.285714	0.294872	0.303797	0.312500	55
56	0.211268	0.222222	0.232877	0.243243	0.253333	0.263158	0.272727	0.282051	0.291139	0.300000	56
57	0.197183	0.208333	0.219178	0.229730	0.240000	0.250000	0.259740	0.269231	0.278481	0.287500	57
58	0.183099	0.194444	0.205479	0.216216	0.226667	0.236842	0.246753	0.256410	0.265823	0.275000	58
59	0.169014	0.180556	0.191781	0.202703	0.213333	0.223684	0.233766	0.243590	0.253165	0.262500	59
60	0.154930	0.166667	0.178082	0.189189	0.200000	0.210526	0.220779	0.230769	0.240506	0.250000	60
61	0.140845	0.152778	0.164384	0.175676	0.186667	0.197368	0.207792	0.217949	0.227848	0.237500	61
62	0.126761	0.138889	0.150685	0.162162	0.173333	0.184211	0.194805	0.205128	0.215190	0.225000	62
63	0.112676	0.125000	0.136986	0.148649	0.160000	0.171053	0.181818	0.192308	0.202532	0.212500	63
64	0.098592	0.111111	0.123288	0.135135	0.146667	0.157895	0.168831	0.179487	0.189873	0.200000	64
65	0.084507	0.097222	0.109589	0.121622	0.133333	0.144737	0.155844	0.166667	0.177215	0.187500	65
66	0.070423	0.083333	0.095890	0.108108	0.120000	0.131579	0.142857	0.153846	0.164557	0.175000	66
67	0.056338	0.069444	0.082192	0.094595	0.106667	0.118421	0.129870	0.141026	0.151899	0.162500	67
68	0.042254	0.055556	0.068493	0.081081	0.093333	0.105263	0.116883	0.128205	0.139240	0.150000	68
69	0.028169	0.041667	0.054795	0.067568	0.080000	0.092105	0.103896	0.115385	0.126582	0.137500	69
70	0.014085	0.027778	0.041096	0.054054	0.066667	0.078947	0.090909	0.102564	0.113924	0.125000	70
71	0.000000	0.013889	0.027397	0.040541	0.053333	0.065789	0.077922	0.089744	0.101266	0.112500	71
72		0.000000	0.013699	0.027027	0.040000	0.052632	0.064935	0.076923	0.088608	0.100000	72
73			0.000000	0.013513	0.026667	0.039474	0.051948	0.064103	0.075949	0.087500	73
74				0.000000	0.013333	0.026316	0.038961	0.051282	0.063291	0.075000	74
75					0.000000	0.013158	0.025974	0.038462	0.050633	0.062500	75
76						0.000000	0.012987	0.025641	0.037975	0.050000	76
77							0.000000	0.012820	0.025316	0.037500	77
78								0.000000	0.012658	0.025000	78
79									0.000000	0.012500	79
80										0.000000	80

81–90 years probable life

Age, years	81	82	83	84	85	86	87	88	89	90	Age, years
1	0.987654	0.987805	0.987952	0.988095	0.988235	0.988372	0.988506	0.988636	0.988764	0.988889	1
2	0.975309	0.975610	0.975904	0.976190	0.976471	0.976744	0.977011	0.977273	0.977528	0.977778	2
3	0.962963	0.963415	0.963855	0.964286	0.964706	0.965116	0.965517	0.965909	0.966292	0.966667	3
4	0.950617	0.951220	0.951807	0.952381	0.952941	0.953488	0.954023	0.954545	0.955056	0.955556	4
5	0.938272	0.939024	0.939759	0.940476	0.941176	0.941860	0.942529	0.943182	0.943820	0.944444	5
6	0.925926	0.926829	0.927711	0.928571	0.929412	0.930233	0.931034	0.931818	0.932584	0.933333	6
7	0.913580	0.914634	0.915663	0.916667	0.917647	0.918605	0.919540	0.920455	0.921348	0.922222	7
8	0.901235	0.902439	0.903614	0.904762	0.905882	0.906977	0.908046	0.909091	0.910112	0.911111	8
9	0.888889	0.890244	0.891566	0.892857	0.894118	0.895349	0.896552	0.897727	0.898876	0.900000	9
10	0.876543	0.878049	0.879518	0.880952	0.882353	0.883721	0.885057	0.886364	0.887640	0.888889	10
11	0.864198	0.865854	0.867470	0.869048	0.870588	0.872093	0.873563	0.875000	0.876404	0.877778	11
12	0.851852	0.853659	0.855422	0.857143	0.858824	0.860465	0.862069	0.863636	0.865169	0.866667	12
13	0.839506	0.841463	0.843373	0.845238	0.847059	0.848837	0.850575	0.852273	0.853933	0.855556	13
14	0.827160	0.829268	0.831325	0.833333	0.835294	0.837209	0.839080	0.840909	0.842697	0.844444	14
15	0.814815	0.817073	0.819277	0.821429	0.823529	0.825581	0.827586	0.829545	0.831461	0.833333	15
16	0.802469	0.804878	0.807229	0.809524	0.811765	0.813953	0.816092	0.818182	0.820225	0.822222	16
17	0.790123	0.792683	0.795181	0.797619	0.800000	0.802326	0.804598	0.806818	0.808989	0.811111	17
18	0.777778	0.780488	0.783133	0.785714	0.788235	0.790698	0.793103	0.795455	0.797753	0.800000	18
19	0.765432	0.768293	0.771084	0.773810	0.776471	0.779070	0.781609	0.784091	0.786517	0.788889	19
20	0.753086	0.756098	0.759036	0.761905	0.764706	0.767442	0.770115	0.772727	0.775281	0.777778	20

TABLE C.1. EXPECTANCY-LIFE FACTORS FOR UNIT PROPERTIES
0 Percent Interest Rate (Continued)

81–90 years probable life

Age, years	81	82	83	84	85	86	87	88	89	90	Age, years
21	0.740741	0.743902	0.746988	0.750000	0.752941	0.755814	0.758621	0.761364	0.764045	0.766667	21
22	0.728395	0.731707	0.734940	0.738095	0.741176	0.744186	0.747126	0.750000	0.752809	0.755556	22
23	0.716049	0.719512	0.722892	0.726190	0.729412	0.732558	0.735632	0.738636	0.741573	0.744444	23
24	0.703704	0.707317	0.710843	0.714286	0.717647	0.720930	0.724138	0.727273	0.730337	0.733333	24
25	0.691358	0.695122	0.698795	0.702381	0.705882	0.709302	0.712644	0.715909	0.719101	0.722222	25
26	0.679012	0.682927	0.686747	0.690476	0.694118	0.697674	0.701149	0.704545	0.707865	0.711111	26
27	0.666667	0.670732	0.674699	0.678571	0.682353	0.686047	0.689655	0.693182	0.696629	0.700000	27
28	0.654321	0.658537	0.662651	0.666667	0.670588	0.674419	0.678161	0.681818	0.685393	0.688889	28
29	0.641975	0.646341	0.650602	0.654762	0.658824	0.662791	0.666667	0.670455	0.674157	0.677778	29
30	0.629630	0.634146	0.638554	0.642857	0.647059	0.651163	0.655172	0.659091	0.662921	0.666667	30
31	0.617284	0.621951	0.626506	0.630952	0.635294	0.639535	0.643678	0.647727	0.651685	0.655556	31
32	0.604938	0.609756	0.614458	0.619048	0.623529	0.627907	0.632184	0.636364	0.640449	0.644444	32
33	0.592593	0.597561	0.602410	0.607143	0.611765	0.616279	0.620690	0.625000	0.629213	0.633333	33
34	0.580247	0.585366	0.590361	0.595238	0.600000	0.604651	0.609195	0.613636	0.617978	0.622222	34
35	0.567901	0.573171	0.578313	0.583333	0.588235	0.593023	0.597701	0.602273	0.606742	0.611111	35
36	0.555556	0.560976	0.566265	0.571429	0.576471	0.581395	0.586207	0.590909	0.595506	0.600000	36
37	0.543210	0.548780	0.554217	0.559524	0.564706	0.569767	0.574713	0.579545	0.584270	0.588889	37
38	0.530864	0.536585	0.542169	0.547619	0.552941	0.558140	0.563218	0.568182	0.573034	0.577778	38
39	0.518519	0.524390	0.530120	0.535714	0.541176	0.546512	0.551724	0.556818	0.561798	0.566667	39
40	0.506173	0.512195	0.518072	0.523810	0.529412	0.534884	0.540230	0.545455	0.550562	0.555556	40
41	0.493827	0.500000	0.506024	0.511905	0.517647	0.523256	0.528736	0.534091	0.539326	0.544444	41
42	0.481481	0.487805	0.493976	0.500000	0.505882	0.511628	0.517241	0.522727	0.528090	0.533333	42
43	0.469136	0.475610	0.481928	0.488095	0.494118	0.500000	0.505747	0.511364	0.516854	0.522222	43
44	0.456790	0.463415	0.469880	0.476190	0.482353	0.488372	0.494253	0.500000	0.505618	0.511111	44
45	0.444444	0.451220	0.457831	0.464286	0.470588	0.476744	0.482759	0.488636	0.494382	0.500000	45
46	0.432099	0.439024	0.445783	0.452381	0.458824	0.465116	0.471264	0.477273	0.483146	0.488889	46
47	0.419753	0.426829	0.433735	0.440476	0.447059	0.453488	0.459770	0.465909	0.471910	0.477778	47
48	0.407407	0.414634	0.421687	0.428571	0.435294	0.441860	0.448276	0.454545	0.460674	0.466667	48
49	0.395062	0.402439	0.409639	0.416667	0.423529	0.430233	0.436782	0.443182	0.449438	0.455556	49
50	0.382716	0.390244	0.397590	0.404762	0.411765	0.418605	0.425287	0.431818	0.438202	0.444444	50
51	0.370370	0.378049	0.385542	0.392857	0.400000	0.406977	0.413793	0.420455	0.426966	0.433333	51
52	0.358025	0.365854	0.373494	0.380952	0.388235	0.395349	0.402299	0.409091	0.415730	0.422222	52
53	0.345679	0.353659	0.361446	0.369048	0.376471	0.383721	0.390805	0.397727	0.404494	0.411111	53
54	0.333333	0.341463	0.349398	0.357143	0.364706	0.372093	0.379310	0.386364	0.393258	0.400000	54
55	0.320988	0.329268	0.337349	0.345238	0.352941	0.360465	0.367816	0.375000	0.382022	0.388889	55
56	0.308642	0.317073	0.325301	0.333333	0.341176	0.348837	0.356322	0.363636	0.370787	0.377778	56
57	0.296296	0.304878	0.313253	0.321429	0.329412	0.337209	0.344828	0.352273	0.359551	0.366667	57
58	0.283951	0.292683	0.301205	0.309524	0.317647	0.325581	0.333333	0.340909	0.348315	0.355556	58
59	0.271605	0.280488	0.289157	0.297619	0.305882	0.313953	0.321839	0.329545	0.337079	0.344444	59
60	0.259259	0.268293	0.277108	0.285714	0.294118	0.302326	0.310345	0.318182	0.325843	0.333333	60
61	0.246914	0.256098	0.265060	0.273810	0.282353	0.290698	0.298851	0.306818	0.314607	0.322222	61
62	0.234568	0.243902	0.253012	0.261905	0.270588	0.279070	0.287356	0.295455	0.303371	0.311111	62
63	0.222222	0.231707	0.240964	0.250000	0.258824	0.267442	0.275862	0.284091	0.292135	0.300000	63
64	0.209877	0.219512	0.228916	0.238095	0.247059	0.255814	0.264368	0.272727	0.280899	0.288889	64
65	0.197531	0.207317	0.216867	0.226190	0.235294	0.244186	0.252874	0.261364	0.269663	0.277778	65
66	0.185185	0.195122	0.204819	0.214286	0.223529	0.232558	0.241379	0.250000	0.258427	0.266667	66
67	0.172840	0.182927	0.192771	0.202381	0.211765	0.220930	0.229885	0.238636	0.247191	0.255556	67
68	0.160494	0.170732	0.180723	0.190476	0.200000	0.209302	0.218391	0.227273	0.235955	0.244444	68
69	0.148148	0.158537	0.168675	0.178571	0.188235	0.197674	0.206897	0.215909	0.224719	0.233333	69
70	0.135802	0.146341	0.156626	0.166667	0.176471	0.186047	0.195402	0.204545	0.213483	0.222222	70
71	0.123457	0.134146	0.144578	0.154762	0.164706	0.174419	0.183908	0.193182	0.202247	0.211111	71
72	0.111111	0.121951	0.132530	0.142857	0.152941	0.162791	0.172414	0.181818	0.191011	0.200000	72
73	0.098765	0.109756	0.120482	0.130952	0.141176	0.151163	0.160920	0.170455	0.179775	0.188889	73
74	0.086420	0.097561	0.108434	0.119048	0.129412	0.139535	0.149425	0.159091	0.168539	0.177778	74
75	0.074074	0.085366	0.096386	0.107143	0.117647	0.127907	0.137931	0.147727	0.157303	0.166667	75
76	0.061728	0.073171	0.084337	0.095238	0.105882	0.116279	0.126437	0.136364	0.146067	0.155556	76
77	0.049383	0.060976	0.072289	0.083333	0.094118	0.104651	0.114943	0.125000	0.134831	0.144444	77
78	0.037037	0.048780	0.060241	0.071429	0.082353	0.093023	0.103448	0.113636	0.123596	0.133333	78
79	0.024691	0.036585	0.048193	0.059524	0.070588	0.081395	0.091954	0.102273	0.112360	0.122222	79
80	0.012346	0.024390	0.036145	0.047619	0.058824	0.069767	0.080460	0.090909	0.101124	0.111111	80

TABLE C.1. EXPECTANCY-LIFE FACTORS FOR UNIT PROPERTIES
0 Percent Interest Rate (Continued)

81–90 years probable life

Age, years	81	82	83	84	85	86	87	88	89	90	Age, years
81	0.000000	0.012195	0.024096	0.035714	0.047059	0.058140	0.068966	0.079545	0.089888	0.100000	81
82		0.000000	0.012048	0.023810	0.035294	0.046512	0.057471	0.068182	0.078652	0.088889	82
83			0.000000	0.011905	0.023529	0.034884	0.045977	0.056818	0.067416	0.077778	83
84				0.000000	0.011765	0.023256	0.034483	0.045455	0.056180	0.066667	84
85					0.000000	0.011628	0.022988	0.034091	0.044944	0.055556	85
86						0.000000	0.011494	0.022727	0.033708	0.044444	86
87							0.000000	0.011364	0.022472	0.033333	87
88								0.000000	0.011236	0.022222	88
89									0.000000	0.011111	89
90										0.000000	90

91–100 years probable life

Age, years	91	92	93	94	95	96	97	98	99	100	Age, years
1	0.989011	0.989130	0.989247	0.989362	0.989474	0.989583	0.989691	0.989796	0.989899	0.990000	1
2	0.978022	0.978261	0.978495	0.978723	0.978947	0.979167	0.979381	0.979592	0.979798	0.980000	2
3	0.967033	0.967391	0.967742	0.968085	0.968421	0.968750	0.969072	0.969388	0.969697	0.970000	3
4	0.956044	0.956522	0.956989	0.957447	0.957895	0.958333	0.958763	0.959184	0.959596	0.960000	4
5	0.945055	0.945652	0.946237	0.946809	0.947368	0.947917	0.948454	0.948980	0.949495	0.950000	5
6	0.934066	0.934783	0.935484	0.936170	0.936842	0.937500	0.938144	0.938776	0.939394	0.940000	6
7	0.923077	0.923913	0.924731	0.925532	0.926316	0.927083	0.927835	0.928571	0.929293	0.930000	7
8	0.912088	0.913043	0.913978	0.914894	0.915789	0.916667	0.917526	0.918367	0.919192	0.920000	8
9	0.901099	0.902174	0.903226	0.904255	0.905263	0.906250	0.907216	0.908163	0.909091	0.910000	9
10	0.890110	0.891304	0.892473	0.893617	0.894737	0.895833	0.896907	0.897959	0.898990	0.900000	10
11	0.879121	0.880435	0.881720	0.882979	0.884211	0.885417	0.886598	0.887755	0.888889	0.890000	11
12	0.868132	0.869565	0.870968	0.872340	0.873684	0.875000	0.876289	0.877551	0.878788	0.880000	12
13	0.857143	0.858696	0.860215	0.861702	0.863158	0.864583	0.865979	0.867347	0.868687	0.870000	13
14	0.846154	0.847826	0.849462	0.851064	0.852632	0.854167	0.855670	0.857143	0.858586	0.860000	14
15	0.835165	0.836957	0.838710	0.840426	0.842105	0.843750	0.845361	0.846939	0.848485	0.850000	15
16	0.824176	0.826087	0.827957	0.829787	0.831579	0.833333	0.835052	0.836735	0.838384	0.840000	16
17	0.813187	0.815217	0.817204	0.819149	0.821053	0.822917	0.824742	0.826531	0.828283	0.830000	17
18	0.802198	0.804348	0.806452	0.808511	0.810526	0.812500	0.814433	0.816327	0.818182	0.820000	18
19	0.791209	0.793478	0.795699	0.797872	0.800000	0.802083	0.804124	0.806122	0.808081	0.810000	19
20	0.780220	0.782609	0.784946	0.787234	0.789474	0.791667	0.793814	0.795918	0.797980	0.800000	20
21	0.769231	0.771739	0.774194	0.776596	0.778947	0.781250	0.783505	0.785714	0.787879	0.790000	21
22	0.758242	0.760870	0.763441	0.765957	0.768421	0.770833	0.773196	0.775510	0.777778	0.780000	22
23	0.747253	0.750000	0.752688	0.755319	0.757895	0.760417	0.762887	0.765306	0.767677	0.770000	23
24	0.736264	0.739130	0.741935	0.744681	0.747368	0.750000	0.752577	0.755102	0.757576	0.760000	24
25	0.725275	0.728261	0.731183	0.734043	0.736842	0.739583	0.742268	0.744898	0.747475	0.750000	25
26	0.714286	0.717391	0.720430	0.723404	0.726316	0.729167	0.731959	0.734694	0.737374	0.740000	26
27	0.703297	0.706522	0.709677	0.712766	0.715789	0.718750	0.721649	0.724490	0.727273	0.730000	27
28	0.692308	0.695652	0.698925	0.702128	0.705263	0.708333	0.711340	0.714286	0.717172	0.720000	28
29	0.681319	0.684783	0.688172	0.691489	0.694737	0.697917	0.701031	0.704082	0.707071	0.710000	29
30	0.670330	0.673913	0.677419	0.680851	0.684211	0.687500	0.690722	0.693878	0.696970	0.700000	30
31	0.659341	0.663043	0.666667	0.670213	0.673684	0.677083	0.680412	0.683673	0.686869	0.690000	31
32	0.648352	0.652174	0.655914	0.659574	0.663158	0.666667	0.670103	0.673469	0.676768	0.680000	32
33	0.637363	0.641304	0.645161	0.648936	0.652632	0.656250	0.659794	0.663265	0.666667	0.670000	33
34	0.626374	0.630435	0.634409	0.638298	0.642105	0.645833	0.649485	0.653061	0.656566	0.660000	34
35	0.615385	0.619565	0.623656	0.627660	0.631579	0.635417	0.639175	0.642857	0.646465	0.650000	35
36	0.604396	0.608696	0.612903	0.617021	0.621053	0.625000	0.628866	0.632653	0.636364	0.640000	36
37	0.593407	0.597826	0.602151	0.606383	0.610526	0.614583	0.618557	0.622449	0.626263	0.630000	37
38	0.582418	0.586957	0.591398	0.595745	0.600000	0.604167	0.608247	0.612245	0.616162	0.620000	38
39	0.571429	0.576087	0.580645	0.585106	0.589474	0.593750	0.597938	0.602041	0.606061	0.610000	39
40	0.560440	0.565217	0.569892	0.574468	0.578947	0.583333	0.587629	0.591837	0.595960	0.600000	40
41	0.549451	0.554348	0.559140	0.563830	0.568421	0.572917	0.577320	0.581633	0.585859	0.590000	41
42	0.538462	0.543478	0.548387	0.553191	0.557895	0.562500	0.567010	0.571429	0.575758	0.580000	42
43	0.527473	0.532609	0.537634	0.542553	0.547368	0.552083	0.556701	0.561224	0.565657	0.570000	43
44	0.516484	0.521739	0.526882	0.531915	0.536842	0.541667	0.546392	0.551020	0.555556	0.560000	44
45	0.505495	0.510870	0.516129	0.521277	0.526316	0.531250	0.536082	0.540816	0.545455	0.550000	45

TABLE C.1. EXPECTANCY-LIFE FACTORS FOR UNIT PROPERTIES
0 Percent Interest Rate (*Continued*)

91-100 years probable life

Age, years	91	92	93	94	95	96	97	98	99	100	Age, years
46	0.494505	0.500000	0.505376	0.510638	0.515789	0.520833	0.525773	0.530612	0.535354	0.540000	46
47	0.483516	0.489130	0.494624	0.500000	0.505263	0.510417	0.515464	0.520408	0.525253	0.530000	47
48	0.472527	0.478261	0.483871	0.489362	0.494737	0.500000	0.505155	0.510204	0.515152	0.520000	48
49	0.461538	0.467391	0.473118	0.478723	0.484211	0.489583	0.494845	0.500000	0.505051	0.510000	49
50	0.450549	0.456522	0.462366	0.468085	0.473684	0.479167	0.484536	0.489796	0.494950	0.500000	50
51	0.439560	0.445652	0.451613	0.457447	0.463158	0.468750	0.474227	0.479592	0.484849	0.490000	51
52	0.428571	0.434783	0.440860	0.446809	0.452632	0.458333	0.463918	0.469388	0.474747	0.480000	52
53	0.417582	0.423913	0.430108	0.436170	0.442105	0.447917	0.453608	0.459184	0.464646	0.470000	53
54	0.406593	0.413043	0.419355	0.425532	0.431579	0.437500	0.443299	0.448980	0.454545	0.460000	54
55	0.395604	0.402174	0.408602	0.414894	0.421053	0.427083	0.432990	0.438775	0.444444	0.450000	55
56	0.384615	0.391304	0.397849	0.404255	0.410526	0.416667	0.422680	0.428571	0.434343	0.440000	56
57	0.373626	0.380435	0.387097	0.393617	0.400000	0.406250	0.412371	0.418367	0.424242	0.430000	57
58	0.362637	0.369565	0.376344	0.382979	0.389474	0.395833	0.402062	0.408163	0.414141	0.420000	58
59	0.351648	0.358696	0.365591	0.372340	0.378947	0.385417	0.391753	0.397959	0.404040	0.410000	59
60	0.340659	0.347826	0.354839	0.361702	0.368421	0.375000	0.381443	0.387755	0.393939	0.400000	60
61	0.329670	0.336957	0.344086	0.351064	0.357895	0.364583	0.371134	0.377551	0.383838	0.390000	61
62	0.318681	0.326087	0.333333	0.340426	0.347368	0.354167	0.360825	0.367347	0.373737	0.380000	62
63	0.307692	0.315217	0.322581	0.329787	0.336842	0.343750	0.350515	0.357143	0.363636	0.370000	63
64	0.296703	0.304348	0.311828	0.319149	0.326316	0.333333	0.340206	0.346939	0.353535	0.360000	64
65	0.285714	0.293478	0.301075	0.308511	0.315789	0.322917	0.329897	0.336735	0.343434	0.350000	65
66	0.274725	0.282609	0.290323	0.297872	0.305263	0.312500	0.319588	0.326531	0.333333	0.340000	66
67	0.263736	0.271739	0.279570	0.287234	0.294737	0.302083	0.309278	0.316327	0.323232	0.330000	67
68	0.252747	0.260870	0.268817	0.276596	0.284211	0.291667	0.298969	0.306122	0.313131	0.320000	68
69	0.241758	0.250000	0.258065	0.265957	0.273684	0.281250	0.288660	0.295918	0.303030	0.310000	69
70	0.230769	0.239130	0.247312	0.255319	0.263158	0.270833	0.278351	0.285714	0.292929	0.300000	70
71	0.219780	0.228261	0.236559	0.244681	0.252632	0.260417	0.268041	0.275510	0.282828	0.290000	71
72	0.208791	0.217391	0.225806	0.234043	0.242105	0.250000	0.257732	0.265306	0.272727	0.280000	72
73	0.197802	0.206522	0.215054	0.223404	0.231579	0.239583	0.247423	0.255102	0.262626	0.270000	73
74	0.186813	0.195652	0.204301	0.212766	0.221053	0.229167	0.237113	0.244898	0.252525	0.260000	74
75	0.175824	0.184783	0.193548	0.202128	0.210526	0.218750	0.226804	0.234694	0.242424	0.250000	75
76	0.164835	0.173913	0.182796	0.191489	0.200000	0.208333	0.216495	0.224490	0.232323	0.240000	76
77	0.153846	0.163043	0.172043	0.180851	0.189474	0.197917	0.206186	0.214286	0.222222	0.230000	77
78	0.142857	0.152174	0.161290	0.170213	0.178947	0.187500	0.195876	0.204082	0.212121	0.220000	78
79	0.131868	0.141304	0.150538	0.159574	0.168421	0.177083	0.185567	0.193878	0.202020	0.210000	79
80	0.120879	0.130435	0.139785	0.148936	0.157895	0.166667	0.175258	0.183673	0.191919	0.200000	80
81	0.109890	0.119565	0.129032	0.138298	0.147368	0.156250	0.164948	0.173469	0.181818	0.190000	81
82	0.098901	0.108696	0.118280	0.127660	0.136842	0.145833	0.154639	0.163265	0.171717	0.180000	82
83	0.087912	0.097826	0.107527	0.117021	0.126316	0.135417	0.144330	0.153061	0.161616	0.170000	83
84	0.076923	0.086957	0.096774	0.106383	0.115789	0.125000	0.134021	0.142857	0.151515	0.160000	84
85	0.065934	0.076087	0.086022	0.095745	0.105263	0.114583	0.123711	0.132653	0.141414	0.150000	85
86	0.054945	0.065217	0.075269	0.085106	0.094737	0.104167	0.113402	0.122449	0.131313	0.140000	86
87	0.043956	0.054348	0.064516	0.074468	0.084211	0.093750	0.103093	0.112245	0.121212	0.130000	87
88	0.032967	0.043478	0.053763	0.063830	0.073684	0.083333	0.092784	0.102041	0.111111	0.120000	88
89	0.021978	0.032609	0.043011	0.053191	0.063158	0.072917	0.082474	0.091837	0.101010	0.110000	89
90	0.010989	0.021739	0.032258	0.042553	0.052632	0.062500	0.072165	0.081633	0.090909	0.100000	90
91	0.000000	0.010870	0.021505	0.031915	0.042105	0.052083	0.061856	0.071429	0.080808	0.090000	91
92		0.000000	0.010753	0.021277	0.031579	0.041667	0.051546	0.061224	0.070707	0.080000	92
93			0.000000	0.010638	0.021053	0.031250	0.041237	0.051020	0.060606	0.070000	93
94				0.000000	0.010526	0.020833	0.030928	0.040816	0.050505	0.060000	94
95					0.000000	0.010417	0.020619	0.030612	0.040404	0.050000	95
96						0.000000	0.010309	0.020408	0.030303	0.040000	96
97							0.000000	0.010204	0.020202	0.030000	97
98								0.000000	0.010101	0.020000	98
99									0.000000	0.010000	99
100										0.000000	100

TABLE C.1. EXPECTANCY-LIFE FACTORS FOR UNIT PROPERTIES
2 Percent Interest Rate

1-10 years probable life

Age, years	1	2	3	4	5	6	7	8	9	10	Age, years
1	0.000000	0.504950	0.673245	0.757376	0.807841	0.841474	0.865488	0.883490	0.897485	0.908673	1
2		0.000000	0.339956	0.509900	0.611840	0.679778	0.728286	0.764650	0.792919	0.815520	2
3			0.000000	0.257474	0.411918	0.514848	0.588340	0.643433	0.686262	0.720504	3
4				0.000000	0.207998	0.346619	0.445594	0.519792	0.577472	0.623588	4
5					0.000000	0.175025	0.299994	0.393678	0.466506	0.524733	5
6						0.000000	0.151482	0.265042	0.353320	0.423901	6
7							0.000000	0.133833	0.237871	0.321053	7
8								0.000000	0.120113	0.216147	8
9									0.000000	0.109144	9
10										0.000000	10

11-20 years probable life

Age, years	11	12	13	14	15	16	17	18	19	20	Age, years
1	0.917822	0.925440	0.931882	0.937398	0.942175	0.946350	0.950030	0.953298	0.956218	0.958843	1
2	0.834001	0.849390	0.862401	0.873544	0.883193	0.891627	0.899061	0.905662	0.911561	0.916863	2
3	0.748503	0.771818	0.791531	0.808413	0.823031	0.835809	0.847072	0.857073	0.866010	0.874044	3
4	0.661295	0.692695	0.719243	0.741979	0.761666	0.778875	0.794044	0.807512	0.819549	0.830368	4
5	0.572343	0.611989	0.645509	0.674217	0.699074	0.720803	0.739955	0.756960	0.772158	0.785819	5
6	0.481612	0.529669	0.570301	0.605099	0.635230	0.661569	0.684784	0.705398	0.723819	0.740378	6
7	0.389066	0.445703	0.493589	0.534599	0.570109	0.601150	0.628510	0.652803	0.674514	0.694029	7
8	0.294669	0.360057	0.415342	0.462689	0.503686	0.539523	0.571110	0.599157	0.624222	0.646753	8
9	0.198385	0.272669	0.335531	0.389341	0.435934	0.476663	0.512563	0.544438	0.572925	0.598531	9
10	0.100174	0.183593	0.254123	0.314526	0.366827	0.412546	0.452844	0.488625	0.520602	0.549345	10
11	0.000000	0.092705	0.171087	0.238214	0.296338	0.347147	0.391931	0.431695	0.467232	0.499176	11
12		0.000000	0.086391	0.160377	0.224440	0.280440	0.329800	0.373627	0.412795	0.448002	12
13			0.000000	0.080982	0.151103	0.212398	0.266426	0.314398	0.357269	0.395806	13
14				0.000000	0.076300	0.142996	0.201785	0.253984	0.300633	0.342565	14
15					0.000000	0.072206	0.135851	0.192361	0.242864	0.288260	15
16						0.000000	0.068598	0.129506	0.183939	0.232868	16
17							0.000000	0.065394	0.123836	0.176369	17
18								0.000000	0.062531	0.118730	18
19									0.000000	0.059958	19
20										0.000000	20

21-30 years probable life

Age, years	21	22	23	24	25	26	27	28	29	30	Age, years
1	0.961215	0.963369	0.965332	0.967129	0.968780	0.970301	0.971707	0.973010	0.974222	0.975350	1
2	0.921655	0.926005	0.929970	0.933600	0.936935	0.940008	0.942848	0.945481	0.947928	0.950207	2
3	0.881303	0.887893	0.893902	0.899401	0.904453	0.909108	0.913412	0.917401	0.921108	0.924561	3
4	0.840144	0.849020	0.857112	0.864518	0.871322	0.877591	0.883387	0.888759	0.893752	0.898403	4
5	0.798162	0.809369	0.819586	0.828937	0.837528	0.845444	0.852762	0.859545	0.865848	0.871721	5
6	0.755341	0.768925	0.781309	0.792645	0.803058	0.812654	0.821524	0.829746	0.837387	0.844505	6
7	0.711663	0.727672	0.742268	0.755627	0.767898	0.779208	0.789661	0.799351	0.808356	0.816746	7
8	0.667112	0.685594	0.702445	0.717868	0.732036	0.745092	0.757161	0.768348	0.778745	0.788430	8
9	0.621669	0.642674	0.661826	0.679355	0.695456	0.710295	0.724011	0.736726	0.748542	0.759549	9
10	0.575318	0.598896	0.620394	0.640071	0.658145	0.674802	0.690199	0.704471	0.717734	0.730090	10
11	0.528039	0.554243	0.578134	0.600001	0.620087	0.638599	0.655709	0.671570	0.686310	0.700042	11
12	0.479815	0.508696	0.535028	0.559130	0.581269	0.601671	0.620531	0.638012	0.654258	0.669393	12
13	0.430627	0.462239	0.491061	0.517441	0.541674	0.564005	0.584648	0.603783	0.621565	0.638131	13
14	0.380454	0.414852	0.446214	0.474919	0.501287	0.525586	0.548048	0.568869	0.588218	0.606244	14
15	0.329279	0.366518	0.400470	0.431546	0.460092	0.486399	0.510716	0.533256	0.554204	0.573719	15

TABLE C.1.   EXPECTANCY-LIFE FACTORS FOR UNIT PROPERTIES
2 Percent Interest Rate (Continued)

21–30 years probable life

Age, years	21	22	23	24	25	26	27	28	29	30	Age, years
16	0.277080	0.317217	0.353811	0.387306	0.418073	0.446428	0.472637	0.496932	0.519510	0.540543	16
17	0.223836	0.266930	0.306220	0.342181	0.375214	0.405657	0.433797	0.459881	0.484122	0.506704	17
18	0.169528	0.215637	0.257676	0.296154	0.331498	0.364071	0.394180	0.422089	0.448026	0.472188	18
19	0.114134	0.163318	0.208161	0.249206	0.286908	0.321653	0.353770	0.383541	0.411208	0.436982	19
20	0.057632	0.109953	0.157656	0.201319	0.241425	0.278387	0.312552	0.344222	0.373654	0.401072	20
21	0.000000	0.055521	0.106141	0.152474	0.195033	0.234255	0.270510	0.304117	0.335348	0.364443	21
22		0.000000	0.053596	0.102652	0.147714	0.189241	0.227627	0.263209	0.296277	0.327082	22
23			0.000000	0.051834	0.099448	0.143327	0.183887	0.221484	0.256424	0.288974	23
24				0.000000	0.050216	0.096494	0.139272	0.178924	0.215774	0.250104	24
25					0.000000	0.048725	0.093764	0.135513	0.174311	0.210456	25
26						0.000000	0.047346	0.091233	0.132019	0.170015	26
27							0.000000	0.046068	0.088881	0.128765	27
28								0.000000	0.044881	0.086691	28
29									0.000000	0.043774	29
30										0.000000	30

31–40 years probable life

Age, years	31	32	33	34	35	36	37	38	39	40	Age, years
1	0.976404	0.977389	0.978313	0.979181	0.979998	0.980767	0.981493	0.982179	0.982829	0.983444	1
2	0.952335	0.954327	0.956193	0.957946	0.959596	0.961150	0.962616	0.964002	0.965314	0.966557	2
3	0.927786	0.930802	0.933631	0.936287	0.938785	0.941140	0.943362	0.945462	0.947449	0.949333	3
4	0.902745	0.906808	0.910617	0.914194	0.917559	0.920730	0.923722	0.926551	0.929227	0.931764	4
5	0.877204	0.882333	0.887142	0.891659	0.895908	0.899911	0.903690	0.907261	0.910641	0.913843	5
6	0.851151	0.857370	0.863199	0.868673	0.873824	0.878677	0.883257	0.887586	0.891682	0.895564	6
7	0.824578	0.831906	0.838776	0.845228	0.851298	0.857018	0.862415	0.867517	0.872345	0.876920	7
8	0.797473	0.805934	0.813865	0.821314	0.828322	0.834925	0.841157	0.847047	0.852621	0.857903	8
9	0.769826	0.779442	0.788456	0.796922	0.804886	0.812391	0.819473	0.826167	0.832502	0.838505	9
10	0.741627	0.752420	0.762539	0.772041	0.780981	0.789406	0.797356	0.804870	0.811981	0.818719	10
11	0.712863	0.724858	0.736103	0.746664	0.756599	0.765961	0.774796	0.783147	0.791049	0.798538	11
12	0.683524	0.696744	0.709138	0.720778	0.731729	0.742047	0.751785	0.760989	0.769699	0.777953	12
13	0.653598	0.668069	0.681635	0.694375	0.706361	0.717655	0.728314	0.738388	0.747922	0.756956	13
14	0.623073	0.638820	0.653581	0.667444	0.680486	0.692776	0.704374	0.715335	0.725709	0.735539	14
15	0.591938	0.608985	0.624966	0.639974	0.654093	0.667398	0.679955	0.691821	0.703052	0.713695	15
16	0.560181	0.578554	0.595779	0.611955	0.627173	0.641513	0.655047	0.667837	0.679942	0.691413	16
17	0.527788	0.547515	0.566008	0.583375	0.599714	0.615111	0.629641	0.643374	0.656370	0.668685	17
18	0.494748	0.515855	0.535641	0.554224	0.571706	0.588180	0.603727	0.618420	0.632326	0.645503	18
19	0.461046	0.483561	0.504668	0.524490	0.543138	0.560711	0.577295	0.592968	0.607802	0.621858	19
20	0.426671	0.450622	0.473074	0.494161	0.513999	0.532692	0.550334	0.567007	0.582786	0.597739	20
21	0.391608	0.417024	0.440849	0.463226	0.484277	0.504113	0.522834	0.540527	0.557271	0.573138	21
22	0.355844	0.382753	0.407980	0.431671	0.453960	0.474963	0.494784	0.513517	0.531245	0.548045	22
23	0.319364	0.347798	0.374453	0.399486	0.423037	0.445229	0.466173	0.485966	0.504699	0.522450	23
24	0.282155	0.312143	0.340255	0.366657	0.391496	0.414901	0.436989	0.457865	0.477622	0.496343	24
25	0.244202	0.275775	0.305374	0.333172	0.359323	0.383966	0.407222	0.429202	0.450003	0.469714	25
26	0.205490	0.238680	0.269795	0.299017	0.326507	0.352413	0.376860	0.399965	0.421832	0.442553	26
27	0.166003	0.200843	0.233504	0.264178	0.293035	0.320228	0.345890	0.370144	0.393098	0.414848	27
28	0.125727	0.162250	0.196488	0.228643	0.258894	0.287400	0.314301	0.339726	0.363788	0.386589	28
29	0.084645	0.122884	0.158731	0.192397	0.224070	0.253915	0.280728	0.308700	0.333893	0.357766	29
30	0.042742	0.082731	0.120219	0.155427	0.188549	0.219760	0.249215	0.277054	0.303400	0.328365	30
31	0.000000	0.041775	0.080937	0.117716	0.152318	0.184923	0.215693	0.244774	0.272297	0.298377	31
32		0.000000	0.040869	0.079252	0.115362	0.149388	0.181500	0.211849	0.240571	0.267788	32
33			0.000000	0.040018	0.077667	0.113143	0.146623	0.178266	0.208212	0.236588	33
34				0.000000	0.039218	0.076173	0.111049	0.144010	0.175205	0.204764	34
35					0.000000	0.038464	0.074763	0.109070	0.141538	0.172304	35
36						0.000000	0.037752	0.073431	0.107197	0.139194	36
37							0.000000	0.037079	0.072170	0.105422	37
38								0.000000	0.036442	0.070975	38
39									0.000000	0.035839	39
40										0.000000	40

TABLE C.1. EXPECTANCY-LIFE FACTORS FOR UNIT PROPERTIES
2 Percent Interest Rate (*Continued*)

Age, years	41	42	43	44	45	46	47	48	49	50	Age, years
1	0.984028	0.984583	0.985110	0.985612	0.986090	0.986547	0.986982	0.987398	0.987796	0.988177	1
2	0.967737	0.968857	0.969922	0.970936	0.971903	0.972824	0.973704	0.974544	0.975348	0.976117	2
3	0.951120	0.952817	0.954431	0.955967	0.957431	0.958827	0.960160	0.961433	0.962651	0.963816	3
4	0.934170	0.936456	0.938630	0.940699	0.942670	0.944550	0.946345	0.948060	0.949700	0.951269	4
5	0.916882	0.919768	0.922512	0.925125	0.927614	0.929988	0.932254	0.934420	0.936490	0.938472	5
6	0.899247	0.902746	0.906073	0.909239	0.912256	0.915134	0.917881	0.920506	0.923016	0.925418	6
7	0.881261	0.885383	0.889304	0.893036	0.896592	0.899983	0.903221	0.906314	0.909272	0.912103	7
8	0.862914	0.867674	0.872200	0.876509	0.880614	0.884530	0.888268	0.891839	0.895254	0.898522	8
9	0.844200	0.849610	0.854754	0.859651	0.864317	0.868767	0.873015	0.877074	0.880955	0.884669	9
10	0.825112	0.831185	0.836959	0.842456	0.847694	0.852689	0.857457	0.862013	0.866370	0.870539	10
11	0.805643	0.812391	0.818809	0.824917	0.830738	0.836289	0.841589	0.846652	0.851493	0.856127	11
12	0.785784	0.793222	0.800295	0.807028	0.813443	0.819562	0.825402	0.830983	0.836319	0.841426	12
13	0.765528	0.773669	0.781411	0.788780	0.795802	0.802499	0.808893	0.815001	0.820842	0.826441	13
14	0.744866	0.753725	0.762149	0.770168	0.777809	0.785096	0.792053	0.798699	0.805055	0.811137	14
15	0.723792	0.733382	0.742502	0.751183	0.759472	0.767345	0.774876	0.782071	0.788952	0.795536	15
16	0.702296	0.712633	0.722462	0.731819	0.740735	0.749238	0.757355	0.765111	0.772527	0.779624	16
17	0.680370	0.691468	0.702022	0.712068	0.721640	0.730769	0.739484	0.747811	0.755773	0.763393	17
18	0.658005	0.669880	0.681172	0.691921	0.702163	0.711931	0.721256	0.730165	0.738685	0.746838	18
19	0.635193	0.647860	0.659906	0.671371	0.682297	0.692716	0.702663	0.712167	0.721255	0.729951	19
20	0.611925	0.625400	0.638214	0.650411	0.662033	0.673117	0.683699	0.693808	0.703476	0.712727	20
21	0.588192	0.602491	0.616088	0.629031	0.641364	0.653126	0.664355	0.675083	0.685341	0.695158	21
22	0.563984	0.579124	0.593520	0.607224	0.620282	0.632735	0.644624	0.655983	0.666844	0.677238	22
23	0.539292	0.555289	0.570501	0.584980	0.598778	0.611937	0.624499	0.636500	0.647977	0.658960	23
24	0.514106	0.530977	0.547021	0.562292	0.576843	0.590722	0.603971	0.616629	0.628733	0.640316	24
25	0.488416	0.506180	0.523071	0.539150	0.554471	0.569083	0.583032	0.596359	0.609104	0.621299	25
26	0.462212	0.480886	0.498643	0.515545	0.531650	0.547011	0.561675	0.575685	0.589082	0.601902	26
27	0.435485	0.455086	0.473725	0.491468	0.508374	0.524498	0.539890	0.554597	0.568659	0.582117	27
28	0.408223	0.428771	0.448310	0.466909	0.484632	0.501535	0.517670	0.533087	0.547828	0.561936	28
29	0.380415	0.401929	0.422386	0.441860	0.460415	0.478112	0.495006	0.511146	0.526581	0.541351	29
30	0.352051	0.374550	0.395944	0.416309	0.435713	0.454221	0.471888	0.488768	0.504909	0.520355	30
31	0.323121	0.346624	0.368973	0.390247	0.410518	0.429852	0.448308	0.465941	0.482803	0.498939	31
32	0.293611	0.318139	0.341462	0.363664	0.384819	0.404995	0.424256	0.442658	0.460255	0.477095	32
33	0.263512	0.289085	0.313402	0.336550	0.358606	0.379642	0.399723	0.418909	0.437256	0.454813	33
34	0.232810	0.259449	0.284780	0.308893	0.331868	0.353781	0.374700	0.394686	0.413797	0.432086	34
35	0.201494	0.229221	0.255586	0.280682	0.304596	0.327404	0.349176	0.369978	0.389869	0.408905	35
36	0.169552	0.198388	0.225808	0.251908	0.276778	0.300498	0.323141	0.344775	0.365463	0.385260	36
37	0.136971	0.166938	0.195434	0.222558	0.248404	0.273054	0.296596	0.319069	0.340568	0.361142	37
38	0.103739	0.134860	0.164452	0.192622	0.219463	0.245062	0.269500	0.292849	0.315175	0.336541	38
39	0.069842	0.102140	0.132852	0.162086	0.189942	0.216510	0.241872	0.266104	0.289275	0.311449	39
40	0.035267	0.068765	0.100619	0.130940	0.159831	0.187387	0.213692	0.238824	0.262857	0.285855	40
41	0.000000	0.034723	0.067741	0.099171	0.129118	0.157681	0.184948	0.210999	0.235910	0.259749	41
42		0.000000	0.034206	0.066766	0.097791	0.127381	0.155629	0.182617	0.208424	0.233120	42
43			0.000000	0.033714	0.065837	0.096475	0.125723	0.153667	0.180389	0.205960	43
44				0.000000	0.033245	0.064952	0.095220	0.124139	0.151792	0.178255	44
45					0.000000	0.032797	0.064106	0.094020	0.122624	0.149997	45
46						0.000000	0.032371	0.063298	0.092873	0.121174	46
47							0.000000	0.031963	0.062526	0.091774	47
48								0.000000	0.031573	0.061787	48
49									0.000000	0.031199	49
50										0.000000	50

TABLE C.1.   EXPECTANCY-LIFE FACTORS FOR UNIT PROPERTIES
2 Percent Interest Rate (*Continued*)

55–100 years probable life

Age, years	55	60	65	70	75	80	85	90	95	100	Age, years
1	0.989857	0.991232	0.992374	0.993332	0.994145	0.994839	0.995437	0.995954	0.996404	0.996797	1
2	0.979510	0.982289	0.984595	0.986531	0.988173	0.989575	0.990782	0.991827	0.992736	0.993530	2
3	0.968957	0.973167	0.976661	0.979594	0.982081	0.984206	0.986035	0.987618	0.989056	0.990198	3
4	0.958193	0.963862	0.968568	0.972519	0.975868	0.978730	0.981192	0.983324	0.985179	0.986800	4
5	0.947213	0.954371	0.960313	0.965301	0.969530	0.973143	0.976253	0.978944	0.981286	0.983333	5
6	0.936014	0.944691	0.951893	0.957940	0.963065	0.967446	0.971215	0.974477	0.977316	0.979797	6
7	0.924591	0.934816	0.943304	0.950431	0.956472	0.961634	0.966076	0.969921	0.973266	0.976190	7
8	0.912940	0.924745	0.934544	0.942772	0.949746	0.955706	0.960834	0.965273	0.969135	0.972511	8
9	0.901055	0.914472	0.925609	0.934960	0.942886	0.949659	0.955488	0.960533	0.964922	0.968758	9
10	0.888933	0.903993	0.916495	0.926991	0.935889	0.943492	0.950034	0.955697	0.960625	0.964931	10
11	0.876568	0.893305	0.907198	0.918863	0.928751	0.937201	0.944472	0.950765	0.956241	0.961027	11
12	0.863956	0.882403	0.897716	0.910573	0.921471	0.930784	0.938798	0.945734	0.951770	0.957045	12
13	0.851092	0.871283	0.888044	0.902117	0.914045	0.924239	0.933011	0.940603	0.947209	0.952983	13
14	0.837970	0.859941	0.878179	0.893491	0.906471	0.917563	0.927108	0.935369	0.942557	0.948840	14
15	0.824586	0.848372	0.868116	0.884694	0.898746	0.910754	0.921087	0.930030	0.937813	0.944614	15
16	0.810935	0.836571	0.857852	0.875720	0.890865	0.903808	0.914945	0.924585	0.932973	0.940303	16
17	0.797010	0.824535	0.847383	0.866567	0.882828	0.896724	0.908681	0.919031	0.928036	0.935907	17
18	0.782807	0.812257	0.836705	0.857230	0.874629	0.889497	0.902291	0.913365	0.923001	0.931422	18
19	0.768320	0.799735	0.825812	0.847707	0.866267	0.882127	0.895774	0.907587	0.917865	0.926848	19
20	0.753543	0.786961	0.814702	0.837994	0.857737	0.874608	0.889126	0.901692	0.912626	0.922182	20
21	0.738470	0.773933	0.803370	0.828086	0.849037	0.866940	0.882345	0.895680	0.907283	0.917423	21
22	0.723096	0.760643	0.791811	0.817980	0.840162	0.859118	0.875429	0.889548	0.901832	0.912568	22
23	0.707415	0.747088	0.780021	0.807672	0.831110	0.851140	0.868374	0.883293	0.896273	0.907617	23
24	0.691420	0.733262	0.767996	0.797158	0.821878	0.843002	0.861179	0.876913	0.890602	0.902567	24
25	0.675105	0.719159	0.755729	0.786433	0.812460	0.834701	0.853839	0.870405	0.884818	0.897412	25
26	0.658464	0.704775	0.743218	0.775494	0.802854	0.826234	0.846353	0.863767	0.878919	0.892161	26
27	0.641489	0.690102	0.730456	0.764336	0.793056	0.817598	0.838716	0.856996	0.872901	0.886801	27
28	0.624176	0.675136	0.717439	0.752955	0.783062	0.808789	0.830928	0.850090	0.866763	0.881335	28
29	0.606516	0.659871	0.704161	0.741347	0.772868	0.799805	0.822983	0.843046	0.860502	0.875758	29
30	0.588503	0.644300	0.690618	0.729506	0.762471	0.790640	0.814879	0.835861	0.854116	0.870071	30
31	0.570130	0.628418	0.676804	0.717429	0.751865	0.781292	0.806614	0.828532	0.847603	0.864270	31
32	0.551389	0.612219	0.662714	0.705110	0.741047	0.771757	0.798183	0.821057	0.840959	0.858352	32
33	0.532273	0.595605	0.648342	0.692544	0.730013	0.762032	0.789583	0.813432	0.834182	0.852317	33
34	0.512775	0.578841	0.633683	0.679727	0.718758	0.752111	0.780812	0.805654	0.827269	0.846160	34
35	0.492888	0.561650	0.618730	0.666654	0.707278	0.741993	0.771865	0.797721	0.820219	0.839881	35
36	0.472602	0.544115	0.603478	0.653320	0.695569	0.731672	0.762739	0.789630	0.813027	0.833476	36
37	0.451911	0.526229	0.587922	0.639719	0.683625	0.721145	0.753430	0.781376	0.805692	0.826942	37
38	0.430805	0.507986	0.572054	0.625845	0.671443	0.710407	0.743936	0.772958	0.798210	0.820278	38
39	0.409278	0.489378	0.555869	0.611694	0.659016	0.699455	0.734251	0.764371	0.790578	0.813481	39
40	0.387320	0.470397	0.539360	0.597261	0.646342	0.688283	0.724373	0.755612	0.782793	0.806548	40
41	0.364923	0.451037	0.522521	0.582538	0.633413	0.676888	0.714297	0.746679	0.774853	0.799476	41
42	0.342078	0.431290	0.505345	0.567521	0.620226	0.665265	0.704020	0.737566	0.766754	0.792263	42
43	0.318777	0.411148	0.487826	0.552204	0.606776	0.653409	0.693537	0.728271	0.758493	0.784906	43
44	0.295009	0.390603	0.469956	0.536581	0.593056	0.641317	0.682845	0.718791	0.750067	0.777401	44
45	0.270766	0.369647	0.451729	0.520645	0.579062	0.628983	0.671938	0.709121	0.741472	0.769746	45
46	0.246038	0.348272	0.433137	0.504390	0.564789	0.616402	0.660814	0.699257	0.732706	0.761939	46
47	0.220815	0.326469	0.414174	0.487810	0.550229	0.603569	0.649467	0.689196	0.723764	0.753975	47
48	0.195088	0.304231	0.394831	0.470909	0.535379	0.590479	0.637893	0.678934	0.714643	0.745851	48
49	0.168846	0.281548	0.375101	0.453649	0.520231	0.577129	0.626088	0.668467	0.705340	0.737565	49
50	0.142080	0.258410	0.354977	0.436054	0.504781	0.563510	0.614046	0.657790	0.695851	0.729114	50
55	0.000000	0.135596	0.248155	0.342659	0.422768	0.491223	0.550129	0.601117	0.645481	0.684253	55
60		0.000000	0.130216	0.239544	0.332219	0.411413	0.479559	0.538545	0.589868	0.634723	60
65			0.000000	0.125697	0.232246	0.323296	0.401644	0.469461	0.528468	0.580037	65
70				0.000000	0.121867	0.226007	0.315619	0.393186	0.460676	0.519660	70
75					0.000000	0.118593	0.220641	0.308973	0.385829	0.452998	75
80						0.000000	0.115778	0.215995	0.303192	0.379399	80
85							0.000000	0.113339	0.211954	0.298139	85
90								0.000000	0.111220	0.208421	90
95									0.000000	0.109366	95
100										0.000000	100

TABLE C.1. EXPECTANCY-LIFE FACTORS FOR UNIT PROPERTIES
5 Percent Interest Rate

1–10 years probable life

Age, years	1	2	3	4	5	6	7	8	9	10	Age, years
1	0.000000	0.512195	0.682791	0.767988	0.819025	0.852983	0.877180	0.895278	0.909310	0.920495	1
2		0.000000	0.349722	0.524376	0.629002	0.698614	0.748219	0.785320	0.814085	0.837016	2
3			0.000000	0.268583	0.429477	0.536527	0.612811	0.669864	0.714100	0.749362	3
4				0.000000	0.219976	0.366336	0.470631	0.548636	0.609114	0.657325	4
5					0.000000	0.187636	0.321343	0.421346	0.498880	0.560687	5
6						0.000000	0.164590	0.287691	0.383134	0.459217	6
7							0.000000	0.147354	0.261601	0.352673	7
8								0.000000	0.133991	0.240802	8
9									0.000000	0.123338	9
10										0.000000	10

11–20 years probable life

Age, years	11	12	13	14	15	16	17	18	19	20	Age, years
1	0.929611	0.937175	0.943544	0.948976	0.953658	0.957730	0.961301	0.964454	0.967255	0.969757	1
2	0.855703	0.871208	0.884266	0.895401	0.904998	0.913347	0.920667	0.927130	0.932873	0.938003	2
3	0.778099	0.801943	0.822023	0.839147	0.853906	0.866744	0.878001	0.887941	0.896771	0.904660	3
4	0.696615	0.729215	0.756669	0.780080	0.800259	0.817811	0.833202	0.846791	0.858865	0.869651	4
5	0.611057	0.652850	0.688046	0.718060	0.743930	0.766432	0.786163	0.803585	0.819063	0.832891	5
6	0.521221	0.572667	0.615993	0.652939	0.684784	0.712484	0.736772	0.758218	0.777271	0.794293	6
7	0.426893	0.488475	0.540337	0.584562	0.622681	0.655838	0.684911	0.710582	0.733390	0.753765	7
8	0.327849	0.400073	0.460898	0.512767	0.557472	0.596360	0.630458	0.660565	0.687314	0.711210	8
9	0.223852	0.307252	0.377487	0.437381	0.489004	0.533908	0.573281	0.608047	0.638935	0.666528	9
10	0.114656	0.209789	0.289905	0.358226	0.417112	0.468334	0.513246	0.552903	0.588137	0.619612	10
11	0.000000	0.107453	0.197945	0.275113	0.341625	0.399480	0.450210	0.495002	0.534799	0.570350	11
12		0.000000	0.101386	0.187845	0.262364	0.327184	0.384021	0.434206	0.478794	0.518625	12
13			0.000000	0.096213	0.179140	0.251274	0.314523	0.370370	0.419988	0.464314	13
14				0.000000	0.091755	0.171568	0.241550	0.303343	0.358243	0.407287	14
15					0.000000	0.087876	0.164928	0.232964	0.293410	0.347408	15
16						0.000000	0.084475	0.159066	0.225335	0.284536	16
17							0.000000	0.081473	0.153857	0.218520	17
18								0.000000	0.078805	0.149204	18
19									0.000000	0.076421	19
20										0.000000	20

21–30 years probable life

Age, years	21	22	23	24	25	26	27	28	29	30	Age, years
1	0.972004	0.974029	0.975863	0.977529	0.979048	0.980436	0.981708	0.982877	0.983954	0.984949	1
2	0.942608	0.946760	0.950520	0.953935	0.957047	0.959893	0.962502	0.964899	0.967107	0.969145	2
3	0.911742	0.918128	0.923909	0.929160	0.933947	0.938323	0.942335	0.946021	0.949417	0.952550	3
4	0.879333	0.888064	0.895967	0.903148	0.909692	0.915675	0.921160	0.926200	0.930842	0.935126	4
5	0.845304	0.856497	0.866629	0.875834	0.884224	0.891895	0.898926	0.905387	0.911338	0.916831	5
6	0.809573	0.823351	0.835823	0.847155	0.857483	0.866925	0.875580	0.883534	0.890860	0.897621	6
7	0.772055	0.788548	0.803478	0.817042	0.829405	0.840707	0.851068	0.860588	0.869357	0.877451	7
8	0.732662	0.752005	0.769515	0.785423	0.799923	0.813178	0.825329	0.836495	0.846780	0.856272	8
9	0.691299	0.713635	0.733854	0.752223	0.768966	0.784273	0.798304	0.811197	0.823073	0.834034	9
10	0.647868	0.673346	0.696410	0.717363	0.736462	0.753922	0.769927	0.784635	0.798181	0.810685	10
11	0.602265	0.631042	0.657093	0.680761	0.702333	0.722054	0.740131	0.756744	0.772045	0.786167	11
12	0.554382	0.586624	0.615811	0.642328	0.666497	0.688592	0.708846	0.727459	0.744602	0.760424	12
13	0.504105	0.539985	0.572465	0.601973	0.628869	0.653458	0.675997	0.696709	0.715786	0.733394	13
14	0.451315	0.491014	0.526951	0.559601	0.589360	0.616566	0.641505	0.664422	0.685530	0.705012	14
15	0.395884	0.439594	0.479162	0.515110	0.547876	0.577830	0.605288	0.630520	0.653761	0.675212	15

TABLE C.1.   EXPECTANCY-LIFE FACTORS FOR UNIT PROPERTIES
5 Percent Interest Rate (Continued)

21–30 years probable life

Age, years	21	22	23	24	25	26	27	28	29	30	Age, years
16	0.337682	0.385603	0.428983	0.468395	0.504317	0.537157	0.567260	0.594924	0.620403	0.643921	16
17	0.276570	0.328913	0.376296	0.419344	0.458581	0.494451	0.527332	0.557548	0.585378	0.611065	17
18	0.212403	0.269388	0.320974	0.367840	0.410557	0.449609	0.485406	0.518302	0.548602	0.576567	18
19	0.145027	0.206886	0.262886	0.313761	0.360133	0.402525	0.441385	0.477095	0.509986	0.540344	19
20	0.074282	0.141260	0.201893	0.256978	0.307187	0.353087	0.395162	0.433827	0.469440	0.502310	20
21	0.000000	0.072353	0.137851	0.197356	0.251594	0.301177	0.346628	0.388396	0.426866	0.462374	21
22		0.000000	0.070607	0.134753	0.193221	0.246672	0.295668	0.340693	0.382164	0.420441	22
23			0.000000	0.069020	0.131930	0.189441	0.242160	0.290605	0.335227	0.376412	23
24				0.000000	0.067574	0.129349	0.185976	0.238013	0.285943	0.330181	24
25					0.000000	0.066252	0.126983	0.182791	0.234194	0.281638	25
26						0.000000	0.065040	0.124808	0.179859	0.230669	26
27							0.000000	0.063926	0.122806	0.177151	27
28								0.000000	0.062901	0.120957	28
29									0.000000	0.061954	29
30										0.000000	30

31–40 years probable life

Age, years	31	32	33	34	35	36	37	38	39	40	Age, years
1	0.985868	0.986720	0.987510	0.988245	0.988928	0.989566	0.990160	0.990716	0.991235	0.991722	1
2	0.971029	0.972775	0.974395	0.975901	0.977303	0.978609	0.979828	0.980967	0.982033	0.983030	2
3	0.955448	0.958133	0.960625	0.962941	0.965096	0.967105	0.968980	0.970731	0.972370	0.973903	3
4	0.939089	0.942760	0.946166	0.949333	0.952280	0.955026	0.957589	0.959984	0.962223	0.964320	4
5	0.921911	0.926617	0.930985	0.935044	0.938822	0.942343	0.945629	0.948699	0.951570	0.954258	5
6	0.903875	0.909668	0.915044	0.920040	0.924691	0.929026	0.933071	0.936849	0.940384	0.943693	6
7	0.884936	0.891871	0.898306	0.904287	0.909854	0.915043	0.919884	0.924408	0.928638	0.932599	7
8	0.865051	0.873184	0.880731	0.887746	0.894275	0.900360	0.906039	0.911344	0.916306	0.920951	8
9	0.844171	0.853563	0.862278	0.870378	0.877917	0.884944	0.891501	0.897627	0.903356	0.908720	9
10	0.822248	0.832960	0.842902	0.852141	0.860741	0.868756	0.876236	0.883224	0.889760	0.895878	10
11	0.799228	0.811328	0.822557	0.832993	0.842707	0.851760	0.860208	0.868101	0.875483	0.882394	11
12	0.775057	0.788614	0.801194	0.812887	0.823770	0.833913	0.843379	0.852222	0.860492	0.868235	12
13	0.749678	0.764764	0.778764	0.791776	0.803887	0.815175	0.825708	0.835549	0.844752	0.853369	13
14	0.723030	0.739722	0.755212	0.769609	0.783010	0.795499	0.807154	0.818042	0.828225	0.837759	14
15	0.695049	0.713428	0.730483	0.746334	0.761088	0.774839	0.787671	0.799660	0.810872	0.821369	15
16	0.665669	0.685819	0.704517	0.721896	0.738071	0.753147	0.767215	0.780358	0.792651	0.804159	16
17	0.634821	0.656829	0.677253	0.696235	0.713903	0.730370	0.745736	0.760092	0.773519	0.786089	17
18	0.602430	0.626390	0.648625	0.669291	0.688526	0.706454	0.723183	0.738812	0.753430	0.767116	18
19	0.568419	0.594429	0.618567	0.641000	0.661881	0.681342	0.699503	0.716469	0.732337	0.747193	19
20	0.532708	0.560870	0.587005	0.611295	0.633903	0.654975	0.674638	0.693008	0.710189	0.726275	20
21	0.495211	0.525633	0.553865	0.580104	0.604527	0.627289	0.648530	0.668374	0.686934	0.704310	21
22	0.455840	0.488635	0.519068	0.547354	0.573681	0.598219	0.621117	0.642509	0.662516	0.681248	22
23	0.414500	0.449786	0.482532	0.512966	0.541294	0.567695	0.592333	0.615350	0.636878	0.657032	23
24	0.371092	0.408995	0.444168	0.476859	0.507287	0.535646	0.562110	0.586833	0.609957	0.631605	24
25	0.325515	0.366164	0.403887	0.438946	0.471579	0.501994	0.530375	0.556891	0.581690	0.604907	25
26	0.277659	0.321192	0.361591	0.399138	0.434087	0.466659	0.497054	0.525451	0.552010	0.576875	26
27	0.227409	0.273971	0.317180	0.357340	0.394719	0.429557	0.462067	0.492439	0.520846	0.547440	27
28	0.174648	0.224389	0.270549	0.313451	0.353384	0.390601	0.425331	0.457777	0.488123	0.516534	28
29	0.119248	0.172328	0.221587	0.267368	0.309981	0.349696	0.386758	0.421382	0.453765	0.484083	29
30	0.061078	0.117664	0.170176	0.218981	0.264408	0.306747	0.346256	0.383166	0.417689	0.450009	30
31	0.000000	0.060267	0.116195	0.168175	0.216557	0.261649	0.303729	0.343041	0.379809	0.414231	31
32		0.000000	0.059514	0.114828	0.166313	0.214297	0.259075	0.300908	0.340034	0.376664	32
33			0.000000	0.058815	0.113557	0.164578	0.212189	0.256670	0.298271	0.337219	33
34				0.000000	0.058163	0.112372	0.162959	0.210219	0.254420	0.295802	34
35					0.000000	0.057556	0.111267	0.161445	0.208377	0.252314	35
36						0.000000	0.056990	0.110234	0.160031	0.206652	36
37							0.000000	0.056461	0.109268	0.158706	37
38								0.000000	0.055966	0.108363	38
39									0.000000	0.055503	39
40										0.000000	40

TABLE C.1. EXPECTANCY-LIFE FACTORS FOR UNIT PROPERTIES
5 Percent Interest Rate (*Continued*)

41–50 years probable life

Age, years	41	42	43	44	45	46	47	48	49	50	Age, years
1	0.992178	0.992605	0.993007	0.993384	0.993738	0.994072	0.994386	0.994682	0.994960	0.995223	1
2	0.983964	0.984841	0.985664	0.986437	0.987163	0.987847	0.988491	0.989097	0.989669	0.990208	2
3	0.975340	0.976688	0.977954	0.979142	0.980260	0.981311	0.982301	0.983234	0.984113	0.984941	3
4	0.966285	0.968128	0.969858	0.971483	0.973011	0.974449	0.975802	0.977077	0.978278	0.979412	4
5	0.956777	0.959140	0.961357	0.963441	0.965400	0.967243	0.968978	0.970612	0.972153	0.973605	5
6	0.946793	0.949702	0.952432	0.954997	0.957408	0.959677	0.961813	0.963825	0.965721	0.967509	6
7	0.936311	0.939792	0.943060	0.946130	0.949017	0.951733	0.954289	0.956697	0.958967	0.961108	7
8	0.925304	0.929387	0.933220	0.936821	0.940206	0.943391	0.946389	0.949214	0.951876	0.954386	8
9	0.913747	0.918462	0.922888	0.927045	0.930955	0.934632	0.938095	0.941356	0.944430	0.947329	9
10	0.901612	0.906990	0.912039	0.916782	0.921241	0.925436	0.929385	0.933105	0.936612	0.939919	10
11	0.888870	0.894945	0.900647	0.906004	0.911041	0.915779	0.920240	0.924442	0.928403	0.932138	11
12	0.875492	0.882297	0.888686	0.894688	0.900331	0.905640	0.910638	0.915346	0.919783	0.923968	12
13	0.861444	0.869018	0.876127	0.882806	0.889086	0.894994	0.900556	0.905795	0.910733	0.915390	13
14	0.846694	0.855074	0.862940	0.870331	0.877279	0.883815	0.889969	0.895766	0.901230	0.906382	14
15	0.831206	0.840433	0.849094	0.857231	0.864881	0.872078	0.878853	0.885236	0.891252	0.896925	15
16	0.814944	0.825060	0.834555	0.843476	0.851863	0.859754	0.867182	0.874179	0.880775	0.886994	16
17	0.797869	0.808918	0.819290	0.829034	0.838195	0.846813	0.854927	0.862570	0.869774	0.876567	17
18	0.779940	0.791969	0.803261	0.813869	0.823843	0.833226	0.842059	0.850380	0.858223	0.865619	18
19	0.761115	0.774173	0.786431	0.797946	0.808773	0.818959	0.828548	0.837580	0.846094	0.854123	19
20	0.741349	0.755487	0.768759	0.781227	0.792950	0.803978	0.814361	0.824141	0.833359	0.842053	20
21	0.720594	0.735866	0.750203	0.763673	0.776336	0.788249	0.799465	0.810050	0.819987	0.829378	21
22	0.698801	0.715265	0.730720	0.745240	0.758891	0.771733	0.783824	0.795213	0.805947	0.816071	22
23	0.675919	0.693634	0.710263	0.725886	0.740574	0.754392	0.767401	0.779655	0.791205	0.802097	23
24	0.651892	0.670921	0.688783	0.705564	0.721340	0.736183	0.750156	0.763319	0.775726	0.787426	24
25	0.626665	0.647072	0.666229	0.684226	0.701146	0.717064	0.732050	0.746167	0.759472	0.772020	25
26	0.600176	0.622031	0.642547	0.661821	0.679941	0.696989	0.713038	0.728157	0.742406	0.755844	26
27	0.572362	0.595738	0.617681	0.638295	0.657677	0.675910	0.693076	0.709246	0.724487	0.738860	27
28	0.543158	0.568130	0.591571	0.613594	0.634299	0.653778	0.672116	0.689390	0.705671	0.721026	28
29	0.512494	0.539142	0.564157	0.587657	0.609752	0.630538	0.650505	0.668541	0.685915	0.702301	29
30	0.480296	0.508704	0.535371	0.560424	0.583978	0.606137	0.626998	0.646650	0.665171	0.682639	30
31	0.446489	0.476744	0.505146	0.531829	0.556915	0.580516	0.602734	0.623664	0.643390	0.661994	31
32	0.410991	0.443187	0.473410	0.501804	0.528499	0.553613	0.577257	0.599528	0.620520	0.640317	32
33	0.373718	0.407952	0.440088	0.470278	0.498662	0.525366	0.550505	0.574186	0.596507	0.617556	33
34	0.334582	0.370955	0.405099	0.437176	0.467333	0.495706	0.522416	0.547577	0.571292	0.593657	34
35	0.293488	0.332108	0.368360	0.402418	0.434439	0.464563	0.492923	0.519638	0.544817	0.568563	35
36	0.250340	0.291318	0.329785	0.365923	0.399899	0.431863	0.461955	0.490301	0.517018	0.542215	36
37	0.205035	0.248489	0.289281	0.327603	0.363632	0.397528	0.429438	0.459498	0.487830	0.514549	37
38	0.157465	0.203519	0.246752	0.287367	0.325552	0.361476	0.395296	0.427154	0.457182	0.485500	38
39	0.107516	0.156300	0.202096	0.245119	0.285568	0.323622	0.359447	0.393194	0.425001	0.454998	39
40	0.055069	0.106721	0.155207	0.200758	0.243584	0.283875	0.321805	0.357535	0.391211	0.422971	40
41	0.000000	0.054662	0.105974	0.154180	0.199502	0.242140	0.282281	0.320093	0.355732	0.389343	41
42		0.000000	0.054280	0.105273	0.153215	0.198319	0.240781	0.280779	0.318479	0.354033	42
43			0.000000	0.053920	0.104614	0.152307	0.197205	0.239500	0.279364	0.316958	43
44				0.000000	0.053583	0.103994	0.151451	0.196157	0.238292	0.278029	44
45					0.000000	0.053265	0.103410	0.150646	0.195167	0.237154	45
46						0.000000	0.052966	0.102860	0.149886	0.194235	46
47							0.000000	0.052684	0.102340	0.149170	47
48								0.000000	0.052419	0.101852	48
49									0.000000	0.052168	49
50										0.000000	50

TABLE C.1. EXPECTANCY-LIFE FACTORS FOR UNIT PROPERTIES
5 Percent Interest Rate (*Continued*)

Age, years	55	60	65	70	75	80	85	90	95	100	Age, years
					55–100 years probable life						
1	0.996333	0.997172	0.997811	0.998301	0.998678	0.998970	0.999197	0.999373	0.999510	0.999617	1
2	0.992483	0.994202	0.995512	0.996517	0.997291	0.997889	0.998354	0.998714	0.998995	0.999215	2
3	0.988440	0.991084	0.993099	0.994643	0.995834	0.996754	0.997468	0.998023	0.998455	0.998792	3
4	0.984195	0.987810	0.990564	0.992676	0.994304	0.995562	0.996538	0.997297	0.997888	0.998349	4
5	0.979738	0.984373	0.987904	0.990611	0.992697	0.994311	0.995562	0.996535	0.997292	0.997883	5
6	0.975058	0.980763	0.985110	0.988443	0.991011	0.992997	0.994537	0.995734	0.996667	0.997394	6
7	0.970144	0.976973	0.982176	0.986166	0.989239	0.991617	0.993461	0.994894	0.996010	0.996880	7
8	0.964985	0.972993	0.979096	0.983775	0.987380	0.990168	0.992331	0.994012	0.995321	0.996341	8
9	0.959567	0.968815	0.975861	0.981264	0.985427	0.988647	0.991144	0.993085	0.994597	0.995775	9
10	0.953879	0.964427	0.972465	0.978628	0.983377	0.987050	0.989898	0.992112	0.993836	0.995181	10
11	0.947906	0.959821	0.968899	0.975861	0.981224	0.985372	0.988590	0.991091	0.993038	0.994557	11
12	0.941634	0.954984	0.965155	0.972954	0.978964	0.983611	0.987216	0.990018	0.992200	0.993902	12
13	0.935049	0.949904	0.961224	0.969903	0.976590	0.981762	0.985774	0.988892	0.991320	0.993213	13
14	0.928134	0.944572	0.957096	0.966699	0.974098	0.979821	0.984259	0.987710	0.990396	0.992491	14
15	0.920874	0.938972	0.952761	0.963335	0.971482	0.977782	0.982669	0.986468	0.989426	0.991732	15
16	0.913251	0.933092	0.948210	0.959802	0.968734	0.975642	0.980999	0.985164	0.988407	0.990936	16
17	0.905247	0.926919	0.943432	0.956093	0.965849	0.973394	0.979246	0.983795	0.987337	0.990100	17
18	0.896842	0.920437	0.938414	0.952199	0.962820	0.971034	0.977405	0.982358	0.986214	0.989221	18
19	0.888018	0.913630	0.933146	0.948110	0.959639	0.968556	0.975472	0.980849	0.985035	0.988299	19
20	0.878752	0.906484	0.927614	0.943816	0.956300	0.965955	0.973443	0.979264	0.983797	0.987331	20
21	0.869023	0.898980	0.921805	0.939308	0.952793	0.963223	0.971312	0.977600	0.982496	0.986315	21
22	0.858807	0.891100	0.915706	0.934574	0.949111	0.960354	0.969074	0.975853	0.981131	0.985247	22
23	0.848080	0.882827	0.909302	0.929603	0.945245	0.957342	0.966725	0.974019	0.979698	0.984126	23
24	0.836817	0.874140	0.902578	0.924384	0.941186	0.954180	0.964258	0.972092	0.978193	0.982950	24
25	0.824991	0.865019	0.895518	0.918905	0.936923	0.950859	0.961668	0.970070	0.976612	0.981714	25
26	0.812574	0.855442	0.888105	0.913151	0.932448	0.947373	0.958948	0.967946	0.974953	0.980416	26
27	0.799536	0.845386	0.880321	0.907109	0.927749	0.943712	0.956092	0.965716	0.973210	0.979054	27
28	0.785846	0.834827	0.872148	0.900765	0.922815	0.939868	0.953093	0.963375	0.971381	0.977624	28
29	0.771471	0.823740	0.863566	0.894104	0.917634	0.935831	0.949949	0.960917	0.969460	0.976122	29
30	0.756378	0.812099	0.854555	0.887110	0.912194	0.931593	0.946639	0.958336	0.967443	0.974545	30
31	0.740530	0.799876	0.845094	0.879767	0.906482	0.927143	0.943168	0.955625	0.965325	0.972889	31
32	0.723890	0.787041	0.835160	0.872056	0.900484	0.922471	0.939523	0.952779	0.963101	0.971150	32
33	0.706417	0.773565	0.824728	0.863960	0.894187	0.917565	0.935696	0.949791	0.960766	0.969324	33
34	0.688071	0.759415	0.813776	0.855458	0.887575	0.912413	0.931678	0.946654	0.958315	0.967407	34
35	0.668808	0.744558	0.802275	0.846532	0.880632	0.907004	0.927458	0.943359	0.955740	0.965395	35
36	0.648582	0.728958	0.790200	0.837160	0.873342	0.901325	0.923028	0.939900	0.953037	0.963281	36
37	0.627344	0.712577	0.777521	0.827319	0.865687	0.895362	0.918376	0.936268	0.950199	0.961062	37
38	0.605044	0.695378	0.764208	0.816985	0.857650	0.889100	0.913492	0.932454	0.947219	0.958732	38
39	0.581630	0.677318	0.750229	0.806135	0.849211	0.882525	0.908363	0.928450	0.944090	0.956286	39
40	0.557044	0.658356	0.735551	0.794743	0.840350	0.875622	0.902978	0.924245	0.940804	0.953717	40
41	0.531229	0.638446	0.720140	0.782781	0.831046	0.868374	0.897324	0.919830	0.937355	0.951019	41
42	0.504124	0.617540	0.703957	0.770221	0.821276	0.860763	0.891387	0.915195	0.933732	0.948187	42
43	0.475663	0.595589	0.686966	0.757033	0.811019	0.852771	0.885153	0.910327	0.929929	0.945214	43
44	0.445779	0.572540	0.669125	0.743185	0.800248	0.844380	0.878608	0.905217	0.925935	0.942091	44
45	0.414402	0.548339	0.650392	0.728645	0.788939	0.835570	0.871735	0.899850	0.921742	0.938812	45
46	0.381455	0.522928	0.630723	0.713379	0.777064	0.826318	0.864519	0.894216	0.917339	0.935370	46
47	0.346861	0.496246	0.610070	0.697348	0.764596	0.816605	0.856942	0.888300	0.912716	0.931755	47
48	0.310537	0.468230	0.588384	0.680517	0.751504	0.806405	0.848986	0.882087	0.907862	0.927960	48
49	0.272397	0.438813	0.565614	0.662843	0.737757	0.795695	0.840632	0.875564	0.902765	0.923975	49
50	0.232350	0.407926	0.541706	0.644286	0.723324	0.784450	0.831861	0.868715	0.897413	0.919790	50
55	0.000000	0.228720	0.402991	0.536619	0.639580	0.719209	0.780969	0.828978	0.866363	0.895513	55
60		0.000000	0.225952	0.399207	0.532700	0.635942	0.716017	0.778263	0.826733	0.864529	60
65			0.000000	0.223830	0.396291	0.529670	0.633120	0.713536	0.776155	0.824983	65
70				0.000000	0.222196	0.394039	0.527319	0.630926	0.711603	0.774512	70
75					0.000000	0.220932	0.392289	0.525492	0.629217	0.710097	75
80						0.000000	0.219951	0.390929	0.524069	0.627885	80
85							0.000000	0.219189	0.389871	0.522960	85
90								0.000000	0.218595	0.389045	90
95									0.000000	0.218133	95
100										0.000000	100

TABLE C.1. EXPECTANCY-LIFE FACTORS FOR UNIT PROPERTIES
8 Percent Interest Rate

1–10 years probable life

Age, years	1	2	3	4	5	6	7	8	9	10	Age, years
1	0.000000	0.519231	0.691966	0.778079	0.829544	0.863685	0.887928	0.905985	0.919920	0.930971	1
2		0.000000	0.359290	0.538405	0.645451	0.716464	0.766889	0.804449	0.833434	0.856419	2
3			0.000000	0.279556	0.446630	0.557466	0.636168	0.694790	0.740029	0.775903	3
4				0.000000	0.231904	0.385748	0.494989	0.576359	0.639152	0.688945	4
5					0.000000	0.200292	0.342516	0.448453	0.530204	0.595032	5
6						0.000000	0.177845	0.310314	0.412541	0.493605	6
7							0.000000	0.161125	0.285464	0.384063	7
8								0.000000	0.148222	0.265759	8
9									0.000000	0.137990	9
10										0.000000	10

11–20 years probable life

Age, years	11	12	13	14	15	16	17	18	19	20	Age, years
1	0.939924	0.947305	0.953478	0.958703	0.963170	0.967023	0.970371	0.973298	0.975872	0.978148	1
2	0.875041	0.890394	0.903235	0.914103	0.923395	0.931408	0.938371	0.944460	0.949815	0.954547	2
3	0.804968	0.828931	0.848972	0.865934	0.880437	0.892944	0.903811	0.913314	0.921672	0.929059	3
4	0.729289	0.762550	0.790368	0.813912	0.834042	0.851403	0.866486	0.879677	0.891278	0.901531	4
5	0.647556	0.690859	0.727075	0.757728	0.783936	0.806538	0.826176	0.843349	0.858453	0.871802	5
6	0.559284	0.613433	0.658719	0.697049	0.729821	0.758084	0.782641	0.804115	0.823001	0.839694	6
7	0.463951	0.529813	0.584895	0.631516	0.671377	0.705754	0.735622	0.761742	0.784714	0.805017	7
8	0.360990	0.439503	0.505165	0.560741	0.608258	0.649237	0.684843	0.715980	0.743363	0.767566	8
9	0.249793	0.341968	0.419056	0.484303	0.540089	0.588199	0.630001	0.666556	0.698705	0.727119	9
10	0.129700	0.236630	0.326059	0.401751	0.466467	0.522279	0.570771	0.613178	0.650474	0.683437	10
11	0.000000	0.122866	0.225622	0.312594	0.386954	0.451084	0.506804	0.555531	0.598384	0.636259	11
12		0.000000	0.117150	0.216304	0.301081	0.374194	0.437719	0.493271	0.542127	0.585308	12
13			0.000000	0.112312	0.208338	0.291152	0.363107	0.426030	0.481369	0.530280	13
14				0.000000	0.108176	0.201468	0.282526	0.353411	0.415751	0.470850	14
15					0.000000	0.104608	0.195498	0.274982	0.344884	0.406666	15
16						0.000000	0.101509	0.190278	0.268347	0.337347	16
17							0.000000	0.098798	0.185687	0.262483	17
18								0.000000	0.096414	0.181629	18
19									0.000000	0.094308	19
20										0.000000	20

21–30 years probable life

Age, years	21	22	23	24	25	26	27	28	29	30	Age, years
1	0.980168	0.981968	0.983578	0.985022	0.986321	0.987493	0.988552	0.989511	0.990381	0.991173	1
2	0.958749	0.962493	0.965842	0.968846	0.971548	0.973985	0.976188	0.978183	0.979993	0.981639	2
3	0.935617	0.941461	0.946687	0.951376	0.955593	0.959397	0.962835	0.965949	0.968774	0.971343	3
4	0.910634	0.918745	0.926000	0.932508	0.938362	0.943641	0.948414	0.952736	0.956658	0.960223	4
5	0.883652	0.894213	0.903658	0.912130	0.919752	0.926626	0.932839	0.938466	0.943572	0.948213	5
6	0.854512	0.867718	0.879528	0.890123	0.899653	0.908249	0.916018	0.923054	0.929439	0.935243	6
7	0.823041	0.839103	0.853468	0.866355	0.877947	0.888401	0.897851	0.906410	0.914176	0.921235	7
8	0.789052	0.808200	0.825323	0.840685	0.854501	0.866966	0.878231	0.888433	0.897691	0.906106	8
9	0.752344	0.774823	0.794927	0.812962	0.829185	0.843816	0.857041	0.869019	0.879888	0.889767	9
10	0.712699	0.738777	0.762099	0.783021	0.801841	0.818815	0.834157	0.848052	0.860660	0.872121	10
11	0.669883	0.699847	0.726645	0.750685	0.772310	0.791813	0.809441	0.825407	0.839895	0.853063	11
12	0.623641	0.657803	0.688354	0.715761	0.740416	0.762651	0.782748	0.800951	0.817468	0.832481	12
13	0.573700	0.612395	0.647001	0.678044	0.705971	0.731156	0.753920	0.774538	0.793247	0.810252	13
14	0.519764	0.563355	0.602338	0.637310	0.668769	0.697141	0.722785	0.746012	0.767088	0.786244	14
15	0.461512	0.510391	0.554103	0.593317	0.628592	0.660405	0.689160	0.715204	0.738836	0.760317	15

TABLE C.1. EXPECTANCY-LIFE FACTORS FOR UNIT PROPERTIES
8 Percent Interest Rate (*Continued*)

21–30 years probable life

Age, years	21	22	23	24	25	26	27	28	29	30	Age, years
16	0.398601	0.453190	0.502009	0.545804	0.585201	0.620730	0.652845	0.681931	0.708325	0.732315	16
17	0.330657	0.391414	0.445748	0.494490	0.538338	0.577882	0.613624	0.645997	0.675372	0.702072	17
18	0.257277	0.324695	0.384986	0.439072	0.487726	0.531605	0.571266	0.607188	0.639784	0.669411	18
19	0.178027	0.252638	0.319362	0.379220	0.433066	0.481626	0.525519	0.565274	0.601347	0.634136	19
20	0.092437	0.174817	0.248489	0.314579	0.374032	0.427649	0.476113	0.520007	0.559837	0.596039	20
21	0.000000	0.090770	0.171946	0.244767	0.310276	0.369354	0.422754	0.471119	0.515005	0.554895	21
22		0.000000	0.089280	0.169371	0.241419	0.306395	0.365126	0.418319	0.466587	0.510459	22
23			0.000000	0.087943	0.167054	0.238400	0.302888	0.361296	0.414295	0.462469	23
24				0.000000	0.086740	0.164964	0.235671	0.299710	0.357820	0.410639	24
25					0.000000	0.085655	0.163077	0.233198	0.296828	0.354662	25
26						0.000000	0.084674	0.161365	0.230955	0.294208	26
27							0.000000	0.083786	0.159813	0.228917	27
28								0.000000	0.082980	0.158403	28
29									0.000000	0.082248	29
30										0.000000	30

31–40 years probable life

Age, years	31	32	33	34	35	36	37	38	39	40	Age, years
1	0.991893	0.992549	0.993148	0.993696	0.994197	0.994655	0.995076	0.995461	0.995815	0.996140	1
2	0.983137	0.984502	0.985749	0.986887	0.987929	0.988883	0.989757	0.990559	0.991295	0.991971	2
3	0.973681	0.975812	0.977757	0.979534	0.981160	0.982649	0.984013	0.985265	0.986413	0.987468	3
4	0.963468	0.966426	0.969126	0.971593	0.973850	0.975916	0.977810	0.979547	0.981141	0.982606	4
5	0.952438	0.956289	0.959804	0.963016	0.965955	0.968645	0.971111	0.973372	0.975448	0.977354	5
6	0.940526	0.945341	0.949737	0.953753	0.957428	0.960792	0.963875	0.966703	0.969298	0.971682	6
7	0.927660	0.933518	0.938864	0.943750	0.948219	0.952311	0.956061	0.959500	0.962657	0.965557	7
8	0.913766	0.920749	0.927122	0.932946	0.938273	0.943151	0.947621	0.951721	0.955484	0.958941	8
9	0.898760	0.906958	0.914440	0.921277	0.927531	0.933258	0.938506	0.943320	0.947738	0.951796	9
10	0.882553	0.892063	0.900743	0.908675	0.915931	0.922574	0.928662	0.934246	0.939372	0.944080	10
11	0.865050	0.875978	0.885951	0.895065	0.903402	0.911035	0.918031	0.924447	0.930336	0.935746	11
12	0.846147	0.858605	0.869976	0.880366	0.889871	0.898574	0.906549	0.913864	0.920578	0.926745	12
13	0.825732	0.839843	0.852722	0.864491	0.875257	0.885115	0.894149	0.902549	0.910039	0.917025	13
14	0.803683	0.819579	0.834088	0.847346	0.859474	0.870579	0.880756	0.890090	0.898657	0.906527	14
15	0.779870	0.797695	0.813964	0.828830	0.842429	0.854881	0.866292	0.876758	0.886365	0.895188	15
16	0.754153	0.774060	0.792229	0.808832	0.824020	0.837927	0.850671	0.862360	0.873089	0.882943	16
17	0.726377	0.748533	0.768756	0.787235	0.804139	0.819616	0.833800	0.846810	0.858751	0.869719	17
18	0.696380	0.720965	0.743405	0.763910	0.782666	0.799841	0.815580	0.830016	0.843266	0.855436	18
19	0.663984	0.691192	0.716026	0.738718	0.759477	0.778483	0.795902	0.811878	0.826542	0.840011	19
20	0.628995	0.659036	0.686456	0.711512	0.734431	0.755417	0.774650	0.792289	0.808480	0.823351	20
21	0.591207	0.624308	0.654521	0.682128	0.707383	0.730506	0.751697	0.771133	0.788974	0.805359	21
22	0.550397	0.586802	0.620031	0.650395	0.678170	0.703602	0.726909	0.748285	0.767906	0.785928	22
23	0.506321	0.546296	0.582722	0.616122	0.646620	0.674545	0.700137	0.723609	0.745154	0.764942	23
24	0.458719	0.502548	0.542553	0.579108	0.612546	0.643164	0.671224	0.696959	0.720581	0.742277	24
25	0.407310	0.455302	0.499105	0.539132	0.575747	0.609273	0.639997	0.667177	0.694042	0.717799	25
26	0.351787	0.404275	0.452182	0.495959	0.536004	0.572670	0.606272	0.637092	0.665380	0.691363	26
27	0.291823	0.349166	0.401505	0.449331	0.493081	0.533139	0.569850	0.603520	0.634426	0.662812	27
28	0.227061	0.289648	0.346774	0.398974	0.446724	0.490445	0.530513	0.567263	0.600995	0.631977	28
29	0.157119	0.225370	0.287664	0.344587	0.396659	0.444336	0.488030	0.528105	0.564889	0.598675	29
30	0.081581	0.155948	0.223825	0.285850	0.342588	0.394539	0.442148	0.485814	0.525895	0.562709	30
31	0.000000	0.080973	0.154880	0.222414	0.284192	0.340757	0.392596	0.440141	0.483782	0.523865	31
32		0.000000	0.080418	0.153903	0.221124	0.282673	0.339079	0.390813	0.438299	0.481914	32
33			0.000000	0.079911	0.153011	0.219942	0.281281	0.337539	0.389178	0.436607	33
34				0.000000	0.079448	0.152193	0.218859	0.280003	0.336127	0.387676	34
35					0.000000	0.079023	0.151443	0.217864	0.278832	0.334830	35
36						0.000000	0.078634	0.150755	0.216953	0.277756	36
37							0.000000	0.078277	0.150124	0.216116	37
38								0.000000	0.077949	0.149545	38
39									0.000000	0.077648	39
40										0.000000	40

TABLE C.1. EXPECTANCY-LIFE FACTORS FOR UNIT PROPERTIES
8 Percent Interest Rate (*Continued*)

Age, years	41	42	43	44	45	46	47	48	49	50	Age, years
					41–50 years probable life						
1	0.996439	0.996713	0.996966	0.997198	0.997413	0.997610	0.997792	0.997960	0.998114	0.998257	1
2	0.992592	0.993163	0.993689	0.994173	0.994618	0.995029	0.995407	0.995756	0.996078	0.996375	2
3	0.988438	0.989330	0.990150	0.990905	0.991601	0.992241	0.992832	0.993376	0.993879	0.994342	3
4	0.983952	0.985189	0.986328	0.987376	0.988341	0.989231	0.990051	0.990806	0.991503	0.992146	4
5	0.979106	0.980717	0.982200	0.983565	0.984821	0.985979	0.987047	0.988031	0.988938	0.989775	5
6	0.973873	0.975888	0.977742	0.979448	0.981020	0.982468	0.983802	0.985033	0.986168	0.987215	6
7	0.968222	0.970672	0.972927	0.975003	0.976914	0.978675	0.980299	0.981795	0.983175	0.984449	7
8	0.962118	0.965039	0.967727	0.970201	0.972480	0.974579	0.976514	0.978298	0.979944	0.981462	8
9	0.955526	0.958955	0.962111	0.965016	0.967691	0.970156	0.972428	0.974522	0.976454	0.978236	9
10	0.948406	0.952385	0.956046	0.959416	0.962519	0.965378	0.968014	0.970444	0.972685	0.974752	10
11	0.940717	0.945289	0.949495	0.953367	0.956933	0.960219	0.963247	0.966039	0.968614	0.970989	11
12	0.932413	0.937625	0.942421	0.946835	0.950901	0.954646	0.958099	0.961282	0.964217	0.966926	12
13	0.923445	0.929348	0.934780	0.939781	0.944386	0.948628	0.952539	0.956144	0.959469	0.962537	13
14	0.913759	0.920409	0.926529	0.932161	0.937349	0.942129	0.946534	0.950595	0.954341	0.957797	14
15	0.903298	0.910755	0.917617	0.923933	0.929750	0.935109	0.940048	0.944602	0.948803	0.952678	15
16	0.892000	0.900329	0.907992	0.915046	0.921543	0.927528	0.933044	0.938130	0.942821	0.947149	16
17	0.879799	0.889068	0.897597	0.905448	0.912679	0.919340	0.925480	0.931141	0.936362	0.941178	17
18	0.866621	0.876907	0.886371	0.895082	0.903106	0.910497	0.917310	0.923591	0.929385	0.934729	18
19	0.852390	0.863773	0.874246	0.883887	0.892767	0.900947	0.908487	0.915438	0.921850	0.927765	19
20	0.837019	0.849588	0.861152	0.871797	0.881601	0.890633	0.898958	0.906633	0.913713	0.920243	20
21	0.820419	0.834268	0.847010	0.858739	0.869542	0.879494	0.888667	0.897124	0.904924	0.912120	21
22	0.802491	0.817723	0.831737	0.844637	0.856518	0.867463	0.877552	0.886853	0.895432	0.903347	22
23	0.783129	0.799853	0.815241	0.829407	0.842452	0.854471	0.865548	0.875761	0.885181	0.893872	23
24	0.762218	0.780555	0.797426	0.812957	0.827261	0.840438	0.852584	0.863782	0.874110	0.883638	24
25	0.739634	0.759712	0.778186	0.795192	0.810854	0.825284	0.838583	0.850844	0.862154	0.872587	25
26	0.715243	0.737203	0.757407	0.776006	0.793136	0.808916	0.823461	0.836871	0.849240	0.860651	26
27	0.688901	0.712892	0.734966	0.755285	0.773999	0.791240	0.807130	0.821781	0.835294	0.847760	27
28	0.660452	0.686637	0.710729	0.732906	0.753331	0.772149	0.789493	0.805483	0.820232	0.833838	28
29	0.629726	0.658281	0.684553	0.708737	0.731010	0.751531	0.770444	0.787881	0.803965	0.818802	29
30	0.596543	0.627656	0.656283	0.682635	0.706904	0.729263	0.749872	0.768872	0.786397	0.802563	30
31	0.560705	0.594582	0.625751	0.654444	0.680869	0.705214	0.727654	0.748342	0.767423	0.785025	31
32	0.522000	0.558862	0.592778	0.623998	0.652751	0.679242	0.703658	0.726169	0.746931	0.766085	32
33	0.480198	0.520284	0.557165	0.591117	0.622384	0.651191	0.677742	0.702222	0.724800	0.745629	33
34	0.435053	0.478620	0.518704	0.555604	0.589588	0.620897	0.649754	0.676359	0.700898	0.723536	34
35	0.386295	0.433622	0.477167	0.517251	0.554167	0.588179	0.619526	0.648428	0.675085	0.699676	35
36	0.333638	0.385025	0.432306	0.475830	0.515913	0.552843	0.586880	0.618262	0.647205	0.673907	36
37	0.276767	0.332540	0.383856	0.431094	0.474599	0.514680	0.551623	0.585683	0.617096	0.646077	37
38	0.215347	0.275857	0.331531	0.382780	0.429980	0.473465	0.513545	0.550497	0.584578	0.616020	38
39	0.149013	0.214638	0.275019	0.330601	0.381791	0.428952	0.472420	0.512496	0.549459	0.583559	39
40	0.077372	0.148523	0.213986	0.274248	0.329746	0.380878	0.428006	0.471456	0.511530	0.548501	40
41	0.000000	0.077117	0.148071	0.213386	0.273540	0.328959	0.380038	0.427132	0.470567	0.510638	41
42		0.000000	0.076883	0.147656	0.212836	0.272886	0.328233	0.379262	0.426327	0.469747	42
43			0.000000	0.076668	0.147275	0.212327	0.272284	0.327563	0.378547	0.425584	43
44				0.000000	0.076470	0.146923	0.211859	0.271728	0.326945	0.377887	44
45					0.000000	0.076287	0.146599	0.211426	0.271215	0.326376	45
46						0.000000	0.076119	0.146300	0.211027	0.270743	46
47							0.000000	0.075963	0.146024	0.210659	47
48								0.000000	0.075820	0.145769	48
49									0.000000	0.075688	49
50										0.000000	50

TABLE C.1.　EXPECTANCY-LIFE FACTORS FOR UNIT PROPERTIES
8 Percent Interest Rate (Continued)

55–100 years probable life

Age, years	55	60	65	70	75	80	85	90	95	100	Age, years
1	0.998822	0.999202	0.999459	0.999632	0.999750	0.999830	0.999884	0.999921	0.999947	0.999964	1
2	0.997550	0.998340	0.998874	0.999235	0.999480	0.999647	0.999760	0.999837	0.999889	0.999924	2
3	0.996176	0.997410	0.998243	0.998806	0.999189	0.999449	0.999625	0.999745	0.999826	0.999882	3
4	0.994692	0.996404	0.997561	0.998343	0.998874	0.999235	0.999479	0.999646	0.999759	0.999836	4
5	0.993089	0.995319	0.996824	0.997843	0.998534	0.999003	0.999322	0.999539	0.999686	0.999787	5
6	0.991359	0.994146	0.996029	0.997303	0.998167	0.998754	0.999152	0.999423	0.999608	0.999733	6
7	0.989489	0.992880	0.995170	0.996720	0.997771	0.998484	0.998969	0.999299	0.999523	0.999675	7
8	0.987470	0.991513	0.994242	0.996090	0.997343	0.998193	0.998771	0.999164	0.999431	0.999613	8
9	0.985290	0.990036	0.993240	0.995409	0.996880	0.997879	0.998557	0.999019	0.999332	0.999546	9
10	0.982935	0.988440	0.992158	0.994674	0.996381	0.997539	0.998326	0.998862	0.999225	0.999473	10
11	0.980392	0.986718	0.990989	0.993880	0.995841	0.997172	0.998077	0.998692	0.999110	0.999394	11
12	0.977646	0.984857	0.989727	0.993023	0.995259	0.996776	0.997808	0.998509	0.998985	0.999310	12
13	0.974679	0.982848	0.988364	0.992097	0.994630	0.996349	0.997517	0.998311	0.998851	0.999218	13
14	0.971476	0.980678	0.986891	0.991098	0.993950	0.995887	0.997202	0.998097	0.998705	0.999119	14
15	0.968016	0.978334	0.985301	0.990018	0.993216	0.995388	0.996863	0.997866	0.998548	0.999012	15
16	0.964279	0.975803	0.983584	0.988852	0.992424	0.994849	0.996497	0.997617	0.998379	0.998897	16
17	0.960244	0.973069	0.981729	0.987592	0.991568	0.994267	0.996101	0.997348	0.998195	0.998772	17
18	0.955885	0.970117	0.979726	0.986232	0.990643	0.993638	0.995673	0.997057	0.997998	0.998638	18
19	0.951178	0.966928	0.977563	0.984763	0.989645	0.992960	0.995212	0.996743	0.997784	0.998492	19
20	0.946094	0.963484	0.975227	0.983176	0.988567	0.992226	0.994713	0.996404	0.997553	0.998335	20
21	0.940604	0.959765	0.972704	0.981463	0.987402	0.991435	0.994175	0.996037	0.997304	0.998166	21
22	0.934674	0.955748	0.969978	0.979612	0.986145	0.990580	0.993593	0.995642	0.997035	0.997982	22
23	0.928270	0.951410	0.967035	0.977613	0.984786	0.989656	0.992965	0.995214	0.996744	0.997785	23
24	0.921354	0.946725	0.963857	0.975455	0.983319	0.988659	0.992287	0.994753	0.996430	0.997571	24
25	0.913884	0.941665	0.960424	0.973123	0.981735	0.987581	0.991554	0.994255	0.996091	0.997340	25
26	0.905817	0.936200	0.956717	0.970606	0.980024	0.986418	0.990763	0.993716	0.995725	0.997091	26
27	0.897104	0.930298	0.952713	0.967886	0.978176	0.985162	0.989908	0.993135	0.995329	0.996822	27
28	0.887695	0.923924	0.948388	0.964950	0.976181	0.983805	0.988986	0.992507	0.994902	0.996531	28
29	0.877532	0.917041	0.943718	0.961778	0.974025	0.982340	0.987989	0.991829	0.994441	0.996217	29
30	0.866557	0.909606	0.938674	0.958353	0.971697	0.980757	0.986912	0.991097	0.993943	0.995878	30
31	0.854704	0.901576	0.933227	0.954654	0.969183	0.979047	0.985750	0.990306	0.993405	0.995512	31
32	0.841902	0.892904	0.927344	0.950658	0.966468	0.977201	0.984494	0.989452	0.992824	0.995117	32
33	0.828076	0.883539	0.920990	0.946343	0.963536	0.975207	0.983138	0.988529	0.992196	0.994690	33
34	0.813144	0.873424	0.914128	0.941683	0.960369	0.973054	0.981674	0.987533	0.991518	0.994228	34
35	0.797017	0.862500	0.906717	0.936650	0.956948	0.970729	0.980092	0.986457	0.990786	0.993730	35
36	0.779601	0.850702	0.898713	0.931215	0.953254	0.968217	0.978384	0.985295	0.989996	0.993192	36
37	0.760791	0.837960	0.890069	0.925344	0.949265	0.965505	0.976539	0.984040	0.989142	0.992611	37
38	0.740476	0.824199	0.880733	0.919004	0.944956	0.962575	0.974547	0.982685	0.988219	0.991984	38
39	0.718536	0.809337	0.870650	0.912157	0.940303	0.959412	0.972395	0.981221	0.987223	0.991306	39
40	0.694841	0.793286	0.859761	0.904761	0.935277	0.955995	0.970071	0.979640	0.986148	0.990574	40
41	0.669250	0.775951	0.848000	0.896775	0.929850	0.952304	0.967561	0.977933	0.984986	0.989784	41
42	0.641612	0.757229	0.835299	0.888149	0.923988	0.948319	0.964851	0.976089	0.983732	0.988930	42
43	0.611763	0.737009	0.821582	0.878833	0.917657	0.944015	0.961923	0.974097	0.982377	0.988008	43
44	0.579527	0.715172	0.806767	0.868772	0.910820	0.939366	0.958761	0.971947	0.980913	0.987013	44
45	0.544711	0.691588	0.790767	0.857907	0.903435	0.934345	0.955347	0.969624	0.979333	0.985937	45
46	0.507110	0.666117	0.773487	0.846171	0.895460	0.928923	0.951659	0.967115	0.977626	0.984776	46
47	0.466500	0.638609	0.754824	0.833498	0.886847	0.923067	0.947676	0.964406	0.975783	0.983522	47
48	0.422643	0.608900	0.734669	0.819810	0.877545	0.916742	0.943375	0.961480	0.973792	0.982167	48
49	0.375276	0.576814	0.712901	0.805027	0.867499	0.909912	0.938729	0.958319	0.971642	0.980704	49
50	0.324120	0.542161	0.689392	0.789061	0.856649	0.902535	0.933712	0.954906	0.969320	0.979124	50
55	0.000000	0.322603	0.540439	0.687905	0.787905	0.855795	0.901923	0.933281	0.954607	0.969113	55
60		0.000000	0.321578	0.539273	0.686897	0.787120	0.855215	0.901507	0.932989	0.954403	60
65			0.000000	0.320885	0.538483	0.686212	0.786586	0.854821	0.901225	0.932789	65
70				0.000000	0.320414	0.537946	0.685747	0.786223	0.854553	0.901032	70
75					0.000000	0.320095	0.537582	0.685431	0.785977	0.854370	75
80						0.000000	0.319878	0.537334	0.685216	0.785809	80
85							0.000000	0.319731	0.537165	0.685070	85
90								0.000000	0.319630	0.537051	90
95									0.000000	0.319562	95
100										0.000000	100

TABLE C.2. EXPECTANCY-LIFE FACTORS FOR GROUP PROPERTIES UNIT SUMMATION PROCEDURE

Type Curve L_2

10 Years Average Life

Age	Percent surviving	0%	2%	4%	6%	8%
1	99.8894	0.87557	0.88400	0.89180	0.89899	0.90560
2	99.2093	0.75796	0.77263	0.78634	0.79910	0.81096
3	97.6156	0.65004	0.66901	0.68691	0.70373	0.71948
4	94.8566	0.55259	0.57420	0.59477	0.61427	0.63268
5	90.0774	0.46959	0.49265	0.51479	0.53595	0.55607
6	82.7811	0.40321	0.42707	0.45017	0.47240	0.49368
7	73.5362	0.35139	0.37576	0.39952	0.42255	0.44470
8	63.4216	0.31058	0.33530	0.35958	0.38326	0.40617
9	53.4482	0.27736	0.30229	0.32696	0.35118	0.37473
10	44.2768	0.24900	0.27396	0.29886	0.32345	0.34749
11	36.1931	0.22363	0.24840	0.27328	0.29801	0.32233
12	29.2188	0.20023	0.22453	0.24912	0.27372	0.29805
13	23.2502	0.17842	0.20198	0.22600	0.25019	0.27424
14	18.1618	0.15818	0.18076	0.20397	0.22749	0.25101
15	13.8551	0.13956	0.16100	0.18321	0.20586	0.22863
16	10.2653	0.12260	0.14278	0.16383	0.18544	0.20729
17	7.3445	0.10720	0.12604	0.14583	0.16628	0.18706
18	5.0429	0.09327	0.11068	0.12912	0.14829	0.16789
19	3.2984	0.08060	0.09654	0.11355	0.13136	0.14965
20	2.0352	0.06904	0.08347	0.09899	0.11533	0.13220
21	1.1690	0.05848	0.07135	0.08531	0.10010	0.11544
22	0.6133	0.04877	0.06005	0.07240	0.08554	0.09925
23	0.2856	0.03981	0.04950	0.06016	0.07159	0.08356
24	0.1129	0.03159	0.03962	0.04852	0.05813	0.06831
25	3.501*$^{-2}$	0.02397	0.03031	0.03740	0.04514	0.05344
26	7.314*$^{-3}$	0.01687	0.02151	0.02674	0.03255	0.03887
27	7.092*$^{-4}$	0.01021	0.01316	0.01648	0.02028	0.02442
28	7.641*$^{-5}$	0.00395	0.00522	0.00659	0.00823	0.00996
28.69	0.0000	0.00000	0.00000	0.00000	0.00000	0.00000

Type Curve L_2
20 Years Average Life

Age	Percent surviving	0%	2%	4%	6%	8%
1	99.9852	0.93706	0.94577	0.95323	0.95955	0.96488
2	99.8894	0.87519	0.89156	0.90571	0.91781	0.92810
3	99.6473	0.81518	0.83817	0.85824	0.87556	0.89040
4	99.2093	0.75747	0.78610	0.81134	0.83332	0.85228
5	98.5398	0.70228	0.73562	0.76530	0.79136	0.81402
6	97.6156	0.64959	0.68683	0.72025	0.74982	0.77574
7	96.4179	0.59951	0.63974	0.67621	0.70875	0.73744
8	94.8566	0.55226	0.59482	0.63373	0.66869	0.69972
9	92.7782	0.50867	0.55297	0.59379	0.63073	0.66372
10	90.0774	0.46921	0.51480	0.55716	0.59573	0.63035
11	86.7286	0.43398	0.48056	0.52416	0.56410	0.60012
12	82.7811	0.40278	0.45015	0.49479	0.53591	0.57316
13	78.3388	0.37527	0.42327	0.46881	0.51099	0.54935
14	73.5362	0.35097	0.39951	0.44588	0.48903	0.52841
15	68.5180	0.32944	0.37844	0.42556	0.46962	0.50998
16	63.4216	0.31020	0.35962	0.40743	0.45236	0.49363
17	58.3665	0.29286	0.34262	0.39107	0.43681	0.47896
18	53.4482	0.27703	0.32706	0.37609	0.42259	0.46556
19	48.7366	0.26240	0.31261	0.36214	0.40933	0.45307
20	44.2768	0.24870	0.29900	0.34893	0.39672	0.44116
21	40.0932	0.23574	0.28600	0.33622	0.38450	0.42954
22	36.1931	0.22337	0.27345	0.32383	0.37249	0.41803
23	32.5723	0.21147	0.26125	0.31164	0.36054	0.40648
24	29.2188	0.20000	0.24932	0.29958	0.34859	0.39478
25	26.1170	0.18891	0.23764	0.28762	0.33661	0.38293

20 Years Average Life (Continued)

Age	Percent surviving	0%	2%	4%	6%	8%
26	23.2502	0.17821	0.22621	0.27578	0.32459	0.37091
27	20.6030	0.16790	0.21505	0.26407	0.31257	0.35876
28	18.1618	0.15798	0.20418	0.25253	0.30060	0.34654
29	15.9154	0.14847	0.19362	0.24119	0.28871	0.33429
30	13.8551	0.13938	0.18341	0.23009	0.27696	0.32207
31	11.9737	0.13070	0.17353	0.21925	0.26537	0.30992
32	10.2653	0.12243	0.16401	0.20869	0.25397	0.29786
33	8.7241	0.11455	0.15484	0.19840	0.24276	0.28591
34	7.3445	0.10705	0.14600	0.18839	0.23175	0.27407
35	6.1198	0.09992	0.13749	0.17864	0.22093	0.26234
36	5.0429	0.09312	0.12928	0.16913	0.21028	0.25071
37	4.1055	0.08664	0.12136	0.15986	0.19979	0.23916
38	3.2984	0.08045	0.11370	0.15080	0.18945	0.22768
39	2.6118	0.07454	0.10629	0.14194	0.17923	0.21625
40	2.0352	0.06890	0.09912	0.13325	0.16913	0.20485
41	1.5579	0.06350	0.09217	0.12474	0.15913	0.19348
42	1.1690	0.05834	0.08542	0.11638	0.14921	0.18212
43	0.8576	0.05339	0.07886	0.10817	0.13937	0.17076
44	0.6132	0.04864	0.07249	0.10008	0.12960	0.15938
45	0.4258	0.04409	0.06628	0.09212	0.11988	0.14797
46	0.2856	0.03973	0.06024	0.08427	0.11019	0.13653
47	0.1840	0.03553	0.05434	0.07652	0.10054	0.12503
48	0.1129	0.03148	0.04859	0.06886	0.09092	0.11348
49	6.525*$^{-2}$	0.02760	0.04298	0.06130	0.08125	0.10187
50	3.501*$^{-2}$	0.02387	0.03749	0.05381	0.07167	0.09018
51	1.707*$^{-2}$	0.02026	0.03212	0.04646	0.06213	0.07842
52	7.314*$^{-3}$	0.01679	0.02687	0.03914	0.05256	0.06658
53	2.614*$^{-3}$	0.01344	0.02173	0.03184	0.04294	0.05465
54	7.092*$^{-4}$	0.01020	0.01667	0.02456	0.03324	0.04257
55	1.203*$^{-4}$	0.00706	0.01166	0.01728	0.02347	0.03029
56	7.652*$^{-6}$	0.00403	0.00671	0.01000	0.01363	0.01774
57	2.686*$^{-8}$	0.00109	0.00180	0.00272	0.00371	0.00488
57.37	0.0000	0.00000	0.00000	0.00000	0.00000	0.00000

Type Curve L_2
25 Years Average Life

Age	Percent surviving	0%	2%	4%	6%	8%
1	99.9922	0.94957	0.95824	0.96537	0.97115	0.97580
2	99.9420	0.89971	0.91624	0.92996	0.94118	0.95028
3	99.8132	0.85088	0.87446	0.89422	0.91051	0.92383
4	99.5767	0.80339	0.83312	0.85846	0.87946	0.89676
5	99.2093	0.75742	0.79275	0.82293	0.84825	0.86926
6	98.6935	0.71306	0.75317	0.78776	0.81700	0.84145
7	98.0168	0.67033	0.71454	0.75301	0.78579	0.81338
8	97.1714	0.62922	0.67688	0.71871	0.75462	0.78505
9	96.1396	0.58974	0.64022	0.68492	0.72357	0.75652
10	94.8566	0.55220	0.60496	0.65206	0.69307	0.72823
11	93.2414	0.51700	0.57159	0.62069	0.66373	0.70083
12	91.2359	0.48442	0.54045	0.59125	0.63603	0.67482
13	88.8144	0.45455	0.51175	0.56398	0.61029	0.65058
14	85.9843	0.42736	0.48552	0.53899	0.58665	0.62828
15	82.7811	0.40273	0.46168	0.51625	0.56513	0.60798
16	79.2606	0.38044	0.44008	0.49565	0.54564	0.58961
17	75.4912	0.36028	0.42052	0.47701	0.52805	0.57308
18	71.5468	0.34200	0.40279	0.46013	0.51217	0.55819
19	67.5009	0.32537	0.38665	0.44480	0.49779	0.54477
20	63.4216	0.31016	0.37188	0.43081	0.48471	0.53261

* Condensed from the usual form 3.501×10^{-2}.

TABLE C.2.　EXPECTANCY-LIFE FACTORS FOR GROUP PROPERTIES
UNIT SUMMATION PROCEDURE
Type Curve L_2 (*Continued*)

Age	Percent surviving	Interest rate					Age	Percent surviving	Interest rate				
		0%	2%	4%	6%	8%			0%	2%	4%	6%	8%
	25 Years Average Life (*Continued*)							30 Years Average Life					
21	59.3692	0.29615	0.35826	0.41792	0.47270	0.52149	1	99.9954	0.95792	0.96653	0.97331	0.97855	0.98258
22	55.3941	0.28316	0.34561	0.40595	0.46157	0.51120	2	99.9658	0.91621	0.93265	0.94591	0.95618	0.96414
23	51.5357	0.27101	0.33374	0.39470	0.45111	0.50156	3	99.8894	0.87512	0.89894	0.91807	0.93314	0.94490
24	47.8234	0.25955	0.32248	0.38400	0.44115	0.49237	4	99.7476	0.83487	0.86531	0.89002	0.90962	0.92504
25	44.2768	0.24867	0.31171	0.37372	0.43153	0.48346	5	99.5251	0.79559	0.83204	0.86189	0.88578	0.90471
26	40.9072	0.23825	0.30131	0.36371	0.42211	0.47471	6	99.2093	0.75738	0.79923	0.83382	0.86172	0.88398
27	37.7192	0.22822	0.29120	0.35389	0.41280	0.46598	7	98.7903	0.72030	0.76696	0.80588	0.83752	0.86293
28	34.7118	0.21852	0.28130	0.34418	0.40350	0.45718	8	98.2608	0.68435	0.73526	0.77811	0.81320	0.84158
29	31.8806	0.20912	0.27158	0.33453	0.39416	0.44826	9	97.6156	0.64953	0.70416	0.75052	0.78878	0.81991
30	29.2188	0.19997	0.26201	0.32491	0.38474	0.43917	10	96.8504	0.61582	0.67363	0.72312	0.76424	0.79791
31	26.7180	0.19107	0.25257	0.31531	0.37524	0.42990	11	95.9455	0.58328	0.64380	0.69602	0.73971	0.77569
32	24.3698	0.18242	0.24327	0.30573	0.36564	0.42044	12	94.8566	0.55215	0.61492	0.66952	0.71550	0.75250
33	22.1658	0.17401	0.23411	0.29619	0.35598	0.41081	13	93.5365	0.52264	0.58730	0.64396	0.69197	0.73190
34	20.0987	0.16586	0.22511	0.28670	0.34626	0.40104	14	91.9500	0.49494	0.56115	0.61962	0.66943	0.71105
35	18.1618	0.15796	0.21628	0.27727	0.33651	0.39115	15	90.0774	0.46910	0.53663	0.59667	0.64810	0.69125
36	16.3495	0.15032	0.20764	0.26795	0.32676	0.38118	16	87.9152	0.44516	0.51379	0.57523	0.62812	0.67266
37	14.6574	0.14294	0.19919	0.25873	0.31704	0.37115	17	85.4751	0.42305	0.49263	0.55533	0.60955	0.65536
38	13.0814	0.13584	0.19095	0.24965	0.30737	0.36109	18	82.7811	0.40269	0.47310	0.53694	0.59239	0.63937
39	11.6184	0.12899	0.18292	0.24070	0.29776	0.35101	19	79.8666	0.38397	0.45510	0.52001	0.57661	0.62469
40	10.2653	0.12240	0.17511	0.23191	0.28823	0.34094	20	76.7708	0.36675	0.43854	0.50444	0.56213	0.61124
41	9.0193	0.11607	0.16750	0.22326	0.27878	0.33089	21	73.5363	0.35089	0.42329	0.49013	0.54885	0.59896
42	7.8774	0.10998	0.16010	0.21478	0.26941	0.32085	22	70.2060	0.33626	0.40922	0.47696	0.53668	0.58773
43	6.8364	0.10414	0.15291	0.20642	0.26013	0.31083	23	66.8215	0.32272	0.39619	0.46480	0.52548	0.57744
44	5.8929	0.09851	0.14591	0.19822	0.25092	0.30083	24	63.4216	0.31014	0.38408	0.45352	0.51514	0.56798
45	5.0429	0.09310	0.13909	0.19015	0.24179	0.29084	25	60.0405	0.29839	0.37277	0.44301	0.50553	0.55923
46	4.2822	0.08790	0.13245	0.18220	0.23272	0.28084	26	56.7079	0.28737	0.36214	0.43315	0.49654	0.55107
47	3.6062	0.08287	0.12597	0.17437	0.22371	0.27084	27	53.4482	0.27697	0.35209	0.42381	0.48804	0.54338
48	3.0099	0.07804	0.11965	0.16665	0.21474	0.26083	28	50.2809	0.26710	0.34251	0.41490	0.47993	0.53604
49	2.4880	0.07338	0.11348	0.15903	0.20582	0.25078	29	47.2204	0.25768	0.33331	0.40632	0.47211	0.52896
50	2.0352	0.06888	0.10745	0.15150	0.19692	0.24071	30	44.2768	0.24865	0.32443	0.39799	0.46448	0.52204
51	1.6460	0.06455	0.10155	0.14406	0.18806	0.23060	31	41.4563	0.23994	0.31579	0.38982	0.45697	0.51518
52	1.3147	0.06036	0.09578	0.13670	0.17921	0.22044	32	38.7616	0.23151	0.30734	0.38178	0.44951	0.50832
53	1.0357	0.05632	0.09013	0.12941	0.17038	0.21023	33	36.1931	0.22332	0.29904	0.37379	0.44204	0.50140
54	0.8037	0.05241	0.08460	0.12219	0.16155	0.19996	34	33.7488	0.21534	0.29086	0.36584	0.43451	0.49438
55	0.6133	0.04863	0.07917	0.11503	0.15272	0.18962	35	31.4255	0.20756	0.28277	0.35788	0.42692	0.48721
56	0.4592	0.04497	0.07397	0.10793	0.14389	0.17920	36	29.2188	0.19995	0.27477	0.34992	0.41922	0.47988
57	0.3366	0.04144	0.06861	0.10088	0.13505	0.16871	37	27.1240	0.19252	0.26685	0.34193	0.41143	0.47237
58	0.2408	0.03801	0.06347	0.09387	0.12619	0.15812	38	25.1361	0.18526	0.25900	0.33393	0.40352	0.46469
59	0.1675	0.03469	0.05843	0.08691	0.11731	0.14745	39	23.2502	0.17817	0.25123	0.32592	0.39552	0.45684
60	0.1129	0.03147	0.05346	0.07999	0.10840	0.13667	40	21.4619	0.17125	0.24356	0.31790	0.38743	0.44883
61	7.320*⁻²	0.02836	0.04858	0.07310	0.09947	0.12579	41	19.7670	0.16451	0.23598	0.30989	0.37927	0.44068
62	4.537*⁻²	0.02533	0.04377	0.06624	0.09050	0.11480	42	18.1618	0.15794	0.22850	0.30191	0.37106	0.43240
63	2.661*⁻²	0.02240	0.03903	0.05942	0.08150	0.10370	43	16.6431	0.15156	0.22115	0.29397	0.36280	0.42402
64	1.457*⁻²	0.01956	0.03437	0.05262	0.07246	0.09248	44	15.2083	0.14536	0.21391	0.28607	0.35453	0.41556
65	7.314*⁻³	0.01681	0.02978	0.04585	0.06340	0.08117	45	13.8551	0.13934	0.20688	0.27824	0.34625	0.40702
66	3.270*⁻³	0.01413	0.02525	0.03910	0.05428	0.06972	46	12.5813	0.13351	0.19992	0.27049	0.33797	0.39844
67	1.246*⁻³	0.01153	0.02078	0.03234	0.04509	0.05809	47	11.3853	0.12786	0.19310	0.26281	0.32971	0.38980
68	3.754*⁻⁴	0.00902	0.01639	0.02565	0.03590	0.04642	48	10.2653	0.12239	0.18642	0.25521	0.32148	0.38114
69	7.714*⁻⁵	0.00657	0.01200	0.01893	0.02663	0.03463	49	9.2196	0.11710	0.17987	0.24770	0.31326	0.37244
70	7.652*⁻⁶	0.00415	0.00759	0.01210	0.01716	0.02252	50	8.2466	0.11198	0.17347	0.24028	0.30508	0.36372
71	1.194*⁻⁷	0.00173	0.00317	0.00511	0.00735	0.00978	51	7.3445	0.10702	0.16720	0.23294	0.29693	0.35498
71.71	0.0000	0.00000	0.00000	0.00000	0.00000	0.00000	52	6.5113	0.10222	0.16106	0.22568	0.28881	0.34621
							53	5.7448	0.09758	0.15504	0.21851	0.28071	0.33741
							54	5.0429	0.09308	0.14915	0.21141	0.27264	0.32858
							55	4.4030	0.08873	0.14338	0.20438	0.26458	0.31970

* Condensed from the usual form 7.320×10^{-2}.

TABLE C.2. EXPECTANCY-LIFE FACTORS FOR GROUP PROPERTIES UNIT SUMMATION PROCEDURE
Type Curve L_2 (*Continued*)

30 Years Average Life (*Continued*)

Age	Percent surviving	Interest rate				
		0%	2%	4%	6%	8%
56	3.8225	0.08451	0.13771	0.19741	0.25654	0.31078
57	3.2984	0.08042	0.13215	0.19050	0.24850	0.30181
58	2.8279	0.07646	0.12669	0.18365	0.24046	0.29278
59	2.4079	0.07261	0.12132	0.17696	0.23243	0.28367
60	2.0352	0.06888	0.11605	0.17010	0.22439	0.27448
61	1.7067	0.06525	0.11086	0.16340	0.21634	0.26519
62	1.4190	0.06173	0.10576	0.15673	0.20827	0.25579
63	1.1690	0.05831	0.10073	0.15010	0.20019	0.24625
64	0.9535	0.05499	0.09578	0.14350	0.19208	0.23655
65	0.7692	0.05176	0.09090	0.13693	0.18395	0.22838
66	0.6133	0.04862	0.08610	0.13038	0.17579	0.21883
67	0.4825	0.04556	0.08136	0.12386	0.16759	0.20918
68	0.3742	0.04259	0.07668	0.11736	0.15936	0.19943
69	0.2856	0.03970	0.07206	0.11087	0.15109	0.18958
70	0.2141	0.03688	0.06749	0.10440	0.14277	0.17962
71	0.1572	0.03414	0.06298	0.09794	0.13440	0.16954
72	0.1129	0.03146	0.05853	0.09148	0.12599	0.15935
73	7.891*$^{-2}$	0.02886	0.05412	0.08504	0.11752	0.14904
74	5.351*$^{-2}$	0.02632	0.04976	0.07860	0.10900	0.13860
75	3.501*$^{-2}$	0.02384	0.04546	0.07216	0.10042	0.12804
76	2.195*$^{-2}$	0.02143	0.04119	0.06572	0.09178	0.11734
77	1.308*$^{-2}$	0.01908	0.03697	0.05929	0.08309	0.10652
78	7.314*$^{-3}$	0.01678	0.03279	0.05285	0.07432	0.09554
79	3.776*$^{-3}$	0.01455	0.02864	0.04640	0.06548	0.08441
80	1.756*$^{-3}$	0.01236	0.02452	0.03993	0.05656	0.07315
81	7.092*$^{-4}$	0.01021	0.02042	0.03342	0.04753	0.06169
82	2.336*$^{-4}$	0.00810	0.01634	0.02687	0.03838	0.04996
83	5.604*$^{-5}$	0.00603	0.01226	0.02028	0.02908	0.03795
84	7.652*$^{-6}$	0.00400	0.00818	0.01364	0.01961	0.02565
85	3.023*$^{-7}$	0.00200	0.00410	0.00691	0.00994	0.01303
86		0.00001	0.00002	0.00004	0.00006	0.00008
86.06	0.0000	0.00000	0.00000	0.00000	0.00000	0.00000

Type Curve L_2
40 Years Average Life

Age	Percent surviving	Interest rate				
		0%	2%	4%	6%	8%
1	99.9980	0.96842	0.97681	0.98287	0.98714	0.99014
2	99.9852	0.93700	0.95331	0.96520	0.97366	0.97966
3	99.9519	0.90586	0.92963	0.94713	0.95968	0.96864
4	99.8894	0.87510	0.90588	0.92875	0.94528	0.95717
5	99.7901	0.84482	0.88215	0.91014	0.93053	0.94530
6	99.6473	0.81507	0.85850	0.89137	0.91550	0.93309
7	99.4553	0.78591	0.83500	0.87249	0.90022	0.92058
8	99.2093	0.75736	0.81169	0.85355	0.88473	0.90778
9	98.9052	0.72944	0.78859	0.83456	0.86906	0.89472
10	98.5398	0.70216	0.76573	0.81555	0.85321	0.88139
11	98.1105	0.67552	0.74311	0.79653	0.83719	0.86780
12	97.6156	0.64951	0.72074	0.77750	0.82098	0.85392
13	97.0534	0.62413	0.69861	0.75845	0.80459	0.83973
14	96.4179	0.59938	0.67676	0.73941	0.78802	0.82525
15	95.6925	0.57534	0.65528	0.72050	0.77140	0.81058

40 Years Average Life (*Continued*)

Age	Percent surviving	Interest rate				
		0%	2%	4%	6%	8%
16	94.8566	0.55213	0.63431	0.70186	0.75489	0.79588
17	93.8903	0.52984	0.61399	0.68365	0.73863	0.78132
18	92.7782	0.50854	0.59442	0.66600	0.72278	0.76705
19	91.5091	0.48828	0.57567	0.64901	0.70746	0.75319
20	90.0774	0.46908	0.55782	0.63276	0.69275	0.73984
21	88.4825	0.45094	0.54087	0.61729	0.67872	0.72708
22	86.7286	0.43385	0.52484	0.60263	0.66541	0.71496
23	84.8242	0.41777	0.50973	0.58880	0.65284	0.70350
24	82.7811	0.40266	0.49550	0.57577	0.64101	0.69271
25	80.6138	0.38848	0.48212	0.56354	0.62990	0.68260
26	78.3388	0.37515	0.46955	0.55206	0.61951	0.67314
27	75.9735	0.36264	0.45774	0.54129	0.60979	0.66432
28	73.5363	0.35087	0.44664	0.53120	0.60070	0.65609
29	71.0452	0.33979	0.43619	0.52174	0.59221	0.64843
30	68.5180	0.32934	0.42634	0.51284	0.58427	0.64129
31	65.9716	0.31946	0.41704	0.50448	0.57683	0.63462
32	63.4216	0.31011	0.40824	0.49658	0.56983	0.62838
33	60.8823	0.30123	0.39987	0.48910	0.56323	0.62252
34	58.3665	0.29277	0.39190	0.48198	0.55698	0.61699
35	55.8853	0.28469	0.38427	0.47518	0.55103	0.61174
36	53.4482	0.27694	0.37694	0.46865	0.54532	0.60671
37	51.0632	0.26950	0.36986	0.46235	0.53981	0.60188
38	48.7366	0.26232	0.36301	0.45623	0.53446	0.59717
39	46.4733	0.25537	0.35633	0.45024	0.52922	0.59257
40	44.2768	0.24863	0.34981	0.44437	0.52406	0.58801
41	42.1497	0.24207	0.34341	0.43857	0.51893	0.58348
42	40.0932	0.23567	0.33711	0.43281	0.51382	0.57892
43	38.1077	0.22942	0.33089	0.42708	0.50868	0.57432
44	36.1931	0.22330	0.32473	0.42135	0.50350	0.56965
45	34.3484	0.21730	0.31862	0.41560	0.49826	0.56489
46	32.5723	0.21141	0.31254	0.40982	0.49293	0.56002
47	30.8630	0.20562	0.30650	0.40401	0.48753	0.55502
48	29.2188	0.19994	0.30049	0.39816	0.48202	0.54989
49	27.6374	0.19435	0.29450	0.39226	0.47642	0.54463
50	26.1170	0.18886	0.28853	0.38632	0.47072	0.53923
51	24.6552	0.18346	0.28259	0.38033	0.46491	0.53369
52	23.2502	0.17816	0.27668	0.37430	0.45901	0.52801
53	21.9001	0.17295	0.27080	0.36824	0.45302	0.52221
54	20.6030	0.16784	0.26496	0.36215	0.44695	0.51628
55	19.3574	0.16284	0.25916	0.35604	0.44081	0.51023
56	18.1618	0.15793	0.25341	0.34992	0.43459	0.50408
57	17.0148	0.15312	0.24771	0.34378	0.42832	0.49783
58	15.9154	0.14842	0.24207	0.33765	0.42199	0.49149
59	14.8625	0.14382	0.23648	0.33145	0.41562	0.48507
60	13.8551	0.13933	0.23096	0.32540	0.40921	0.47857
61	12.8924	0.13494	0.22550	0.31929	0.40276	0.47201
62	11.9737	0.13065	0.22010	0.31320	0.39630	0.46538
63	11.0982	0.12647	0.21478	0.30714	0.38981	0.45870
64	10.2653	0.12238	0.20952	0.30109	0.38330	0.45196
65	9.4742	0.11840	0.20433	0.29508	0.37677	0.44518
66	8.7241	0.11451	0.19921	0.28909	0.37023	0.43834
67	8.0145	0.11071	0.19416	0.28312	0.36368	0.43146
68	7.3445	0.10701	0.18918	0.27719	0.35711	0.42453
69	6.7132	0.10340	0.18426	0.27128	0.35053	0.41755
70	6.1198	0.09987	0.17940	0.26539	0.34394	0.41053

* Condensed from the usual form 7.891×10^{-2}.

TABLE C.2. EXPECTANCY-LIFE FACTORS FOR GROUP PROPERTIES
UNIT SUMMATION PROCEDURE
Type Curve L_2 (Continued)

Age	Percent surviving	Interest rate					Age	Percent surviving	Interest rate				
		0%	2%	4%	6%	8%			0%	2%	4%	6%	8%
40 Years Average Life (Continued)							50 Years Average Life (Continued)						
71	5.5634	0.09643	0.17461	0.25953	0.33732	0.40345	6	99.8132	0.85082	0.89451	0.92471	0.94491	0.95848
72	5.0429	0.09307	0.16988	0.25369	0.33069	0.39632	7	99.7100	0.82689	0.87667	0.91138	0.93477	0.95058
73	4.5573	0.08980	0.16520	0.24786	0.32404	0.38914	8	99.5767	0.80332	0.85885	0.89792	0.92443	0.94246
74	4.1055	0.08659	0.16058	0.24206	0.31737	0.38190	9	99.4106	0.78014	0.84109	0.88435	0.91391	0.93414
75	3.6863	0.08347	0.15601	0.23627	0.31067	0.37460	10	99.2093	0.75734	0.82340	0.87068	0.90322	0.92562
76	3.2984	0.08041	0.15149	0.23049	0.30394	0.36724	11	98.9708	0.73496	0.80581	0.85693	0.89237	0.91691
77	2.9407	0.07743	0.14702	0.22472	0.29719	0.35981	12	98.6935	0.71293	0.78831	0.84312	0.88136	0.90800
78	2.6118	0.07451	0.14260	0.21897	0.29040	0.35232	13	98.3758	0.69141	0.77091	0.82923	0.87018	0.89889
79	2.3104	0.07166	0.13822	0.21322	0.28359	0.34475	14	98.0168	0.67025	0.75363	0.81528	0.85885	0.88956
80	2.0352	0.06887	0.13389	0.20748	0.27673	0.33711	15	97.6156	0.64950	0.73646	0.80126	0.84734	0.88000
81	1.7848	0.06614	0.12960	0.20174	0.26984	0.32940	16	97.1714	0.62914	0.71939	0.78716	0.83565	0.87019
82	1.5579	0.06347	0.12535	0.19600	0.26291	0.32160	17	96.6818	0.60918	0.70244	0.77299	0.82376	0.86013
83	1.3531	0.06086	0.12113	0.19026	0.25593	0.31372	18	96.1396	0.58966	0.68565	0.75881	0.81176	0.84986
84	1.1690	0.05830	0.11696	0.18453	0.24892	0.30576	19	95.5349	0.57062	0.66909	0.74468	0.79969	0.83944
85	1.0043	0.05580	0.11282	0.17879	0.24185	0.29771	20	94.8566	0.55212	0.65284	0.73068	0.78763	0.82896
86	0.8576	0.05336	0.10871	0.17304	0.23474	0.28956	21	94.0948	0.53420	0.63696	0.71691	0.77568	0.81050
87	0.7277	0.05096	0.10464	0.16730	0.22758	0.28133	22	93.2414	0.51692	0.62151	0.70342	0.76391	0.80815
88	0.6133	0.04861	0.10059	0.16154	0.22037	0.27299	23	92.2898	0.50029	0.60654	0.69028	0.75239	0.79796
89	0.5130	0.04631	0.09658	0.15578	0.21310	0.26455	24	91.2359	0.48434	0.59210	0.67754	0.74118	0.78801
90	0.4258	0.04406	0.09260	0.15000	0.20577	0.25601	25	90.0774	0.46906	0.57820	0.66524	0.73032	0.77834
91	0.3503	0.04185	0.08864	0.14422	0.19839	0.24736	26	88.8144	0.45447	0.56486	0.65341	0.71984	0.76899
92	0.2856	0.03969	0.08471	0.13842	0.19095	0.23860	27	87.4488	0.44055	0.55210	0.64207	0.70978	0.75999
93	0.2305	0.03757	0.08080	0.13261	0.18345	0.22973	28	85.9843	0.42728	0.53990	0.63122	0.70016	0.75137
94	0.1840	0.03549	0.07692	0.12679	0.17588	0.22074	29	84.4263	0.41466	0.52827	0.62086	0.69097	0.74313
95	0.1451	0.03346	0.07307	0.12094	0.16824	0.21164	30	82.7811	0.40265	0.51719	0.61101	0.68222	0.73528
96	0.1129	0.03146	0.06923	0.11508	0.16055	0.20241	31	81.0565	0.39123	0.50664	0.60163	0.67391	0.72783
97	8.653^{*-2}	0.02950	0.06542	0.10920	0.15278	0.19305	32	79.2606	0.38037	0.49660	0.59273	0.66603	0.72077
98	6.525^{*-2}	0.02758	0.06162	0.10331	0.14494	0.18356	33	77.4025	0.37004	0.48706	0.58428	0.65857	0.71409
99	4.830^{*-2}	0.02569	0.05785	0.09739	0.13702	0.17393	34	75.4912	0.36021	0.47799	0.57627	0.65151	0.70778
100	3.501^{*-2}	0.02384	0.05409	0.09145	0.12902	0.16416	35	73.5363	0.35085	0.46935	0.56868	0.64484	0.70183
101	2.478^{*-2}	0.02203	0.05035	0.08549	0.12095	0.15426	36	71.5468	0.34194	0.46114	0.56147	0.63853	0.69621
102	1.707^{*-2}	0.02024	0.04663	0.07950	0.11281	0.14421	37	69.5321	0.33343	0.45330	0.55463	0.63256	0.69091
103	1.138^{*-2}	0.01850	0.04293	0.07350	0.10459	0.13402	38	67.5009	0.32531	0.44583	0.54812	0.62692	0.68592
104	7.314^{*-3}	0.01678	0.03924	0.06748	0.09629	0.12368	39	65.4614	0.31754	0.43869	0.54193	0.62156	0.68119
105	4.493^{*-3}	0.01511	0.03557	0.06142	0.08792	0.11320	40	63.4216	0.31010	0.43185	0.53603	0.61648	0.67673
106	2.614^{*-3}	0.01348	0.03189	0.05533	0.07950	0.10264	41	61.3887	0.30296	0.42529	0.53039	0.61165	0.67249
107	1.422^{*-3}	0.01187	0.02823	0.04920	0.07100	0.09197	42	59.3692	0.29610	0.41899	0.52498	0.60703	0.66846
108	7.092^{*-4}	0.01028	0.02457	0.04303	0.06241	0.08117	43	57.3693	0.28948	0.41291	0.51978	0.60261	0.66461
109	3.159^{*-4}	0.00871	0.02091	0.03682	0.05370	0.07020	44	55.3941	0.28310	0.40703	0.51477	0.59835	0.66092
110	1.203^{*-4}	0.00716	0.01727	0.03057	0.04484	0.05902	45	53.4482	0.27694	0.40134	0.50991	0.59424	0.65736
111	3.645^{*-5}	0.00563	0.01363	0.02428	0.03581	0.04756	46	51.5357	0.27096	0.39580	0.50519	0.59025	0.65391
112	7.652^{*-6}	0.00411	0.00999	0.01792	0.02658	0.03574	47	49.6599	0.26515	0.39040	0.50058	0.58635	0.65055
113	8.204^{*-7}	0.00261	0.00635	0.01148	0.01712	0.02343	48	47.8234	0.25950	0.38512	0.49606	0.58253	0.64727
114	2.686^{*-8}	0.00111	0.00271	0.00495	0.00741	0.01039	49	46.0286	0.25400	0.37994	0.49161	0.57876	0.64399
114.7	0.0000	0.00000	0.00000	0.00000	0.00000	0.00000	50	44.2768	0.24862	0.37484	0.48721	0.57502	0.64076
							51	42.5695	0.24336	0.36982	0.48285	0.57130	0.63752
							52	40.9072	0.23821	0.36485	0.47850	0.56757	0.63428
		Type Curve L_2					53	39.2905	0.23315	0.35993	0.47417	0.56382	0.63100
		50 Years Average Life					54	37.7102	0.22818	0.35504	0.46982	0.56003	0.62767
							55	36.1931	0.22329	0.35018	0.46546	0.55621	0.62428
1	99.9989	0.97473	0.98286	0.98824	0.99170	0.99394	56	34.7118	0.21848	0.34534	0.46107	0.55232	0.62083
2	99.9922	0.94953	0.96547	0.97609	0.98298	0.98749	57	33.2746	0.21375	0.34051	0.45664	0.54837	0.61729
3	99.9748	0.92449	0.94788	0.96362	0.97391	0.98069	58	31.8806	0.20908	0.33570	0.45218	0.54435	0.61366
4	99.9420	0.89966	0.93016	0.95087	0.96451	0.97356	59	30.5290	0.20447	0.33088	0.44768	0.54026	0.60994
5	99.8894	0.87509	0.91235	0.93789	0.95484	0.96614	60	29.2188	0.19993	0.32608	0.44312	0.53608	0.60612

* Condensed from the usual form 8.653×10^{-2}.

TABLE C.2. EXPECTANCY-LIFE FACTORS FOR GROUP PROPERTIES
UNIT SUMMATION PROCEDURE
Type Curve L_2 (Continued)

Age	Percent surviving	Interest rate					Age	Percent surviving	Interest rate				
		0%	2%	4%	6%	8%			0%	2%	4%	6%	8%
50 Years Average Life (Continued)							50 Years Average Life (Continued)						
61	27.9488	0.19545	0.32128	0.43852	0.53182	0.60220	106	1.0357	0.05630	0.12970	0.21315	0.28748	0.35012
62	26.7180	0.19104	0.31648	0.43387	0.52747	0.59818	107	0.9142	0.05433	0.12599	0.20797	0.28115	0.34302
63	25.5253	0.18668	0.31169	0.42917	0.52304	0.59405	108	0.8037	0.05239	0.12228	0.20277	0.27476	0.33584
64	24.3698	0.18238	0.30690	0.42442	0.51853	0.58981	109	0.7036	0.05048	0.11857	0.19755	0.26832	0.32856
65	23.2502	0.17815	0.30212	0.41964	0.51393	0.58548	110	0.6133	0.04861	0.11485	0.19232	0.26182	0.32119
66	22.1658	0.17398	0.29735	0.41480	0.50926	0.58104	111	0.5320	0.04677	0.11112	0.18706	0.25527	0.31372
67	21.1156	0.16987	0.29259	0.40994	0.50452	0.57650	112	0.4592	0.04496	0.10737	0.18178	0.24865	0.30615
68	20.0987	0.16582	0.28785	0.40503	0.49970	0.57188	113	0.3942	0.04317	0.10358	0.17648	0.24197	0.29848
69	19.1143	0.16184	0.28312	0.40009	0.49481	0.56716	114	0.3366	0.04142	0.09976	0.17116	0.23523	0.29070
70	18.1618	0.15792	0.27842	0.39514	0.48986	0.56236	115	0.2856	0.03969	0.09798	0.16581	0.22843	0.28296
71	17.2404	0.15407	0.27374	0.39015	0.48486	0.55747	116	0.2408	0.03799	0.09446	0.16044	0.22156	0.27498
72	16.3495	0.15029	0.26908	0.38515	0.47980	0.55251	117	0.2016	0.03632	0.09096	0.15505	0.21462	0.26690
73	15.4887	0.14657	0.26445	0.38013	0.47469	0.54748	118	0.1675	0.03468	0.08746	0.14963	0.20762	0.25871
74	14.6574	0.14291	0.25985	0.37510	0.46953	0.54238	119	0.1381	0.03305	0.08398	0.14418	0.20055	0.25041
75	13.8551	0.13933	0.25528	0.37006	0.46433	0.53722	120	0.1129	0.03146	0.08050	0.13871	0.19340	0.24197
76	13.0814	0.13581	0.25075	0.36501	0.45910	0.53199	121	9.137^{*-2}	0.02989	0.07703	0.13320	0.18619	0.23342
77	12.3360	0.13235	0.24625	0.35996	0.45382	0.52671	122	7.320^{*-2}	0.02834	0.07357	0.12768	0.17890	0.22475
78	11.6184	0.12896	0.24179	0.35490	0.44852	0.52137	123	5.799^{*-2}	0.02682	0.07012	0.12212	0.17153	0.21595
79	10.9283	0.12564	0.23736	0.34985	0.44318	0.51598	124	4.537^{*-2}	0.02532	0.06667	0.11652	0.16408	0.20701
80	10.2653	0.12238	0.23297	0.34479	0.43782	0.51054	125	3.501^{*-2}	0.02384	0.06323	0.11091	0.15657	0.19795
81	9.6291	0.11918	0.22862	0.33974	0.43242	0.50505	126	2.661^{*-2}	0.02239	0.05980	0.10527	0.14897	0.18876
82	9.0193	0.11605	0.22430	0.33469	0.42700	0.49951	127	1.988^{*-2}	0.02096	0.05637	0.09958	0.14128	0.17941
83	8.4355	0.11297	0.22003	0.32965	0.42155	0.49393	128	1.457^{*-2}	0.01955	0.05296	0.09388	0.13353	0.16995
84	7.8774	0.10996	0.21579	0.32460	0.41608	0.48829	129	1.045^{*-2}	0.01816	0.04954	0.08814	0.12568	0.16033
85	7.3445	0.10701	0.21158	0.31956	0.41058	0.48261	130	7.314^{*-3}	0.01680	0.04615	0.08238	0.11778	0.15060
86	6.8364	0.10411	0.20741	0.31453	0.40506	0.47689	131	4.973^{*-3}	0.01545	0.04275	0.07659	0.10978	0.14071
87	6.3527	0.10127	0.20328	0.30949	0.39951	0.47111	132	3.270^{*-3}	0.01412	0.03935	0.07075	0.10168	0.13067
88	5.8929	0.09848	0.19918	0.30446	0.39393	0.46529	133	2.067^{*-3}	0.01280	0.03593	0.06478	0.09340	0.12023
89	5.4565	0.09575	0.19511	0.29943	0.38832	0.45941	134	1.246^{*-3}	0.01152	0.03256	0.05894	0.08515	0.10987
90	5.0429	0.09307	0.19107	0.29439	0.38269	0.45345	135	7.092^{*-4}	0.01025	0.02918	0.05302	0.07680	0.09933
91	4.6517	0.09044	0.18706	0.28936	0.37702	0.44750	136	3.754^{*-4}	0.00901	0.02582	0.04708	0.06838	0.08866
92	4.2822	0.08786	0.18308	0.28433	0.37132	0.44147	137	1.810^{*-4}	0.00786	0.02261	0.04122	0.05991	0.07787
93	3.9340	0.08533	0.17913	0.27929	0.36559	0.43538	138	7.714^{*-5}	0.00669	0.01936	0.03528	0.05129	0.06701
94	3.6062	0.08285	0.17521	0.27424	0.35983	0.42922	139	2.764^{*-5}	0.00551	0.01606	0.02925	0.04250	0.05598
95	3.2984	0.08041	0.17131	0.26919	0.35402	0.42301	140	7.652^{*-6}	0.00432	0.01267	0.02309	0.03353	0.04466
96	3.0099	0.07802	0.16743	0.26413	0.34819	0.41674	141	1.389^{*-6}	0.00311	0.00916	0.01673	0.02430	0.03287
97	2.7400	0.07566	0.16358	0.25906	0.34231	0.41040	142	1.194^{*-7}	0.00186	0.00552	0.01008	0.01469	0.02030
98	2.4880	0.07336	0.15975	0.25398	0.33640	0.40399	143	1.138^{*-8}	0.00057	0.00171	0.00313	0.00457	0.00651
99	2.2533	0.07109	0.15594	0.24889	0.33044	0.39752	143.4	0.0000	0.00000	0.00000	0.00000	0.00000	0.00000
100	2.0352	0.06886	0.15215	0.24379	0.32444	0.39098							
101	1.8330	0.06668	0.14838	0.23867	0.31840	0.38436							
102	1.6460	0.06453	0.14462	0.23354	0.31231	0.37767							
103	1.4734	0.06242	0.14087	0.22838	0.30618	0.37090							
104	1.3147	0.06034	0.13714	0.22321	0.30000	0.36406							
105	1.1690	0.05830	0.13342	0.21832	0.29377	0.35714							

* Condensed from the usual form 9.137×10^{-2}.

TABLE C.2. EXPECTANCY-LIFE FACTORS FOR GROUP PROPERTIES
UNIT SUMMATION PROCEDURE
Type Curve S_2

10 Years Average Life

Age	Percent surviving	0%	2%	4%	6%	8%
1	99.9944	0.88677	0.89531	0.90322	0.91051	0.91723
2	99.8756	0.77469	0.78971	0.80376	0.81576	0.82908
3	99.2931	0.66682	0.68632	0.70477	0.72218	0.73854
4	97.7066	0.56675	0.58943	0.61023	0.63049	0.64972
5	94.5472	0.47708	0.50058	0.52331	0.54518	0.56614
6	89.3835	0.39888	0.42258	0.44573	0.46823	0.48998
7	82.0454	0.33192	0.35505	0.37787	0.40024	0.42205
8	72.6843	0.27522	0.29726	0.31919	0.34089	0.36222
9	61.7653	0.22746	0.24804	0.26872	0.28936	0.30981
10	50.0000	0.18725	0.20617	0.22534	0.24464	0.26391
11	38.2347	0.15333	0.17045	0.18796	0.20572	0.22358
12	27.3157	0.12461	0.13986	0.15558	0.17166	0.18795
13	17.9546	0.10016	0.11350	0.12737	0.14167	0.15624
14	10.6165	0.07923	0.09065	0.10258	0.11505	0.12780
15	5.4528	0.06121	0.07070	0.08068	0.09122	0.10206
16	2.2933	0.04564	0.05316	0.06116	0.06970	0.07855
17	0.7069	0.03205	0.03761	0.04368	0.05014	0.05692
18	0.1244	0.02007	0.02371	0.02788	0.03219	0.03682
19	5.623^{*-3}	0.00949	0.01126	0.01342	0.01557	0.01793
20	0.0000	0.00000	0.00000	0.00000	0.00000	0.00000

Type Curve S_2
20 Years Average Life

Age	Percent surviving	0%	2%	4%	6%	8%
1	99.9998	0.94326	0.95205	0.95957	0.96592	0.97124
2	99.9944	0.88660	0.90320	0.91758	0.92986	0.94027
3	99.9651	0.83020	0.85364	0.87418	0.89192	0.90706
4	99.8756	0.77440	0.80372	0.82970	0.85237	0.87191
5	99.6734	0.71965	0.75391	0.78458	0.81163	0.83518
6	99.2931	0.66644	0.70472	0.73937	0.77022	0.79734
7	98.6624	0.61520	0.65666	0.69457	0.72867	0.75890
8	97.7066	0.56632	0.61017	0.65069	0.68748	0.72039
9	96.3555	0.52006	0.56561	0.60813	0.64709	0.68226
10	94.5472	0.47662	0.52325	0.56721	0.60786	0.64484
11	92.2337	0.43608	0.48325	0.52816	0.57005	0.60847
12	89.3835	0.39842	0.44568	0.49110	0.53384	0.57334
13	85.9845	0.36360	0.41055	0.45611	0.49934	0.53958
14	82.0454	0.33149	0.37782	0.42319	0.46659	0.50729
15	77.5955	0.30195	0.34739	0.39229	0.43558	0.47647
16	72.6843	0.27482	0.31915	0.36334	0.40628	0.44712
17	67.3797	0.24992	0.29296	0.33624	0.37862	0.41919
18	61.7653	0.22708	0.26868	0.31088	0.35250	0.39261
19	55.9372	0.20613	0.24618	0.28715	0.32785	0.36731
20	50.0000	0.18690	0.22530	0.26492	0.30455	0.34321
21	44.0628	0.16924	0.20592	0.24407	0.28250	0.32022
22	38.2347	0.15301	0.18791	0.22450	0.26162	0.29825
23	32.6203	0.13808	0.17115	0.20610	0.24179	0.27722
24	27.3157	0.12432	0.15553	0.18877	0.22294	0.25704
25	22.4045	0.11162	0.14095	0.17242	0.20497	0.23764
26	17.9546	0.09989	0.12731	0.15696	0.18782	0.21894
27	14.0155	0.08905	0.11453	0.14230	0.17139	0.20088
28	10.6165	0.07900	0.10254	0.12839	0.15563	0.18339
29	7.7663	0.06966	0.09126	0.11515	0.14048	0.16641
30	5.4528	0.06099	0.08064	0.10253	0.12587	0.14989
31	3.6446	0.05292	0.07061	0.09046	0.11175	0.13377
32	2.2933	0.04539	0.06113	0.07891	0.09809	0.11801
33	1.3376	0.03837	0.05214	0.06782	0.08482	0.10257
34	0.7069	0.03179	0.04362	0.05716	0.07190	0.08741
35	0.3266	0.02564	0.03553	0.04689	0.05932	0.07250

20 Years Average Life (Continued)

Age	Percent surviving	0%	2%	4%	6%	8%
36	0.1244	0.01989	0.02784	0.03697	0.04705	0.05778
37	3.492^{*-2}	0.01449	0.02052	0.02737	0.03504	0.04321
38	5.623^{*-3}	0.00942	0.01349	0.01803	0.02323	0.02876
39	2.341^{*-4}	0.00463	0.00669	0.00892	0.01158	0.01437
40	0.0000	0.00000	0.00000	0.00000	0.00000	0.00000

Type Curve S_2
25 Years Average Life

Age	Percent surviving	0%	2%	4%	6%	8%
1	99.9999	0.95461	0.96334	0.97051	0.97629	0.98089
2	99.9980	0.90924	0.92596	0.93985	0.95117	0.96027
3	99.9872	0.86397	0.88794	0.90808	0.92466	0.93811
4	99.9535	0.81895	0.84941	0.87529	0.89681	0.91444
5	99.8756	0.77436	0.81057	0.84167	0.86780	0.88940
6	99.7258	0.73045	0.77167	0.80746	0.83782	0.86314
7	99.4711	0.68746	0.73298	0.77291	0.80711	0.83590
8	99.0751	0.64563	0.69475	0.73830	0.77596	0.80793
9	98.4996	0.60517	0.65725	0.70390	0.74462	0.77949
10	97.7067	0.56626	0.62070	0.66996	0.71335	0.75081
11	96.6605	0.52904	0.58528	0.63668	0.68237	0.72213
12	95.3288	0.49360	0.55114	0.60426	0.65188	0.69365
13	93.6846	0.46000	0.51840	0.57282	0.62204	0.66553
14	91.7072	0.42826	0.48711	0.54248	0.59297	0.63792
15	89.3835	0.39837	0.45732	0.51330	0.56477	0.61092
16	86.7081	0.37029	0.42904	0.48533	0.53750	0.58461
17	83.6845	0.34396	0.40223	0.45857	0.51120	0.55904
18	80.3244	0.31932	0.37688	0.43303	0.48588	0.53425
19	76.6482	0.29628	0.35294	0.40868	0.46154	0.51023
20	72.6843	0.27477	0.33034	0.38548	0.43817	0.48700
21	68.4683	0.25468	0.30902	0.36341	0.41574	0.46454
22	64.0423	0.23593	0.28892	0.34239	0.39421	0.44282
23	59.4540	0.21844	0.26996	0.32239	0.37355	0.42181
24	54.7550	0.20211	0.25208	0.30335	0.35371	0.40149
25	50.0000	0.18686	0.23521	0.28521	0.33465	0.38182
26	45.2450	0.17365	0.21928	0.26792	0.31632	0.36275
27	40.5460	0.15930	0.20423	0.25142	0.29868	0.34425
28	35.9577	0.14685	0.19000	0.23566	0.28168	0.32628
29	31.5317	0.13520	0.17652	0.22063	0.26527	0.30880
30	27.3157	0.12428	0.16375	0.20616	0.24942	0.29176
31	23.3518	0.11405	0.15164	0.19233	0.23408	0.27515
32	19.6756	0.10444	0.14014	0.17905	0.21922	0.25891
33	16.3155	0.09542	0.12920	0.16629	0.20479	0.24302
34	13.2919	0.08694	0.11879	0.15401	0.19077	0.22744
35	10.6165	0.07896	0.10886	0.14216	0.17712	0.21215
36	8.2928	0.07144	0.09939	0.13073	0.16382	0.19711
37	6.3154	0.06435	0.09034	0.11968	0.15082	0.18230
38	4.6712	0.05766	0.08168	0.10898	0.13811	0.16769
39	3.3396	0.05134	0.07338	0.09861	0.12567	0.15325
40	2.2933	0.04536	0.06542	0.08854	0.11346	0.13897
41	1.5004	0.03971	0.05778	0.07874	0.10146	0.12482
42	0.9249	0.03435	0.05043	0.06921	0.08966	0.11079
43	0.5289	0.02927	0.04336	0.05991	0.07804	0.09685
44	0.2742	0.02445	0.03654	0.05084	0.06658	0.08298
45	0.1244	0.01987	0.02996	0.04197	0.05526	0.06917
46	4.653^{*-2}	0.01553	0.02362	0.03330	0.04406	0.05536
47	1.284^{*-2}	0.01142	0.01748	0.02480	0.03294	0.04154
48	2.032^{*-3}	0.00750	0.01150	0.01645	0.02190	0.02770
49	8.331^{*-5}	0.00371	0.00568	0.00819	0.01093	0.01386
50	0.0000	0.00000	0.00000	0.00000	0.00000	0.00000

* Condensed from the usual form 5.623×10^{-3}.

TABLE C.2. EXPECTANCY-LIFE FACTORS FOR GROUP PROPERTIES
UNIT SUMMATION PROCEDURE
Type Curve S_2 (Continued)

Age	Percent surviving	Interest rate					Age	Percent surviving	Interest rate				
		0%	2%	4%	6%	8%			0%	2%	4%	6%	8%
		30 Years Average Life							40 Years Average Life				
1	100.0000	0.96217	0.97081	0.97761	0.98282	0.98676	1	100.0000	0.97163	0.98004	0.98608	0.99026	0.99309
2	99.9991	0.92435	0.94105	0.95433	0.96462	0.97246	2	99.9998	0.94325	0.95968	0.97162	0.97994	0.98564
3	99.9944	0.88657	0.91073	0.93017	0.94538	0.95707	3	99.9985	0.91489	0.93893	0.95658	0.96901	0.97760
4	99.9794	0.84891	0.87993	0.90516	0.92510	0.94058	4	99.9944	0.88657	0.91780	0.94098	0.95746	0.96895
5	99.9442	0.81146	0.84873	0.87937	0.90384	0.92300	5	99.9846	0.85830	0.89631	0.92482	0.94529	0.95968
6	99.8756	0.77434	0.81726	0.85293	0.88168	0.90441	6	99.9651	0.83014	0.87450	0.90813	0.93251	0.94978
7	99.7571	0.73769	0.78566	0.82595	0.85874	0.88489	7	99.9308	0.80213	0.85241	0.89094	0.91912	0.93927
8	99.5699	0.70165	0.75408	0.79858	0.83515	0.86456	8	99.8756	0.77432	0.83010	0.87329	0.90518	0.92817
9	99.2931	0.66636	0.72269	0.77099	0.81106	0.84355	9	99.7924	0.74678	0.80763	0.85523	0.89071	0.91649
10	98.9051	0.63195	0.69163	0.74333	0.78661	0.82200	10	99.6734	0.71956	0.78506	0.83683	0.87577	0.90429
11	98.3835	0.59854	0.66105	0.71576	0.76196	0.80005	11	99.5099	0.69273	0.76247	0.81815	0.86040	0.89160
12	97.7067	0.56623	0.63109	0.68841	0.73726	0.77783	12	99.2931	0.66634	0.73991	0.79924	0.84466	0.87847
13	96.8538	0.53509	0.60184	0.66141	0.71262	0.75548	13	99.0137	0.64044	0.71746	0.78019	0.82862	0.86495
14	95.8062	0.50518	0.57340	0.63488	0.68817	0.73311	14	98.6624	0.61509	0.69517	0.76104	0.81233	0.85109
15	94.5472	0.47654	0.54584	0.60889	0.66401	0.71082	15	98.2297	0.59033	0.67312	0.74186	0.79585	0.83694
16	93.0633	0.44918	0.51922	0.58354	0.64022	0.68871	16	97.7067	0.56620	0.65134	0.72272	0.77924	0.82256
17	91.3442	0.42312	0.49358	0.55888	0.61688	0.66684	17	97.0846	0.54274	0.62989	0.70366	0.76254	0.80800
18	89.3835	0.39834	0.46892	0.53494	0.59403	0.64529	18	96.3555	0.51995	0.60881	0.68474	0.74582	0.79330
19	87.1784	0.37481	0.44527	0.51176	0.57173	0.62409	19	95.5119	0.49787	0.58815	0.66599	0.72911	0.77850
20	84.7305	0.35252	0.42261	0.48935	0.55000	0.60328	20	94.5472	0.47651	0.56792	0.64747	0.71246	0.76364
21	82.0454	0.33141	0.40094	0.46771	0.52885	0.58289	21	93.4560	0.45587	0.54816	0.62919	0.69590	0.74877
22	79.1329	0.31144	0.38023	0.44686	0.50829	0.56294	22	92.2337	0.43596	0.52889	0.61120	0.67947	0.73392
23	76.0066	0.29257	0.36045	0.42676	0.48833	0.54342	23	90.8769	0.41678	0.51011	0.59352	0.66319	0.71910
24	72.6843	0.27474	0.34158	0.40741	0.46896	0.52435	24	89.3835	0.39831	0.49184	0.57616	0.64710	0.70430
25	69.1867	0.25791	0.32357	0.38878	0.45017	0.50572	25	87.7526	0.38055	0.47409	0.55914	0.63119	0.68968
26	65.5381	0.24202	0.30640	0.37086	0.43194	0.48752	26	85.9845	0.36349	0.45686	0.54247	0.61550	0.67512
27	61.7653	0.22701	0.29002	0.35360	0.41425	0.46973	27	84.0812	0.34710	0.44014	0.52616	0.60004	0.66068
28	57.8973	0.21285	0.27439	0.33700	0.39709	0.45235	28	82.0454	0.33138	0.42394	0.51022	0.58481	0.64637
29	53.9649	0.19947	0.25948	0.32101	0.38043	0.43536	29	79.8817	0.31630	0.40824	0.49464	0.56982	0.63220
30	50.0000	0.18684	0.24526	0.30560	0.36425	0.41873	30	77.5955	0.30184	0.39304	0.47943	0.55508	0.61817
31	46.0351	0.17491	0.23167	0.29075	0.34853	0.40246	31	75.1937	0.28799	0.37832	0.46457	0.54058	0.60428
32	42.1027	0.16363	0.21869	0.27643	0.33323	0.38651	32	72.6843	0.27472	0.36408	0.45008	0.52632	0.59056
33	38.2347	0.15296	0.20628	0.26261	0.31835	0.37087	33	70.0763	0.26200	0.35030	0.43593	0.51232	0.57698
34	34.4619	0.14287	0.19441	0.24926	0.30384	0.35551	34	67.3797	0.24982	0.33696	0.42213	0.49855	0.56355
35	30.8133	0.13332	0.18304	0.23635	0.28969	0.34043	35	64.6055	0.23816	0.32407	0.40866	0.48502	0.55026
36	27.3157	0.12427	0.17216	0.22386	0.27588	0.32559	36	61.7653	0.22698	0.31159	0.39552	0.47172	0.53713
37	23.9933	0.11570	0.16172	0.21176	0.26239	0.31098	37	58.8716	0.21628	0.29952	0.38270	0.45864	0.52413
38	20.8671	0.10757	0.15170	0.20003	0.24919	0.29657	38	55.9372	0.20604	0.28783	0.37018	0.44578	0.51126
39	17.9546	0.09986	0.14208	0.18865	0.23626	0.28235	39	52.9755	0.19622	0.27653	0.35796	0.43313	0.49853
40	15.2695	0.09253	0.13284	0.17759	0.22359	0.26831	40	50.0000	0.18681	0.26558	0.34603	0.42069	0.48592
41	12.8216	0.08557	0.12395	0.16683	0.21115	0.25442	41	47.0245	0.17780	0.25498	0.33437	0.40843	0.47343
42	10.6165	0.07896	0.11538	0.15637	0.19894	0.24066	42	44.0628	0.16916	0.24471	0.32297	0.39637	0.46104
43	8.6557	0.07267	0.10713	0.14617	0.18692	0.22703	43	41.1284	0.16088	0.23476	0.31183	0.38448	0.44876
44	6.9367	0.06667	0.09917	0.13622	0.17509	0.21350	44	38.2347	0.15293	0.22512	0.30092	0.37275	0.43657
45	5.4528	0.06097	0.09148	0.12650	0.16343	0.20007	45	35.3945	0.14531	0.21577	0.29025	0.36119	0.42447
46	4.1938	0.05553	0.08406	0.11701	0.15192	0.18671	46	32.6203	0.13800	0.20669	0.27980	0.34978	0.41246
47	3.1462	0.05034	0.07687	0.10772	0.14056	0.17341	47	29.9237	0.13098	0.19788	0.26957	0.33850	0.40051
48	2.2933	0.04538	0.06992	0.09862	0.12932	0.16016	48	27.3157	0.12424	0.18933	0.25953	0.32737	0.38862
49	1.6165	0.04065	0.06318	0.08970	0.11821	0.14695	49	24.8063	0.11777	0.18102	0.24968	0.31636	0.37680
50	1.0949	0.03613	0.05665	0.08095	0.10719	0.13377	50	22.4045	0.11155	0.17295	0.24002	0.30546	0.36502
51	0.7069	0.03181	0.05030	0.07235	0.09627	0.12059	51	20.1184	0.10557	0.16509	0.23053	0.29468	0.35329
52	0.4301	0.02767	0.04414	0.06390	0.08544	0.10742	52	17.9546	0.09983	0.15745	0.22121	0.28400	0.34159
53	0.2429	0.02371	0.03816	0.05559	0.07468	0.09425	53	15.9189	0.09430	0.15001	0.21204	0.27341	0.32992
54	0.1244	0.01992	0.03233	0.04741	0.06400	0.08106	54	14.0155	0.08898	0.14276	0.20302	0.26291	0.31827
55	5.576*⁻²	0.01629	0.02663	0.03934	0.05339	0.06783	55	12.2474	0.08386	0.13570	0.19414	0.25249	0.30663
56	2.062*⁻²	0.01279	0.02107	0.03138	0.04278	0.05455	56	10.6165	0.07893	0.12882	0.18540	0.24214	0.29500
57	5.623*⁻³	0.00941	0.01563	0.02352	0.03219	0.04116	57	9.1231	0.07418	0.12210	0.17678	0.23185	0.28358
58	8.800*⁻⁴	0.00615	0.01032	0.01569	0.02155	0.02764	58	7.7663	0.06960	0.11554	0.16828	0.22163	0.27172
59	3.571*⁻⁵	0.00302	0.00511	0.00787	0.01083	0.01393	59	6.5440	0.06519	0.10914	0.15988	0.21146	0.26006
60	0.0000	0.00000	0.00000	0.00000	0.00000	0.00000	60	5.4528	0.06093	0.10288	0.15160	0.20133	0.24838

* Condensed from the usual form 5.576×10^{-2}.

TABLE C.2.   EXPECTANCY-LIFE FACTORS FOR GROUP PROPERTIES UNIT SUMMATION PROCEDURE
Type Curve S_2 (Continued)

Age	Percent surviving	Interest rate					Age	Percent surviving	Interest rate				
		0%	2%	4%	6%	8%			0%	2%	4%	6%	8%
40 Years Average Life (Continued)							**50 Years Average Life (Continued)**						
61	4.4881	0.05682	0.09676	0.14342	0.19124	0.23667	6	99.9872	0.86394	0.90841	0.93903	0.95892	0.97161
62	3.6445	0.05286	0.09077	0.13533	0.18119	0.22493	7	99.9743	0.84138	0.89218	0.92752	0.95070	0.96560
63	2.9154	0.04904	0.08492	0.12732	0.17117	0.21314	8	99.9535	0.81890	0.87572	0.91565	0.94208	0.95921
64	2.2933	0.04534	0.07918	0.11940	0.16117	0.20131	9	99.9217	0.79654	0.85905	0.90344	0.93307	0.95244
65	1.7703	0.04177	0.07356	0.11156	0.15119	0.18943	10	99.8756	0.77431	0.84219	0.89089	0.92369	0.94530
66	1.3376	0.03832	0.06805	0.10379	0.14122	0.17748	11	99.8117	0.75225	0.82518	0.87803	0.91394	0.93779
67	0.9863	0.03498	0.06265	0.09609	0.13126	0.16547	12	99.7258	0.73040	0.80806	0.86490	0.90386	0.92993
68	0.7069	0.03176	0.05734	0.08845	0.12130	0.15338	13	99.6138	0.70877	0.79084	0.85151	0.89346	0.92174
69	0.4901	0.02863	0.05214	0.08087	0.11134	0.14122	14	99.4711	0.68740	0.77358	0.83791	0.88276	0.91322
70	0.3266	0.02561	0.04702	0.07334	0.10137	0.12897	15	99.2931	0.66632	0.75630	0.82412	0.87180	0.90442
71	0.2076	0.02268	0.04200	0.06586	0.09140	0.11664	16	99.0751	0.64556	0.73904	0.81017	0.86059	0.89534
72	0.1244	0.01985	0.03706	0.05843	0.08140	0.10421	17	98.8121	0.62515	0.72182	0.79610	0.84918	0.88600
73	6.918*$^{-2}$	0.01710	0.03220	0.05105	0.07139	0.09168	18	98.4996	0.60510	0.70469	0.78194	0.83757	0.87644
74	3.492*$^{-2}$	0.01444	0.02741	0.04369	0.06134	0.07902	19	98.1326	0.58544	0.68768	0.76771	0.82581	0.86668
75	1.543*$^{-2}$	0.01186	0.02271	0.03636	0.05125	0.06623	20	97.7067	0.56619	0.67080	0.75345	0.81392	0.85673
76	5.623*$^{-3}$	0.00936	0.01808	0.02905	0.04112	0.05332	21	97.2173	0.54736	0.65409	0.73919	0.80192	0.84662
77	1.513*$^{-3}$	0.00694	0.01351	0.02176	0.03095	0.04026	22	96.6605	0.52897	0.63757	0.72494	0.78984	0.83637
78	2.341*$^{-4}$	0.00459	0.00898	0.01449	0.02071	0.02704	23	96.0321	0.51102	0.62126	0.71075	0.77770	0.82600
79	9.363*$^{-6}$	0.00228	0.00448	0.00724	0.01039	0.01363	24	95.3288	0.49353	0.60518	0.69662	0.76552	0.81553
80	0.0000	0.00000	0.00000	0.00000	0.00000	0.00000	25	94.5472	0.47650	0.58934	0.68257	0.75332	0.80498
							26	93.6846	0.45993	0.57377	0.66864	0.74113	0.79437
							27	92.7386	0.44383	0.55847	0.65482	0.72896	0.78371
	Type Curve S_2						28	91.7073	0.42819	0.54345	0.64114	0.71682	0.77302
	50 Years Average Life						29	90.5892	0.41301	0.52872	0.62761	0.70473	0.76230
							30	89.3835	0.39830	0.51428	0.61424	0.69270	0.75158
1	100.0000	0.97730	0.98546	0.99078	0.99409	0.99611	31	88.0897	0.38403	0.50015	0.60104	0.68074	0.74086
2	99.9999	0.95460	0.97062	0.98120	0.98782	0.99190	32	86.7081	0.37022	0.48632	0.58801	0.66885	0.73015
3	99.9995	0.93190	0.95550	0.97124	0.98118	0.98737	33	85.2393	0.35684	0.47279	0.57516	0.65705	0.71945
4	99.9980	0.90922	0.94008	0.96089	0.97416	0.98248	34	83.6845	0.34389	0.45957	0.56250	0.64535	0.70878
5	99.9944	0.88656	0.92438	0.95015	0.96674	0.97723	35	82.0454	0.33136	0.44665	0.55003	0.63374	0.69814

* Condensed from the usual form 6.918×10^{-2}.

TABLE C.2. EXPECTANCY-LIFE FACTORS FOR GROUP PROPERTIES UNIT SUMMATION PROCEDURE
Type Curve S_2 (Continued)

50 Years Average Life (Continued)

Age	Percent surviving	0%	2%	4%	6%	8%
36	80.3244	0.31925	0.43403	0.53775	0.62223	0.68754
37	78.5242	0.30754	0.42170	0.52567	0.61083	0.67697
38	76.6482	0.29622	0.40967	0.51377	0.59954	0.66645
39	74.7002	0.28528	0.39793	0.50207	0.58835	0.65597
40	72.6843	0.27470	0.38647	0.49056	0.57728	0.64553
41	70.6053	0.26449	0.37529	0.47924	0.56631	0.63514
42	68.4683	0.25462	0.36438	0.46810	0.55545	0.62480
43	66.2787	0.24508	0.35374	0.45715	0.54470	0.61450
44	64.0423	0.23587	0.34336	0.44638	0.53405	0.60424
45	61.7653	0.22697	0.33323	0.43578	0.52351	0.59403
46	59.4540	0.21838	0.32334	0.42536	0.51307	0.58386
47	57.1150	0.21007	0.31370	0.41510	0.50272	0.57373
48	54.7550	0.20205	0.30428	0.40501	0.49248	0.56364
49	52.3810	0.19429	0.29510	0.39507	0.48232	0.55358
50	50.0000	0.18680	0.28612	0.38529	0.47225	0.54356
51	47.6190	0.17956	0.27736	0.37566	0.46227	0.53357
52	45.2450	0.17256	0.26881	0.36617	0.45237	0.52360
53	42.8850	0.16579	0.26045	0.35682	0.44254	9.51366
54	40.5460	0.15925	0.25228	0.34761	0.43279	0.50373
55	38.2347	0.15292	0.24430	0.33853	0.42311	0.49382
56	35.9577	0.14680	0.23650	0.32957	0.41350	0.48392
57	33.7213	0.14088	0.22886	0.32074	0.40395	0.47404
58	31.5317	0.13515	0.22140	0.31201	0.39445	0.46416
59	29.3947	0.12960	0.21409	0.30340	0.38501	0.45428
60	27.3157	0.12423	0.20694	0.29490	0.37562	0.44440
61	25.2999	0.11904	0.19994	0.28649	0.36628	0.43451
62	23.3518	0.11400	0.19308	0.27819	0.35698	0.42461
63	21.4758	0.10912	0.18636	0.26997	0.34771	0.41470
64	19.6756	0.10440	0.17977	0.26185	0.33848	0.40477
65	17.9546	0.09982	0.17331	0.25381	0.32929	0.39482
66	16.3156	0.09538	0.16697	0.24585	0.32012	0.38484
67	14.7607	0.09107	0.16076	0.23796	0.31097	0.37484
68	13.2919	0.08690	0.15465	0.23015	0.30184	0.36479
69	11.9103	0.08285	0.14866	0.22241	0.29273	0.35472
70	10.6165	0.07892	0.14278	0.21474	0.28363	0.34460

50 Years Average Life (Continued)

Age	Percent surviving	0%	2%	4%	6%	8%
71	9.4108	0.07510	0.13699	0.20712	0.27454	0.33443
72	8.2928	0.07140	0.13131	0.19956	0.26545	0.32421
73	7.2614	0.06781	0.12572	0.19206	0.25636	0.31394
74	6.3154	0.06432	0.12022	0.18461	0.24728	0.30362
75	5.4528	0.06092	0.11481	0.17721	0.23819	0.29322
76	4.6712	0.05763	0.10926	0.16985	0.22909	0.28277
77	3.9679	0.05442	0.10423	0.16254	0.21998	0.27224
78	3.3395	0.05131	0.09906	0.15526	0.21086	0.26164
79	2.7827	0.04828	0.09397	0.14803	0.20172	0.25096
80	2.2933	0.04534	0.08895	0.14082	0.19255	0.24020
81	1.8674	0.04247	0.08400	0.13365	0.18336	0.22934
82	1.5004	0.03968	0.07912	0.12651	0.17415	0.21840
83	1.1879	0.03696	0.07430	0.11939	0.16491	0.20736
84	0.9249	0.03432	0.06954	0.11229	0.15563	0.19622
85	0.7069	0.03175	0.06484	0.10522	0.14632	0.18498
86	0.5289	0.02924	0.06020	0.09816	0.13697	0.17363
87	0.3862	0.02680	0.05562	0.09113	0.12758	0.16216
88	0.2742	0.02442	0.05108	0.08411	0.11814	0.15058
89	0.1883	0.02210	0.04660	0.07710	0.10866	0.13888
90	0.1244	0.01984	0.04217	0.07010	0.09913	0.12705
91	7.834*$^{-2}$	0.01764	0.03778	0.06311	0.08954	0.11508
92	4.653*$^{-2}$	0.01549	0.03344	0.05613	0.07991	0.10299
93	2.566*$^{-2}$	0.01338	0.02913	0.04915	0.07021	0.09078
94	1.284*$^{-2}$	0.01131	0.02486	0.04217	0.06043	0.07844
95	5.623*$^{-3}$	0.00928	0.02063	0.03519	0.05057	0.06594
96	2.032*$^{-3}$	0.00729	0.01644	0.02819	0.04063	0.05325
97	5.413*$^{-4}$	0.00535	0.01229	0.02118	0.03061	0.04035
98	8.331*$^{-5}$	0.00349	0.00818	0.01415	0.02051	0.02720
99	3.310*$^{-6}$	0.00171	0.00408	0.00710	0.01032	0.01376
100	0.0000	0.00000	0.00000	0.00000	0.00000	0.00000

* Condensed from the usual form 7.834×10^{-2}.

TABLE C.2. EXPECTANCY-LIFE FACTORS FOR GROUP PROPERTIES
UNIT SUMMATION PROCEDURE
Type Curve R_2

10 Years Average Life

Age	Percent surviving	0%	2%	4%	6%	8%
1	98.8936	0.87602	0.88445	0.89224	0.89941	0.90600
2	97.3737	0.76863	0.78350	0.79739	0.81031	0.82229
3	95.3294	0.67099	0.69058	0.70905	0.72642	0.74267
4	92.6306	0.58163	0.60439	0.62609	0.64668	0.66614
5	89.1267	0.49996	0.52454	0.54823	0.57094	0.59259
6	84.6471	0.42572	0.45098	0.47557	0.49937	0.52227
7	79.0113	0.35882	0.38379	0.40834	0.43234	0.45565
8	72.0573	0.29922	0.32314	0.34690	0.37034	0.39330
9	63.7000	0.24688	0.26920	0.29158	0.31386	0.33589
10	54.0251	0.20164	0.22200	0.24261	0.26331	0.28394
11	43.3960	0.16318	0.18139	0.20000	0.21885	0.23778
12	32.5113	0.13087	0.14688	0.16338	0.18025	0.19731
13	22.3191	0.10368	0.11757	0.13185	0.14682	0.16181
14	13.7424	0.08092	0.09216	0.10436	0.11704	0.12971
15	7.3294	0.06041	0.06925	0.07913	0.08906	0.09939
16	3.1142	0.04120	0.04778	0.05512	0.06235	0.07018
17	0.8223	0.02353	0.02768	0.03235	0.03685	0.04183
18	4.561^{*-2}	0.00777	0.00939	0.01126	0.01298	0.01483
18.58	0.0000	0.00000	0.00000	0.00000	0.00000	0.00000

Type Curve R_2
20 Years Average Life

Age	Percent surviving	0%	2%	4%	6%	8%
1	99.4922	0.93415	0.94284	0.95025	0.95652	0.96176
2	98.8936	0.87551	0.89187	0.90598	0.91800	0.92813
3	98.1918	0.82047	0.84359	0.86373	0.88103	0.89573
4	97.3737	0.76818	0.79720	0.82273	0.84486	0.86381
5	96.4247	0.71828	0.75237	0.78268	0.80918	0.83207
6	95.3294	0.67056	0.70896	0.74344	0.77387	0.80036
7	94.0707	0.62490	0.66687	0.70494	0.73885	0.76861
8	92.6306	0.58121	0.62606	0.66716	0.70410	0.73679
9	90.9895	0.53944	0.58652	0.63009	0.66962	0.70489
10	89.1267	0.49955	0.54825	0.59377	0.63545	0.67294
11	87.0201	0.46151	0.51126	0.55824	0.60164	0.64099
12	84.6471	0.42532	0.47560	0.52355	0.56824	0.60910
13	81.9848	0.39096	0.44130	0.48977	0.53534	0.57734
14	79.0113	0.35843	0.40838	0.45696	0.50303	0.54583
15	75.5072	0.32773	0.37692	0.42521	0.47141	0.51466
16	72.0573	0.29885	0.34694	0.39460	0.44059	0.48396
17	68.0540	0.27178	0.31849	0.36521	0.41067	0.45386
18	63.7000	0.24652	0.29160	0.33712	0.38176	0.42449
19	59.0122	0.22304	0.26631	0.31039	0.35397	0.39599
20	54.0251	0.20131	0.24262	0.28508	0.32739	0.36846
21	48.7940	0.18128	0.22052	0.26121	0.30208	0.34200
22	43.3960	0.16287	0.19999	0.23880	0.27807	0.31670
23	37.9299	0.14601	0.18096	0.21782	0.25538	0.29256
24	32.5113	0.13058	0.16335	0.19820	0.23397	0.26959
25	27.2660	0.11646	0.14705	0.17984	0.21374	0.24770
26	22.3191	0.10350	0.13190	0.16259	0.19454	0.22674
27	17.7824	0.09152	0.11772	0.14626	0.17617	0.20650
28	13.7424	0.08034	0.10431	0.13062	0.15838	0.18670
29	10.2523	0.06983	0.09139	0.11516	0.14079	0.16685
30	7.3294	0.05969	0.07877	0.10007	0.12324	0.14678
31	4.9608	0.04993	0.06648	0.08530	0.10573	0.12652
32	3.1142	0.04057	0.05450	0.07077	0.08829	0.10612
33	1.7492	0.03165	0.04289	0.05644	0.07093	0.08558
34	0.8223	0.02322	0.03172	0.04234	0.05366	0.06493
35	0.2804	0.01528	0.02103	0.02852	0.03651	0.04430

20 Years Average Life (Continued)

Age	Percent surviving	0%	2%	4%	6%	8%
36	4.561^{*-2}	0.00785	0.01092	0.01506	0.01951	0.02372
37	6.598^{*-5}	0.00102	0.00143	0.00203	0.00267	0.00325
37.16	0.0000	0.00000	0.00000	0.00000	0.00000	0.00000

Type Curve R_2
25 Years Average Life

Age	Percent surviving	0%	2%	4%	6%	8%
1	99.6007	0.94639	0.95504	0.96212	0.96782	0.97236
2	99.1447	0.89839	0.91488	0.92852	0.93959	0.94846
3	98.6260	0.85307	0.87667	0.89639	0.91252	0.92554
4	98.0380	0.80975	0.83978	0.86511	0.88601	0.90300
5	97.3737	0.76813	0.80393	0.83442	0.85979	0.88057
6	96.6257	0.72803	0.76896	0.80417	0.83372	0.85810
7	95.7861	0.68935	0.73480	0.77429	0.80773	0.83552
8	94.8465	0.65201	0.70140	0.74474	0.78176	0.81276
9	93.7978	0.61596	0.66873	0.71549	0.75579	0.78980
10	92.6306	0.58116	0.63678	0.68655	0.72982	0.76661
11	91.3348	0.54759	0.60555	0.65792	0.70384	0.74320
12	89.8998	0.51523	0.57503	0.62960	0.67788	0.71957
13	88.3145	0.48406	0.54525	0.60163	0.65194	0.69573
14	86.5675	0.45408	0.51621	0.57403	0.62607	0.67170
15	84.6471	0.42527	0.48795	0.54684	0.60029	0.64752
16	82.5415	0.39764	0.46047	0.52008	0.57464	0.62322
17	80.2394	0.37118	0.43382	0.49381	0.54919	0.59885
18	77.7303	0.34588	0.40801	0.46807	0.52397	0.57448
19	75.0052	0.32176	0.38307	0.44290	0.49905	0.55015
20	72.0573	0.29880	0.35904	0.41837	0.47450	0.52594
21	68.8830	0.27701	0.33594	0.39451	0.45037	0.50191
22	65.4830	0.25637	0.31380	0.37138	0.42673	0.47816
23	61.8634	0.23688	0.29262	0.34902	0.40365	0.45475
24	58.0372	0.21852	0.27244	0.32748	0.38118	0.43176
25	54.0251	0.20127	0.25326	0.30678	0.35939	0.40925
26	49.8563	0.18511	0.23508	0.28695	0.33832	0.38730
27	45.5694	0.17000	0.21789	0.26801	0.31800	0.36595
28	41.2116	0.15591	0.20166	0.24995	0.29844	0.34524
29	36.8384	0.14278	0.18637	0.23277	0.27967	0.32519
30	32.5113	0.13055	0.17198	0.21642	0.26164	0.30578
31	28.2951	0.11915	0.15841	0.20085	0.24432	0.28699
32	24.2545	0.10852	0.14560	0.18599	0.22764	0.26874
33	20.4497	0.09857	0.13345	0.17176	0.21150	0.25093
34	16.9324	0.08919	0.12187	0.15802	0.19577	0.23342
35	13.7424	0.08031	0.11074	0.14466	0.18031	0.21606
36	10.9050	0.07184	0.09995	0.13154	0.16495	0.19864
37	8.4307	0.06368	0.08942	0.11856	0.14957	0.18102
38	6.3169	0.05580	0.07906	0.10561	0.13405	0.16304
39	4.5509	0.04815	0.06886	0.09266	0.11833	0.14465
40	3.1142	0.04075	0.05880	0.07971	0.10242	0.12583
41	1.9857	0.03360	0.04894	0.06683	0.08639	0.10668
42	1.1436	0.02676	0.03935	0.05409	0.07036	0.08732
43	0.5629	0.02024	0.03004	0.04155	0.05438	0.06784
44	0.2120	0.01403	0.02101	0.02923	0.03849	0.04828
45	4.561^{*-2}	0.00811	0.01226	0.01715	0.02272	0.02865
46	1.281^{*-3}	0.00248	0.00378	0.00531	0.00707	0.00897
46.45	0.0000	0.00000	0.00000	0.00000	0.00000	0.00000

* Condensed from the usual form 4.561 $\times$ 10^{-2}.

TABLE C.2. EXPECTANCY-LIFE FACTORS FOR GROUP PROPERTIES
UNIT SUMMATION PROCEDURE
Type Curve R_2 (*Continued*)

Age	Percent surviving	Interest rate					Age	Percent surviving	Interest rate				
		0%	2%	4%	6%	8%			0%	2%	4%	6%	8%
	30 Years Average Life							40 Years Average Life					
1	99.6710	0.95471	0.96327	0.97000	0.97515	0.97905	1	99.7568	0.96531	0.97366	0.97965	0.98381	0.98667
2	99.3034	0.91399	0.93047	0.94352	0.95360	0.96127	2	99.4922	0.93397	0.95021	0.96195	0.97014	0.97580
3	98.8936	0.87541	0.89920	0.91822	0.93302	0.94436	3	99.2050	0.90414	0.92782	0.94511	0.95724	0.96566
4	98.4380	0.83839	0.86893	0.89357	0.91289	0.92779	4	98.8936	0.87538	0.90610	0.92872	0.94471	0.95585
5	97.9327	0.80267	0.83940	0.86932	0.89298	0.91135	5	98.5564	0.84748	0.88485	0.91260	0.93236	0.94620
6	97.3737	0.76810	0.81050	0.84537	0.87316	0.89489	6	98.1918	0.82035	0.86397	0.89666	0.92010	0.93661
7	96.7565	0.73458	0.78214	0.82163	0.85336	0.87834	7	97.7982	0.79389	0.84340	0.88083	0.90786	0.92700
8	96.0767	0.70206	0.75427	0.79806	0.83353	0.86165	8	97.3737	0.76807	0.82308	0.86506	0.89560	0.91735
9	95.3294	0.67048	0.72688	0.77462	0.81363	0.84477	9	96.9165	0.74284	0.80300	0.84934	0.88329	0.90761
10	94.5095	0.63982	0.69992	0.75131	0.79365	0.82768	10	96.4247	0.71817	0.78313	0.83362	0.87090	0.89775
11	93.6118	0.61004	0.67341	0.72811	0.77356	0.81036	11	95.8964	0.69405	0.76345	0.81791	0.85841	0.88776
12	92.6306	0.58113	0.64733	0.70503	0.75337	0.79279	12	95.3294	0.67046	0.74397	0.80218	0.84581	0.87762
13	91.5602	0.55307	0.62168	0.68207	0.73308	0.77497	13	94.7216	0.64738	0.72466	0.78644	0.83309	0.86731
14	90.3943	0.52586	0.59647	0.65923	0.71268	0.75690	14	94.0707	0.62480	0.70554	0.77068	0.82024	0.85682
15	89.1267	0.49947	0.57171	0.63652	0.69220	0.73858	15	93.3746	0.60271	0.68659	0.75489	0.80726	0.84614
16	87.7508	0.47391	0.54740	0.61397	0.67163	0.72001	16	92.6306	0.58110	0.66781	0.73908	0.79413	0.83527
17	86.2598	0.44917	0.52356	0.59159	0.65100	0.70121	17	91.8365	0.55998	0.64922	0.72324	0.78086	0.82419
18	84.6471	0.42525	0.50021	0.56941	0.63033	0.68219	18	90.9895	0.53933	0.63080	0.70738	0.76745	0.81289
19	82.9057	0.40214	0.47735	0.54743	0.60964	0.66296	19	90.0872	0.51916	0.61257	0.69150	0.75389	0.80138
20	81.0292	0.37984	0.45501	0.52570	0.58896	0.64356	20	89.1267	0.49944	0.59452	0.67560	0.74018	0.78966
21	79.0113	0.35836	0.43320	0.50424	0.56833	0.62402	21	88.1053	0.48020	0.57667	0.65970	0.72634	0.77771
22	76.8463	0.33769	0.41195	0.48309	0.54776	0.60436	22	87.0201	0.46141	0.55902	0.64380	0.71235	0.76553
23	74.5295	0.31783	0.39127	0.46226	0.52731	0.58462	23	85.8683	0.44309	0.54158	0.62790	0.69824	0.75314
24	72.0573	0.29878	0.37118	0.44180	0.50701	0.56484	24	84.6471	0.42522	0.52436	0.61203	0.68400	0.74053
25	69.4278	0.28053	0.35170	0.42174	0.48690	0.54508	25	83.3535	0.40781	0.50736	0.59618	0.66964	0.72771
26	66.6411	0.26310	0.33285	0.40211	0.46703	0.52536	26	81.9848	0.39086	0.49059	0.58037	0.65518	0.71468
27	63.7000	0.24646	0.31465	0.38295	0.44744	0.50575	27	80.5383	0.37437	0.47406	0.56461	0.64062	0.70146
28	60.6101	0.23061	0.29710	0.36427	0.42816	0.48629	28	79.0113	0.35833	0.45778	0.54892	0.62598	0.68804
29	57.3808	0.21554	0.28023	0.34612	0.40924	0.46702	29	77.4017	0.34275	0.44177	0.53331	0.61128	0.67444
30	54.0251	0.20125	0.26403	0.32851	0.39072	0.44800	30	75.7072	0.32763	0.42603	0.51779	0.59651	0.66068
31	50.5605	0.18771	0.24850	0.31147	0.37262	0.42926	31	73.9261	0.31296	0.41058	0.50239	0.58172	0.64677
32	47.0087	0.17490	0.23365	0.29500	0.35498	0.41085	32	72.0573	0.29875	0.39541	0.48711	0.56690	0.63272
33	43.3960	0.16281	0.21947	0.27911	0.33782	0.39280	33	70.1000	0.28500	0.38056	0.47198	0.55209	0.61856
34	39.7526	0.15140	0.20595	0.26381	0.32113	0.37512	34	68.0540	0.27169	0.36601	0.45701	0.53729	0.60429
35	36.1123	0.14066	0.19306	0.24908	0.30494	0.35782	35	65.9202	0.25884	0.35179	0.44221	0.52254	0.58996
36	32.5113	0.13053	0.18078	0.23491	0.28922	0.34091	36	63.7000	0.24643	0.33790	0.42761	0.50784	0.57556
37	28.9873	0.12098	0.16906	0.22127	0.27395	0.32436	37	61.3961	0.23447	0.32435	0.41322	0.49322	0.56114
38	25.5780	0.11197	0.15788	0.20810	0.25910	0.30814	38	59.0122	0.22296	0.31115	0.39906	0.47871	0.54670
39	22.3191	0.10345	0.14718	0.19538	0.24461	0.29219	39	56.5531	0.21188	0.29830	0.38514	0.46432	0.53227
40	19.2431	0.09536	0.13690	0.18301	0.23040	0.27644	40	54.0251	0.20123	0.28581	0.37146	0.45007	0.51788
41	16.3771	0.08766	0.12698	0.17095	0.21641	0.26079	41	51.4357	0.19100	0.27368	0.35806	0.43597	0.50355
42	13.7424	0.08029	0.11735	0.15910	0.20252	0.24513	42	48.7940	0.18119	0.26191	0.34493	0.42205	0.48929
43	11.3528	0.07320	0.10795	0.14738	0.18864	0.22934	43	46.1102	0.17179	0.25051	0.33208	0.40832	0.47512
44	9.2150	0.06635	0.09872	0.13573	0.17468	0.21332	44	43.3960	0.16279	0.23947	0.31952	0.39479	0.46107
45	7.3294	0.05969	0.08961	0.12407	0.16056	0.19695	45	40.6646	0.15417	0.22878	0.30726	0.38147	0.44714
46	5.6904	0.05314	0.08029	0.11226	0.14627	0.18024	46	37.9299	0.14593	0.21845	0.29528	0.36836	0.43335
47	4.2891	0.04679	0.07122	0.10039	0.13166	0.16285	47	35.2069	0.13805	0.20846	0.28360	0.35547	0.41969
48	3.1142	0.04061	0.06230	0.08848	0.11680	0.14489	48	32.5113	0.13051	0.19879	0.27219	0.34279	0.40617
49	2.1533	0.03456	0.05351	0.07657	0.10174	0.12650	49	29.8590	0.12329	0.18945	0.26106	0.33031	0.39278
50	1.3939	0.02863	0.04485	0.06470	0.08656	0.10772	50	27.2660	0.11639	0.18040	0.25017	0.31802	0.37952
51	0.8223	0.02287	0.03636	0.05290	0.07127	0.08871	51	24.7478	0.10977	0.17163	0.23952	0.30590	0.36634
52	0.4224	0.01735	0.02807	0.04118	0.05593	0.06957	52	22.3191	0.10343	0.16311	0.22908	0.29392	0.35325
53	0.1729	0.01208	0.01998	0.02954	0.04049	0.05028	53	19.9933	0.09733	0.15482	0.21881	0.28205	0.34018
54	4.561*-2	0.00710	0.01207	0.01800	0.02491	0.03087	54	17.7824	0.09145	0.14674	0.20869	0.27025	0.32710
55	3.441*-3	0.00248	0.00433	0.00653	0.00915	0.01133	55	15.6961	0.08577	0.13882	0.19868	0.25848	0.31396
55.75	0.0000	0.00000	0.00000	0.00000	0.00000	0.00000	56	13.7424	0.08025	0.13105	0.18874	0.24668	0.30070
							57	11.9267	0.07494	0.12340	0.17883	0.23480	0.28726
							58	10.2523	0.06973	0.11582	0.16891	0.22281	0.27357
							59	8.7201	0.06465	0.10831	0.15894	0.21064	0.25958
							60	7.3294	0.05967	0.10084	0.14891	0.19827	0.24524

* Condensed from the usual form 4.561×10^{-2}.

TABLE C.2.   EXPECTANCY-LIFE FACTORS FOR GROUP PROPERTIES
UNIT SUMMATION PROCEDURE
Type Curve R_2 (Continued)

40 Years Average Life (Continued)

Age	Percent surviving	0%	2%	4%	6%	8%
61	6.0775	0.05480	0.09340	0.13878	0.18565	0.23050
62	4.9608	0.05001	0.08598	0.12856	0.17279	0.21534
63	3.9746	0.04531	0.07858	0.11824	0.15967	0.19975
64	3.1142	0.04055	0.07103	0.10766	0.14624	0.18383
65	2.3741	0.03596	0.06365	0.09715	0.13266	0.16747
66	1.7492	0.03148	0.05638	0.08665	0.11889	0.15072
67	1.2340	0.02711	0.04923	0.07618	0.10493	0.13364
68	0.8223	0.02289	0.04220	0.06574	0.09083	0.11624
69	0.5073	0.01881	0.03526	0.05533	0.07666	0.09853
70	0.2804	0.01486	0.02842	0.04496	0.06244	0.08055
71	0.1309	0.01096	0.02165	0.03461	0.04817	0.06231
72	4.561*$^{-2}$	0.00717	0.01502	0.02424	0.03385	0.04384
73	8.395*$^{-3}$	0.00355	0.00849	0.01385	0.01943	0.02517
74	6.596*$^{-5}$	0.00011	0.00208	0.00344	0.00485	0.00628
74.33	0.00000	0.00000	0.00000	0.00000	0.00000	0.00000

Type Curve R_2
50 Years Average Life

Age	Percent surviving	0%	2%	4%	6%	8%
1	99.8071	0.97181	0.97991	0.98521	0.98853	0.99064
2	99.6007	0.94626	0.96211	0.97254	0.97913	0.98330
3	99.3802	0.92187	0.94514	0.96058	0.97037	0.97659
4	99.1447	0.89829	0.92866	0.94898	0.96194	0.97020
5	98.8936	0.87536	0.91253	0.93760	0.95369	0.96398
6	98.6260	0.85298	0.89666	0.92637	0.94554	0.95785
7	98.3411	0.83110	0.88099	0.91522	0.93744	0.95177
8	98.0380	0.80967	0.86549	0.90412	0.92936	0.94569
9	97.7158	0.78866	0.85013	0.89304	0.92163	0.93960
10	97.3737	0.76806	0.83489	0.88196	0.91312	0.93346
11	97.0107	0.74782	0.81977	0.87087	0.90493	0.92726
12	96.6257	0.72796	0.80474	0.85976	0.89667	0.92099
13	96.2179	0.70845	0.78980	0.84861	0.88833	0.91463
14	95.7861	0.68928	0.77494	0.83743	0.87991	0.90818
15	95.3294	0.67044	0.76016	0.82619	0.87139	0.90162
16	94.8465	0.65194	0.74546	0.81490	0.86276	0.89494
17	94.3364	0.63375	0.73084	0.80356	0.85403	0.88814
18	93.7978	0.61589	0.71628	0.79217	0.84519	0.88120
19	93.2297	0.59834	0.70181	0.78071	0.83623	0.87414
20	92.6306	0.58109	0.68740	0.76919	0.82714	0.86692
21	91.9995	0.56416	0.67307	0.75761	0.81793	0.85956
22	91.3348	0.54752	0.65882	0.74597	0.80859	0.85204
23	90.6354	0.53119	0.64464	0.73428	0.79912	0.84436
24	89.8998	0.51516	0.63055	0.72252	0.78953	0.83653
25	89.1267	0.49943	0.61654	0.71070	0.77979	0.82852
26	88.3145	0.48400	0.60262	0.69884	0.76993	0.82034
27	87.4620	0.46886	0.58879	0.68692	0.75993	0.81200
28	86.5675	0.45401	0.57505	0.67496	0.74980	0.80347
29	85.6297	0.43946	0.56141	0.66295	0.73955	0.79478
30	84.6471	0.42521	0.54788	0.65090	0.72916	0.78590
31	83.6181	0.41124	0.53445	0.63882	0.71865	0.77685
32	82.5415	0.39758	0.52114	0.62671	0.70802	0.76762
33	81.4157	0.38420	0.50795	0.61458	0.69727	0.75822
34	80.2394	0.37111	0.49488	0.60244	0.68641	0.74865
35	79.0113	0.35832	0.48195	0.59029	0.67544	0.73891
36	77.7303	0.34582	0.46915	0.57813	0.66437	0.72900
37	76.3953	0.33361	0.45649	0.56599	0.65321	0.71893
38	75.0052	0.32170	0.44398	0.55386	0.64196	0.70872
39	73.5594	0.31007	0.43163	0.54175	0.63063	0.69835
40	72.0573	0.29874	0.41944	0.52968	0.61924	0.68783

50 Years Average Life (Continued)

Age	Percent surviving	0%	2%	4%	6%	8%
41	70.4985	0.28770	0.40742	0.51766	0.60778	0.67719
42	68.8830	0.27695	0.39558	0.50568	0.59628	0.66642
43	67.2109	0.26648	0.38391	0.49377	0.58473	0.65553
44	65.4830	0.25631	0.37243	0.48193	0.57316	0.64454
45	63.7000	0.24642	0.36115	0.47017	0.56157	0.63346
46	61.8634	0.23682	0.35006	0.45850	0.54997	0.62229
47	59.9751	0.22750	0.33917	0.44693	0.53838	0.61105
48	58.0372	0.21846	0.32849	0.43548	0.52681	0.59975
49	56.0528	0.20970	0.31802	0.42414	0.51526	0.58840
50	54.0251	0.20122	0.30777	0.41292	0.50375	0.57702
51	51.9581	0.19300	0.29773	0.40185	0.49229	0.56561
52	49.8563	0.18506	0.28791	0.39091	0.48090	0.55420
53	47.7249	0.17738	0.27831	0.38013	0.46957	0.54278
54	45.5694	0.16995	0.26894	0.36949	0.45832	0.53136
55	43.3960	0.16278	0.25978	0.35902	0.44715	0.51997
56	41.2116	0.15586	0.25085	0.34870	0.43608	0.50861
57	39.0232	0.14918	0.24213	0.33855	0.42510	0.49728
58	36.8384	0.14273	0.23363	0.32856	0.41422	0.48599
59	34.6651	0.13650	0.22533	0.31873	0.40344	0.47474
60	32.5113	0.13050	0.21724	0.30905	0.39276	0.46353
61	30.3853	0.12470	0.20934	0.29953	0.38217	0.45236
62	28.2951	0.11911	0.20164	0.29015	0.37167	0.44122
63	26.2489	0.11370	0.19411	0.28091	0.36125	0.43011
64	24.2545	0.10848	0.18674	0.27179	0.35090	0.41901
65	22.3191	0.10342	0.17954	0.26277	0.34060	0.40791
66	20.4497	0.09852	0.17247	0.25385	0.33033	0.39678
67	18.6523	0.09377	0.16552	0.24501	0.32007	0.38559
68	16.9324	0.08915	0.15869	0.23621	0.30980	0.37433
69	15.2946	0.08466	0.15195	0.22745	0.29948	0.36295
70	13.7424	0.08027	0.14528	0.21870	0.28910	0.35143
71	12.2786	0.07599	0.13868	0.20993	0.27861	0.33972
72	10.9050	0.07180	0.13212	0.20113	0.26799	0.32779
73	9.6223	0.06768	0.12560	0.19227	0.25721	0.31559
74	8.4307	0.06364	0.11909	0.18333	0.24624	0.30309
75	7.3294	0.05967	0.11259	0.17430	0.23506	0.29027
76	6.3169	0.05576	0.10609	0.16517	0.22365	0.27708
77	5.3915	0.05191	0.09959	0.15592	0.21200	0.26351
78	4.5509	0.04812	0.09308	0.14666	0.20010	0.24955
79	3.7927	0.04439	0.08658	0.13709	0.18794	0.23520
80	3.1142	0.04072	0.08008	0.12752	0.17555	0.22045
81	2.5127	0.03711	0.07360	0.11785	0.16293	0.20531
82	1.9857	0.03357	0.06714	0.10812	0.15010	0.18981
83	1.5303	0.03019	0.06053	0.09829	0.13700	0.17325
84	1.1436	0.02682	0.05416	0.08839	0.12369	0.15654
85	0.8223	0.02349	0.04763	0.07841	0.11022	0.13973
86	0.5630	0.02020	0.04137	0.06845	0.09662	0.12282
87	0.3612	0.01698	0.03510	0.05844	0.08294	0.10580
88	0.2120	0.01384	0.02897	0.04842	0.06915	0.08858
89	0.1092	0.01076	0.02293	0.03844	0.05523	0.07105
90	4.561*$^{-2}$	0.00776	0.01692	0.02847	0.04116	0.05314
91	1.287*$^{-2}$	0.00487	0.01089	0.01843	0.02681	0.03471
92	1.281*$^{-3}$	0.00209	0.00481	0.00820	0.01202	0.01555
92.91	0.0000	0.00000	0.00000	0.00000	0.00000	0.00000

* Condensed from the usual form 4.561×10^{-2}.

TABLE C.3. EXPECTANCY-LIFE FACTORS FOR GROUP PROPERTIES CALCULATED BY AVERAGE LIFE AND UNIT SUMMATION PROCEDURES
Type Curve L_2

Age, % of average life	Percent surviving	Expectancy-life factor		Age, % of average life	Percent surviving	Expectancy-life factor	
		Average life	Unit summation			Average life	Unit summation
(1)	(2)	(3)	(4)	(1)	(2)	(3)	(4)
1	99.999807	0.990004	0.987358	56	85.984315	0.535016	0.427285
2	99.998891	0.980013	0.974726	57	85.216607	0.529790	0.420894
3	99.996579	0.970036	0.962115	58	84.426261	0.524703	0.414660
4	99.992212	0.960078	0.949533	59	83.614134	0.519751	0.408580
5	99.985158	0.950145	0.936989	60	82.781134	0.514931	0.402650
6	99.974812	0.940243	0.924491	61	81.928238	0.510239	0.396868
7	99.960598	0.930376	0.912046	62	81.056472	0.505673	0.391229
8	99.941968	0.920548	0.899660	63	80.166901	0.501229	0.385730
9	99.918399	0.910764	0.887340	64	79.260622	0.496903	0.380368
10	99.889398	0.901027	0.875090	65	78.338763	0.492691	0.375139
11	99.854493	0.891341	0.862916	66	77.402470	0.488591	0.370039
12	99.813241	0.881707	0.850823	67	76.452903	0.484597	0.365064
13	99.765222	0.872129	0.838814	68	75.491231	0.480707	0.360211
14	99.710041	0.862609	0.826892	69	74.518626	0.476915	0.355476
15	99.647326	0.853148	0.815060	70	73.536255	0.473220	0.350854
16	99.576728	0.843750	0.803322	71	72.545280	0.469616	0.346343
17	99.497920	0.834414	0.791680	72	71.546848	0.466099	0.341938
18	99.410598	0.825143	0.780135	73	70.542090	0.462667	0.337636
19	99.314481	0.815936	0.768688	74	69.532118	0.459315	0.333433
20	99.209306	0.806796	0.757343	75	68.518019	0.456039	0.329325
21	99.094830	0.797722	0.746103	76	67.500852	0.452835	0.325310
22	98.970833	0.788716	0.734956	77	66.481645	0.449701	0.321383
23	98.837111	0.779776	0.723886	78	65.461397	0.446632	0.317542
24	98.693480	0.770903	0.712928	79	64.441067	0.443624	0.313782
25	98.539775	0.762098	0.702114	80	63.421582	0.440675	0.310100
26	98.375848	0.753360	0.691412	81	62.403830	0.437781	0.306494
27	98.201568	0.744688	0.680787	82	61.388656	0.434938	0.302960
28	98.016821	0.736082	0.670253	83	60.376869	0.432142	0.299495
29	97.821510	0.727542	0.659825	84	59.369235	0.429392	0.296096
30	97.615552	0.719066	0.649498	85	58.366476	0.426683	0.292760
31	97.398879	0.710655	0.639269	86	57.369276	0.424013	0.289485
32	97.171372	0.702307	0.629139	87	56.378274	0.421378	0.286267
33	96.932624	0.694024	0.619108	88	55.394068	0.418776	0.283105
34	96.681829	0.685812	0.609180	89	54.417216	0.416204	0.279995
35	96.417909	0.677675	0.599360	90	53.448233	0.413659	0.276935
36	96.139623	0.669622	0.589655	91	52.487594	0.411138	0.273923
37	95.845705	0.661660	0.580071	92	51.535736	0.408639	0.270957
38	95.534922	0.653797	0.570615	93	50.593050	0.406160	0.268034
39	95.205597	0.646041	0.561295	94	49.659898	0.403699	0.265152
40	94.856560	0.638400	0.552116	95	48.736601	0.401252	0.262309
41	94.486655	0.630879	0.543084	96	47.823448	0.398818	0.259503
42	94.094806	0.623486	0.534204	97	46.920692	0.396395	0.256733
43	93.680009	0.616224	0.525482	98	46.028551	0.393981	0.253997
44	93.241387	0.609100	0.516920	99	45.147216	0.391575	0.251293
45	92.778200	0.602116	0.508522	100	44.276847	0.389174	0.248620
46	92.289842	0.595275	0.500291	101	43.417573	0.386777	0.245976
47	91.775845	0.588581	0.492229	102	42.569500	0.384383	0.243360
48	91.235878	0.582035	0.484336	103	41.732707	0.381990	0.240770
49	90.669746	0.575638	0.476614	104	40.907250	0.379597	0.238206
50	90.077384	0.569390	0.469062	105	40.093163	0.377203	0.235665
51	89.458860	0.563293	0.461681	106	39.290458	0.374807	0.233148
52	88.814360	0.557344	0.454469	107	38.499130	0.372408	0.230653
53	88.144190	0.551544	0.447425	108	37.719155	0.370006	0.228180
54	87.448764	0.545890	0.440548	109	36.950494	0.367599	0.225727
55	86.728601	0.540381	0.433835	110	36.193092	0.365187	0.223294

TABLE C.3.   EXPECTANCY-LIFE FACTORS FOR GROUP PROPERTIES
CALCULATED BY AVERAGE LIFE AND UNIT SUMMATION
PROCEDURES

Type Curve L_2 (*Continued*)

Age, % of average life	Percent surviving	Expectancy-life factor		Age, % of average life	Percent surviving	Expectancy-life factor	
		Average life	Unit sum-mation			Average life	Unit sum-mation
(1)	(2)	(3)	(4)	(1)	(2)	(3)	(4)
111	35.446884	0.362769	0.220880	166	8.435485	0.227738	0.112974
112	34.711792	0.360346	0.218484	167	8.153240	0.225449	0.111460
113	33.987724	0.357916	0.216106	168	7.877358	0.223169	0.109961
114	33.274582	0.355480	0.213746	169	7.607786	0.220900	0.108477
115	32.572259	0.353037	0.211403	170	7.344472	0.218640	0.107007
116	31.880642	0.350587	0.209076	171	7.087362	0.216390	0.105551
117	31.199610	0.348130	0.206766	172	6.836401	0.214150	0.104110
118	30.529041	0.345667	0.204472	173	6.591532	0.211920	0.102682
119	29.868804	0.343198	0.202194	174	6.352696	0.209700	0.101269
120	29.218771	0.340721	0.199932	175	6.119834	0.207488	0.099870
121	28.578808	0.338239	0.197685	176	5.892884	0.205287	0.098484
122	27.948779	0.335751	0.195453	177	5.671783	0.203094	0.097111
123	27.328552	0.333258	0.193237	178	5.456467	0.200911	0.095752
124	26.717990	0.330759	0.191036	179	5.246870	0.198738	0.094406
125	26.116962	0.328256	0.188850	180	5.042923	0.196573	0.093072
126	25.525332	0.325748	0.186680	181	4.844559	0.194417	0.091751
127	24.942972	0.323237	0.184525	182	4.651707	0.192270	0.090443
128	24.369753	0.320722	0.182385	183	4.464294	0.190131	0.089147
129	23.805548	0.318205	0.180260	184	4.282248	0.188002	0.087863
130	23.250237	0.315686	0.178151	185	4.105494	0.185880	0.086591
131	22.703700	0.313165	0.176057	186	3.933956	0.183768	0.085332
132	22.165819	0.310643	0.173979	187	3.767558	0.181663	0.084084
133	21.636482	0.308120	0.171917	188	3.606220	0.179567	0.082848
134	21.115580	0.305598	0.169870	189	3.449865	0.177478	0.081623
135	20.603011	0.303076	0.167839	190	3.298411	0.175398	0.080409
136	20.098673	0.300556	0.165824	191	3.151777	0.173326	0.079207
137	19.602469	0.298038	0.163825	192	3.009882	0.171261	0.078016
138	19.114307	0.295522	0.161842	193	2.872643	0.169204	0.076835
139	18.634099	0.293008	0.159875	194	2.739975	0.167155	0.075665
140	18.161760	0.290499	0.157925	195	2.611795	0.165113	0.074506
141	17.697209	0.287993	0.155991	196	2.488018	0.163079	0.073357
142	17.240369	0.285492	0.154073	197	2.368557	0.161051	0.072219
143	16.791166	0.282996	0.152172	198	2.253328	0.159031	0.071091
144	16.349531	0.280505	0.150287	199	2.142245	0.157019	0.069972
145	15.915396	0.278020	0.148419	200	2.035219	0.155013	0.068864
146	15.488697	0.275542	0.146568	201	1.932165	0.153014	0.067766
147	15.069374	0.273070	0.144733	202	1.832994	0.151022	0.066678
148	14.657367	0.270605	0.142914	203	1.737621	0.149037	0.065598
149	14.252621	0.268148	0.141112	204	1.645958	0.147058	0.064528
150	13.855081	0.265698	0.139327	205	1.557916	0.145086	0.063468
151	13.464696	0.263256	0.137558	206	1.473410	0.143121	0.062417
152	13.081416	0.260823	0.135806	207	1.392351	0.141132	0.061375
153	12.705191	0.258399	0.134071	208	1.314653	0.139209	0.060342
154	12.335974	0.255983	0.132352	209	1.240229	0.137263	0.059318
155	11.973718	0.253576	0.130649	210	1.168992	0.135322	0.058303
156	11.618379	0.251179	0.128963	211	1.100858	0.133388	0.057296
157	11.269910	0.248791	0.127292	212	1.035738	0.131460	0.056298
158	10.928268	0.246412	0.125638	213	0.973550	0.129539	0.055308
159	10.593406	0.244043	0.124000	214	0.914207	0.127623	0.054327
160	10.265282	0.241684	0.122378	215	0.857626	0.125712	0.053354
161	9.943851	0.239335	0.120772	216	0.803724	0.123808	0.052390
162	9.629067	0.236995	0.119182	217	0.752418	0.121909	0.051434
163	9.320885	0.234666	0.117607	218	0.703625	0.120016	0.050485
164	9.019259	0.232347	0.116147	219	0.657266	0.118129	0.049545
165	8.724141	0.230037	0.114503	220	0.613258	0.116247	0.048612

TABLE C.3. EXPECTANCY-LIFE FACTORS FOR GROUP PROPERTIES CALCULATED BY AVERAGE LIFE AND UNIT SUMMATION PROCEDURES
Type Curve L_2 (Continued)

| Age, % of average life | Percent surviving | Expectancy-life factor | | Age, % of average life | Percent surviving | Expectancy-life factor | |
		Average life	Unit summation			Average life	Unit summation
(1)	(2)	(3)	(4)	(1)	(2)	(3)	(4)
221	0.571524	0.114371	0.047687	256	1.45737*-2	0.051734	0.019549
222	0.531984	0.112480	0.046769	257	1.23784*-2	0.050022	0.018852
223	0.494561	0.110634	0.045859	258	1.04531*-2	0.048315	0.018161
224	0.459179	0.108774	0.044956	259	8.77280*-3	0.046611	0.017475
225	0.425762	0.106919	0.044060	260	7.31384*-3	0.044912	0.016795
226	0.394237	0.105069	0.043172	261	6.05413*-3	0.043217	0.016119
227	0.364530	0.103224	0.042291	262	4.97294*-3	0.041526	0.015449
228	0.336568	0.101384	0.041418	263	4.05096*-3	0.039839	0.014784
229	0.310282	0.099549	0.040551	264	3.27022*-3	0.038156	0.014122
230	0.285603	0.097719	0.039691	265	2.61411*-3	0.036478	0.013460
231	0.262462	0.095894	0.038838	266	2.06728*-3	0.034804	0.012803
232	0.240792	0.094074	0.037992	267	1.61567*-3	0.033135	0.012158
233	0.220529	0.092259	0.037152	268	1.24639*-3	0.031471	0.011520
234	0.201607	0.090448	0.036319	269	9.47756*-4	0.029812	0.010885
235	0.183966	0.088643	0.035494	270	7.09195*-4	0.028159	0.010254
236	0.167543	0.086841	0.034675	271	5.21216*-4	0.026511	0.009630
237	0.152279	0.085045	0.033861	272	3.75360*-4	0.024869	0.009011
238	0.138116	0.083253	0.033052	273	2.64162*-4	0.023234	0.008398
239	0.124998	0.081465	0.032251	274	1.81034*-4	0.021607	0.007791
240	0.112869	0.079682	0.031457	275	1.20312*-4	0.019988	0.007189
241	0.101676	0.077903	0.030670	276	7.71288*-5	0.018380	0.006589
242	9.13671*-2	0.076129	0.029889	277	4.73736*-5	0.016784	0.005989
243	8.18917*-2	0.074359	0.029113	278	2.76319*-5	0.015203	0.005389
244	7.32011*-2	0.072594	0.028343	279	1.51239*-5	0.013641	0.004789
245	6.52482*-2	0.070833	0.027579	280	7.64047*-6	0.012105	0.004189
246	5.79875*-2	0.069076	0.026820	281	3.47912*-6	0.010604	0.003589
247	5.13750*-2	0.067323	0.026067	282	1.37772*-6	0.009151	0.002989
248	4.53683*-2	0.065524	0.025320	283	4.47984*-7	0.007765	0.002389
249	3.99267*-2	0.063830	0.024580	284	1.08143*-7	0.006453	0.001789
250	3.50111*-2	0.062090	0.023845	285	1.55959*-8	0.005073	0.001189
251	3.05840*-2	0.060353	0.023115	286	1.13774*-10	0.005000	0.000589
252	2.66094*-2	0.058621	0.022391				
253	2.30531*-2	0.056893	0.021672				
254	1.98822*-2	0.055170	0.020958				
255	1.70656*-2	0.053450	0.020251				

* Condensed from the usual form 9.13671 × 10⁻².

TABLE C.3. EXPECTANCY-LIFE FACTORS FOR GROUP PROPERTIES CALCULATED BY AVERAGE LIFE AND UNIT SUMMATION PROCEDURES
Type Curve S_2

Age, % of average life	Percent surviving	Expectancy-life factor Average life	Expectancy-life factor Unit summation	Age, % of average life	Percent surviving	Expectancy-life factor Average life	Expectancy-life factor Unit summation
(1)	(2)	(3)	(4)	(1)	(2)	(3)	(4)
1	100.000000	0.990000	0.988650	51	94.126215	0.527042	0.468154
2	99.999997	0.980000	0.977299	52	93.684619	0.519502	0.459928
3	99.999978	0.970000	0.965949	53	93.222164	0.512055	0.451819
4	99.999917	0.960001	0.954599	54	92.738598	0.504699	0.443826
5	99.999766	0.950002	0.943251	55	92.233696	0.497434	0.435949
6	99.999457	0.940005	0.931904	56	91.707265	0.490261	0.428188
7	99.998897	0.930010	0.920560	57	91.159143	0.483179	0.420543
8	99.997966	0.920019	0.909220	58	90.589201	0.476187	0.413013
9	99.996518	0.910032	0.897886	59	89.997341	0.469286	0.405597
10	99.994376	0.900052	0.886560	60	89.383496	0.462474	0.398296
11	99.991336	0.890079	0.875244	61	88.747635	0.455752	0.391108
12	99.987165	0.880116	0.863941	62	88.089759	0.449118	0.384033
13	99.981599	0.870164	0.852652	63	87.409902	0.442573	0.377069
14	99.974348	0.860227	0.841381	64	86.708131	0.436115	0.370216
15	99.965090	0.850306	0.830131	65	85.984550	0.429742	0.363473
16	99.953478	0.840405	0.818905	66	85.239294	0.423456	0.356838
17	99.939138	0.830525	0.807706	67	84.472532	0.417254	0.350311
18	99.921669	0.820669	0.796539	68	83.684466	0.411136	0.343891
19	99.900648	0.810840	0.785406	69	82.875333	0.405101	0.337576
20	99.875625	0.801042	0.774312	70	82.045402	0.399149	0.331365
21	99.846130	0.791278	0.763260	71	81.194976	0.393277	0.325258
22	99.811674	0.781549	0.752254	72	80.324388	0.387485	0.319252
23	99.771748	0.771860	0.741298	73	79.434005	0.381773	0.313346
24	99.725825	0.762213	0.730395	74	78.524226	0.376138	0.307539
25	99.673624	0.752611	0.719551	75	77.595477	0.370580	0.301830
26	99.613806	0.743058	0.708768	76	76.648220	0.365098	0.296217
27	99.546587	0.733557	0.698050	77	75.682941	0.359691	0.290699
28	99.471128	0.724109	0.687401	78	74.700159	0.354357	0.285275
29	99.386843	0.714719	0.676824	79	73.700418	0.349096	0.279943
30	99.293139	0.705389	0.666324	80	72.684292	0.343907	0.274702
31	99.189418	0.696121	0.655903	81	71.652379	0.338788	0.269550
32	99.075081	0.686919	0.645565	82	70.605303	0.333738	0.264486
33	98.949525	0.677785	0.635313	83	69.543714	0.328756	0.259509
34	98.812152	0.668720	0.625150	84	68.468282	0.323841	0.254617
35	98.662362	0.659727	0.615079	85	67.379703	0.318992	0.249808
36	98.499563	0.650809	0.605103	86	66.278692	0.314208	0.245082
37	98.323167	0.641968	0.595223	87	65.165984	0.309488	0.240437
38	98.132596	0.633205	0.585443	88	64.042335	0.304831	0.235871
39	97.927280	0.624522	0.575765	89	62.908516	0.300234	0.231384
40	97.706661	0.615921	0.566191	90	61.765316	0.295699	0.226973
41	97.470194	0.607403	0.556722	91	60.613539	0.291223	0.222638
42	97.217348	0.598970	0.547361	92	59.454003	0.286805	0.218377
43	96.947609	0.590622	0.538109	93	58.287537	0.282444	0.214189
44	96.660480	0.582362	0.528967	94	57.114983	0.278140	0.210072
45	96.355482	0.574190	0.519937	95	55.937193	0.273891	0.206026
46	96.032159	0.566106	0.511020	96	54.755025	0.269697	0.202048
47	95.690073	0.558112	0.502217	97	53.569348	0.265555	0.198138
48	95.328812	0.550208	0.493528	98	52.381032	0.261466	0.194294
49	94.947987	0.542395	0.484954	99	51.190957	0.257429	0.190516
50	94.547234	0.534673	0.476496	100	50.000000	0.253441	0.186802

TABLE C.3.   EXPECTANCY-LIFE FACTORS FOR GROUP PROPERTIES
CALCULATED BY AVERAGE LIFE AND UNIT SUMMATION PROCEDURES
Type Curve S_2 (*Continued*)

Age, % of average life	Percent surviving	Expectancy-life factor		Age, % of average life	Percent surviving	Expectancy-life factor	
		Average life	Unit summation			Average life	Unit summation
(1)	(2)	(3)	(4)	(1)	(2)	(3)	(4)
101	48.809043	0.249503	0.183150	151	5.052013	0.098830	0.059265
102	47.618966	0.245614	0.179560	152	4.671188	0.096479	0.057628
103	46.430653	0.241772	0.176030	153	4.309927	0.094147	0.056014
104	45.244975	0.237977	0.172560	154	3.967841	0.091833	0.054424
105	44.062807	0.234227	0.169148	155	3.644518	0.089536	0.052857
106	42.885017	0.230523	0.165793	156	3.339520	0.087257	0.051311
107	41.712463	0.226862	0.162494	157	3.052391	0.084994	0.049785
108	40.545997	0.223245	0.159249	158	2.782652	0.082749	0.048280
109	39.386461	0.219670	0.156059	159	2.529806	0.080520	0.046797
110	38.234684	0.216137	0.152921	160	2.293339	0.078306	0.045335
111	37.091484	0.212644	0.149835	161	2.072720	0.076109	0.043893
112	35.957665	0.209192	0.146800	162	1.867404	0.073927	0.042470
113	34.834016	0.205778	0.143815	163	1.676833	0.071761	0.041066
114	33.721308	0.202403	0.140878	164	1.500437	0.069610	0.039680
115	32.620297	0.199066	0.137990	165	1.337638	0.067473	0.038312
116	31.531718	0.195766	0.135148	166	1.187848	0.065351	0.036962
117	30.456287	0.192502	0.132352	167	1.050475	0.063243	0.035632
118	29.394697	0.189275	0.129602	168	0.924919	0.061149	0.034320
119	28.347621	0.186080	0.126896	169	0.810582	0.059070	0.033026
120	27.315708	0.182921	0.124233	170	0.706862	0.057004	0.031748
121	26.299582	0.179795	0.121613	171	0.613157	0.054951	0.030487
122	25.299841	0.176703	0.119035	172	0.528872	0.052911	0.029242
123	24.317059	0.173642	0.116497	173	0.453413	0.050885	0.028013
124	23.351780	0.170613	0.114000	174	0.386194	0.048872	0.026800
125	22.404523	0.167615	0.111542	175	0.326638	0.046871	0.025602
126	21.475774	0.164648	0.109123	176	0.274175	0.044883	0.024420
127	20.565995	0.161710	0.106742	177	0.228252	0.042907	0.023254
128	19.675612	0.158802	0.104398	178	0.188326	0.040943	0.022104
129	18.805024	0.155922	0.102090	179	0.153870	0.038992	0.020968
130	17.954598	0.153070	0.099818	180	0.124376	0.037053	0.019845
131	17.124667	0.150247	0.097581	181	$9.93524 *^{-2}$	0.035126	0.018754
132	16.315534	0.147450	0.095378	182	$7.83306 *^{-2}$	0.033211	0.017671
133	15.527468	0.144679	0.093209	183	$6.08622 *^{-2}$	0.031308	0.016596
134	14.760706	0.141935	0.091074	184	$4.65220 *^{-2}$	0.029417	0.015529
135	14.015450	0.130216	0.088971	185	$3.49103 *^{-2}$	0.027538	0.014471
136	13.291869	0.136523	0.086899	186	$2.56524 *^{-2}$	0.025672	0.013422
137	12.590099	0.133854	0.084859	187	$1.84007 *^{-2}$	0.023819	0.012383
138	11.910241	0.131209	0.082849	188	$1.28351 *^{-2}$	0.021979	0.011354
139	11.252365	0.128588	0.080869	189	$8.66393 *^{-3}$	0.020153	0.010335
140	10.616504	0.125991	0.078919	190	$5.62422 *^{-3}$	0.018343	0.009327
141	10.002659	0.123415	0.076998	191	$3.48232 *^{-3}$	0.016550	0.008330
142	9.410799	0.120863	0.075105	192	$2.03372 *^{-3}$	0.014777	0.007345
143	8.840857	0.118332	0.073240	193	$1.10291 *^{-3}$	0.013029	0.006372
144	8.292735	0.115823	0.071403	194	$5.42850 *^{-4}$	0.011312	0.005412
145	7.766305	0.113335	0.069592	195	$2.34042 *^{-4}$	0.009641	0.004466
146	7.261402	0.110867	0.067808	196	$8.32856 *^{-5}$	0.008041	0.003535
147	6.777836	0.108421	0.066050	197	$2.18850 *^{-5}$	0.006572	0.002620
148	6.315381	0.105993	0.064317	198	$3.30905 *^{-6}$	0.005399	0.001724
149	5.873785	0.103587	0.062609	199	$1.32090 *^{-7}$	0.005000	0.000849
150	5.452766	0.101199	0.060925	200	0.000000	0.000000	0.000000

* Condensed from the usual form 9.93524×10^{-2}.

TABLE C.3. EXPECTANCY-LIFE FACTORS FOR GROUP PROPERTIES
CALCULATED BY AVERAGE LIFE AND UNIT SUMMATION PROCEDURES
Type Curve R_2

Age, % of average life	Percent surviving	Expectancy-life factor		Age, % of average life	Percent surviving	Expectancy-life factor	
		Average life	Unit summation			Average life	Unit summation
(1)	(2)	(3)	(4)	(1)	(2)	(3)	(4)
1	99.905169	0.990944	0.985414	51	88.725573	0.577136	0.491676
2	99.807067	0.981914	0.971811	52	88.314544	0.569798	0.483996
3	99.705605	0.972908	0.958835	53	87.893407	0.562505	0.476390
4	99.600695	0.963927	0.946260	54	87.461981	0.555255	0.468857
5	99.492244	0.954972	0.933957	55	87.020081	0.548049	0.461398
6	99.380161	0.946044	0.921870	56	86.567526	0.540888	0.454013
7	99.264351	0.937142	0.909992	57	86.104130	0.533772	0.446701
8	99.144719	0.928267	0.898290	58	85.629710	0.526702	0.439463
9	99.021166	0.919419	0.886750	59	85.144083	0.519677	0.432298
10	98.893593	0.910598	0.875359	60	84.647065	0.512699	0.425207
11	98.761899	0.901806	0.864106	61	84.138474	0.505768	0.418189
12	98.625982	0.893042	0.852983	62	83.618129	0.498884	0.411244
13	98.485737	0.884306	0.841983	63	83.085851	0.492048	0.404373
14	98.341058	0.875600	0.831101	64	82.541463	0.485260	0.397575
15	98.191836	0.866923	0.820332	65	81.984792	0.478521	0.390850
16	98.037963	0.858276	0.809672	66	81.415667	0.471831	0.384198
17	97.879326	0.849659	0.799217	67	80.833918	0.465191	0.377619
18	97.715812	0.841072	0.788664	68	80.239384	0.458601	0.371113
19	97.547306	0.832516	0.778311	69	79.631907	0.452061	0.364680
20	97.373690	0.823992	0.768055	70	79.011334	0.445573	0.351321
21	97.194847	0.815499	0.757893	71	78.377518	0.439135	0.352034
22	97.010654	0.807038	0.747824	72	77.730321	0.432750	0.345821
23	96.820990	0.798609	0.737847	73	77.069611	0.426417	0.339681
24	96.625728	0.790212	0.727959	74	76.395264	0.420137	0.333614
25	96.424742	0.781849	0.718159	75	75.707172	0.413910	0.327620
26	96.217904	0.773519	0.708446	76	75.005227	0.407737	0.321698
27	96.005083	0.765223	0.698790	77	74.289341	0.401618	0.315849
28	95.786146	0.756960	0.689277	78	73.559434	0.395553	0.310074
29	95.560957	0.748732	0.679819	79	72.815442	0.389544	0.304372
30	95.329381	0.740539	0.670443	80	72.057316	0.383590	0.298742
31	95.091277	0.732381	0.661149	81	71.285018	0.377691	0.293185
32	94.846506	0.724258	0.651937	82	70.498527	0.371849	0.287700
33	94.594923	0.716171	0.642806	83	69.697846	0.366064	0.282288
34	94.336384	0.708120	0.633754	84	68.882993	0.360335	0.276948
35	94.070739	0.700105	0.624782	85	68.054005	0.354663	0.271680
36	93.797841	0.692128	0.615888	86	67.210947	0.349049	0.266485
37	93.517536	0.684187	0.607073	87	66.353898	0.343493	0.261362
38	93.229671	0.676284	0.598335	88	65.482963	0.337995	0.256311
39	92.934090	0.668420	0.589675	89	64.598277	0.332555	0.251331
40	92.630635	0.660593	0.581092	90	63.699997	0.327175	0.246423
41	92.319143	0.652805	0.572586	91	62.788308	0.321853	0.241586
42	91.999455	0.645056	0.564156	92	61.863420	0.316590	0.236820
43	91.671405	0.637346	0.555802	93	60.925581	0.311386	0.232125
44	91.334826	0.629677	0.547524	94	59.975065	0.306242	0.227501
45	90.989550	0.622047	0.539321	95	59.012172	0.301157	0.222947
46	90.635405	0.614458	0.531193	96	58.037245	0.296132	0.218463
47	90.272221	0.606910	0.523141	97	57.050649	0.291167	0.214048
48	89.899822	0.599403	0.515163	98	56.052792	0.286261	0.209702
49	89.518033	0.591939	0.507260	99	55.044118	0.281415	0.205425
50	89.126676	0.584516	0.499431	100	54.025098	0.276629	0.201217

TABLE C.3. EXPECTANCY-LIFE FACTORS FOR GROUP PROPERTIES
CALCULATED BY AVERAGE LIFE AND UNIT SUMMATION PROCEDURES
Type Curve R_2 (*Continued*)

Age, % of average life	Percent surviving	Expectancy-life factor		Age, % of average life	Percent surviving	Expectancy-life factor	
		Average life	Unit summation			Average life	Unit summation
(1)	(2)	(3)	(4)	(1)	(2)	(3)	(4)
101	52.996242	0.271902	0.197077	146	9.622345	0.110077	0.067683
102	51.958098	0.267235	0.193004	147	9.015187	0.107154	0.065654
103	50.911253	0.262627	0.188998	148	8.430722	0.104235	0.063643
104	49.856322	0.258078	0.185058	149	7.868833	0.101322	0.061649
105	48.793961	0.253588	0.181184	150	7.329370	0.098411	0.059671
106	47.724858	0.249157	0.177376	151	6.812139	0.095504	0.057709
107	46.649738	0.244785	0.173632	152	6.316922	0.092599	0.055761
108	45.569366	0.240469	0.169952	153	5.843470	0.089696	0.053828
109	44.484524	0.236211	0.166336	154	5.391513	0.086794	0.051910
110	43.396042	0.232011	0.162782	155	4.960762	0.083898	0.050007
111	42.304772	0.227867	0.159289	156	4.550914	0.081004	0.048119
112	41.211602	0.223778	0.155858	157	4.161655	0.078113	0.046245
113	40.117432	0.219745	0.152487	158	3.792661	0.075226	0.044386
114	39.023208	0.215767	0.149176	159	3.443606	0.072345	0.042541
115	37.929874	0.211842	0.145923	160	3.114157	0.069469	0.040711
116	36.838412	0.207971	0.142727	161	2.803979	0.066601	0.038897
117	35.749814	0.204151	0.139588	162	2.512738	0.063740	0.037099
118	34.665084	0.200383	0.136504	163	2.240094	0.060890	0.035319
119	33.585247	0.196665	0.133475	164	1.985704	0.058050	0.033554
120	32.511310	0.192996	0.130500	165	1.749220	0.055222	0.031808
121	31.444312	0.189375	0.127576	166	1.530285	0.052407	0.030080
122	30.385275	0.185802	0.124704	167	1.328528	0.049607	0.028371
123	29.335168	0.182274	0.121882	168	1.143562	0.046821	0.026681
124	28.295102	0.178790	0.119109	169	0.974979	0.044053	0.025010
125	27.266031	0.175349	0.116383	170	0.822348	0.041301	0.023358
126	26.248932	0.171950	0.113704	171	0.685186	0.038568	0.021726
127	25.244775	0.168591	0.111069	172	0.562991	0.035854	0.020114
128	24.254487	0.165270	0.108478	173	0.455208	0.033159	0.018519
129	23.278979	0.161986	0.105930	174	0.361230	0.030485	0.016944
130	22.319126	0.158737	0.103422	175	0.280397	0.027832	0.015390
131	21.375759	0.155522	0.100954	176	0.211982	0.025201	0.013858
132	20.449671	0.152339	0.098523	177	0.155196	0.022593	0.012347
133	19.541616	0.149185	0.096129	178	0.109175	0.020009	0.010857
134	18.652297	0.146060	0.093770	179	7.29837*$^{-2}$	0.017451	0.009389
135	17.782360	0.142961	0.091445	180	4.56098*$^{-2}$	0.014924	0.007944
136	16.932406	0.139886	0.089152	181	2.59620*$^{-2}$	0.012434	0.006524
137	16.102977	0.136833	0.086889	182	1.28698*$^{-2}$	0.009997	0.005128
138	15.294557	0.133802	0.084656	183	5.08426*$^{-3}$	0.007649	0.003757
139	14.507570	0.130789	0.082451	184	1.28068*$^{-3}$	0.005515	0.002415
140	13.742387	0.127793	0.080272	185	6.59603*$^{-5}$	0.004988	0.001100
141	12.999319	0.124812	0.078118				
142	12.278611	0.121844	0.075988				
143	11.580451	0.118889	0.073881				
144	10.904978	0.115943	0.071795				
145	10.252267	0.113006	0.069730				

* Condensed from the usual form 7.29837 $\times$ 10^{-2}.

APPENDIX D

Compound Interest Factors

The tables of compound interest factors, D.1 to D.22, on the following pages are for interest rates of each one-half percent from 1 to 8½, 9, 10, 12, 15, 20, and 25 percent. The interest periods are consecutive from 1 to 40, then for 40, 45, 50, 55, 60, 65, 70, 75, 80, 90, and 100.

These compound interest factors are from original calculations made by the authors on business machines. These 22 tables may be reproduced in whole or in part only by specific permission of the authors and publisher.

For other fractional interest rates from ¼ to 10½ percent and for 10-place tables the reader is referred to Kent's tables.[1] Kent gives the factors for each interest period 1 to 100 and up to 300 periods for interest rates of less than 1 percent.

[1] Frederick C. Kent and Maude E. Kent, "Compound Interest and Annuity Tables," 1st ed. (11th impression), New York, McGraw-Hill Book Company, Inc., 1926.

TABLE D.1. 1 PERCENT COMPOUND INTEREST FACTORS FOR ONE DOLLAR

	Single payment		Annuities (uniform series payments)				
	Compound amount	Present worth	Compound amount	Sinking fund	Present worth	Capital recovery	
n	Given P To find S $(1 + i)^n$	Given S To find P $\dfrac{1}{(1 + i)^n}$	Given R To find S $\dfrac{(1 + i)^n - 1}{i}$	Given S To find R $\dfrac{i}{(1 + i)^n - 1}$	Given R To find P $\dfrac{(1 + i)^n - 1}{i(1 + i)^n}$	Given P To find R $\dfrac{i(1 + i)^n}{(1 + i)^n - 1}$	n
	k_1	k_2	k_3	k_4	k_5	k_6	
1	1.0100 0000	0.990099	1.000000	1.000000	0.990099	1.010000	1
2	1.0201 0000	0.980296	2.010000	0.497512	1.970395	0.507512	2
3	1.0303 0100	0.970590	3.030100	0.330022	2.940985	0.340022	3
4	1.0406 0401	0.960980	4.060401	0.246281	3.901966	0.256281	4
5	1.0510 1005	0.951466	5.101005	0.196040	4.853431	0.206040	5
6	1.0615 2015	0.942045	6.152015	0.162548	5.795476	0.172548	6
7	1.0721 3535	0.932718	7.213535	0.138628	6.728195	0.148628	7
8	1.0828 5671	0.923483	8.285671	0.120690	7.651678	0.130690	8
9	1.0936 8527	0.914340	9.368527	0.106740	8.566018	0.116740	9
10	1.1046 2213	0.905287	10.462213	0.095582	9.471305	0.105582	10
11	1.1156 6835	0.896324	11.566835	0.086454	10.367628	0.096454	11
12	1.1268 2503	0.887449	12.682503	0.078849	11.255077	0.088849	12
13	1.1380 9328	0.878663	13.809328	0.072415	12.133740	0.082415	13
14	1.1494 7421	0.869963	14.947421	0.066901	13.003703	0.076901	14
15	1.1609 6896	0.861349	16.096896	0.062124	13.865053	0.072124	15
16	1.1725 7864	0.852821	17.257864	0.057945	14.717874	0.067945	16
17	1.1843 0443	0.844377	18.430443	0.054258	15.562251	0.064258	17
18	1.1961 4748	0.836017	19.614748	0.050982	16.398269	0.060982	18
19	1.2081 0895	0.827740	20.810895	0.048052	17.226008	0.058052	19
20	1.2201 9004	0.819544	22.019004	0.045415	18.045553	0.055415	20
21	1.2323 9194	0.811430	23.239194	0.043031	18.856983	0.053031	21
22	1.2447 1586	0.803396	24.471586	0.040864	19.660379	0.050864	22
23	1.2571 6302	0.795442	25.716302	0.038886	20.455821	0.048886	23
24	1.2697 3465	0.787566	26.973465	0.037073	21.243387	0.047073	24
25	1.2824 3200	0.779768	28.243200	0.035407	22.023156	0.045407	25
26	1.2952 5631	0.772048	29.525631	0.033869	22.795204	0.043869	26
27	1.3082 0888	0.764404	30.820888	0.032446	23.559608	0.042446	27
28	1.3212 9097	0.756836	32.129097	0.031124	24.316443	0.041124	28
29	1.3345 0388	0.749342	33.450388	0.029895	25.065785	0.039895	29
30	1.3478 4892	0.741923	34.784892	0.028748	25.807708	0.038748	30
31	1.3613 2740	0.734577	36.132740	0.027676	26.542285	0.037676	31
32	1.3749 4068	0.727304	37.494068	0.026671	27.269589	0.036671	32
33	1.3886 9009	0.720103	38.869009	0.025727	27.989693	0.035727	33
34	1.4025 7699	0.712973	40.257699	0.024840	28.702666	0.034840	34
35	1.4166 0276	0.705914	41.660276	0.024004	29.408580	0.034004	35
36	1.4307 6878	0.698925	43.076878	0.023214	30.107505	0.033214	36
37	1.4450 7647	0.692005	44.507647	0.022468	30.799510	0.032468	37
38	1.4595 2724	0.685153	45.952724	0.021761	31.484663	0.031761	38
39	1.4741 2251	0.678370	47.412251	0.021092	32.163033	0.031092	39
40	1.4888 6373	0.671653	48.886373	0.020456	32.834686	0.030456	40
45	1.5648 1075	0.639055	56.481075	0.017705	36.094508	0.027705	45
50	1.6446 3182	0.608039	64.463182	0.015513	39.196118	0.025513	50
55	1.7285 2457	0.578528	72.852457	0.013726	42.147192	0.023726	55
60	1.8166 9670	0.550450	81.669670	0.012244	44.955038	0.022244	60
65	1.9093 6649	0.523734	90.936649	0.010997	47.626608	0.020997	65
70	2.0067 6337	0.498315	100.676337	0.009933	50.168514	0.019933	70
75	2.1091 2847	0.474129	110.912847	0.009016	52.587051	0.019016	75
80	2.2167 1522	0.451118	121.671522	0.008219	54.888206	0.018219	80
90	2.4486 3267	0.408391	144.863267	0.006903	59.160881	0.016903	90
100	2.7048 1383	0.369711	170.481383	0.005866	63.028879	0.015866	100

TABLE D.2. 1½ PERCENT COMPOUND INTEREST FACTORS FOR ONE DOLLAR

	Single payment		Annuities (uniform series payments)				
	Compound amount	Present worth	Compound amount	Sinking fund	Present worth	Capital recovery	
n	Given P To find S $(1+i)^n$	Given S To find P $\dfrac{1}{(1+i)^n}$	Given R To find S $\dfrac{(1+i)^n-1}{i}$	Given S To find R $\dfrac{i}{(1+i)^n-1}$	Given R To find P $\dfrac{(1+i)^n-1}{i(1+i)^n}$	Given P To find R $\dfrac{i(1+i)^n}{(1+i)^n-1}$	n
	k_1	k_2	k_3	k_4	k_5	k_6	
1	1.0150 0000	0.985222	1.000000	1.000000	0.985222	1.015000	1
2	1.0302 2500	0.970662	2.015000	0.496278	1.955883	0.511278	2
3	1.0456 7838	0.956317	3.045225	0.328383	2.912200	0.343383	3
4	1.0613 6355	0.942184	4.090903	0.244445	3.854385	0.259445	4
5	1.0772 8400	0.928260	5.152267	0.194089	4.782645	0.209089	5
6	1.0934 4326	0.914542	6.229551	0.160525	5.697187	0.175525	6
7	1.1098 4491	0.901027	7.322994	0.136556	6.598214	0.151556	7
8	1.1264 9259	0.887711	8.432839	0.118584	7.485925	0.133584	8
9	1.1433 8998	0.874592	9.559332	0.104610	8.360517	0.119610	9
10	1.1605 4083	0.861667	10.702722	0.093434	9.222185	0.108434	10
11	1.1779 4894	0.848933	11.863262	0.084294	10.071118	0.099294	11
12	1.1956 1817	0.836387	13.041211	0.076680	10.907505	0.091680	12
13	1.2135 5244	0.824027	14.236830	0.070240	11.731532	0.085240	13
14	1.2317 5573	0.811849	15.450382	0.064723	12.543382	0.079723	14
15	1.2502 3207	0.799852	16.682138	0.059944	13.343233	0.074944	15
16	1.2689 8555	0.788031	17.932370	0.055765	14.131264	0.070765	16
17	1.2880 2033	0.776385	19.201355	0.052080	14.907649	0.067080	17
18	1.3073 4064	0.764912	20.489376	0.048806	15.672561	0.063806	18
19	1.3269 5075	0.753607	21.796716	0.045878	16.426168	0.060878	19
20	1.3468 5501	0.742470	23.123667	0.043246	17.168639	0.058246	20
21	1.3670 5783	0.731498	24.470522	0.040865	17.900137	0.055865	21
22	1.3875 6370	0.720688	25.837580	0.038703	18.620824	0.053703	22
23	1.4083 7715	0.710037	27.225144	0.036731	19.330861	0.051731	23
24	1.4295 0281	0.699544	28.633521	0.034924	20.030405	0.049924	24
25	1.4509 4535	0.689206	30.063024	0.033263	20.719611	0.048263	25
26	1.4727 0953	0.679021	31.513969	0.031732	21.398632	0.046732	26
27	1.4948 0018	0.668986	32.986678	0.030315	22.067617	0.045315	27
28	1.5172 2218	0.659099	34.481479	0.029001	22.726717	0.044001	28
29	1.5399 8051	0.649359	35.998701	0.027779	23.376076	0.042779	29
30	1.5630 8022	0.639762	37.538681	0.026639	24.015838	0.041639	30
31	1.5865 2642	0.630308	39.101762	0.025574	24.646146	0.040574	31
32	1.6103 2432	0.620993	40.688288	0.024577	25.267139	0.039577	32
33	1.6344 7918	0.611816	42.298612	0.023641	25.878954	0.038641	33
34	1.6589 9637	0.602774	43.933092	0.022762	26.481728	0.037762	34
35	1.6838 8132	0.593866	45.592088	0.021934	27.075595	0.036934	35
36	1.7091 3954	0.585090	47.275969	0.021152	27.660684	0.036152	36
37	1.7347 7663	0.576443	48.985109	0.020414	28.237127	0.035414	37
38	1.7607 9828	0.567924	50.719885	0.019716	28.805052	0.034716	38
39	1.7872 1025	0.559531	52.480684	0.019055	29.364583	0.034055	39
40	1.8140 1841	0.551262	54.267894	0.018427	29.915845	0.033427	40
45	1.9542 1301	0.511715	63.614201	0.015720	32.552337	0.030720	45
50	2.1052 4242	0.475005	73.682828	0.013572	34.999688	0.028572	50
55	2.2679 4398	0.440928	84.529599	0.011830	37.271467	0.026830	55
60	2.4432 1978	0.409296	96.214652	0.010393	39.380269	0.025393	60
65	2.6320 4158	0.379933	108.802772	0.009191	41.337786	0.024191	65
70	2.8354 5629	0.352677	122.363753	0.008172	43.154872	0.023172	70
75	3.0545 9171	0.327376	136.972781	0.007301	44.841600	0.022301	75
80	3.2906 6279	0.303890	152.710852	0.006548	46.407323	0.021548	80
90	3.8189 4851	0.261852	187.929900	0.005321	49.209855	0.020321	90
100	4.4320 4565	0.225629	228.803043	0.004371	51.624704	0.019371	100

TABLE D.3. 2 PERCENT COMPOUND INTEREST FACTORS FOR ONE DOLLAR

	Single payment		Annuities (uniform series payments)				
	Compound amount	Present worth	Compound amount	Sinking fund	Present worth	Capital recovery	
n	Given P To find S $(1 + i)^n$	Given S To find P $\dfrac{1}{(1 + i)^n}$	Given R To find S $\dfrac{(1 + i)^n - 1}{i}$	Given S To find R $\dfrac{i}{(1 + i)^n - 1}$	Given R To find P $\dfrac{(1 + i)^n - 1}{i(1 + i)^n}$	Given P To find R $\dfrac{i(1 + i)^n}{(1 + i)^n - 1}$	n
	k_1	k_2	k_3	k_4	k_5	k_6	
1	1.0200 0000	0.980392	1.000000	1.000000	0.980392	1.020000	1
2	1.0404 0000	0.961169	2.020000	0.495050	1.941561	0.515050	2
3	1.0612 0800	0.942322	3.060400	0.326755	2.883883	0.346755	3
4	1.0824 3216	0.923845	4.121608	0.242624	3.807729	0.262624	4
5	1.1040 8080	0.905731	5.204040	0.192158	4.713460	0.212158	5
6	1.1261 6242	0.887971	6.308121	0.158526	5.601431	0.178526	6
7	1.1486 8567	0.870560	7.434283	0.134512	6.471991	0.154512	7
8	1.1716 5938	0.853490	8.582969	0.116510	7.325481	0.136510	8
9	1.1950 9257	0.836755	9.754628	0.102515	8.162237	0.122515	9
10	1.2189 9442	0.820348	10.949721	0.091327	8.982585	0.111327	10
11	1.2433 7431	0.804263	12.168715	0.082178	9.786848	0.102178	11
12	1.2682 4179	0.788493	13.412090	0.074560	10.575341	0.094560	12
13	1.2936 0663	0.773033	14.680332	0.068118	11.348374	0.088118	13
14	1.3194 7876	0.757875	15.973938	0.062602	12.106249	0.082602	14
15	1.3458 6834	0.743015	17.293417	0.057825	12.849264	0.077825	15
16	1.3727 8571	0.728446	18.639285	0.053650	13.577709	0.073650	16
17	1.4002 4142	0.714163	20.012071	0.049970	14.291872	0.069970	17
18	1.4282 4625	0.700159	21.412312	0.046702	14.992031	0.066702	18
19	1.4568 1117	0.686431	22.840559	0.043782	15.678462	0.063782	19
20	1.4859 4740	0.672971	24.297370	0.041157	16.351433	0.061157	20
21	1.5156 6634	0.659776	25.783317	0.038785	17.011209	0.058785	21
22	1.5459 7967	0.646839	27.298984	0.036631	17.658048	0.056631	22
23	1.5768 9926	0.634156	28.844963	0.034668	18.292204	0.054668	23
24	1.6084 3725	0.621721	30.421862	0.032871	18.913926	0.052871	24
25	1.6406 0599	0.609531	32.030300	0.031220	19.523456	0.051220	25
26	1.6734 1811	0.597579	33.670906	0.029699	20.121036	0.049699	26
27	1.7068 8648	0.585862	35.344324	0.028293	20.706898	0.048293	27
28	1.7410 2421	0.574375	37.051210	0.026990	21.281272	0.046990	28
29	1.7758 4469	0.563112	38.792235	0.025778	21.844385	0.045778	29
30	1.8113 6158	0.552071	40.568079	0.024650	22.396456	0.044650	30
31	1.8475 8882	0.541246	42.379441	0.023596	22.937702	0.043596	31
32	1.8845 4059	0.530633	44.227030	0.022611	23.468335	0.042611	32
33	1.9222 3140	0.520229	46.111570	0.021687	23.988564	0.041687	33
34	1.9606 7603	0.510028	48.033802	0.020819	24.498592	0.040819	34
35	1.9998 8955	0.500028	49.994478	0.020002	24.998619	0.040002	35
36	2.0398 8734	0.490223	51.994367	0.019233	25.488842	0.039233	36
37	2.0806 8509	0.480611	54.034255	0.018507	25.969453	0.038507	37
38	2.1222 9879	0.471187	56.114940	0.017821	26.440641	0.037821	38
39	2.1647 4477	0.461948	58.237238	0.017171	26.902589	0.037171	39
40	2.2080 3966	0.452890	60.401983	0.016556	27.355479	0.036556	40
45	2.4378 5421	0.410197	71.892710	0.013910	29.490160	0.033910	45
50	2.6915 8803	0.371528	84.579401	0.011823	31.423606	0.031823	50
55	2.9717 3067	0.336504	98.586534	0.010143	33.174788	0.030143	55
60	3.2810 3079	0.304782	114.051539	0.008768	34.760887	0.028768	60
65	3.6225 2311	0.276051	131.126155	0.007626	36.197466	0.027626	65
70	3.9995 5822	0.250028	149.977911	0.006668	37.498619	0.026668	70
75	4.4158 3546	0.226458	170.791773	0.005855	38.677114	0.025855	75
80	4.8754 3916	0.205110	193.771958	0.005161	39.744514	0.025161	80
90	5.9431 3313	0.168261	247.156656	0.004046	41.586929	0.024046	90
100	7.2446 4612	0.138033	312.232306	0.003203	43.098352	0.023203	100

TABLE D.4.   2½ PERCENT COMPOUND INTEREST FACTORS FOR ONE DOLLAR

n	Single payment		Annuities (uniform series payments)				n
	Compound amount	Present worth	Compound amount	Sinking fund	Present worth	Capital recovery	
n	Given P To find S $(1+i)^n$	Given S To find P $\dfrac{1}{(1+i)^n}$	Given R To find S $\dfrac{(1+i)^n-1}{i}$	Given S To find R $\dfrac{i}{(1+i)^n-1}$	Given R To find P $\dfrac{(1+i)^n-1}{i(1+i)^n}$	Given P To find R $\dfrac{i(1+i)^n}{(1+i)^n-1}$	n
	k_1	k_2	k_3	k_4	k_5	k_6	
1	1.0250 0000	0.975610	1.000000	1.000000	0.975610	1.025000	1
2	1.0506 2500	0.951814	2.025000	0.493827	1.927424	0.518827	2
3	1.0768 9063	0.928599	3.075625	0.325137	2.856024	0.350137	3
4	1.1038 1289	0.905951	4.152516	0.240818	3.761974	0.265818	4
5	1.1314 0821	0.883854	5.256329	0.190247	4.645828	0.215247	5
6	1.1596 9342	0.862297	6.387737	0.156550	5.508125	0.181550	6
7	1.1886 8575	0.841265	7.547430	0.132495	6.349391	0.157495	7
8	1.2184 0290	0.820747	8.736116	0.114467	7.170137	0.139467	8
9	1.2488 6297	0.800728	9.954519	0.100457	7.970866	0.125457	9
10	1.2800 8454	0.781198	11.203382	0.089259	8.752064	0.114259	10
11	1.3120 8666	0.762145	12.483466	0.080106	9.514209	0.105106	11
12	1.3448 8882	0.743556	13.795553	0.072487	10.257765	0.097487	12
13	1.3785 1104	0.725420	15.140442	0.066048	10.983185	0.091048	13
14	1.4129 7382	0.707727	16.518953	0.060537	11.690912	0.085537	14
15	1.4482 9817	0.690466	17.931927	0.055766	12.381378	0.080766	15
16	1.4845 0562	0.673625	19.380225	0.051599	13.055003	0.076599	16
17	1.5216 1826	0.657195	20.864730	0.047928	13.712198	0.072928	17
18	1.5596 5872	0.641166	22.386349	0.044670	14.353364	0.069670	18
19	1.5986 5019	0.625528	23.946007	0.041761	14.978891	0.066761	19
20	1.6386 1644	0.610271	25.544658	0.039147	15.589162	0.064147	20
21	1.6795 8185	0.595386	27.183274	0.036787	16.184549	0.061787	21
22	1.7215 7140	0.580865	28.862856	0.034647	16.765413	0.059647	22
23	1.7646 1068	0.566697	30.584427	0.032696	17.332110	0.057696	23
24	1.8087 2595	0.552875	32.349038	0.030913	17.884986	0.055913	24
25	1.8539 4410	0.539391	34.157764	0.029276	18.424376	0.054276	25
26	1.9002 9270	0.526235	36.011708	0.027769	18.950611	0.052769	26
27	1.9478 0002	0.513400	37.912001	0.026377	19.464011	0.051377	27
28	1.9964 9502	0.500878	39.859801	0.025088	19.964889	0.050088	28
29	2.0464 0739	0.488661	41.856296	0.023891	20.453550	0.048891	29
30	2.0975 6758	0.476743	43.902703	0.022778	20.930293	0.047778	30
31	2.1500 0677	0.465115	46.000271	0.021739	21.395407	0.046739	31
32	2.2037 5694	0.453771	48.150278	0.020768	21.849178	0.045768	32
33	2.2588 5086	0.442703	50.354034	0.019859	22.291881	0.044859	33
34	2.3153 2213	0.431905	52.612885	0.019007	22.723786	0.044007	34
35	2.3732 0519	0.421371	54.928207	0.018206	23.145157	0.043206	35
36	2.4325 3532	0.411094	57.301413	0.017452	23.556251	0.042452	36
37	2.4933 4870	0.401067	59.733948	0.016741	23.957318	0.041741	37
38	2.5556 8242	0.391285	62.227297	0.016070	24.348603	0.041070	38
39	2.6195 7448	0.381741	64.782979	0.015436	24.730344	0.040436	39
40	2.6850 6384	0.372431	67.402554	0.014836	25.102775	0.039836	40
45	3.0379 0328	0.329174	81.516131	0.012268	26.833024	0.037268	45
50	3.4371 0872	0.290942	97.484349	0.010258	28.362312	0.035258	50
55	3.8887 7303	0.257151	115.550921	0.008654	29.713979	0.033654	55
60	4.3997 8975	0.227284	135.991590	0.007353	30.908656	0.032353	60
65	4.9779 5826	0.200886	159.118330	0.006285	31.964577	0.031285	65
70	5.6321 0286	0.177554	185.284114	0.005397	32.897857	0.030397	70
75	6.3722 0743	0.156931	214.888297	0.004654	33.722740	0.029654	75
80	7.2095 6782	0.138705	248.382713	0.004026	34.451817	0.029026	80
90	9.2288 5633	0.108356	329.154253	0.003038	35.665768	0.028038	90
100	11.8137 1635	0.084647	432.548654	0.002312	36.614105	0.027312	100

TABLE D.5. 3 PERCENT COMPOUND INTEREST FACTORS FOR ONE DOLLAR

	Single payment		Annuities (uniform series payments)				
	Compound amount	Present worth	Compound amount	Sinking fund	Present worth	Capital recovery	
n	Given P To find S $(1+i)^n$	Given S To find P $\dfrac{1}{(1+i)^n}$	Given R To find S $\dfrac{(1+i)^n - 1}{i}$	Given S To find R $\dfrac{i}{(1+i)^n - 1}$	Given R To find P $\dfrac{(1+i)^n - 1}{i(1+i)^n}$	Given P To find R $\dfrac{i(1+i)^n}{(1+i)^n - 1}$	n
	k_1	k_2	k_3	k_4	k_5	k_6	
1	1.0300 0000	0.970874	1.000000	1.000000	0.970874	1.030000	1
2	1.0609 0000	0.942596	2.030000	0.492611	1.913470	0.522611	2
3	1.0927 2700	0.915142	3.090900	0.323530	2.828611	0.353530	3
4	1.1255 0881	0.888487	4.183627	0.239027	3.717098	0.269027	4
5	1.1592 7407	0.862609	5.309136	0.188355	4.579707	0.218355	5
6	1.1940 5230	0.837484	6.468410	0.154598	5.417191	0.184598	6
7	1.2298 7387	0.813092	7.662462	0.130506	6.230283	0.160506	7
8	1.2667 7008	0.789409	8.892336	0.112456	7.019692	0.142456	8
9	1.3047 7318	0.766417	10.159106	0.098434	7.786109	0.128434	9
10	1.3439 1638	0.744094	11.463879	0.087231	8.530203	0.117231	10
11	1.3842 3387	0.722421	12.807796	0.078077	9.252624	0.108077	11
12	1.4257 6089	0.701380	14.192030	0.070462	9.954004	0.100462	12
13	1.4685 3371	0.680951	15.617790	0.064030	10.634955	0.094030	13
14	1.5125 8972	0.661118	17.086324	0.058526	11.296073	0.088526	14
15	1.5579 6742	0.641862	18.598914	0.053767	11.937935	0.083767	15
16	1.6047 0644	0.623167	20.156881	0.049611	12.561102	0.079611	16
17	1.6528 4763	0.605016	21.761588	0.045953	13.166118	0.075953	17
18	1.7024 3306	0.587395	23.414435	0.042709	13.753513	0.072709	18
19	1.7535 0605	0.570286	25.116868	0.039814	14.323799	0.069814	19
20	1.8061 1123	0.553676	26.870374	0.037216	14.877475	0.067216	20
21	1.8602 9457	0.537549	28.676486	0.034872	15.415024	0.064872	21
22	1.9161 0341	0.521893	30.536780	0.032747	15.936917	0.062747	22
23	1.9735 8651	0.506692	32.452884	0.030814	16.443608	0.060814	23
24	2.0327 9411	0.491934	34.426470	0.029047	16.935542	0.059047	24
25	2.0937 7793	0.477606	36.459264	0.027428	17.413148	0.057428	25
26	2.1565 9127	0.463695	38.553042	0.025938	17.876842	0.055938	26
27	2.2212 8901	0.450189	40.709634	0.024564	18.327031	0.054564	27
28	2.2879 2768	0.437077	42.930923	0.023293	18.764108	0.053293	28
29	2.3565 6551	0.424346	45.218850	0.022115	19.188455	0.052115	29
30	2.4272 6247	0.411987	47.575416	0.021019	19.600441	0.051019	30
31	2.5000 8035	0.399987	50.002678	0.019999	20.000428	0.049999	31
32	2.5750 8276	0.388337	52.502759	0.019047	20.388766	0.049047	32
33	2.6523 3524	0.377026	55.077841	0.018156	20.765792	0.048156	33
34	2.7319 0530	0.366045	57.730177	0.017322	21.131837	0.047322	34
35	2.8138 6245	0.355383	60.462082	0.016539	21.487220	0.046539	35
36	2.8982 7833	0.345032	63.275944	0.015804	21.832252	0.045804	36
37	2.9852 2668	0.334983	66.174223	0.015112	22.167235	0.045112	37
38	3.0747 8348	0.325226	69.159449	0.014459	22.492462	0.044459	38
39	3.1670 2698	0.315754	72.234233	0.013844	22.808215	0.043844	39
40	3.2620 3779	0.306557	75.401260	0.013262	23.114772	0.043262	40
45	3.7815 9584	0.264439	92.719861	0.010785	24.518713	0.040785	45
50	4.3839 0602	0.228107	112.796867	0.008865	25.729764	0.038865	50
55	5.0821 4859	0.196767	136.071620	0.007349	26.774428	0.037349	55
60	5.8916 0310	0.169733	163.053437	0.006133	27.675564	0.036133	60
65	6.8299 8273	0.146413	194.332758	0.005146	28.452892	0.035146	65
70	7.9178 2191	0.126297	230.594064	0.004337	29.123421	0.034337	70
75	9.1789 2567	0.108945	272.630856	0.003668	29.701826	0.033668	75
80	10.6408 9056	0.093977	321.363019	0.003112	30.200763	0.033112	80
90	14.3004 6711	0.069928	443.348904	0.002256	31.002407	0.032256	90
100	19.2186 3198	0.052033	607.287733	0.001647	31.598905	0.031647	100

TABLE D.6. 3½ PERCENT COMPOUND INTEREST FACTORS FOR ONE DOLLAR

	Single payment		Annuities (uniform series payments)				
	Compound amount	Present worth	Compound amount	Sinking fund	Present worth	Capital recovery	
n	Given P To find S $(1+i)^n$	Given S To find P $\dfrac{1}{(1+i)^n}$	Given R To find S $\dfrac{(1+i)^n-1}{i}$	Given S To find R $\dfrac{i}{(1+i)^n-1}$	Given R To find P $\dfrac{(1+i)^n-1}{i(1+i)^n}$	Given P To find R $\dfrac{i(1+i)^n}{(1+i)^n-1}$	n
	k_1	k_2	k_3	k_4	k_5	k_6	
1	1.0350 0000	0.966184	1.000000	1.000000	0.966184	1.035000	1
2	1.0712 2500	0.933511	2.035000	0.491400	1.899694	0.526400	2
3	1.1087 1788	0.901943	3.106225	0.321934	2.801637	0.356934	3
4	1.1475 2300	0.871442	4.214943	0.237251	3.673079	0.272251	4
5	1.1876 8631	0.841973	5.362466	0.186481	4.515052	0.221481	5
6	1.2292 5533	0.813501	6.550152	0.152668	5.328553	0.187668	6
7	1.2722 7926	0.785991	7.779408	0.128544	6.114544	0.163544	7
8	1.3168 0904	0.759412	9.051687	0.110477	6.873956	0.145477	8
9	1.3628 9735	0.733731	10.368496	0.096446	7.607687	0.131446	9
10	1.4105 9876	0.708919	11.731393	0.085241	8.316605	0.120241	10
11	1.4599 6972	0.684946	13.141992	0.076092	9.001551	0.111092	11
12	1.5110 6866	0.661783	14.601962	0.068484	9.663334	0.103484	12
13	1.5639 5606	0.639404	16.113030	0.062062	10.302738	0.097062	13
14	1.6186 9452	0.617782	17.676986	0.056571	10.920520	0.091571	14
15	1.6753 4883	0.596891	19.295681	0.051825	11.517411	0.086825	15
16	1.7339 8604	0.576706	20.971030	0.047685	12.094117	0.082685	16
17	1.7946 7555	0.557204	22.705016	0.044043	12.651321	0.079043	17
18	1.8574 8920	0.538361	24.499691	0.040817	13.189682	0.075817	18
19	1.9225 0132	0.520156	26.357180	0.037940	13.709837	0.072940	19
20	1.9897 8886	0.502566	28.279682	0.035361	14.212403	0.070361	20
21	2.0594 3147	0.485571	30.269471	0.033037	14.697974	0.068037	21
22	2.1315 1158	0.469151	32.328902	0.030932	15.167125	0.065932	22
23	2.2061 1448	0.453286	34.460414	0.029019	15.620410	0.064019	23
24	2.2833 2849	0.437957	36.666528	0.027273	16.058368	0.062273	24
25	2.3632 4498	0.423147	38.949857	0.025674	16.481515	0.060674	25
26	2.4459 5856	0.408838	41.313102	0.024205	16.890352	0.059205	26
27	2.5315 6711	0.395012	43.759060	0.022852	17.285365	0.057852	27
28	2.6201 7196	0.381654	46.290627	0.021603	17.667019	0.056603	28
29	2.7118 7798	0.368748	48.910799	0.020445	18.035767	0.055445	29
30	2.8067 9370	0.356278	51.622677	0.019371	18.392045	0.054371	30
31	2.9050 3148	0.344230	54.429471	0.018372	18.736276	0.053372	31
32	3.0067 0759	0.332590	57.334502	0.017442	19.068865	0.052442	32
33	3.1119 4235	0.321343	60.341210	0.016572	19.390208	0.051572	33
34	3.2208 6033	0.310476	63.453152	0.015760	19.700684	0.050760	34
35	3.3335 9045	0.299977	66.674013	0.014998	20.000661	0.049998	35
36	3.4502 6611	0.289833	70.007603	0.014284	20.290494	0.049284	36
37	3.5710 2543	0.280032	73.457869	0.013613	20.570525	0.048613	37
38	3.6960 1132	0.270562	77.028895	0.012982	20.841087	0.047982	38
39	3.8253 7171	0.261413	80.724906	0.012388	21.102500	0.047388	39
40	3.9592 5972	0.252572	84.550278	0.011827	21.355072	0.046827	40
45	4.7023 5855	0.212659	105.781673	0.009453	22.495450	0.044453	45
50	5.5849 2686	0.179053	130.997910	0.007634	23.455618	0.042634	50
55	6.6331 4114	0.150758	160.946890	0.006213	24.264053	0.041213	55
60	7.8780 9090	0.126934	196.516883	0.005089	24.944734	0.040089	60
65	9.3567 0068	0.106875	238.762876	0.004188	25.517849	0.039188	65
70	11.1128 2526	0.089986	288.937865	0.003461	26.000397	0.038461	70
75	13.1985 5038	0.075766	348.530011	0.002869	26.406689	0.037869	75
80	15.6757 3754	0.063793	419.306787	0.002385	26.748776	0.037385	80
90	22.1121 7595	0.045224	603.205027	0.001658	27.279316	0.036658	90
100	31.1914 0798	0.032060	862.611657	0.001159	27.655425	0.036159	100

TABLE D.7. 4 PERCENT COMPOUND INTEREST FACTORS FOR ONE DOLLAR

	Single payment		Annuities (uniform series payments)				
	Compound amount	Present worth	Compound amount	Sinking fund	Present worth	Capital recovery	
n	Given P To find S $(1+i)^n$	Given S To find P $\dfrac{1}{(1+i)^n}$	Given R To find S $\dfrac{(1+i)^n-1}{i}$	Given S To find R $\dfrac{i}{(1+i)^n-1}$	Given R To find P $\dfrac{(1+i)^n-1}{i(1+i)^n}$	Given P To find R $\dfrac{i(1+i)^n}{(1+i)^n-1}$	n
	k_1	k_2	k_3	k_4	k_5	k_6	
1	1.0400 0000	0.961538	1.000000	1.000000	0.961538	1.040000	1
2	1.0816 0000	0.924556	2.040000	0.490196	1.886095	0.530196	2
3	1.1248 6400	0.888996	3.121600	0.320349	2.775091	0.360349	3
4	1.1698 5856	0.854804	4.246464	0.235490	3.629895	0.275490	4
5	1.2166 5290	0.821927	5.416323	0.184627	4.451822	0.224627	5
6	1.2653 1902	0.790315	6.632975	0.150762	5.242137	0.190762	6
7	1.3159 3178	0.759918	7.898294	0.126610	6.002055	0.166610	7
8	1.3685 6905	0.730690	9.214226	0.108528	6.732745	0.148528	8
9	1.4233 1181	0.702587	10.582795	0.094493	7.435332	0.134493	9
10	1.4802 4428	0.675564	12.006107	0.083291	8.110896	0.123291	10
11	1.5394 5406	0.649581	13.486351	0.074149	8.760477	0.114149	11
12	1.6010 3222	0.624597	15.025805	0.066552	9.385074	0.106552	12
13	1.6650 7351	0.600574	16.626838	0.060144	9.985648	0.100144	13
14	1.7316 7645	0.577475	18.291911	0.054669	10.563123	0.094669	14
15	1.8009 4351	0.555265	20.023588	0.049941	11.118387	0.089941	15
16	1.8729 8125	0.533908	21.824531	0.045820	11.652296	0.085820	16
17	1.9479 0050	0.513373	23.697512	0.042199	12.165669	0.082199	17
18	2.0258 1652	0.493628	25.645413	0.038993	12.659297	0.078993	18
19	2.1068 4918	0.474642	27.671229	0.036139	13.133939	0.076139	19
20	2.1911 2314	0.456387	29.778079	0.033582	13.590326	0.073582	20
21	2.2787 6807	0.438834	31.969202	0.031280	14.029160	0.071280	21
22	2.3699 1879	0.421955	34.247970	0.029199	14.451115	0.069199	22
23	2.4647 1554	0.405726	36.617889	0.027309	14.856842	0.067309	23
24	2.5633 0416	0.390121	39.082604	0.025587	15.246963	0.065587	24
25	2.6658 3633	0.375117	41.645908	0.024012	15.622080	0.064012	25
26	2.7724 6978	0.360689	44.311745	0.022567	15.982769	0.062567	26
27	2.8833 6858	0.346817	47.084214	0.021239	16.329586	0.061239	27
28	2.9987 0332	0.333477	49.967583	0.020013	16.663063	0.060013	28
29	3.1186 5145	0.320651	52.966286	0.018880	16.983715	0.058880	29
30	3.2433 9751	0.308319	56.084938	0.017830	17.292033	0.057830	30
31	3.3731 3341	0.296460	59.328335	0.016855	17.588494	0.056855	31
32	3.5080 5875	0.285058	62.701469	0.015949	17.873551	0.055949	32
33	3.6483 8110	0.274094	66.209527	0.015104	18.147646	0.055104	33
34	3.7943 1634	0.263552	69.857909	0.014315	18.411198	0.054315	34
35	3.9460 8899	0.253415	73.652225	0.013577	18.664613	0.053577	35
36	4.1039 3255	0.243669	77.598314	0.012887	18.908282	0.052887	36
37	4.2680 8986	0.234297	81.702246	0.012240	19.142579	0.052240	37
38	4.4388 1345	0.225285	85.970336	0.011632	19.367864	0.051632	38
39	4.6163 6599	0.216621	90.409150	0.011061	19.584485	0.051061	39
40	4.8010 2063	0.208289	95.025516	0.010523	19.792774	0.050523	40
45	5.8411 7568	0.171198	121.029392	0.008262	20.720040	0.048262	45
50	7.1066 8335	0.140713	152.667084	0.006550	21.482185	0.046550	50
55	8.6463 6692	0.115656	191.159173	0.005231	22.108612	0.045231	55
60	10.5196 2741	0.095060	237.990685	0.004202	22.623490	0.044202	60
65	12.7987 3522	0.078133	294.968380	0.003390	23.046682	0.043390	65
70	15.5716 1835	0.064219	364.290459	0.002745	23.394515	0.042745	70
75	18.9452 5466	0.052784	448.631367	0.002229	23.680408	0.042229	75
80	23.0497 9907	0.043384	551.244977	0.001814	23.915392	0.041814	80
90	34.1193 3334	0.029309	827.983334	0.001208	24.267278	0.041208	90
100	50.5049 4818	0.019800	1,237.623705	0.000808	24.504999	0.040808	100

TABLE D.8.　4½ PERCENT COMPOUND INTEREST FACTORS FOR ONE DOLLAR

	Single payment		Annuities (uniform series payments)				
	Compound amount	Present worth	Compound amount	Sinking fund	Present worth	Capital recovery	
n	Given P To find S $(1 + i)^n$	Given S To find P $\dfrac{1}{(1 + i)^n}$	Given R To find S $\dfrac{(1 + i)^n - 1}{i}$	Given S To find R $\dfrac{i}{(1 + i)^n - 1}$	Given R To find P $\dfrac{(1 + i)^n - 1}{i(1 + i)^n}$	Given P To find R $\dfrac{i(1 + i)^n}{(1 + i)^n - 1}$	n
	k_1	k_2	k_3	k_4	k_5	k_6	
1	1.0450 0000	0.956938	1.000000	1.000000	0.956938	1.045000	1
2	1.0920 2500	0.915730	2.045000	0.488998	1.872668	0.533998	2
3	1.1411 6613	0.876297	3.137025	0.318773	2.748964	0.363773	3
4	1.1925 1860	0.838561	4.278191	0.233744	3.587526	0.278744	4
5	1.2461 8194	0.802451	5.470710	0.182792	4.389977	0.227792	5
6	1.3022 6012	0.767896	6.716892	0.148878	5.157872	0.193878	6
7	1.3608 6183	0.734828	8.019152	0.124701	5.892701	0.169701	7
8	1.4221 0061	0.703185	9.380014	0.106610	6.595886	0.151610	8
9	1.4860 9514	0.672904	10.802114	0.092574	7.268790	0.137574	9
10	1.5529 6942	0.643928	12.288209	0.081379	7.912718	0.126379	10
11	1.6228 5305	0.616199	13.841179	0.072248	8.528917	0.117248	11
12	1.6958 8143	0.589664	15.464032	0.064666	9.118581	0.109666	12
13	1.7721 9610	0.564272	17.159913	0.058275	9.682852	0.103275	13
14	1.8519 4492	0.539973	18.932109	0.052820	10.222825	0.097820	14
15	1.9352 8244	0.516720	20.784054	0.048114	10.739546	0.093114	15
16	2.0223 7015	0.494469	22.719337	0.044015	11.234015	0.089015	16
17	2.1133 7681	0.473176	24.747707	0.040418	11.707191	0.085418	17
18	2.2084 7877	0.452800	26.855084	0.037237	12.159992	0.082237	18
19	2.3078 6031	0.433302	29.063562	0.034407	12.593294	0.079407	19
20	2.4117 1402	0.414643	31.371423	0.031876	13.007936	0.076876	20
21	2.5202 4116	0.396787	33.783137	0.029601	13.404724	0.074601	21
22	2.6336 5201	0.379701	36.303378	0.027546	13.784425	0.072546	22
23	2.7521 6635	0.363350	38.937030	0.025682	14.147775	0.070682	23
24	2.8760 1383	0.347703	41.689196	0.023987	14.495478	0.068987	24
25	3.0054 3446	0.332731	44.565210	0.022439	14.828209	0.067439	25
26	3.1406 7901	0.318402	47.570645	0.021021	15.146611	0.066021	26
27	3.2820 0956	0.304691	50.711324	0.019719	15.451303	0.064719	27
28	3.4296 9999	0.291571	53.993333	0.018521	15.742874	0.063521	28
29	3.5840 3649	0.279015	57.423033	0.017415	16.021889	0.062415	29
30	3.7453 1813	0.267000	61.007070	0.016392	16.288889	0.061392	30
31	3.9138 5745	0.255502	64.752388	0.015443	16.544391	0.060443	31
32	4.0899 8104	0.244500	68.666245	0.014563	16.788891	0.059563	32
33	4.2740 3018	0.233971	72.756226	0.013745	17.022862	0.058745	33
34	4.4663 6154	0.223896	77.030256	0.012982	17.246758	0.057982	34
35	4.6673 4781	0.214254	81.496618	0.012270	17.461012	0.057270	35
36	4.8773 7846	0.205028	86.163966	0.011606	17.666041	0.056606	36
37	5.0968 6049	0.196199	91.041344	0.010984	17.862240	0.055984	37
38	5.3262 1921	0.187750	96.138205	0.010402	18.049990	0.055402	38
39	5.5658 9908	0.179665	101.464424	0.009856	18.229656	0.054856	39
40	5.8163 6454	0.171929	107.030323	0.009343	18.401584	0.054343	40
45	7.2482 4843	0.137964	138.849965	0.007202	19.156347	0.052202	45
50	9.0326 3627	0.110710	178.503028	0.005602	19.762008	0.050602	50
55	11.2563 0817	0.088839	227.917959	0.004388	20.248021	0.049388	55
60	14.0274 0793	0.071289	289.497954	0.003454	20.638022	0.048454	60
65	17.4807 0239	0.057206	366.237831	0.002730	20.950979	0.047730	65
70	21.7841 3558	0.045905	461.869680	0.002165	21.202112	0.047165	70
75	27.1469 9629	0.036836	581.044362	0.001721	21.403634	0.046721	75
80	33.8300 9643	0.029559	729.557699	0.001371	21.565345	0.046371	80
90	52.5371 0530	0.019034	1,145.269007	0.000873	21.799241	0.045873	90
100	81.5885 1803	0.012257	1,790.855956	0.000558	21.949853	0.045558	100

TABLE D.9. 5 PERCENT COMPOUND INTEREST FACTORS FOR ONE DOLLAR

	Single payment		Annuities (uniform series payments)				
	Compound amount	Present worth	Compound amount	Sinking fund	Present worth	Capital recovery	
n	Given P To find S $(1+i)^n$	Given S To find P $\dfrac{1}{(1+i)^n}$	Given R To find S $\dfrac{(1+i)^n-1}{i}$	Given S To find R $\dfrac{i}{(1+i)^n-1}$	Given R To find P $\dfrac{(1+i)^n-1}{i(1+i)^n}$	Given P To find R $\dfrac{i(1+i)^n}{(1+i)^n-1}$	n
	k_1	k_2	k_3	k_4	k_5	k_6	
1	1.0500 0000	0.952381	1.000000	1.000000	0.952381	1.050000	1
2	1.1025 0000	0.907029	2.050000	0.487805	1.859410	0.537805	2
3	1.1576 2500	0.863838	3.152500	0.317209	2.723248	0.367209	3
4	1.2155 0625	0.822702	4.310125	0.232012	3.545951	0.282012	4
5	1.2762 8156	0.783526	5.525631	0.180975	4.329477	0.230975	5
6	1.3400 9564	0.746215	6.801913	0.147017	5.075692	0.197017	6
7	1.4071 0042	0.710681	8.142008	0.122820	5.786373	0.172820	7
8	1.4774 5544	0.676839	9.549109	0.104722	6.463213	0.154722	8
9	1.5513 2822	0.644609	11.026564	0.090690	7.107822	0.140690	9
10	1.6288 9463	0.613913	12.577893	0.079505	7.721735	0.129505	10
11	1.7103 3936	0.584679	14.206787	0.070389	8.306414	0.120389	11
12	1.7958 5633	0.556837	15.917127	0.062825	8.863252	0.112825	12
13	1.8856 4914	0.530321	17.712983	0.056456	9.393573	0.106456	13
14	1.9799 3160	0.505068	19.598632	0.051024	9.898641	0.101024	14
15	2.0789 2818	0.481017	21.578564	0.046342	10.379658	0.096342	15
16	2.1828 7459	0.458112	23.657492	0.042270	10.837770	0.092270	16
17	2.2920 1832	0.436297	25.840366	0.038699	11.274066	0.088699	17
18	2.4066 1923	0.415521	28.132385	0.035546	11.689587	0.085546	18
19	2.5269 5020	0.395734	30.539004	0.032745	12.085321	0.082745	19
20	2.6532 9771	0.376889	33.065954	0.030243	12.462210	0.080243	20
21	2.7859 6259	0.358942	35.719252	0.027996	12.821153	0.077996	21
22	2.9252 6072	0.341850	38.505214	0.025971	13.163003	0.075971	22
23	3.0715 2376	0.325571	41.430475	0.024137	13.488574	0.074137	23
24	3.2250 9994	0.310068	44.501999	0.022471	13.798642	0.072471	24
25	3.3863 5494	0.295303	47.727099	0.020952	14.093945	0.070952	25
26	3.5556 7269	0.281241	51.113454	0.019564	14.375185	0.069564	26
27	3.7334 5632	0.267848	54.669126	0.018292	14.643034	0.068292	27
28	3.9201 2914	0.255094	58.402583	0.017123	14.898127	0.067123	28
29	4.1161 3560	0.242946	62.322712	0.016046	15.141074	0.066046	29
30	4.3219 4238	0.231377	66.438848	0.015051	15.372451	0.065051	30
31	4.5380 3949	0.220359	70.760790	0.014132	15.592811	0.064132	31
32	4.7649 4147	0.209866	75.298829	0.013280	15.802677	0.063280	32
33	5.0031 8854	0.199873	80.063771	0.012490	16.002549	0.062490	33
34	5.2533 4797	0.190355	85.066959	0.011755	16.192904	0.061755	34
35	5.5160 1537	0.181290	90.320307	0.011072	16.374194	0.061072	35
36	5.7918 1614	0.172657	95.836323	0.010434	16.546852	0.060434	36
37	6.0814 0694	0.164436	101.628139	0.009840	16.711287	0.059840	37
38	6.3854 7729	0.156605	107.709546	0.009284	16.867893	0.059284	38
39	6.7047 5115	0.149148	114.095023	0.008765	17.017041	0.058765	39
40	7.0399 8871	0.142046	120.799774	0.008278	17.159086	0.058278	40
45	8.9850 0779	0.111297	159.700156	0.006262	17.774070	0.056262	45
50	11.4673 9979	0.087204	209.347996	0.004777	18.255925	0.054777	50
55	14.6356 3092	0.068326	272.712618	0.003667	18.633472	0.053667	55
60	18.6791 8589	0.053536	353.583718	0.002828	18.929290	0.052828	60
65	23.8399 0056	0.041946	456.798011	0.002189	19.161070	0.052189	65
70	30.4264 2554	0.032866	588.528511	0.001699	19.342677	0.051699	70
75	38.8326 8592	0.025752	756.653718	0.001322	19.484970	0.051322	75
80	49.5614 4107	0.020177	971.228821	0.001030	19.596460	0.051030	80
90	80.7303 6505	0.012387	1,594.607301	0.000627	19.752262	0.050627	90
100	131.5012 5785	0.007604	2,610.025157	0.000383	19.847910	0.050383	100

TABLE D.10. 5½ PERCENT COMPOUND INTEREST FACTORS FOR ONE DOLLAR

	Single payment		Annuities (uniform series payments)				
	Compound amount	Present worth	Compound amount	Sinking fund	Present worth	Capital recovery	
n	Given P To find S $(1 + i)^n$	Given S To find P $\dfrac{1}{(1 + i)^n}$	Given R To find S $\dfrac{(1 + i)^n - 1}{i}$	Given S To find R $\dfrac{i}{(1 + i)^n - 1}$	Given R To find P $\dfrac{(1 + i)^n - 1}{i(1 + i)^n}$	Given P To find R $\dfrac{i(1 + i)^n}{(1 + i)^n - 1}$	n
	k_1	k_2	k_3	k_4	k_5	k_6	
1	1.0550 0000	0.947867	1.000000	1.000000	0.947867	1.055000	1
2	1.1130 2500	0.898452	2.055000	0.486618	1.846320	0.541618	2
3	1.1742 4138	0.851614	3.168025	0.315654	2.697933	0.370654	3
4	1.2388 2465	0.807217	4.342266	0.230294	3.505150	0.285294	4
5	1.3069 6001	0.765134	5.581091	0.179176	4.270284	0.234176	5
6	1.3788 4281	0.725246	6.888051	0.145179	4.995530	0.200179	6
7	1.4546 7916	0.687437	8.266894	0.120964	5.682967	0.175964	7
8	1.5346 8651	0.651599	9.721573	0.102864	6.334566	0.157864	8
9	1.6190 9427	0.617629	11.256260	0.088839	6.952195	0.143839	9
10	1.7081 4446	0.585431	12.875354	0.077668	7.537626	0.132668	10
11	1.8020 9240	0.554911	14.583498	0.068571	8.092536	0.123571	11
12	1.9012 0749	0.525982	16.385591	0.061029	8.618518	0.116029	12
13	2.0057 7390	0.498561	18.286798	0.054684	9.117079	0.109684	13
14	2.1160 9146	0.472569	20.292572	0.049279	9.589648	0.104279	14
15	2.2324 7649	0.447933	22.408663	0.044626	10.037581	0.099626	15
16	2.3552 6270	0.424581	24.641140	0.040583	10.462162	0.095583	16
17	2.4848 0215	0.402447	26.996403	0.037042	10.864609	0.092042	17
18	2.6214 6627	0.381466	29.481205	0.033920	11.246074	0.088920	18
19	2.7656 4691	0.361579	32.102671	0.031150	11.607654	0.086150	19
20	2.9177 5749	0.342729	34.868318	0.028679	11.950382	0.083679	20
21	3.0782 3415	0.324862	37.786076	0.026465	12.275244	0.081465	21
22	3.2475 3703	0.307926	40.864310	0.024471	12.583170	0.079471	22
23	3.4261 5157	0.291873	44.111847	0.022670	12.875042	0.077670	23
24	3.6145 8990	0.276657	47.537998	0.021036	13.151699	0.076036	24
25	3.8133 9235	0.262234	51.152588	0.019549	13.413933	0.074549	25
26	4.0231 2893	0.248563	54.965981	0.018193	13.662495	0.073193	26
27	4.2444 0102	0.235605	58.989109	0.016952	13.898100	0.071952	27
28	4.4778 4307	0.223322	63.233510	0.015814	14.121422	0.070814	28
29	4.7241 2444	0.211679	67.711354	0.014769	14.333101	0.069769	29
30	4.9839 5129	0.200644	72.435478	0.013805	14.533745	0.068805	30
31	5.2580 6861	0.190184	77.419429	0.012917	14.723929	0.067917	31
32	5.5472 6238	0.180269	82.677498	0.012095	14.904198	0.067095	32
33	5.8523 6181	0.170871	88.224760	0.011335	15.075069	0.066335	33
34	6.1742 4171	0.161963	94.077122	0.010630	15.237033	0.065630	34
35	6.5138 2501	0.153520	100.251364	0.009975	15.390552	0.064975	35
36	6.8720 8538	0.145516	106.765189	0.009366	15.536068	0.064366	36
37	7.2500 5008	0.137930	113.637274	0.008800	15.673999	0.063800	37
38	7.6488 0283	0.130739	120.887324	0.008272	15.804738	0.063272	38
39	8.0694 8699	0.123924	128.536127	0.007780	15.928662	0.062780	39
40	8.5133 0877	0.117463	136.605614	0.007320	16.046125	0.062320	40
45	11.1265 5409	0.089875	184.119165	0.005431	16.547726	0.060431	45
50	14.5419 6120	0.068767	246.217476	0.004061	16.931518	0.059061	50
55	19.0057 6171	0.052616	327.377486	0.003055	17.225170	0.058055	55
60	24.8397 7045	0.040258	433.450372	0.002307	17.449854	0.057307	60
65	32.4645 8654	0.030803	572.083392	0.001748	17.621767	0.056748	65
70	42.4299 1623	0.023568	753.271204	0.001328	17.753304	0.056328	70
75	55.4542 0359	0.018033	990.076429	0.001010	17.853947	0.056010	75
80	72.4764 2628	0.013798	1,299.571387	0.000769	17.930953	0.055769	80
90	123.8002 0591	0.008078	2,232.731017	0.000448	18.034954	0.055448	90
100	211.4686 3567	0.004729	3,826.702467	0.000261	18.095839	0.055261	100

TABLE D.11. 6 PERCENT COMPOUND INTEREST FACTORS FOR ONE DOLLAR

	Single payment		Annuities (uniform series payments)				
	Compound amount	Present worth	Compound amount	Sinking fund	Present worth	Capital recovery	
n	Given P To find S $(1 + i)^n$	Given S To find P $\dfrac{1}{(1 + i)^n}$	Given R To find S $\dfrac{(1 + i)^n - 1}{i}$	Given S To find R $\dfrac{i}{(1 + i)^n - 1}$	Given R To find P $\dfrac{(1 + i)^n - 1}{i(1 + i)^n}$	Given P To find R $\dfrac{i(1 + i)^n}{(1 + i)^n - 1}$	n
	k_1	k_2	k_3	k_4	k_5	k_6	
1	1.0600 0000	0.943396	1.000000	1.000000	0.943396	1.060000	1
2	1.1236 0000	0.889996	2.060000	0.485437	1.833393	0.545437	2
3	1.1910 1600	0.839619	3.183600	0.314110	2.673012	0.374110	3
4	1.2624 7696	0.792094	4.374616	0.228591	3.465106	0.288591	4
5	1.3382 2558	0.747258	5.637093	0.177396	4.212364	0.237396	5
6	1.4185 1911	0.704961	6.975319	0.143363	4.917324	0.203363	6
7	1.5036 3026	0.665057	8.393838	0.119135	5.582381	0.179135	7
8	1.5938 4807	0.627412	9.897468	0.101036	6.209794	0.161036	8
9	1.6894 7896	0.591898	11.491316	0.087022	6.801692	0.147022	9
10	1.7908 4770	0.558395	13.180795	0.075868	7.360087	0.135868	10
11	1.8982 9856	0.526788	14.971643	0.066793	7.886875	0.126793	11
12	2.0121 9647	0.496969	16.869941	0.059277	8.383844	0.119277	12
13	2.1329 2826	0.468839	18.882138	0.052960	8.852683	0.112960	13
14	2.2609 0396	0.442301	21.015066	0.047585	9.294984	0.107585	14
15	2.3965 5819	0.417265	23.275970	0.042963	9.712249	0.102963	15
16	2.5403 5168	0.393646	25.672528	0.038952	10.105895	0.098952	16
17	2.6927 7279	0.371364	28.212880	0.035445	10.477260	0.095445	17
18	2.8543 3915	0.350344	30.905653	0.032357	10.827603	0.092357	18
19	3.0255 9950	0.330513	33.759992	0.029621	11.158116	0.089621	19
20	3.2071 3547	0.311805	36.785591	0.027185	11.469921	0.087185	20
21	3.3995 6360	0.294155	39.992727	0.025005	11.764077	0.085005	21
22	3.6035 3742	0.277505	43.392290	0.023046	12.041582	0.083046	22
23	3.8197 4966	0.261797	46.995828	0.021278	12.303379	0.081278	23
24	4.0489 3464	0.246979	50.815577	0.019679	12.550358	0.079679	24
25	4.2918 7072	0.232999	54.864512	0.018227	12.783356	0.078227	25
26	4.5493 8296	0.219810	59.156383	0.016904	13.003166	0.076904	26
27	4.8223 4594	0.207368	63.705766	0.015697	13.210534	0.075697	27
28	5.1116 8670	0.195630	68.528112	0.014593	13.406164	0.074593	28
29	5.4183 8790	0.184557	73.639798	0.013580	13.590721	0.073580	29
30	5.7434 9117	0.174110	79.058186	0.012649	13.764831	0.072649	30
31	6.0881 0064	0.164255	84.801677	0.011792	13.929086	0.071792	31
32	6.4533 8668	0.154957	90.889778	0.011002	14.084043	0.071002	32
33	6.8405 8988	0.146186	97.343165	0.010273	14.230230	0.070273	33
34	7.2510 2528	0.137912	104.183755	0.009598	14.368141	0.069598	34
35	7.6860 8679	0.130105	111.434780	0.008974	14.498246	0.068974	35
36	8.1472 5200	0.122741	119.120867	0.008395	14.620987 '	0.068395	36
37	8.6360 8712	0.115793	127.268119	0.007857	14.736780	0.067857	37
38	9.1542 5235	0.109239	135.904206	0.007358	14.846019	0.067358	38
39	9.7035 0749	0.103056	145.058458	0.006894	14.949075	0.066894	39
40	10.2857 1794	0.097222	154.761966	0.006462	15.046297	0.066462	40
45	13.7646 1083	0.072650	212.743514	0.004700	15.455832	0.064700	45
50	18.4201 5427	0.054288	290.335905	0.003444	15.761861	0.063444	50
55	24.6503 2159	0.040567	394.172027	0.002537	15.990543	0.062537	55
60	32.9876 9085	0.030314	533.128181	0.001876	16.161428	0.061876	60
65	44.1449 7165	0.022653	719.082861	0.001391	16.289123	0.061391	65
70	59.0759 3018	0.016927	967.932170	0.001033	16.384544	0.061033	70
75	79.0569 2079	0.012649	1,300.948680	0.000769	16.455848	0.060769	75
80	105.7959 9348	0.009452	1,746.599891	0.000573	16.509131	0.060573	80
90	189.4645 1123	0.005278	3,141.075187	0.000318	16.578699	0.060318	90
100	339.3020 8351	0.002947	5,638.368059	0.000177	16.617546	0.060177	100

TABLE D.12.   6½ PERCENT COMPOUND INTEREST FACTORS FOR ONE DOLLAR

	Single payment		Annuities (uniform series payments)			
	Compound amount	Present worth	Compound amount	Sinking fund	Present worth	Capital recovery
n	Given P To find S $(1 + i)^n$	Given S To find P $\dfrac{1}{(1 + i)^n}$	Given R To find S $\dfrac{(1 + i)^n - 1}{i}$	Given S To find R $\dfrac{i}{(1 + i)^n - 1}$	Given R To find P $\dfrac{(1 + i)^n - 1}{i(1 + i)^n}$	Given P To find R $\dfrac{i(1 + i)^n}{(1 + i)^n - 1}$	n
	k_1	k_2	k_3	k_4	k_5	k_6	
1	1.0650 0000	0.938967	1.000000	1.000000	0.938967	1.065000	1
2	1.1342 2500	0.881659	2.065000	0.484262	1.820626	0.549262	2
3	1.2079 4963	0.827849	3.199225	0.312576	2.648476	0.377576	3
4	1.2864 6635	0.777323	4.407175	0.226903	3.425799	0.291903	4
5	1.3700 8666	0.729881	5.693641	0.175635	4.155679	0.240635	5
6	1.4591 4230	0.685334	7.063728	0.141568	4.841014	0.206568	6
7	1.5539 8655	0.643506	8.522870	0.117331	5.484520	0.182331	7
8	1.6549 9567	0.604231	10.076856	0.099237	6.088751	0.164237	8
9	1.7625 7039	0.567353	11.731852	0.085238	6.656104	0.150238	9
10	1.8771 3747	0.532726	13.494423	0.074105	7.188830	0.139105	10
11	1.9991 5140	0.500212	15.371560	0.065055	7.689042	0.130055	11
12	2.1290 9624	0.469683	17.370711	0.057568	8.158725	0.122568	12
13	2.2674 8750	0.441017	19.499808	0.051283	8.599742	0.116283	13
14	2.4148 7418	0.414100	21.767295	0.045940	9.013842	0.110940	14
15	2.5718 4101	0.388827	24.182169	0.041353	9.402669	0.106353	15
16	2.7390 1067	0.365095	26.754010	0.037378	9.767764	0.102378	16
17	2.9170 4637	0.342813	29.493021	0.033906	10.110577	0.098906	17
18	3.1066 5438	0.321890	32.410067	0.030855	10.432466	0.095855	18
19	3.3085 8691	0.302244	35.516722	0.028156	10.734710	0.093156	19
20	3.5236 4506	0.283797	38.825309	0.025756	11.018507	0.090756	20
21	3.7526 8199	0.266476	42.348954	0.023613	11.284983	0.088613	21
22	3.9966 0632	0.250212	46.101636	0.021691	11.535196	0.086691	22
23	4.2563 8573	0.234941	50.098242	0.019961	11.770137	0.084961	23
24	4.5330 5081	0.220602	54.354628	0.018398	11.990739	0.083398	24
25	4.8276 9911	0.207138	58.887679	0.016981	12.197877	0.081981	25
26	5.1414 9955	0.194496	63.715378	0.015695	12.392373	0.080695	26
27	5.4756 9702	0.182625	68.856877	0.014523	12.574998	0.079523	27
28	5.8316 1733	0.171479	74.332574	0.013453	12.746477	0.078453	28
29	6.2106 7245	0.161013	80.164192	0.012474	12.907490	0.077474	29
30	6.6143 6616	0.151186	86.374864	0.011577	13.058676	0.076577	30
31	7.0442 9996	0.141959	92.989230	0.010754	13.200635	0.075754	31
32	7.5021 7946	0.133295	100.033530	0.009997	13.333929	0.074997	32
33	7.9898 2113	0.125159	107.535710	0.009299	13.459088	0.074299	33
34	8.5091 5950	0.117520	115.525531	0.008656	13.576609	0.073656	34
35	9.0622 5487	0.110348	124.034690	0.008062	13.686957	0.073062	35
36	9.6513 0143	0.103613	133.096945	0.007513	13.790570	0.072513	36
37	10.2786 3603	0.097289	142.748247	0.007005	13.887859	0.072005	37
38	10.9467 4737	0.091351	153.026883	0.006535	13.979210	0.071535	38
39	11.6582 8595	0.085776	163.973630	0.006099	14.064986	0.071099	39
40	12.4160 7453	0.080541	175.631916	0.005694	14.145527	0.070694	40
45	17.0110 9813	0.058785	246.324587	0.004060	14.480228	0.069060	45
50	23.3066 7868	0.042906	343.179672	0.002914	14.724521	0.067914	50
55	31.9321 6963	0.031316	475.879533	0.002101	14.902825	0.067101	55
60	43.7498 3974	0.022857	657.689842	0.001520	15.032966	0.066520	60
65	59.9410 7195	0.016683	906.785722	0.001103	15.127953	0.066103	65
70	82.1244 6327	0.012177	1,248.068666	0.000801	15.197282	0.065801	70
75	112.5176 3187	0.008887	1,715.655875	0.000583	15.247885	0.065583	75
80	154.1589 0683	0.006487	2,356.290874	0.000424	15.284818	0.065424	80
90	289.3774 5961	0.003456	4,436.576302	0.000225	15.331451	0.065225	90
100	543.2012 7103	0.001841	8,341.558016	0.000120	15.356293	0.065120	100

TABLE D.13. 7 PERCENT COMPOUND INTEREST FACTORS FOR ONE DOLLAR

	Single payment		Annuities (uniform series payments)				
	Compound amount	Present worth	Compound amount	Sinking fund	Present worth	Capital recovery	
n	Given P To find S $(1+i)^n$	Given S To find P $\dfrac{1}{(1+i)^n}$	Given R To find S $\dfrac{(1+i)^n - 1}{i}$	Given S To find R $\dfrac{i}{(1+i)^n - 1}$	Given R To find P $\dfrac{(1+i)^n - 1}{i(1+i)^n}$	Given P To find R $\dfrac{i(1+i)^n}{(1+i)^n - 1}$	n
	k_1	k_2	k_3	k_4	k_5	k_6	
1	1.0700 0000	0.934579	1.000000	1.000000	0.934579	1.070000	1
2	1.1449 0000	0.873439	2.070000	0.483092	1.808018	0.553092	2
3	1.2250 4300	0.816298	3.214900	0.311052	2.624316	0.381052	3
4	1.3107 9601	0.762895	4.439943	0.225228	3.387211	0.295228	4
5	1.4025 5173	0.712986	5.750739	0.173891	4.100197	0.243891	5
6	1.5007 3035	0.666342	7.153291	0.139796	4.766540	0.209796	6
7	1.6057 8148	0.622750	8.654021	0.115553	5.389289	0.185553	7
8	1.7181 8618	0.582009	10.259803	0.097468	5.971299	0.167468	8
9	1.8384 5921	0.543934	11.977989	0.083486	6.515232	0.153486	9
10	1.9671 5136	0.508349	13.816448	0.072378	7.023582	0.142378	10
11	2.1048 5195	0.475093	15.783599	0.063357	7.498674	0.133357	11
12	2.2521 9159	0.444012	17.888451	0.055902	7.942686	0.125902	12
13	2.4098 4500	0.414964	20.140643	0.049651	8.357651	0.119651	13
14	2.5785 3415	0.387817	22.550488	0.044345	8.745468	0.114345	14
15	2.7590 3154	0.362446	25.129022	0.039795	9.107914	0.109795	15
16	2.9521 6375	0.338735	27.888054	0.035858	9.446649	0.105858	16
17	3.1588 1521	0.316574	30.840217	0.032425	9.763223	0.102425	17
18	3.3799 3228	0.295864	33.999033	0.029413	10.059087	0.099413	18
19	3.6165 2754	0.276508	37.378965	0.026753	10.335595	0.096753	19
20	3.8696 8446	0.258419	40.995492	0.024393	10.594014	0.094393	20
21	4.1405 6237	0.241513	44.865177	0.022289	10.835527	0.092289	21
22	4.4304 0174	0.225713	49.005739	0.020406	11.061240	0.090406	22
23	4.7405 2986	0.210947	53.436141	0.018714	11.272187	0.088714	23
24	5.0723 6695	0.197147	58.176671	0.017189	11.469334	0.087189	24
25	5.4274 3264	0.184249	63.249038	0.015811	11.653583	0.085811	25
26	5.8073 5292	0.172195	68.676470	0.014561	11.825779	0.084561	26
27	6.2138 6763	0.160930	74.483823	0.013426	11.986709	0.083426	27
28	6.6488 3836	0.150402	80.697691	0.012392	12.137111	0.082392	28
29	7.1142 5705	0.140563	87.346529	0.011449	12.277674	0.081449	29
30	7.6122 5504	0.131367	94.460786	0.010586	12.409041	0.080586	30
31	8.1451 1290	0.122773	102.073041	0.009797	12.531814	0.079797	31
32	8.7152 7080	0.114741	110.218154	0.009073	12.646555	0.079073	32
33	9.3253 3975	0.107235	118.933425	0.008408	12.753790	0.078408	33
34	9.9781 1354	0.100219	128.258765	0.007797	12.854009	0.077797	34
35	10.6765 8148	0.093663	138.236878	0.007234	12.947672	0.077234	35
36	11.4239 4219	0.087535	148.913460	0.006715	13.035208	0.076715	36
37	12.2236 1814	0.081809	160.337402	0.006237	13.117017	0.076237	37
38	13.0792 7141	0.076457	172.561020	0.005795	13.193473	0.075795	38
39	13.9948 2041	0.071455	185.640292	0.005387	13.264928	0.075387	39
40	14.9744 5784	0.066780	199.635112	0.005009	13.331709	0.075009	40
45	21.0024 5176	0.047613	285.749311	0.003500	13.605522	0.073500	45
50	29.4570 2506	0.033945	406.528929	0.002460	13.800746	0.072460	50
55	41.3150 0148	0.024204	575.928593	0.001736	13.939939	0.071736	55
60	57.9464 2683	0.017257	813.520383	0.001229	14.039181	0.071229	60
65	81.2728 6124	0.012304	1,146.755161	0.000872	14.109940	0.070872	65
70	113.9893 9220	0.008773	1,614.134174	0.000620	14.160389	0.070620	70
75	159.8760 1931	0.006255	2,269.657419	0.000441	14.196359	0.070441	75
80	224.2343 8758	0.004460	3,189.062680	0.000314	14.222005	0.070314	80
90	441.1029 7988	0.002267	6,287.185427	0.000159	14.253328	0.070159	90
100	867.7163 2557	0.001152	12,381.661794	0.000081	14.269251	0.070081	100

TABLE D.14. 7½ PERCENT COMPOUND INTEREST FACTORS FOR ONE DOLLAR

	Single payment		Annuities (uniform series payments)				
	Compound amount	Present worth	Compound amount	Sinking fund	Present worth	Capital recovery	
n	Given P To find S $(1+i)^n$	Given S To find P $\dfrac{1}{(1+i)^n}$	Given R To find S $\dfrac{(1+i)^n-1}{i}$	Given S To find R $\dfrac{i}{(1+i)^n-1}$	Given R To find P $\dfrac{(1+i)^n-1}{i(1+i)^n}$	Given P To find R $\dfrac{i(1+i)^n}{(1+i)^n-1}$	n
	k_1	k_2	k_3	k_4	k_5	k_6	
1	1.0750 0000	0.930233	1.000000	1.000000	0.930233	1.075000	1
2	1.1556 2500	0.865333	2.075000	0.481928	1.795565	0.556928	2
3	1.2422 9688	0.804961	3.230625	0.309538	2.600526	0.384538	3
4	1.3354 6914	0.748801	4.472922	0.223568	3.349326	0.298568	4
5	1.4356 2933	0.696559	5.808391	0.172165	4.045885	0.247165	5
6	1.5433 0153	0.647962	7.244020	0.138045	4.693846	0.213045	6
7	1.6590 4914	0.602755	8.787322	0.113800	5.296601	0.188800	7
8	1.7834 7783	0.560702	10.446371	0.095727	5.857304	0.170727	8
9	1.9172 3866	0.521583	12.229849	0.081767	6.378887	0.156767	9
10	2.0610 3156	0.485194	14.147087	0.070686	6.864081	0.145686	10
11	2.2156 0893	0.451343	16.208119	0.061697	7.315424	0.136697	11
12	2.3817 7960	0.419854	18.423728	0.054278	7.735278	0.129278	12
13	2.5604 1307	0.390562	20.805508	0.048064	8.125840	0.123064	13
14	2.7524 4405	0.363313	23.365921	0.042797	8.489154	0.117797	14
15	2.9588 7735	0.337966	26.118365	0.038287	8.827120	0.113287	15
16	3.1807 9315	0.314387	29.077242	0.034391	9.141507	0.109391	16
17	3.4193 5264	0.292453	32.258035	0.031000	9.433960	0.106000	17
18	3.6758 0409	0.272049	35.677388	0.028029	9.706009	0.103029	18
19	3.9514 8940	0.253069	39.353192	0.025411	9.959078	0.100411	19
20	4.2478 5110	0.235413	43.304681	0.023092	10.194491	0.098092	20
21	4.5664 3993	0.218989	47.552532	0.021029	10.413480	0.096029	21
22	4.9089 2293	0.203711	52.118972	0.019187	10.617191	0.094187	22
23	5.2770 9215	0.189498	57.027895	0.017535	10.806689	0.092535	23
24	5.6728 7406	0.176277	62.304987	0.016050	10.982967	0.091050	24
25	6.0983 3961	0.163979	67.977862	0.014711	11.146946	0.089711	25
26	6.5557 1508	0.152539	74.076201	0.013500	11.299485	0.088500	26
27	7.0473 9371	0.141896	80.631916	0.012402	11.441381	0.087402	27
28	7.5759 4824	0.131997	87.679310	0.011405	11.573378	0.086405	28
29	8.1441 4436	0.122788	95.255258	0.010498	11.696165	0.085498	29
30	8.7549 5519	0.114221	103.399403	0.009671	11.810386	0.084671	30
31	9.4115 7683	0.106252	112.154358	0.008916	11.916638	0.083916	31
32	10.1174 4509	0.098839	121.565935	0.008226	12.015478	0.083226	32
33	10.8762 5347	0.091943	131.683380	0.007594	12.107421	0.082594	33
34	11.6919 7248	0.085529	142.559633	0.007015	12.192950	0.082015	34
35	12.5688 7042	0.079562	154.251606	0.006483	12.272511	0.081483	35
36	13.5115 3570	0.074011	166.820476	0.005994	12.346522	0.080994	36
37	14.5249 0088	0.068847	180.332012	0.005545	12.415370	0.080545	37
38	15.6142 6844	0.064044	194.856913	0.005132	12.479414	0.080132	38
39	16.7853 3858	0.059576	210.471181	0.004751	12.538989	0.079751	39
40	18.0442 3897	0.055419	227.256520	0.004400	12.594409	0.079400	40
45	25.9048 3863	0.038603	332.064515	0.003011	12.818629	0.078011	45
50	37.1897 4603	0.026889	482.529947	0.002072	12.974812	0.077072	50
55	53.3906 9004	0.018730	698.542534	0.001432	13.083602	0.076432	55
60	76.6492 4036	0.013046	1,008.656538	0.000991	13.159381	0.075991	60
65	110.0398 9729	0.009088	1,453.865297	0.000688	13.212165	0.075688	65
70	157.9765 0360	0.006330	2,093.020048	0.000478	13.248933	0.075478	70
75	226.7957 0141	0.004409	3,010.609352	0.000332	13.274543	0.075332	75
80	325.5945 6000	0.003071	4,327.927467	0.000231	13.292383	0.075231	80
90	671.0606 6463	0.001490	8,934.142195	0.000112	13.313464	0.075112	90
100	1,383.0772 0993	0.000723	18,427.696132	0.000054	13.323693	0.075054	100

TABLE D.15. 8 PERCENT COMPOUND INTEREST FACTORS FOR ONE DOLLAR

	Single payment		Annuities (uniform series payments)				
	Compound amount	Present worth	Compound amount	Sinking fund	Present worth	Capital recovery	
n	Given P To find S $(1+i)^n$	Given S To find P $\dfrac{1}{(1+i)^n}$	Given R To find S $\dfrac{(1+i)^n-1}{i}$	Given S To find R $\dfrac{i}{(1+i)^n-1}$	Given R To find P $\dfrac{(1+i)^n-1}{i(1+i)^n}$	Given P To find R $\dfrac{i(1+i)^n}{(1+i)^n-1}$	n
	k_1	k_2	k_3	k_4	k_5	k_6	
1	1.0800 0000	0.925926	1.000000	1.000000	0.925926	1.080000	1
2	1.1664 0000	0.857339	2.080000	0.480769	1.783265	0.560769	2
3	1.2597 1200	0.793832	3.246400	0.308034	2.577097	0.388034	3
4	1.3604 8896	0.735030	4.506112	0.221921	3.312127	0.301921	4
5	1.4693 2808	0.680583	5.866601	0.170456	3.992710	0.250456	5
6	1.5868 7432	0.630170	7.335929	0.136315	4.622880	0.216315	6
7	1.7138 2427	0.583490	8.922803	0.112072	5.206370	0.192072	7
8	1.8509 3021	0.540269	10.636628	0.094015	5.746639	0.174015	8
9	1.9990 0463	0.500249	12.487558	0.080080	6.246888	0.160080	9
10	2.1589 2500	0.463193	14.486562	0.069029	6.710081	0.149029	10
11	2.3316 3900	0.428883	16.645487	0.060076	7.138964	0.140076	11
12	2.5181 7012	0.397114	18.977126	0.052695	7.536078	0.132695	12
13	2.7196 2373	0.367698	21.495297	0.046522	7.903776	0.126522	13
14	2.9371 9362	0.340461	24.214920	0.041297	8.244237	0.121297	14
15	3.1721 6911	0.315242	27.152114	0.036830	8.559479	0.116830	15
16	3.4259 4264	0.291890	30.324283	0.032977	8.851369	0.112977	16
17	3.7000 1805	0.270269	33.750226	0.029629	9.121638	0.109629	17
18	3.9960 1950	0.250249	37.450244	0.026702	9.371887	0.106702	18
19	4.3157 0106	0.231712	41.446263	0.024128	9.603599	0.104128	19
20	4.6609 5714	0.214548	45.761964	0.021852	9.818147	0.101852	20
21	5.0338 3372	0.198656	50.422921	0.019832	10.016803	0.099832	21
22	5.4365 4041	0.183941	55.456755	0.018032	10.200744	0.098032	22
23	5.8714 6365	0.170435	60.893296	0.016422	10.371059	0.096422	23
24	6.3411 8074	0.157699	66.764759	0.014978	10.528758	0.094978	24
25	6.8484 7520	0.146018	73.105940	0.013679	10.674776	0.093679	25
26	7.3963 5321	0.135202	79.954415	0.012507	10.809978	0.092507	26
27	7.9880 6147	0.125187	87.350768	0.011448	10.935165	0.091448	27
28	8.6271 0639	0.115914	95.338830	0.010489	11.051078	0.090489	28
29	9.3172 7490	0.107328	103.965936	0.009619	11.158406	0.089619	29
30	10.0626 5689	0.099377	113.283211	0.008827	11.257783	0.088827	30
31	10.8676 6944	0.092016	123.345868	0.008107	11.349799	0.088107	31
32	11.7370 8300	0.085200	134.213537	0.007451	11.434999	0.087451	32
33	12.6760 4964	0.078889	145.950620	0.006852	11.513888	0.086852	33
34	13.6901 3361	0.073045	158.626670	0.006304	11.586934	0.086304	34
35	14.7853 4429	0.067635	172.316804	0.005803	11.654568	0.085803	35
36	15.9681 7184	0.062625	187.102148	0.005345	11.717193	0.085345	36
37	17.2456 2558	0.057986	203.070320	0.004924	11.775179	0.084924	37
38	18.6252 7563	0.053690	220.315945	0.004539	11.828869	0.084539	38
39	20.1152 9768	0.049713	238.941221	0.004185	11.878582	0.084185	39
40	21.7245 2150	0.046031	259.056519	0.003860	11.924613	0.083860	40
45	31.9204 4939	0.031328	386.505617	0.002587	12.108402	0.082587	45
50	46.9016 1251	0.021321	573.770156	0.001743	12.233485	0.081743	50
55	68.9138 5611	0.014511	848.923201	0.001178	12.318614	0.081178	55
60	101.2570 6367	0.009876	1,253.213296	0.000798	12.376552	0.080798	60
65	148.7798 4662	0.006721	1,847.248083	0.000541	12.415983	0.080541	65
70	218.6064 0590	0.004574	2,720.080074	0.000368	12.442820	0.080368	70
75	321.2045 2996	0.003113	4,002.556624	0.000250	12.461084	0.080250	75
80	471.9548 3426	0.002119	5,886.935428	0.000170	12.473514	0.080170	80
90	1,018.9150 8928	0.000981	12,723.938616	0.000079	12.487732	0.080079	90
100	2,199.7612 5634	0.000455	27,484.515704	0.000036	12.494318	0.080036	100

TABLE D.16.   8½ PERCENT COMPOUND INTEREST FACTORS FOR ONE DOLLAR

	Single payment		Annuities (uniform series payments)				
	Compound amount	Present worth	Compound amount	Sinking fund	Present worth	Capital recovery	
n	Given P To find S $(1 + i)^n$	Given S To find P $\dfrac{1}{(1 + i)^n}$	Given R To find S $\dfrac{(1 + i)^n - 1}{i}$	Given S To find R $\dfrac{i}{(1 + i)^n - 1}$	Given R To find P $\dfrac{(1 + i)^n - 1}{i(1 + i)^n}$	Given P To find R $\dfrac{i(1 + i)^n}{(1 + i)^n - 1}$	n
	k_1	k_2	k_3	k_4	k_5	k_6	
1	1.0850 0000	0.921659	1.000000	1.000000	0.921659	1.085000	1
2	1.1772 2500	0.849455	2.085000	0.479616	1.771114	0.564616	2
3	1.2772 8913	0.782908	3.262225	0.306539	2.554022	0.391539	3
4	1.3858 5870	0.721574	4.539514	0.220288	3.275597	0.305288	4
5	1.5036 5669	0.665045	5.925373	0.168766	3.940642	0.253766	5
6	1.6314 6751	0.612945	7.429030	0.134607	4.553587	0.219607	6
7	1.7701 4225	0.564926	9.060497	0.110369	5.118514	0.195369	7
8	1.9206 0434	0.520669	10.830639	0.092331	5.639183	0.177331	8
9	2.0838 5571	0.479880	12.751244	0.078424	6.119063	0.163424	9
10	2.2609 8344	0.442285	14.835099	0.067408	6.561348	0.152408	10
11	2.4531 6703	0.407636	17.096083	0.058493	6.968984	0.143493	11
12	2.6616 8623	0.375702	19.549250	0.051153	7.344686	0.136153	12
13	2.8879 2956	0.346269	22.210936	0.045023	7.690955	0.130023	13
14	3.1334 0357	0.319142	25.098866	0.039842	8.010097	0.124842	14
15	3.3997 4288	0.294140	28.232269	0.035420	8.304237	0.120420	15
16	3.6887 2102	0.271097	31.632012	0.031614	8.575333	0.116614	16
17	4.0022 6231	0.249859	35.320733	0.028312	8.825192	0.113312	17
18	4.3424 5461	0.230285	39.322995	0.025430	9.055476	0.110430	18
19	4.7115 6325	0.212244	43.665450	0.022901	9.267720	0.107901	19
20	5.1120 4612	0.195616	48.377013	0.020671	9.463337	0.105671	20
21	5.5465 7005	0.180292	53.489059	0.018695	9.643628	0.103695	21
22	6.0180 2850	0.166167	59.035629	0.016939	9.809796	0.101939	22
23	6.5295 6092	0.153150	65.053658	0.015372	9.962945	0.100372	23
24	7.0845 7360	0.141152	71.583219	0.013970	10.104097	0.098970	24
25	7.6867 6236	0.130094	78.667792	0.012712	10.234191	0.097712	25
26	8.3401 3716	0.119902	86.354555	0.011580	10.354093	0.096580	26
27	9.0490 4881	0.110509	94.694692	0.010560	10.464602	0.095560	27
28	9.8182 1796	0.101851	103.743741	0.009639	10.566453	0.094639	28
29	10.6527 6649	0.093872	113.561959	0.008806	10.660326	0.093806	29
30	11.5582 5164	0.086518	124.214725	0.008051	10.746844	0.093051	30
31	12.5407 0303	0.079740	135.772977	0.007365	10.826584	0.092365	31
32	13.6066 6279	0.073493	148.313680	0.006742	10.900078	0.091742	32
33	14.7632 2913	0.067736	161.920343	0.006176	10.967813	0.091176	33
34	16.0181 0360	0.062429	176.683572	0.005660	11.030243	0.090660	34
35	17.3796 4241	0.057539	192.701675	0.005189	11.087781	0.090189	35
36	18.8569 1201	0.053031	210.081318	0.004760	11.140812	0.089760	36
37	20.4597 4953	0.048876	228.938230	0.004368	11.189689	0.089368	37
38	22.1988 2824	0.045047	249.397979	0.004010	11.234736	0.089010	38
39	24.0857 2865	0.041518	271.596808	0.003682	11.276255	0.088682	39
40	26.1330 1558	0.038266	295.682536	0.003382	11.314520	0.088382	40
45	39.2950 8371	0.025448	450.530397	0.002220	11.465312	0.087220	45
50	59.0863 1551	0.016924	683.368418	0.001463	11.565595	0.086463	50
55	88.8455 3362	0.011255	1,033.476866	0.000968	11.632288	0.085968	55
60	133.5931 8102	0.007485	1,559.919777	0.000641	11.676642	0.085641	60
65	200.8782 8041	0.004978	2,351.509181	0.000425	11.706140	0.085425	65
70	302.0519 7024	0.003311	3,541.787885	0.000282	11.725757	0.085282	70
75	454.1824 6584	0.002202	5,331.558422	0.000188	11.738803	0.085188	75
80	682.9345 0332	0.001464	8,022.758863	0.000125	11.747479	0.085125	80
90	1,544.1036 0392	0.000648	18,154.160046	0.000055	11.757087	0.085055	90
100	3,491.1926 8107	0.000286	41,061.090366	0.000024	11.761336	0.085024	100

TABLE D.17.   9 PERCENT COMPOUND INTEREST FACTORS
FOR ONE DOLLAR

	Single payment		Annuities (uniform series payments)			
	Compound amount	Present worth	Compound amount	Sinking fund	Present worth	Capital recovery
n	Given P To find S $(1+i)^n$	Given S To find P $\dfrac{1}{(1+i)^n}$	Given R To find S $\dfrac{(1+i)^n-1}{i}$	Given S To find R $\dfrac{i}{(1+i)^n-1}$	Given R To find P $\dfrac{(1+i)^n-1}{i(1+i)^n}$	Given P To find R $\dfrac{i(1+i)^n}{(1+i)^n-1}$	n
	k_1	k_2	k_3	k_4	k_5	k_6	
1	1.0900 0000	0.917431	1.000000	1.000000	0.917431	1.090000	1
2	1.1881 0000	0.841680	2.090000	0.478469	1.759111	0.568469	2
3	1.2950 2900	0.772183	3.278100	0.305055	2.531295	0.395055	3
4	1.4115 8161	0.708425	4.573129	0.218669	3.239720	0.308669	4
5	1.5386 2395	0.649931	5.984711	0.167092	3.889651	0.257092	5
6	1.6771 0011	0.596267	7.523335	0.132920	4.485919	0.222920	6
7	1.8280 3912	0.547034	9.200435	0.108691	5.032953	0.198691	7
8	1.9925 6264	0.501866	11.028474	0.090674	5.534819	0.180674	8
9	2.1718 9328	0.460428	13.021036	0.076799	5.995247	0.166799	9
10	2.3673 6367	0.422411	15.192930	0.065820	6.417658	0.155820	10
11	2.5804 2641	0.387533	17.560293	0.056947	6.805191	0.146947	11
12	2.8126 6478	0.355535	20.140720	0.049651	7.160725	0.139651	12
13	3.0658 0461	0.326179	22.953385	0.043567	7.486904	0.133567	13
14	3.3417 2703	0.299246	26.019189	0.038433	7.786150	0.128433	14
15	3.6424 8246	0.274538	29.360916	0.034059	8.060688	0.124059	15
16	3.9703 0588	0.251870	33.003399	0.030300	8.312558	0.120300	16
17	4.3276 3341	0.231073	36.973705	0.027046	8.543631	0.117046	17
18	4.7171 2042	0.211994	41.301338	0.024212	8.755625	0.114212	18
19	5.1416 6125	0.194490	46.018458	0.021730	8.950115	0.111730	19
20	5.6044 1077	0.178431	51.160120	0.019546	9.128546	0.109546	20
21	6.1088 0774	0.163698	56.764530	0.017617	9.292244	0.107617	21
22	6.6586 0043	0.150182	62.873338	0.015905	9.442425	0.105905	22
23	7.2578 7447	0.137781	69.531939	0.014382	9.580207	0.104382	23
24	7.9110 8317	0.126405	76.789813	0.013023	9.706612	0.103023	24
25	8.6230 8066	0.115968	84.700896	0.011806	9.822580	0.101806	25
26	9.3991 5792	0.106393	93.323977	0.010715	9.928972	0.100715	26
27	10.2450 8213	0.097608	102.723135	0.009735	10.026580	0.099735	27
28	11.1671 3952	0.089548	112.968217	0.008852	10.116128	0.098852	28
29	12.1721 8208	0.082155	124.135356	0.008056	10.198283	0.098056	29
30	13.2676 7847	0.075371	136.307539	0.007336	10.273654	0.097336	30
31	14.4617 6953	0.069148	149.575217	0.006686	10.342802	0.096686	31
32	15.7633 2879	0.063438	164.036987	0.006096	10.406240	0.096096	32
33	17.1820 2838	0.058200	179.800315	0.005562	10.464441	0.095562	33
34	18.7284 1093	0.053395	196.982344	0.005077	10.517835	0.095077	34
35	20.4139 6792	0.048986	215.710755	0.004636	10.566821	0.094636	35
36	22.2512 2503	0.044941	236.124723	0.004235	10.611763	0.094235	36
37	24.2538 3528	0.041231	258.375948	0.003870	10.652993	0.093870	37
38	26.4366 8046	0.037826	282.629783	0.003538	10.690820	0.093538	38
39	28.8159 8170	0.034703	309.066463	0.003236	10.725523	0.093236	39
40	31.4094 2005	0.031838	337.882445	0.002960	10.757360	0.092960	40
45	48.3272 8610	0.020692	525.858734	0.001902	10.881197	0.091902	45
50	74.3575 2008	0.013449	815.083556	0.001227	10.961683	0.091227	50
55	114.4082 6162	0.008741	1,260.091796	0.000794	11.013993	0.090794	55
60	176.0312 9196	0.005681	1,944.792133	0.000514	11.047991	0.090514	60
65	270.8459 6262	0.003692	2,998.288474	0.000334	11.070087	0.090334	65
70	416.7300 8618	0.002400	4,619.223180	0.000216	11.084449	0.090216	70
75	641.1908 9332	0.001560	7,113.232148	0.000141	11.093782	0.090141	75
80	986.5516 6813	0.001014	10,950.574090	0.000091	11.099849	0.090091	80
90	2,335.5265 8223	0.000428	25,939.184247	0.000039	11.106354	0.090039	90
100	5,529.0407 9183	0.000181	61,422.675465	0.000016	11.109102	0.090016	100

TABLE D.18. 10 PERCENT COMPOUND INTEREST FACTORS FOR ONE DOLLAR

n	Single payment		Annuities (uniform series payments)				n
	Compound amount	Present worth	Compound amount	Sinking fund	Present worth	Capital recovery	
	Given P To find S $(1+i)^n$	Given S To find P $\dfrac{1}{(1+i)^n}$	Given R To find S $\dfrac{(1+i)^n-1}{i}$	Given S To find R $\dfrac{i}{(1+i)^n-1}$	Given R To find P $\dfrac{(1+i)^n-1}{i(1+i)^n}$	Given P To find R $\dfrac{i(1+i)^n}{(1+i)^n-1}$	
	k_1	k_2	k_3	k_4	k_5	k_6	
1	1.1000 0000	0.909091	1.000000	1.000000	0.909091	1.100000	1
2	1.2100 0000	0.826446	2.100000	0.476190	1.735537	0.576190	2
3	1.3310 0000	0.751315	3.310000	0.302115	2.486852	0.402115	3
4	1.4641 0000	0.683013	4.641000	0.215471	3.169865	0.315471	4
5	1.6105 1000	0.620921	6.105100	0.163797	3.790787	0.263797	5
6	1.7715 6100	0.564474	7.715610	0.129607	4.355261	0.229607	6
7	1.9487 1710	0.513158	9.487171	0.105405	4.868419	0.205405	7
8	2.1435 8881	0.466507	11.435888	0.087444	5.334926	0.187444	8
9	2.3579 4769	0.424098	13.579477	0.073641	5.759024	0.173641	9
10	2.5937 4246	0.385543	15.937425	0.062745	6.144567	0.162745	10
11	2.8531 1671	0.350494	18.531167	0.053963	6.495061	0.153963	11
12	3.1384 2838	0.318631	21.384284	0.046763	6.813692	0.146763	12
13	3.4522 7121	0.289664	24.522712	0.040779	7.103356	0.140779	13
14	3.7974 9834	0.263331	27.974983	0.035746	7.366687	0.135746	14
15	4.1772 4817	0.239392	31.772482	0.031474	7.606080	0.131474	15
16	4.5949 7299	0.217629	35.949730	0.027817	7.823709	0.127817	16
17	5.0544 7028	0.197845	40.544703	0.024664	8.021553	0.124664	17
18	5.5599 1731	0.179859	45.599173	0.021930	8.201412	0.121930	18
19	6.1159 0904	0.163508	51.159090	0.019547	8.364920	0.119547	19
20	6.7274 9995	0.148644	57.274999	0.017460	8.513564	0.117460	20
21	7.4002 4994	0.135131	64.002499	0.015624	8.648694	0.115624	21
22	8.1402 7494	0.122846	71.402749	0.014005	8.771540	0.114005	22
23	8.9543 0243	0.111678	79.543024	0.012572	8.883218	0.112572	23
24	9.8497 3268	0.101526	88.497327	0.011300	8.984744	0.111300	24
25	10.8347 0594	0.092296	98.347059	0.010168	9.077040	0.110168	25
26	11.9181 7654	0.083905	109.181765	0.009159	9.160945	0.109159	26
27	13.1099 9419	0.076278	121.099942	0.008258	9.237223	0.108258	27
28	14.4209 9361	0.069343	134.209936	0.007451	9.306567	0.107451	28
29	15.8630 9297	0.063039	148.630930	0.006728	9.369606	0.106728	29
30	17.4494 0227	0.057309	164.494023	0.006079	9.426914	0.106079	30
31	19.1943 4250	0.052099	181.943425	0.005496	9.479013	0.105496	31
32	21.1137 7675	0.047362	201.137767	0.004972	9.526376	0.104972	32
33	23.2251 5442	0.043057	222.251544	0.004499	9.569432	0.104499	33
34	25.5476 6986	0.039143	245.476699	0.004074	9.608575	0.104074	34
35	28.1024 3685	0.035584	271.024368	0.003690	9.644159	0.103690	35
36	30.9126 8053	0.032349	299.126805	0.003343	9.676508	0.103343	36
37	34.0039 4859	0.029408	330.039486	0.003030	9.705917	0.103030	37
38	37.4043 4344	0.026735	364.043434	0.002747	9.732651	0.102747	38
39	41.1447 7779	0.024304	401.447778	0.002491	9.756956	0.102491	39
40	45.2592 5557	0.022095	442.592556	0.002259	9.779051	0.102259	40
45	72.8904 8369	0.013719	718.904837	0.001391	9.862808	0.101391	45
50	117.3908 5288	0.008519	1,163.908529	0.000859	9.914814	0.100859	50
55	189.0591 4247	0.005289	1,880.591425	0.000532	9.947106	0.100532	55
60	304.4816 3954	0.003284	3,034.816395	0.000330	9.967157	0.100330	60
65	490.3707 2530	0.002039	4,893.707253	0.000204	9.979607	0.100204	65
70	789.7469 5680	0.001266	7,887.469568	0.000127	9.987338	0.100127	70
75	1,271.8953 7140	0.000786	12,708.953714	0.000079	9.992138	0.100079	75
80	2,048.4002 1459	0.000488	20,474.002146	0.000049	9.995118	0.100049	80
90	5,313.0226 1185	0.000188	53,120.226118	0.000019	9.998118	0.100019	90
100	13,780.6123 3982	0.000073	137,796.123398	0.000007	9.999274	0.100007	100

TABLE D.19.   12 PERCENT COMPOUND INTEREST FACTORS FOR ONE DOLLAR

	Single payment		Annuities (uniform series payments)				
	Compound amount	Present worth	Compound amount	Sinking fund	Present worth	Capital recovery	
n	Given P To find S $(1 + i)^n$	Given S To find P $\dfrac{1}{(1 + i)^n}$	Given R To find S $\dfrac{(1 + i)^n - 1}{i}$	Given S To find R $\dfrac{i}{(1 + i)^n - 1}$	Given R To find P $\dfrac{(1 + i)^n - 1}{i(1 + i)^n}$	Given P To find R $\dfrac{i(1 + i)^n}{(1 + i)^n - 1}$	n
	k_1	k_2	k_3	k_4	k_5	k_6	
1	1.1200 0000	0.892857	1.00000	1.000000	0.89286	1.120000	1
2	1.2544 0000	0.797194	2.12000	0.471698	1.69005	0.591698	2
3	1.4049 2800	0.711780	3.37440	0.296349	2.40183	0.416349	3
4	1.5735 1936	0.635518	4.77933	0.209234	3.03735	0.329234	4
5	1.7623 4168	0.567427	6.35285	0.157410	3.60477	0.277410	5
6	1.9738 2269	0.506631	8.11519	0.123226	4.11140	0.243226	6
7	2.2106 8141	0.452349	10.08901	0.099118	4.56375	0.219118	7
8	2.4759 6318	0.403883	12.29969	0.081303	4.96764	0.201303	8
9	2.7730 7876	0.360610	14.77566	0.067679	5.32825	0.187679	9
10	3.1058 4821	0.321973	17.54874	0.056984	5.65023	0.176984	10
11	3.4785 4999	0.287476	20.65458	0.048415	5.93771	0.168415	11
12	3.8959 7599	0.256675	24.13313	0.041437	6.19437	0.161437	12
13	4.3634 9311	0.229174	28.02911	0.035677	6.42356	0.155677	13
14	4.8871 1229	0.204620	32.39260	0.030871	6.62818	0.150871	14
15	5.4735 6576	0.182696	37.27971	0.026824	6.81088	0.146824	15
16	6.1303 9365	0.163122	42.75328	0.023390	6.97399	0.143390	16
17	6.8660 4089	0.145644	48.88367	0.020457	7.11962	0.140457	17
18	7.6899 6580	0.130040	55.74972	0.017937	7.24969	0.137937	18
19	8.6127 6169	0.116107	63.43968	0.015763	7.36578	0.135763	19
20	9.6462 9309	0.103667	72.05244	0.013879	7.46943	0.133879	20
21	10.8038 4826	0.092560	81.69874	0.012240	7.56201	0.132240	21
22	12.1003 1006	0.082643	92.50258	0.010811	7.64462	0.130811	22
23	13.5523 4726	0.073788	104.60289	0.009560	7.71843	0.129560	23
24	15.1786 2893	0.065882	118.15524	0.008463	7.78434	0.128463	24
25	17.0000 6441	0.058823	133.33387	0.007500	7.84314	0.127500	25
26	19.0400 7214	0.052521	150.33393	0.006652	7.89565	0.126652	26
27	21.3248 8079	0.046894	169.37401	0.005904	7.94256	0.125904	27
28	23.8838 6649	0.041869	190.69889	0.005244	7.98441	0.125244	28
29	26.7499 3047	0.037383	214.58275	0.004660	8.02182	0.124660	29
30	29.9599 2212	0.033378	241.33268	0.004144	8.05516	0.124144	30
31	33.5551 1278	0.029802	271.29261	0.003686	8.08499	0.123686	31
32	37.5817 2631	0.026609	304.84772	0.003280	8.11162	0.123280	32
33	42.0915 3347	0.023758	342.42945	0.002920	8.13537	0.122920	33
34	47.1425 1748	0.021212	384.52098	0.002601	8.15654	0.122601	34
35	52.7996 1958	0.018940	431.66350	0.002317	8.17548	0.122317	35
36	59.1355 7393	0.016910	484.46312	0.002064	8.19242	0.122064	36
37	66.2318 4280	0.015098	543.59869	0.001840	8.20749	0.121840	37
38	74.1796 6394	0.013481	609.83053	0.001640	8.22098	0.121640	38
39	83.0812 2361	0.012036	684.01020	0.001462	8.23303	0.121462	39
40	93.0509 7044	0.010747	767.09142	0.001304	8.24375	0.121304	40
41	104.2170 8689	0.009595	860.14239	0.001163	8.25334	0.121163	41
42	116.7231 3732	0.008567	964.35948	0.001037	8.26194	0.121037	42
43	130.7299 1380	0.007649	1,081.08262	0.000925	8.26959	0.120925	43
44	146.4175 0346	0.006830	1,211.81253	0.000825	8.27643	0.120825	44
45	163.9876 0387	0.006098	1,358.23003	0.000736	8.28253	0.120736	45
50	289.0021 8983	0.003460	2,400.01825	0.000417	8.30448	0.120417	50
55	509.3206 0567	0.001963	4,236.00505	0.000236	8.31698	0.120236	55
60	897.5969 3349	0.001114	7,471.64111	0.000134	8.32404	0.120134	60

TABLE D.20.　15 PERCENT COMPOUND INTEREST FACTORS FOR ONE DOLLAR

	Single payment		Annuities (uniform series payments)			
	Compound amount	Present worth	Compound amount	Sinking fund	Present worth	Capital recovery
n	Given P To find S $(1 + i)^n$	Given S To find P $\dfrac{1}{(1 + i)^n}$	Given R To find S $\dfrac{(1 + i)^n - 1}{i}$	Given S To find R $\dfrac{i}{(1 + i)^n - 1}$	Given R To find P $\dfrac{(1 + i)^n - 1}{i(1 + i)^n}$	Given P To find R $\dfrac{i(1 + i)^n}{(1 + i)^n - 1}$	n
	k_1	k_2	k_3	k_4	k_5	k_6	
1	1.1500 0000	0.869565	1.00000	1.000000	0.86957	1.150000	1
2	1.3225 0000	0.756144	2.15000	0.465116	1.62571	0.615116	2
3	1.5208 7500	0.657516	3.47250	0.287977	2.28322	0.437977	3
4	1.7490 0625	0.571753	4.99338	0.200265	2.85498	0.350265	4
5	2.0113 5719	0.497177	6.74238	0.148316	3.35215	0.298316	5
6	2.3130 6077	0.432328	8.75374	0.114237	3.78448	0.264237	6
7	2.6600 1988	0.375937	11.06680	0.090360	4.16043	0.240360	7
8	3.0590 2286	0.326902	13.72682	0.072850	4.48732	0.222850	8
9	3.5178 7629	0.284262	16.78584	0.059574	4.77158	0.209574	9
10	4.0455 5774	0.247185	20.30372	0.049252	5.01877	0.199252	10
11	4.6523 9140	0.214943	24.34928	0.041069	5.23371	0.191069	11
12	5.3502 5011	0.186907	29.00167	0.034481	5.42061	0.184481	12
13	6.1527 8762	0.162528	34.35192	0.029110	5.58316	0.179110	13
14	7.0757 0576	0.141329	40.50471	0.024688	5.72449	0.174688	14
15	8.1370 6163	0.122894	47.58041	0.021017	5.84737	0.171017	15
16	9.3576 2087	0.106865	55.71747	0.017948	5.95422	0.167948	16
17	10.7612 6400	0.092926	65.07509	0.015367	6.04716	0.165367	17
18	12.3754 5361	0.080805	75.83636	0.013186	6.12798	0.163186	18
19	14.2317 7165	0.070265	88.21181	0.011336	6.19824	0.161336	19
20	16.3665 3739	0.061100	102.44358	0.009761	6.25935	0.159761	20
21	18.8215 1800	0.053131	118.81012	0.008417	6.31245	0.158417	21
22	21.6447 4570	0.046201	137.63164	0.007266	6.35865	0.157266	22
23	24.8914 5756	0.040174	159.27638	0.006278	6.39885	0.156278	23
24	28.6251 7619	0.034934	184.16784	0.005430	6.43376	0.155430	24
25	32.9189 5262	0.030378	212.79302	0.004699	6.46417	0.154699	25
26	37.8567 9551	0.026415	245.71197	0.004070	6.49056	0.154070	26
27	43.5353 1484	0.022970	283.56877	0.003526	6.51355	0.153526	27
28	50.0656 1207	0.019974	327.10408	0.003057	6.53351	0.153057	28
29	57.5754 5388	0.017369	377.16969	0.002651	6.55089	0.152651	29
30	66.2117 7199	0.015103	434.74515	0.002300	6.56599	0.152300	30
31	76.1435 3775	0.013133	500.95692	0.001996	6.57912	0.151996	31
32	87.5650 6841	0.011420	577.10046	0.001733	6.59052	0.151733	32
33	100.6998 2867	0.009931	664.66552	0.001505	6.60044	0.151505	33
34	115.8048 0298	0.008635	765.36535	0.001307	6.60908	0.151307	34
35	133.1755 2342	0.007509	881.17016	0.001135	6.61660	0.151135	35
36	153.1518 5194	0.006529	1,014.34568	0.000986	6.62313	0.150986	36
37	176.1246 2973	0.005678	1,167.49753	0.000857	6.62879	0.150857	37
38	202.5433 2419	0.004937	1,343.62216	0.000744	6.63376	0.150744	38
39	232.9248 2281	0.004293	1,546.16549	0.000647	6.63803	0.150647	39
40	267.8635 4623	0.003733	1,779.09031	0.000562	6.64178	0.150562	40
41	308.0430 7817	0.003246	2,046.95385	0.000489	6.64500	0.150489	41
42	354.2495 3990	0.002823	2,354.99693	0.000425	6.64783	0.150425	42
43	407.3869 7088	0.002455	2,709.24647	0.000369	6.65031	0.150369	43
44	468.4950 1651	0.002134	3,116.63344	0.000321	6.65243	0.150321	44
45	538.7692 6899	0.001856	3,585.12846	0.000279	6.65429	0.150279	45
50	1,083.6574 4158	0.000923	7,217.71628	0.000139	6.66049	0.150139	50

TABLE D.21. 20 PERCENT COMPOUND INTEREST FACTORS FOR ONE DOLLAR

	Single payment		Annuities (uniform series payments)				
	Compound amount	Present worth	Compound amount	Sinking fund	Present worth	Capital recovery	
n	Given P To find S $(1+i)^n$	Given S To find P $\dfrac{1}{(1+i)^n}$	Given R To find S $\dfrac{(1+i)^n-1}{i}$	Given S To find R $\dfrac{i}{(1+i)^n-1}$	Given R To find P $\dfrac{(1+i)^n-1}{i(1+i)^n}$	Given P To find R $\dfrac{i(1+i)^n}{(1+i)^n-1}$	n
	k_1	k_2	k_3	k_4	k_5	k_6	
1	1.2000 0000	0.833333	1.00000	1.000000	0.83333	1.200000	1
2	1.4400 0000	0.694444	2.20000	0.454545	1.52778	0.654545	2
3	1.7280 0000	0.578704	3.64000	0.274725	2.10648	0.474725	3
4	2.0736 0000	0.482253	5.36800	0.186289	2.58874	0.386289	4
5	2.4883 2000	0.401878	7.44160	0.134380	2.99061	0.334380	5
6	2.9859 8400	0.334898	9.92992	0.100706	3.32551	0.300706	6
7	3.5831 8080	0.279082	12.91590	0.077424	3.60459	0.277424	7
8	4.2998 1696	0.232568	16.49908	0.060609	3.83717	0.260609	8
9	5.1597 8035	0.193807	20.79890	0.048079	4.03097	0.248079	9
10	6.1917 3642	0.161506	25.95868	0.038523	4.19247	0.238523	10
11	7.4300 8371	0.134588	32.15042	0.031104	4.32706	0.231104	11
12	8.9161 0045	0.112157	39.58050	0.025265	4.43922	0.225265	12
13	10.6993 2054	0.093464	48.49660	0.020620	4.53268	0.220620	13
14	12.8391 8465	0.077887	59.19502	0.016893	4.61057	0.216893	14
15	15.4070 2157	0.064905	72.03511	0.013882	4.67548	0.213882	15
16	18.4884 2589	0.054088	87.44213	0.011436	4.72956	0.211436	16
17	22.1861 1107	0.045073	105.93056	0.009440	4.77464	0.209440	17
18	26.6233 3328	0.037561	128.11667	0.007805	4.81220	0.207805	18
19	31.9479 9994	0.031301	154.74000	0.006462	4.84351	0.206462	19
20	38.3375 9992	0.026084	186.68800	0.005357	4.86957	0.205357	20
21	46.0051 1991	0.021737	225.02560	0.004444	4.89131	0.204444	21
22	55.2061 4389	0.018114	271.03072	0.003690	4.90942	0.203690	22
23	66.2473 7267	0.015095	326.23686	0.003065	4.92453	0.203065	23
24	79.4968 4720	0.012579	392.48424	0.002548	4.93710	0.202548	24
25	95.3962 1664	0.010483	471.98108	0.002119	4.94758	0.202119	25
26	114.4754 5997	0.008735	567.37730	0.001762	4.95633	0.201762	26
27	137.3705 5197	0.007280	681.85276	0.001467	4.96359	0.201467	27
28	164.8446 6236	0.006066	819.22331	0.001221	4.96966	0.201221	28
29	197.8135 9483	0.005055	984.06797	0.001016	4.97473	0.201016	29
30	237.3763 1380	0.004213	1,181.88157	0.000846	4.97894	0.200846	30
31	284.8515 7656	0.003511	1,419.25788	0.000705	4.98244	0.200705	31
32	341.8218 9187	0.002926	1,704.10946	0.000587	4.98537	0.200587	32
33	410.1862 7025	0.002438	2,045.93135	0.000489	4.98780	0.200489	33
34	492.2235 2430	0.002032	2,456.11762	0.000407	4.98985	0.200407	34
35	590.6682 2915	0.001693	2,948.34115	0.000339	4.99154	0.200339	35
36	708.8018 7499	0.001411	3,539.00938	0.000283	4.99293	0.200283	36
37	850.5622 4998	0.001176	4,247.81125	0.000235	4.99413	0.200235	37
38	1,020.6746 9998	0.000980	5,098.37350	0.000196	4.99510	0.200196	38
39	1,224.8096 3997	0.000816	6,119.04820	0.000163	4.99593	0.200163	39
40	1,469.7715 6797	0.000680	7,343.85784	0.000136	4.99660	0.200136	40
41	1,763.7258 8156	0.000567	8,813.62941	0.000113	4.99718	0.200113	41

TABLE D.22.   25 PERCENT COMPOUND INTEREST FACTORS
FOR ONE DOLLAR

	Single payment		Annuities (uniform series payments)			
	Compound amount	Present worth	Compound amount	Sinking fund	Present worth	Capital recovery
n	Given P To find S $(1+i)^n$	Given S To find P $\dfrac{1}{(1+i)^n}$	Given R To find S $\dfrac{(1+i)^n-1}{i}$	Given S To find R $\dfrac{i}{(1+i)^n-1}$	Given R To find P $\dfrac{(1+i)^n-1}{i(1+i)^n}$	Given P To find R $\dfrac{i(1+i)^n}{(1+i)^n-1}$
	k_1	k_2	k_3	k_4	k_5	k_6
1	1.2500 0000	0.800000	1.00000	1.000000	0.80000	1.250000
2	1.5625 0000	0.640000	2.25000	0.444444	1.44000	0.694444
3	1.9531 2500	0.512000	3.81250	0.262295	1.95200	0.512295
4	2.4414 0625	0.409600	5.76562	0.173442	2.36160	0.423442
5	3.0517 5781	0.327680	8.20703	0.121847	2.68928	0.371847
6	3.8146 9727	0.262144	11.25879	0.088819	2.95143	0.338819
7	4.7683 7158	0.209715	15.07349	0.066342	3.16114	0.316342
8	5.9604 6448	0.167772	19.84186	0.050399	3.32891	0.300399
9	7.4505 8060	0.134218	25.80232	0.038756	3.46313	0.288756
10	9.3132 2575	0.107374	33.25290	0.030073	3.57050	0.280073
11	11.6415 3218	0.085899	42.56613	0.023493	3.65640	0.273493
12	14.5519 1523	0.068719	54.20766	0.018448	3.72512	0.268448
13	18.1898 9404	0.054976	68.75958	0.014543	3.78010	0.264543
14	22.7373 6754	0.043980	86.94947	0.011501	3.82408	0.261501
15	28.4217 0943	0.035184	109.68684	0.009117	3.85926	0.259117
16	35.5271 3679	0.028147	138.10855	0.007241	3.88741	0.257241
17	44.4089 2099	0.022518	173.63568	0.005759	3.90993	0.255759
18	55.5111 5123	0.018014	218.04460	0.004586	3.92795	0.254586
19	69.3889 3904	0.014412	273.55576	0.003656	3.94235	0.253656
20	86.7361 7380	0.011529	342.94470	0.002916	3.95388	0.252916
21	108.4202 1725	0.009223	429.68087	0.002327	3.96311	0.252327
22	135.5252 7156	0.007379	538.10109	0.001858	3.97049	0.251858
23	169.4065 8945	0.005903	673.62636	0.001485	3.97638	0.251485
24	211.7582 3681	0.004722	843.03295	0.001186	3.98111	0.251186
25	264.6977 9602	0.003778	1,054.79118	0.000948	3.98489	0.250948
26	330.8722 4502	0.003022	1,319.48898	0.000758	3.98791	0.250758
27	413.5903 0628	0.002418	1,650.36123	0.000606	3.99033	0.250606
28	516.9878 8285	0.001934	2,063.95153	0.000485	3.99226	0.250485
29	646.2348 5356	0.001547	2,580.93941	0.000387	3.99382	0.250387
30	807.7935 6695	0.001238	3,227.17427	0.000310	3.99505	0.250310
31	1,009.7419 5868	0.000990	4,034.96783	0.000248	3.99604	0.250248
32	1,262.1774 4835	0.000792	5,044.70979	0.000198	3.99683	0.250198
33	1,577.7218 1044	0.000634	6,306.88724	0.000159	3.99746	0.250159
34	1,972.1522 6305	0.000507	7,884.60905	0.000127	3.99797	0.250127
35	2,465.1903 2882	0.000406	9,856.76132	0.000101	3.99838	0.250101

INDEX OF COURT DECISIONS AND COMMISSION CASES

A

B

C

D

M

N

O

P

R

INDEX

92